$E^{\ominus}$ cell is proportional to ln K ∴ the $E^{\ominus}$ cell potential can be used to calculate the equilibrium constant

# A2-Level Chemistry

$Cr_2O_7^{2-}$, $CrO_4^{2-}$, $Cr^{3+}_{(hyd)}$, $Cr^{2+}_{(hyd)}$

Yellow Orange Green Blue

$Cr_2O_7^{2-} + Fe_2SO_4 \rightarrow Cr^{3+}$

## The Revision Guide

*Editors:*
Amy Boutal, Mary Falkner, David Hickinson, Sarah Hilton, Paul Jordin, Sharon Keeley,
Simon Little, Tim Major, Sam Norman, Ami Snelling, Michael Southorn, Hayley Thompson.

*Contributors:*
Mike Bossart, Robert Clarke, Ian H. Davis, John Duffy, Lucy Muncaster,
Paul Warren, Chris Workman.

*Proofreaders*:
Barrie Crowther, Julie Wakeling.

Published by Coordination Group Publications Ltd.

This book is suitable for:

***AQA, OCR A, OCR B (Salters) and Edexcel***.

There are notes on the pages to tell you which bits you need to know for each unit of your syllabus.

ISBN: 978 1 84762 265 5

With thanks to Laura Stoney for the copyright research.

Groovy website: www.cgpbooks.co.uk
Jolly bits of clipart from CorelDRAW®
Printed by Elanders Hindson Ltd, Newcastle upon Tyne.

# Contents

## How Science Works



## Section 1 — Elements and Bonding



## Section 2 — Kinetics



## Section 3 — Equilibria



## Section 4 — Acids and Bases



## ection 5 — Isomerism and Carbonyl Compounds



## 6 — More Organic Chemistry



## Section 7 — Synthesis and Analysis



## Section 8 — Thermodynamics



## Section 9 — Period 3, Redox and Electrochemistry



## Section 10 — Transition Metals



## Section 11 — Inorganic Reactions

# The Scientific Process

*'How Science Works' is all about the scientific process — how we develop and test scientific ideas. It's what scientists do all day, every day (well except at coffee time — never come between scientists and their coffee).*

## *Scientists Come Up with **Theories** — Then **Test Them**...*

Science tries to explain **how** and **why** things happen. It's all about seeking and gaining **knowledge** about the world around us. Scientists do this by **asking** questions and **suggesting** answers and then **testing** them, to see if they're correct — this is the **scientific process**.

1) **Ask** a question — make an **observation** and ask **why or how** whatever you've observed happens.
   *E.g. Why does sodium chloride dissolve in water?*
2) **Suggest** an answer, or part of an answer, by forming a **theory** or a **model** (a possible **explanation** of the observations or a description of what you think is actually happening).
   *E.g. Sodium chloride is made up of charged particles, which are pulled apart by the polar water molecules.*
3) Make a **prediction** or **hypothesis** — a **specific testable statement**, based on the theory, about what will happen in a test situation.
   *E.g. A solution of sodium chloride will conduct electricity much better than water does.*
4) Carry out **tests** — to provide **evidence** that will support the prediction or refute it.
   *E.g. Measure the conductivity of water and of sodium chloride solution.*

The evidence supported Quentin's Theory of Flammable Burps.

A theory is only scientific if it can be tested.

## *...Then They **Tell** Everyone About Their **Results**...*

The results are **published** — scientists need to let others know about their work. Scientists publish their results in **scientific journals**. These are just like normal magazines, only they contain **scientific reports** (called papers) instead of the latest celebrity gossip.

1) Scientific reports are similar to the **lab write-ups** you do in school. And just as a lab write-up is **reviewed** (marked) by your teacher, reports in scientific journals undergo **peer review** before they're published.
   Scientists use standard terminology when writing their reports. This way they know that other scientists will understand them. For instance, there are internationally agreed rules for naming organic compounds, so that scientists across the world will know exactly what substance is being referred to.
2) The report is sent out to **peers** — other scientists who are experts in the **same area**. They go through it bit by bit, examining the methods and data, and checking it's all clear and logical. When the report is approved, it's **published**. This makes sure that work published in scientific journals is of a **good standar**
3) But peer review **can't guarantee** the science is **correct** — other scientists still need to **reproduce** it.
4) Sometimes **mistakes** are made and bad work is published. Peer review **isn't perfect** but it's probably the best way for scientists to self-regulate their work and to publish **quality reports**.

## *...Then **Other Scientists** Will **Test** the Theory Too*

1) Other scientists read the published theories and results, and try to **test the theory** themselves. This invo
   - Repeating the **exact same experiments**.
   - Using the theory to make **new predictions** and then testing them with **new experiments**.
2) If all the experiments in the world provide evidence to back it up, the theory is thought of as **scientific 'fact'** (for now).
3) If **new evidence** comes to light that **conflicts** with the current evidence the theory is questioned all over again. More rounds of **testing** will be carried out to try to find out where the theory **falls down**.

This is how the **scientific process works** — **evidence** supports a theory, loads of other scientists read it and test it for themselves, eventually all the scientists in the world **agree** with it and then bingo, you get to **learn** it.

This is exactly how scientists arrived at the structure of the atom — and how they came to the conclusion that electrons are arranged in shells and orbitals. It took years and years for these models to be developed and accepted — this is often the case with the scientific process.

# The Scientific Process

## *If the **Evidence** Supports a Theory, It's **Accepted — for Now***

Our currently accepted theories have survived this '**trial by evidence**'. They've been tested **over and over again** and each time the results have backed them up. **BUT**, and this is a big but (teehee), they never become totally indisputable fact. Scientific **breakthroughs or advances** could provide new ways to question and test the theory, which could lead to **changes and challenges** to it. Then the testing starts all over again...

And this, my friend, is the **tentative nature of scientific knowledge** — it's always **changing** and **evolving**.

In 1865, when Kekulé suggested the structure of benzene was a ring of carbon atoms, joined by alternating single and double bonds, it was widely accepted — it was the best fit for the evidence at the time. It was only once electrons had been discovered and orbital theory was developed that scientists came up with the modern 'delocalised model', which explains the behaviour of benzene better than Kekulé's model. See page 70.

## *Evidence Comes From **Lab Experiments**...*

1) Results from **controlled experiments** in **laboratories** are **great**.
2) A lab is the easiest place to **control variables** so that they're all **kept constant** (except for the one you're investigating).
3) This means you can draw meaningful **conclusions**.

For example, if you're investigating how temperature affects the rate of a reaction you need to keep everything but the temperature constant, e.g. the pH of the solution, the concentration of the solution, etc.

## *...But You **Can't** Always do a Lab Experiment*

There are things you **can't** study in a lab. And outside the lab controlling the variables is tricky, if not impossible.

- *Are increasing $CO_2$ emissions causing climate change?*
  There are other variables which may have an effect, such as changes in solar activity. You can't easily rule out every possibility. Also, climate change is a very **gradual process**. Scientists won't be able to tell if their predictions are correct for donkey's years.
- *Does eating food containing trans fatty acids increase the risk of heart disease and strokes?*
  There are always differences between groups of people. The best you can do is to have a **well-designed study** using **matched groups — choose two groups** of people (those who eat a lot of trans fats and those who don't) which are **as similar as possible** (same mix of ages, same mix of diets etc.). But you still can't rule out every possibility. Taking newborn identical twins and treating them identically, except for making one consume a lot of trans fats and the other none at all, might be a fairer test, but it would present huge **ethical problems**.

Samantha thought her study was very well designed — especially the fitted bookshelf.

See page 65 for more about fats and fatty acids.

## *...nce Helps to Inform **Decision-Making***

... scientific work eventually leads to **important discoveries** that **could** benefit humankind — ...e are often **risks** attached (and almost always **financial costs**).

... that's you, me and everyone else) must weigh up the information in order to **make decisions** — about the way ...vhat we eat, what we drive, and so on. Information is also used by **politicians** to devise policies and laws.

- ...fic advances mean that **hydrogen-oxygen fuel cells** can now be made (see page 148). They're better for the ...**ment** than batteries, because their only waste product is **water**. But you do need to **use energy** to produce ...**rogen** and **oxygen** in the first place. And hydrogen is **highly flammable**, so it's tricky to store safely.
- ...aceutical drugs are really expensive to develop, and drug companies want to make money. So they put most ...heir efforts into developing drugs that they can sell for a good price. Society has to consider the **cost** of buying new drugs — the **NHS** can't afford the most expensive drugs without **sacrificing** something else.
- **Synthetic polymers** are very useful — they're **cheap** to produce and very **durable**. But they're **hard to dispose of** (they don't break down easily). So we need to make choices about how we can best dispose of plastics (see page 102) and whether we should try to **reduce** the amount that we use, or work to develop more **biodegradable plastics**.

## *So there you have it — how science works...*

*Hopefully these pages have given you a nice intro to how science works, e.g. what scientists do to provide you with 'facts'. You need to understand this, as you're expected to know how science works yourselves — for the exam and for life.*

# The Periodic Table and Bonding

*You learnt all about the periodic table and bonding at AS — sadly you still need to know it at A2.*
***Strictly, these pages are for OCR B only, but they're a good recap for anyone who's feeling a bit rusty.***

## *The **Periodic Table** arranges Elements by **Proton Number***

1) The periodic table (there's one inside the front cover) is arranged into **periods** (rows) and **groups** (columns).
2) All the elements **within a period** have the same number of **electron shells** (if you don't worry about the sub-shells).
3) All the elements **within a group** have the same number of **electrons in their outer shell**. This means they have similar chemical properties. The group number tells you the number of electrons in the outer shell, e.g. Group 1 elements have 1 electron in their outer shell, Group 4 elements have 4 electrons, and so on...
4) The table is also split into **blocks** — Groups 1 and 2 are the **s-block**, Groups 3-0 are the **p-block** and the block of elements in between is the **d-block** (see p.153). The blocks help you work out **electronic configurations**.

## ***Ionic Bonding** is When **Ions** are Stuck Together by **Electrostatic Attraction***

1) Ions are formed when **electrons** are **transferred** from one atom to another. Atoms want to lose or gain electrons so that they have a **full outer shell**.

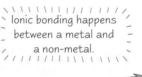

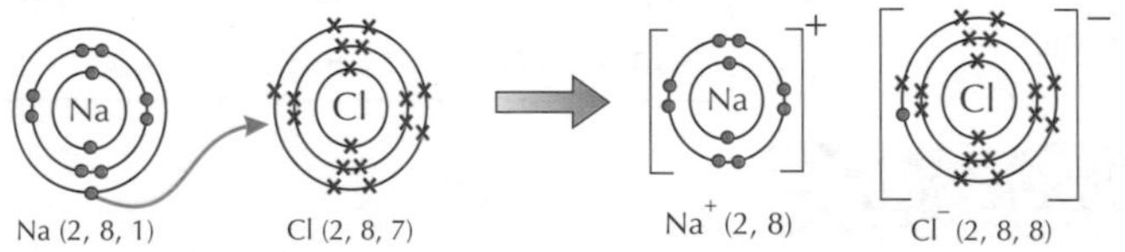


Ionic bonding happens between a metal and a non-metal.

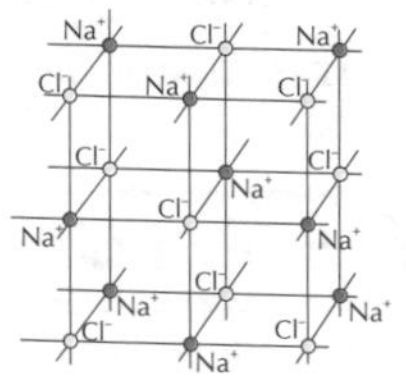


2) **Electrostatic attraction** holds positive and negative ions together in a lattice.

You need to know the names and formulas of these **compound ions**:
sulfate: $\mathbf{SO_4^{2-}}$, carbonate: $\mathbf{CO_3^{2-}}$, nitrate: $\mathbf{NO_3^-}$, hydroxide: $\mathbf{OH^-}$, hydrogencarbonate: $\mathbf{HCO_3^-}$ and ammonium: $\mathbf{NH_4^+}$.

## ***Metals** Have Giant Structures*

1) In metallic lattices, the electrons in the outermost shell of the metal atoms are **delocalised** — they're free to move. This leaves a **positive metal ion**, e.g. $Na^+$, $Mg^{2+}$, $Al^{3+}$.
2) The positive metal ions are **attracted** to the delocalised negative electrons. They form a lattice of closely packed positive ions in a **sea** of delocalised electrons — this is **metallic bonding**.

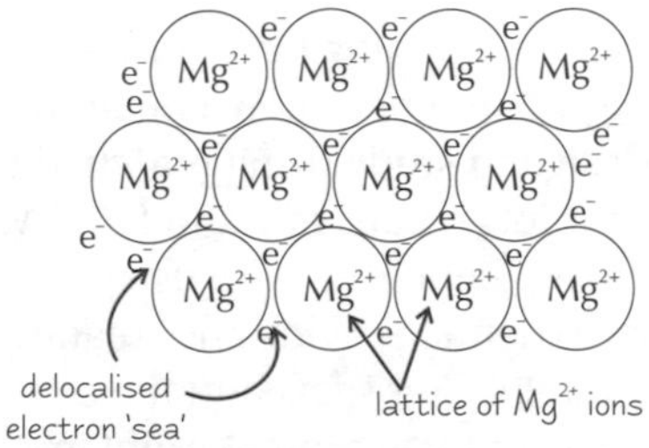


## ***Molecules** are Groups of Atoms **Covalently Bonded** Together*

Covalent bonding between non-

1) In covalent bonding, two atoms **share** electrons, so they've **both** got full outer shells of electrons. Both the positive nuclei are attracted **electrostatically** to the shared electrons.

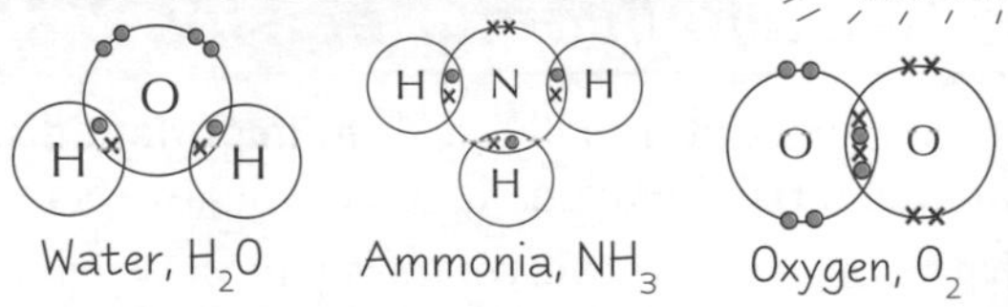


2) In a **dative** (or **coordinate**) covalent bond, one atom donates **both electrons** to a bond. E.g. to form an **ammonium ion** ($NH_4^+$), the nitrogen atom in ammonia **donates a pair of electrons** to a pr

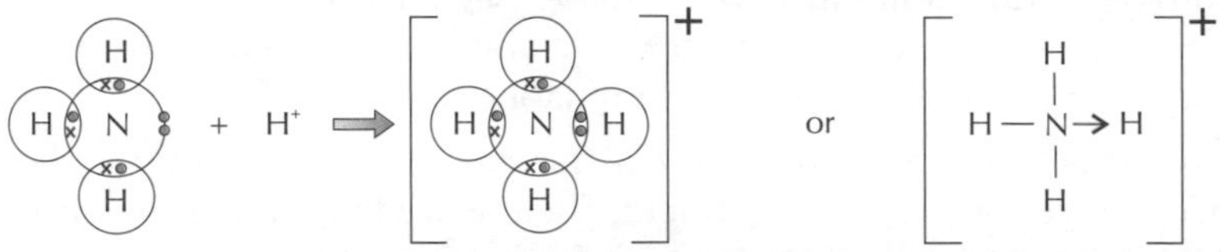

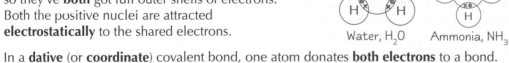

Dative covalent bonding in diagrams by an arrow, away from the 'donor' at

## *Some **Covalently Bonded** Substances Have **Giant Structures***

**Carbon** can form giant networks of **covalently** bonded atoms.

<u>Graphite</u> — each carbon forms 3 covalent bonds. The spare electrons are free to move through the layers and can carry a current. The layers are held together by intermolecular forces (see p7).

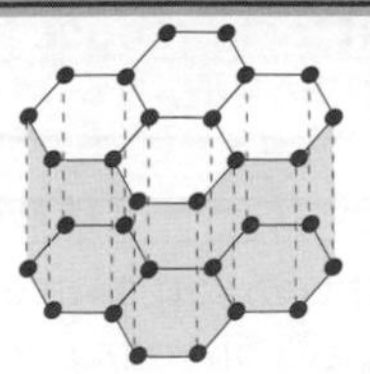

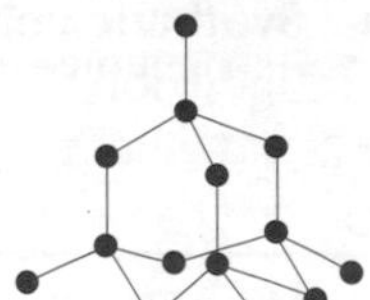

<u>Diamond</u> — each carbon form 4 strong covalent bonds.

# The Periodic Table and Bonding

## Learn the **Properties** of the Main Substance Types

| Bonding | Examples | Melting and boiling points | Typical state at STP | Does solid conduct electricity? | Does liquid conduct electricity? | Is it soluble in water? |
|---|---|---|---|---|---|---|
| Ionic | NaCl<br>$MgCl_2$ | High | Solid | No (ions are held firmly in place) | Yes (ions are free to move) | Yes |
| Simple molecular (covalent) | $CO_2$<br>$I_2$<br>$H_2O$ | Low (have to overcome intermolecular forces, see p 7, not covalent bonds) | Sometimes solid, usually liquid or gas (water is liquid because it has hydrogen bonds) | No | No | Depends on how polarised the molecule is |
| Giant molecular (covalent) | Diamond<br>Graphite<br>$SiO_2$ | High | Solid | No (except graphite) | —<br>(will generally sublime) | No |
| Metallic | Fe<br>Mg | High | Solid | Yes (delocalised electrons) | Yes (delocalised electrons) | No |

## Electron Pairs **Repel** Each Other

The shape of a molecule (or molecular ion) depends on the **number of electron pairs** in the outer shell of the central atom. Electron pairs **repel** each other as much as they can and different **types** of electron pair repel more than others.

*Lone-pair/lone-pair bond angles are the biggest.* *Lone-pair/bonding-pair bond angles are the second biggest.* *Bonding-pair/bonding-pair bond angles are the smallest.*

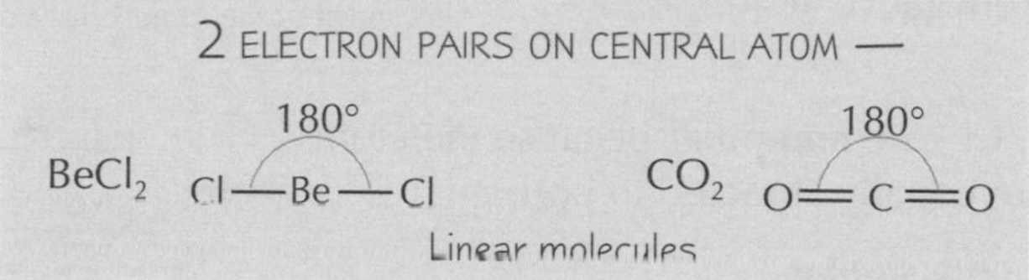


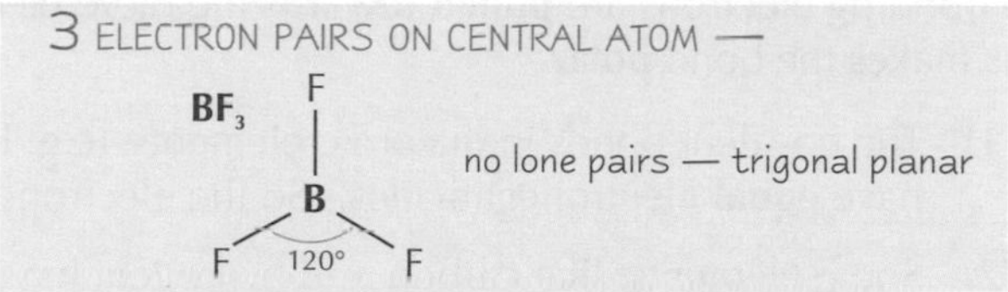


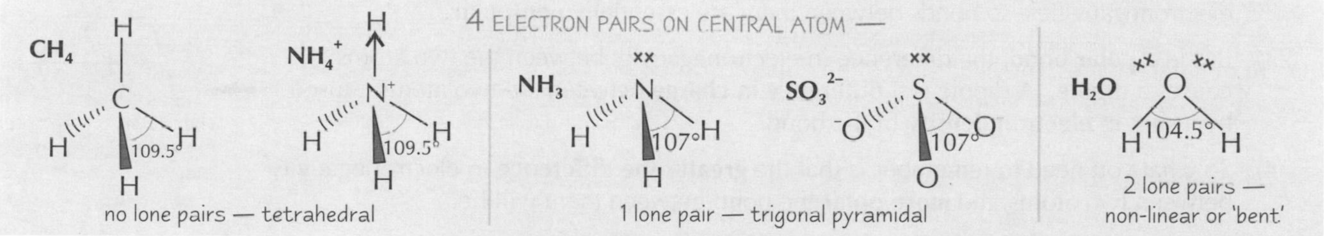

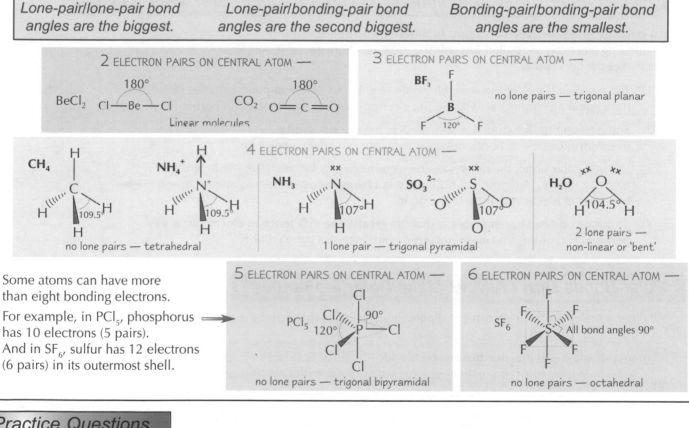

Some atoms can have more than eight bonding electrons.

For example, in $PCl_5$, phosphorus has 10 electrons (5 pairs). And in $SF_6$, sulfur has 12 electrons (6 pairs) in its outermost shell.

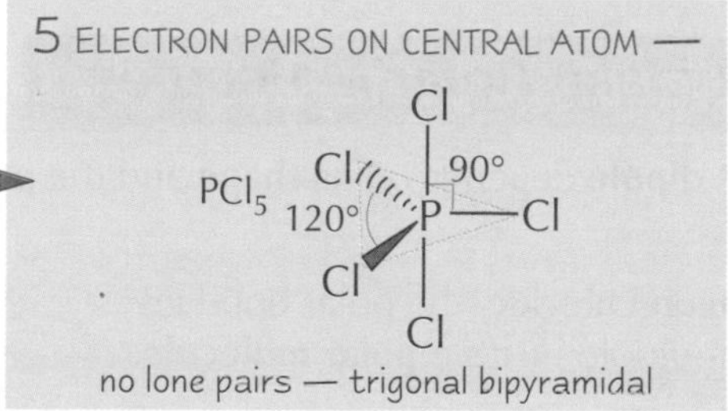


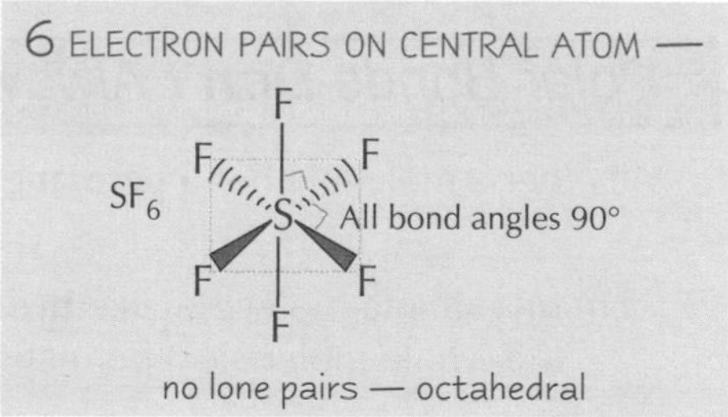


## Practice Questions

Q1 What's the difference between a covalent bond and a dative covalent bond?

Q2 Name the shape formed by a molecule with 4 electron pairs around its central atom (and no lone-pairs).

**Exam Question**

1 a) The molecule ICl contains a covalent bond.
Showing outer-shell electrons only, draw a 'dot-and-cross' diagram to show the bonding in ICl. [2 marks]

b) The molecules $BCl_3$ and $NCl_3$ both consist of a central atom surrounded by three Cl atoms – but they are not the same shape. Predict the shapes of the two molecules and explain why they are different. [3 marks]

c) Sodium chloride and silicon dioxide consist of different types of giant lattice structure.
Name the structures and describe a test that you could do to tell them apart. [4 marks]

## Do you expect me to talk? No, Mr Bond — I expect you to form molecules...

*There's nowt new here. You've just got to make sure it's not been pushed out of your brain by all the new A2 stuff.*

# Electronegativity and Intermolecular Forces

*Pulling power... that's what we're talking about here. The ability to pull electrons.*
***Again, these pages are for OCR B only, but they're worth reading for revision whichever spec you're doing.***

## Some Atoms **Attract** Bonding Electrons More than Other Atoms

The ability to attract the bonding electrons in a covalent bond is called **electronegativity.**

1) Electronegativity is usually measured using the **Pauling scale** — the higher the value, the more electronegative the element.
2) **Fluorine** is the most electronegative element. Oxygen, nitrogen and chlorine are also strongly electronegative.
3) In general, electronegativity **increases across periods** and **decreases down groups** (ignoring the noble gases).

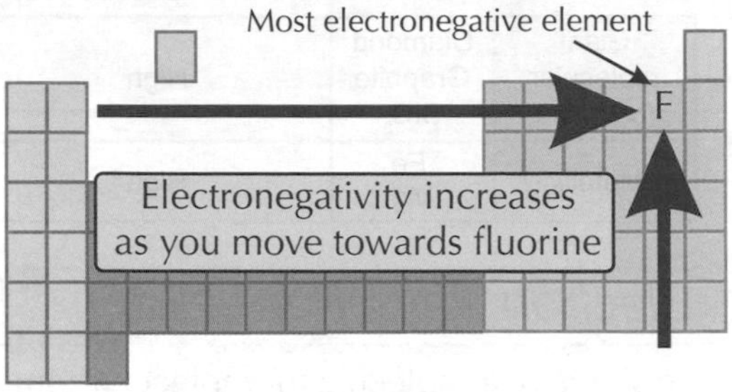


## Covalent Bonds may be Polarised by **Differences** in **Electronegativity**

In a covalent bond between two atoms of **different** electronegativities, the bonding electrons are **pulled towards** the more electronegative atom. This makes the bond **polar**.

So most molecules aren't **purely covalent** — they have some **ionic character**.

1) The covalent bonds in diatomic elements (e.g. $H_2$, $Cl_2$) are **non-polar** because the atoms have **equal** electronegativities. So the electrons are equally attracted to both nuclei.

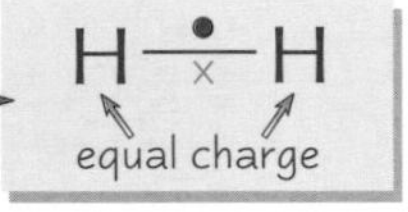


2) Some elements, like carbon and hydrogen, have pretty **similar** electronegativities, so bonds between them are essentially **non-polar**.
3) But in a **polar bond**, the difference in electronegativity between the two atoms causes a **dipole**. A dipole is a **difference in charge** between the two atoms caused by a shift in **electron density** in the bond.

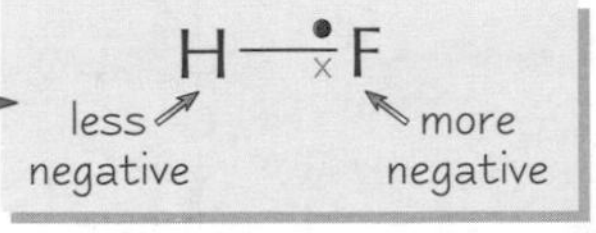


4) So what you need to remember is that the **greater the difference** in electronegativity between two atoms, the **more polar** the bond between them will be.

## Polar Bonds **Don't** Always Make **Polar Molecules**

Whether a molecule has a **permanent dipole** depends on its **shape** and the **polarity** of its bonds.

1) In a simple molecule, like **hydrogen chloride**, the polar bond gives the whole molecule a permanent dipole — it's a **polar molecule**.

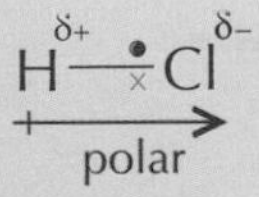


'δ' (delta) means 'slightly', so 'δ+' means 'slightly positive'.

2) A more complicated molecule may have **several polar bonds**. If the polar bonds are arranged so they point in opposite directions, they'll **cancel each other out** — the molecule is **non-polar** overall.

No dipole overall.

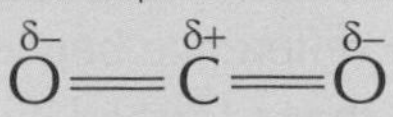


3) If the polar bonds all point in roughly the **same direction**, then the molecule is **polar**.

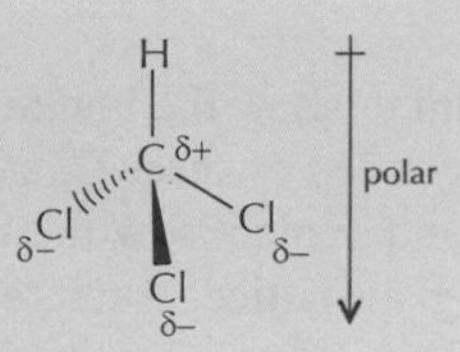


4) **Lone pairs of electrons** on the central atom also have an effect on the overall polarity and may **cancel out** the dipole created by the bonding pairs.

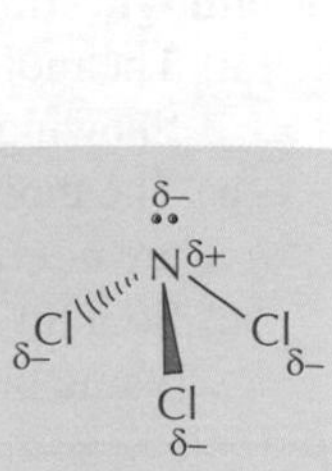


No dipole overall.

# Electronegativity and Intermolecular Forces

## Intermolecular Forces are *Very Weak*

Intermolecular forces are forces **between** molecules. They're much **weaker** than covalent, ionic or metallic bonds. There are three types you need to know about:

### *Permanent Dipole-Permanent Dipole* Bonding

The δ+ and δ– charges on **polar molecules** cause **weak electrostatic forces** of attraction **between** molecules.

The polar molecules in **hydrogen chloride gas** interact in this way.

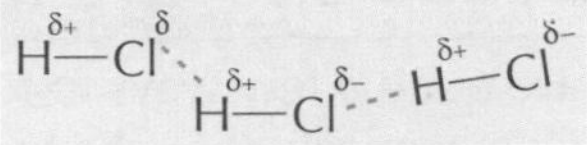

### *Instantaneous Dipole-Induced Dipole* Bonding

...otherwise known as **Van der Waals forces**.

**These forces** cause **all** atoms and molecules to be **attracted** to each other.

1) **Electrons** in charge clouds are always **moving** really quickly. At any one moment, the electrons in an atom are likely to be more to one side than the other. At this moment, the atom has a **temporary dipole**.
2) This dipole can create **another** temporary dipole in the opposite direction on a neighbouring atom. The two dipoles are then **attracted** to each other.

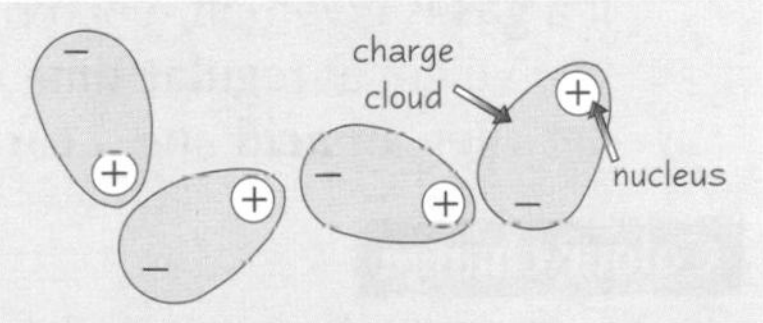


3) Because the electrons are constantly moving, the dipoles are being **created** and **destroyed** all the time. This means that dipole-dipole attractions are only temporary — this is the weakest type of intermolecular bonding.

The **size** and **shape** of molecules affects the **strength** of the **intermolecular forces** between them.
- In organic molecules, the **longer** the carbon chain is, the **stronger** the induced dipole forces will be, because there's **more molecular surface area** and more **electrons** to interact.
- Branched-chain molecules can't **pack closely** together, and they also have smaller **molecular surface areas** — so the instantaneous dipole-dipole forces between them are small.

### *Hydrogen* Bonding

1) Hydrogen bonding happens when **hydrogen** is covalently bonded to **fluorine**, **nitrogen** or **oxygen**. They're all very **electronegative**, so they draw the bonding electrons away from the hydrogen atom.
2) The bond is so **polarised** that the hydrogen atoms form weak bonds with **lone pairs of electrons** on the fluorine, nitrogen or oxygen atoms of **other molecules**.
3) Hydrogen bonding is the strongest of the three types of intermolecular bonding.

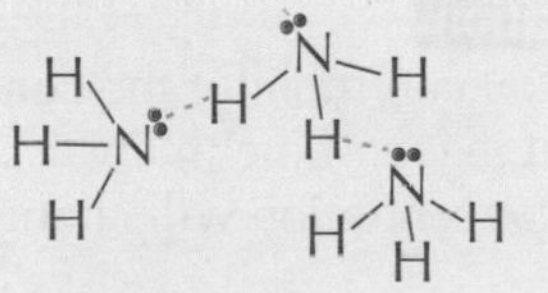

H bonding in ammonia

## Practice Questions

Q1 Write a definition of electronegativity.

Q2 Which element is the most electronegative?

Q3 List the three types of intermolecular bond in order of increasing strength.

**Exam Questions**

1 a) Draw a diagram of two water molecules with a hydrogen bond between them. Show the $\delta^+$ and $\delta^-$ charges on all the oxygen and hydrogen atoms. [2 marks]

b) What is the strongest type of intermolecular bonding holding the molecules in liquid hydrogen bromide together? [1 marks]

2 a) Which element would you expect to be more electronegative — sulfur or oxygen? Explain your answer. [2 marks]

b) The structure of sulfur trioxide is shown on the right. Label each of the S and O atoms with $\delta^+$ or $\delta^-$ to show the polarity of the S=O bonds. [2 marks]

c) Is the sulfur trioxide molecule polar or non-polar overall? Explain your answer. [2 marks]

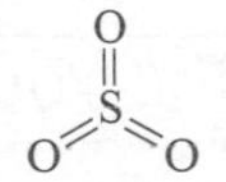

Sulfur trioxide

## Electronegativity — what I feel when I listen to techno...

*All those electrons being pulled around, left, right and centre. Makes me dizzy just thinking about it. It's all pretty logical really though — where you have opposite charges, even the tiny ones that you get from differences in electronegativity, stuff sticks together. And that's how you end up with intermolecular bonding. Delta negative meets delta positive. Ahhh...*

# Rate Graphs and Orders

***These pages are for AQA (Unit 4), OCR A (Unit 5), OCR B (Unit 4) and Edexcel (Unit 4).***

## The **Reaction Rate** tells you How Fast **Reactants** are Converted to **Products**

The **reaction rate** is the **change in the amount** of reactants or products **per unit time** (normally per second).

If the reactants are in **solution**, the rate'll be **change in concentration per second** and the units will be **mol dm$^{-3}$ s$^{-1}$**.

## There are **Loads** of Ways to **Follow the Rate of a Reaction**

Although there are quite a few ways to follow reactions, not every method works for every reaction.
You've got to **pick a property** that **changes** as the reaction goes on.

**Gas volume**

If a **gas** is given off, you could **collect it** in a gas syringe and record how much you've got at **regular time intervals**. For example, this'd work for the reaction between an **acid** and a **carbonate** in which **carbon dioxide gas** is given off.

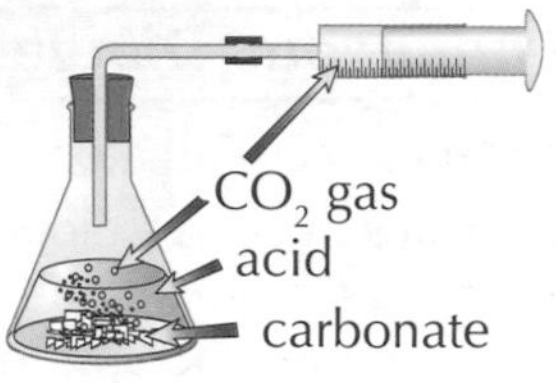
$CO_2$ gas
acid
carbonate

**Colour change**

You can sometimes track the colour change of a reaction using a gadget called a **colorimeter** (see p163).
For example, in the reaction between propanone and iodine, the **brown** colour fades.

$$\underset{\text{colourless}}{CH_3COCH_{3(aq)}} + \underset{\text{brown}}{I_{2(aq)}} \rightarrow \underbrace{CH_3COCH_2I_{(aq)} + H^+_{(aq)} + I^-_{(aq)}}_{\text{colourless}}$$

**Loss of mass**

If a **gas** is given off, the system will **lose mass**. You can measure this at regular intervals with a **balance**.

**pH measurement**

If one of the reactants or products is an **acid or base** you could follow the reaction by monitoring the pH of the reaction mixture. The simplest way to do this is by using a **pH meter** or pH probe connected to a datalogger.

**Titration**

You can monitor the **concentration** of a reactant or product in a solution by taking small samples of the reaction mixture at regular time intervals and **titrating** them. You'll need to **slow** the reaction happening in the sample though, or the concentration will change as you're trying to measure it. One way to do this is to **dilute** the sample with distilled water.

## Work Out **Reaction Rate** from a **Concentration-Time Graph**

By repeatedly taking measurements during a reaction you can plot a **concentration-time** graph. The **gradient** of the line — or the **tangent** if the graph's a curve — is proportional to the **rate** at that point in the reaction.

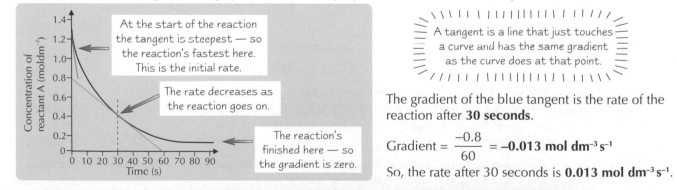

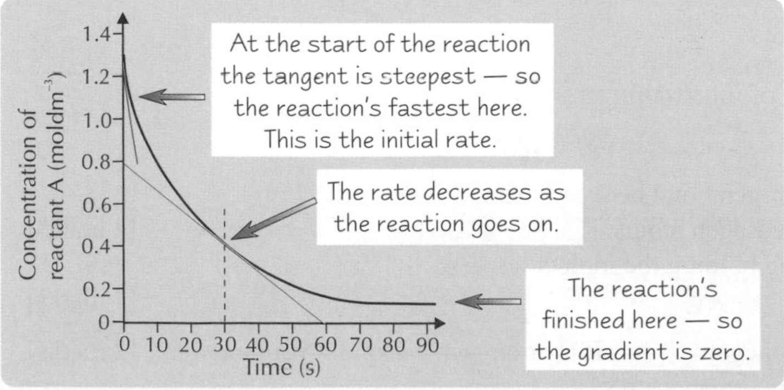
Concentration of reactant A (moldm$^{-3}$)
1.4
1.2
1.0
0.8
0.6
0.4
0.2
0
0 10 20 30 40 50 60 70 80 90
Time (s)
At the start of the reaction the tangent is steepest — so the reaction's fastest here. This is the initial rate.
The rate decreases as the reaction goes on.
The reaction's finished here — so the gradient is zero.

A tangent is a line that just touches a curve and has the same gradient as the curve does at that point.

The gradient of the blue tangent is the rate of the reaction after **30 seconds**.

$$\text{Gradient} = \frac{-0.8}{60} = \mathbf{-0.013\ mol\ dm^{-3}\ s^{-1}}$$

So, the rate after 30 seconds is **0.013 mol dm$^{-3}$ s$^{-1}$**.

## **Orders** Tell You How a Reactant's **Concentration** Affects the **Rate**

1) The **order of reaction** with respect to a particular reactant tells you how the **reactant's concentration** affects the **rate**.

   If you double the reactant's concentration and the rate **stays the same**, the order with respect to that reactant is **0**.
   If you double the reactant's concentration and the rate **also doubles**, the order with respect to that reactant is **1**.
   If you double the reactant's concentration and the rate **quadruples**, the order with respect to that reactant is **2**.

2) You can only find **orders of reaction** from **experiments**. You **can't** work them out from chemical equations.

# Rate Graphs and Orders

## The *Shape* of a *Rate-Concentration Graph* Tells You the *Order*

You can use your concentration-time graph to construct a **rate-concentration graph**, which you can then use to work out the order of the reaction. Here's how:

1) Find the **gradient** (which is the rate, remember) at various points along the concentration-time graph. This gives you a **set of points** for the rate-concentration graph.
2) Just **plot the points** and then **join them up** with a line or smooth curve, and you're done. The **shape** of the new graph tells you the **order**...

The notation [X] means 'the concentration of reactant X'.

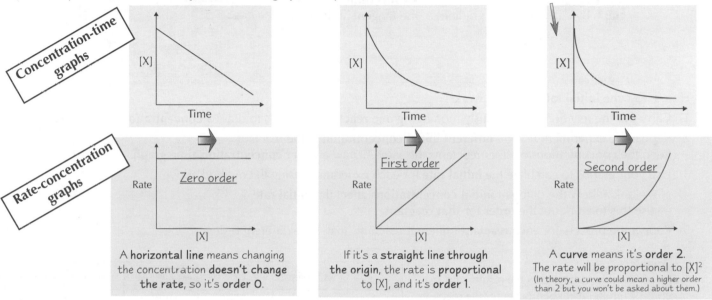

Concentration-time graphs

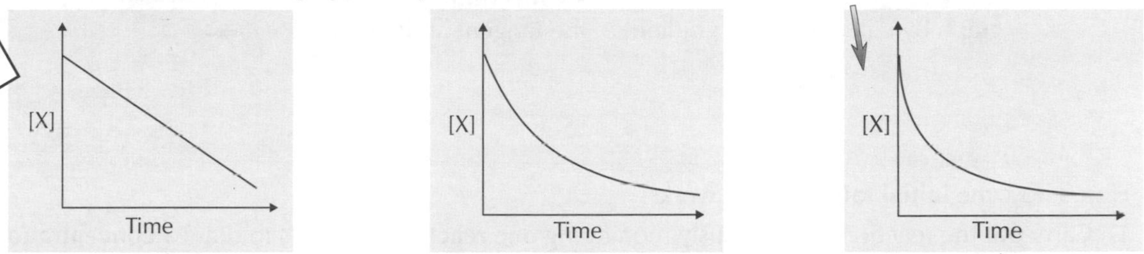


Rate-concentration graphs

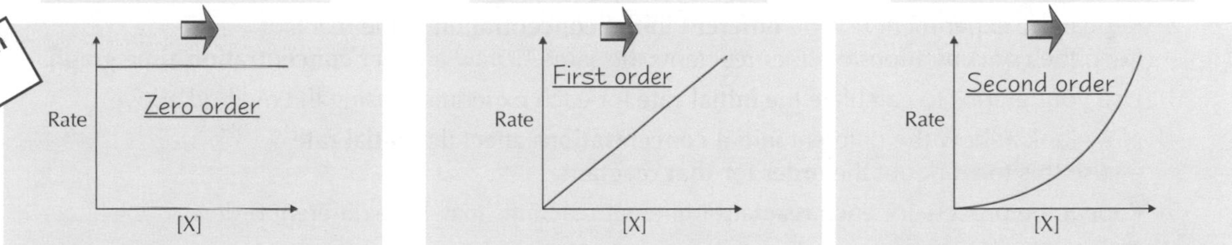


A **horizontal line** means changing the concentration **doesn't change the rate**, so it's **order 0**.

If it's a **straight line through the origin**, the rate is **proportional** to [X], and it's **order 1**.

A **curve** means it's **order 2**. The rate will be proportional to $[X]^2$ (In theory, a curve could mean a higher order than 2 but you won't be asked about them.)

## Practice Questions

Q1 Give two things that could be measured to follow the rate of a reaction.

Q2 What does the gradient of a concentration-time graph tell you?

Q3 If the rate of a reaction doubles when you double the concentration of a reactant, what is the order of reaction with respect to that reactant?

Q4 Sketch a typical rate-concentration graph for a second order reaction.

**Exam Questions**

1 It takes 200 seconds to completely dissolve a 0.4 g piece of magnesium in 25 ml of dilute hydrochloric acid. It takes 100 seconds if the concentration of the acid is doubled.

a) What is the order of the reaction with respect to the concentration of the acid? [1 mark]

b) Sketch a graph to show the relationship between the concentration of the acid and the overall rate of the reaction. [2 marks]

c) What could be measured to follow the rate of this reaction in more detail? [2 marks]

2 The rate of decomposition of hydrogen peroxide was followed by monitoring the concentration of hydrogen peroxide.

$$2H_2O_{2(aq)} \rightarrow 2H_2O_{(l)} + O_{2(g)}$$

| Time (minutes) | 0 | 20 | 40 | 60 | 80 | 100 |
|---|---|---|---|---|---|---|
| $[H_2O_2]$ (mol dm$^{-3}$) | 2.00 | 1.00 | 0.50 | 0.25 | 0.125 | 0.0625 |

a) Suggest an alternative method that could have been used to follow the rate of this reaction. [2 marks]

b) Using the data above, plot a graph and determine the rate of the reaction after 30 minutes. [6 marks]

## *Mmmm, look at those seductive curves...*

*...sorry, chemistry gets me a bit excited sometimes. I think I'm OK now. Remember — the concentration-time graphs on this page slope downwards (i.e. have negative gradients) because they show the concentration of reactants. If you measure the concentration of products instead, the graphs will flip the other way up — they'll slope upwards, but level off in the same way.*

# Initial Rates and Half-Life

*This is where it starts getting a bit mathsy. But don't panic, just take a deep breath and dive in... And don't bash your head on the bottom. Oh, and don't start sentences with 'And' or 'But' — English teachers hate it. 'Butt' is fine though.*
***These pages are for AQA (Unit 4), OCR A (Unit 5), OCR B (Unit 4) and Edexcel (Unit 4).***

## The *Initial Rates Method* can be used to work out *Orders* too

On the previous page, reaction order was found by turning a concentration-time graph into a rate-concentration graph. Another way to find order is by looking at **initial reaction rates.**

The **initial rate of a reaction** is the rate right at the **start** of the reaction. You can find this from a **concentration-time** graph by calculating the **gradient** of the **tangent** at **time = 0.**

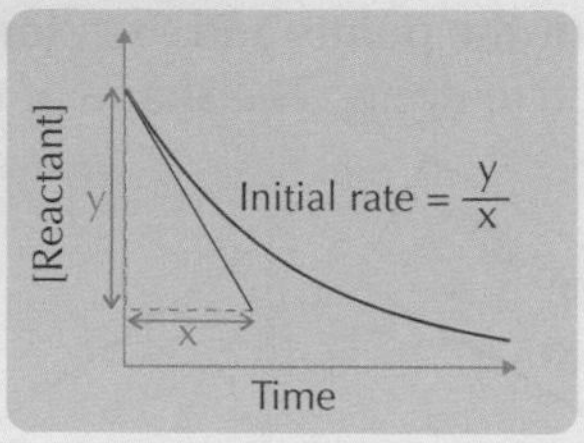


Here's how the **initial rates method** works:

1) Carry out the reaction, continuously monitoring **one reactant**. Use this to draw a **concentration-time graph**.
2) Repeat the experiment using a **different initial concentration** of the reactant.
   Keep the concentrations of other reactants the same. Draw another **concentration-time graph**.
3) Use your graphs to calculate the **initial rate** for each experiment using the method above.
4) Now look at how the different **initial concentrations** affect the **initial rate**
   — use this to work out the **order for that reactant**.
5) Repeat the process for **each reactant** (different reactants may have different orders).

***Example:***
The table on the right shows the results of a series of initial rate experiments for the reaction:

$$NO_{(g)} + CO_{(g)} + O_{2(g)} \rightarrow NO_{2(g)} + CO_{2(g)}$$

Write down the order with respect to each reactant.

| Experiment number | $[NO_{(g)}]$ (mol dm$^{-3}$) | $[CO_{(g)}]$ (mol dm$^{-3}$) | $[O_{2(g)}]$ (mol dm$^{-3}$) | Initial rate (mol dm$^{-3}$ s$^{-1}$) |
|---|---|---|---|---|
| 1 | $2.0 \times 10^{-2}$ | $1.0 \times 10^{-2}$ | $1.0 \times 10^{-2}$ | 0.176 |
| 2 | $4.0 \times 10^{-2}$ | $1.0 \times 10^{-2}$ | $1.0 \times 10^{-2}$ | 0.704 |
| 3 | $2.0 \times 10^{-2}$ | $2.0 \times 10^{-2}$ | $1.0 \times 10^{-2}$ | 0.176 |
| 4 | $2.0 \times 10^{-2}$ | $1.0 \times 10^{-2}$ | $2.0 \times 10^{-2}$ | 0.176 |

1) Look at experiments 1 and 2 — when $[NO_{(g)}]$ doubles (but all the other concentrations stay constant), the rate **quadruples**. So the reaction is **second order** with respect to NO.
2) Look at experiments 1 and 3 — when $[CO_{(g)}]$ doubles (but all the other concentrations stay constant), the rate **stays the same**. So the reaction is **zero order** with respect to CO.
3) Look at experiments 1 and 4 — when $[O_{2(g)}]$ doubles (but all the other concentrations stay constant), the rate **stays the same**. So the reaction is **zero order** with respect to $O_2$.

## *Clock Reactions* can be used to *Simplify* the Initial Rate Method

***Edexcel only***

The method described above is a bit faffy — lots of measuring and drawing graphs.
In clock reactions, the initial rate can be **easily estimated**.

1) In a **clock reaction**, you can easily **measure the time** it takes for a given amount of product to form — usually there's a sudden colour change. The **shorter** the time, the faster the **initial rate**.
2) It's a much easier way to find **initial rates** than drawing lots of **concentration-time graphs**.

The most famous clock reaction is the **iodine-clock** reaction.

- **sodium thiosulfate** solution and **starch** are added to **hydrogen peroxide** and **iodide ions** in acid solution.
- the important product of the reaction that occurs is **iodine** — after a certain amount of time, the solution will **suddenly** turn dark blue as the iodine reacts with the starch.
- varying iodide or hydrogen peroxide concentration while keeping the concentrations of the other reactants constant will give **different times** for the colour change. These can be used to work out the **reaction order**.

# Initial Rates and Half-Life

## *Half-Life is the Time for Half the Reactant to Disappear*

The **half-life ($t_{1/2}$)** of a reaction is the time it takes for **half of the reactant** to be used up.
The **half-life** of a first order reaction is **independent of the concentration**.

***Example:***

This graph shows the decomposition of hydrogen peroxide, $H_2O_2$.

$$2H_2O_{2(aq)} \rightarrow 2H_2O_{(l)} + O_{2(g)}$$

- Use the graph to measure the half-life at various points:
  $[H_2O_2]$ from **4** to **2** mol dm$^{-3}$ = **200 s**,
  $[H_2O_2]$ from **2** to **1** mol dm$^{-3}$ = **200 s**,
  $[H_2O_2]$ from **1** to **0.5** mol dm$^{-3}$ = **200 s**.
- The half-life is constant, regardless of the initial concentration, so it's a **first order reaction** with respect to **$[H_2O_2]$**.

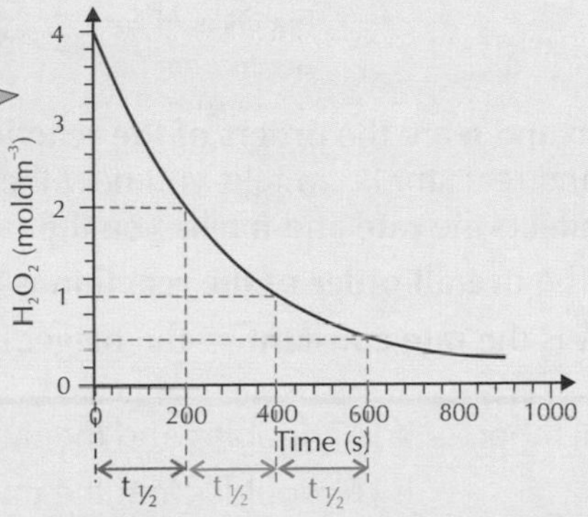


## *Practice Questions*

Q1 What is meant by the 'initial rate' of a reaction?

Q2 Describe how to calculate the initial rate of a reaction.

Q3 What is a clock reaction?

Q4 What does the term 'half-life' of a reaction mean?

**Exam Questions**

1 The table below shows the results of a series of initial rate experiments for the reaction between substances D and E.

| Experiment | [D] (mol dm$^{-3}$) | [E] (mol dm$^{-3}$) | Initial rate × $10^{-3}$ (mol dm$^{-3}$s$^{-1}$) |
|---|---|---|---|
| 1 | 0.2 | 0.2 | 1.30 |
| 2 | 0.4 | 0.2 | 5.20 |
| 3 | 0.2 | 0.4 | 2.60 |

Find the order of the reaction with respect to reactants D and E. Explain your reasoning. [4 marks]

2 The table shows the results of an experiment on the decomposition of nitrogen(V) oxide at constant temperature.

$$2N_2O_{5(g)} \rightarrow 4NO_{2(g)} + O_{2(g)}$$

| **Time (s)** | 0 | 50 | 100 | 150 | 200 | 250 | 300 |
|---|---|---|---|---|---|---|---|
| **$[N_2O_5]$ (mol dm$^{-3}$)** | 2.50 | 1.66 | 1.14 | 0.76 | 0.50 | 0.32 | 0.22 |

a) Plot a graph of these results. [3 marks]

b) From the graph, find the times for the concentration of $N_2O_5$ to decrease:

i) to half its original concentration. [2 marks]

ii) from 2.0 mol dm$^{-3}$ to 1.0 mol dm$^{-3}$. [2 marks]

c) Giving a reason, deduce the order of this reaction. [2 marks]

## *If you thought this was fun, just wait till you get a load of...*

*...page 12. That's even better. It's got a proper maths equation. It's also got shape-shifters, dogs and industrial men. And speaking of other things that are fun, can I recommend... flying kites, peeling bananas, making models of your friends out of apples, the literary works of Virginia Woolf, counting spots on the carpet, eating all the pies and cuddling with a boy.*

# Rate Equations

*Now you're going to take all the stuff you've learned from the previous pages and make a maths equation. Yay!?*
***These pages are for AQA (Unit 4), OCR A (Unit 5), OCR B (Unit 4) and Edexcel (Unit 4).***

## The Rate Equation Links Reaction Rate to Reactant Concentrations

Rate equations look mean, but all they're really telling you is how the **rate** is affected by the **concentrations of reactants**. For a general reaction: **A + B → C + D**, the **rate equation** is:

$$\text{Rate} = k[A]^m[B]^n$$

The units of rate are mol $dm^{-3}$ $s^{-1}$.

Remember — square brackets mean the concentration of whatever's inside them.

1) **m** and **n** are the **orders of the reaction** with respect to reactant A and reactant B. **m** tells you how the **concentration of reactant A** affects the **rate** and **n** tells you the same for **reactant B**.
2) The **overall order of the reaction** is **m + n**.
3) ***k*** is the **rate constant** — the bigger it is, the **faster** the reaction.

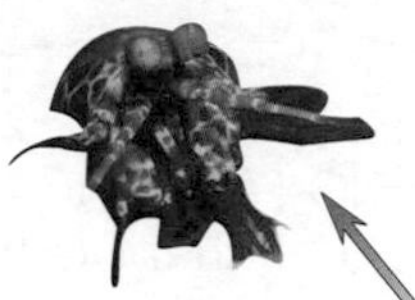

Rate constants are shape-shifters. Here is one in its true form.

Remember — If [A] doubles and the rate **stays the same**, the order with respect to A is **0**.
If [A] doubles and the rate **also doubles**, the order with respect to A is **1**.
If [A] doubles and the rate **quadruples**, the order with respect to A is **2**.

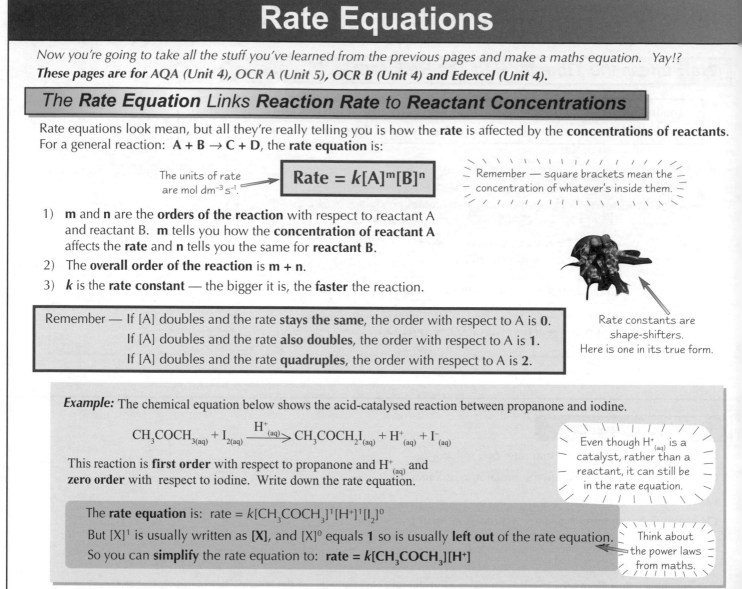

***Example:*** The chemical equation below shows the acid-catalysed reaction between propanone and iodine.

$$CH_3COCH_{3(aq)} + I_{2(aq)} \xrightarrow{H^+_{(aq)}} CH_3COCH_2I_{(aq)} + H^+_{(aq)} + I^-_{(aq)}$$

This reaction is **first order** with respect to propanone and $H^+_{(aq)}$ and **zero order** with respect to iodine. Write down the rate equation.

Even though $H^+_{(aq)}$ is a catalyst, rather than a reactant, it can still be in the rate equation.

The **rate equation** is: rate = $k[CH_3COCH_3]^1[H^+]^1[I_2]^0$
But $[X]^1$ is usually written as **[X]**, and $[X]^0$ equals **1** so is usually **left out** of the rate equation.
So you can **simplify** the rate equation to: **rate = $k[CH_3COCH_3][H^+]$**

Think about the power laws from maths.

## You can Calculate the Rate Constant from the Orders and Rate of Reaction

Once the rate and the orders of the reaction have been found by experiment, you can work out the **rate constant, *k***. The **units** of the rate constant **vary**, so you have to **work them out**.

***Example:***
The reaction below was found to be second order with respect to NO and zero order with respect to CO and $O_2$.
The rate is $1.76 \times 10^{-3}$ mol $dm^{-3}$ $s^{-1}$, when $[NO_{(g)}] = [CO_{(g)}] = [O_{2(g)}] = 2.00 \times 10^{-3}$ mol $dm^{-3}$.

$$NO_{(g)} + CO_{(g)} + O_{2(g)} \rightarrow NO_{2(g)} + CO_{2(g)}$$

Find the value of the rate constant.

First write out the **rate equation**: Rate = $k[NO]^2[CO]^0[O_2]^0 = k[NO]^2$

Next insert the **concentration** and the **rate**. **Rearrange** the equation and calculate the value of ***k***:

$$\text{Rate} = k[NO_{(g)}]^2,\ \text{so, } 1.76 \times 10^{-3} = k \times (2.00 \times 10^{-3})^2 \Rightarrow k = \frac{1.76\times10^{-3}}{(2.00\times10^{-3})^2} = 440$$

Find the **units for *k*** by putting the other units in the rate equation:

$$\text{Rate} = k[NO_{(g)}]^2,\ \text{so mol dm}^{-3}\,\text{s}^{-1} = k \times (\text{mol dm}^{-3})^2 \Rightarrow k = \frac{\text{mol dm}^{-3}\ \text{s}^{-1}}{(\text{mol dm}^{-3})^2} = \frac{\text{s}^{-1}}{\text{mol dm}^{-3}} = \text{dm}^3\ \text{mol}^{-1}\ \text{s}^{-1}$$

So the answer is: **$k$ = 440 $dm^3$ $mol^{-1}$ $s^{-1}$**

# Rate Equations

## *Temperature Changes* Affect the *Rate Constant*

1) Reactions happen when the reactant particles **collide** and have enough energy to **break** the existing bonds.
2) Increasing the temperature **speeds up** the reactant particles, so that they collide **more often**. It also increases the chances of the particles reacting when they do hit each other, as they have more energy.
3) In other words, **increasing temperature** increases the **reaction rate**.
4) According to the rate equation, reaction rate depends **only** on the rate constant and reactant concentrations. Since temperature **does** increase the reaction rate, it must **change the rate constant**.

> The **rate constant** applies to a **particular reaction** at a **certain temperature.**
> At a **higher** temperature, the reaction will have a **higher** rate constant.

## Practice Questions

Q1 Write down a general rate equation for a reaction with reactants A, B and C.

Q2 How do you work out the units of *k*?

Q3 How does temperature affect the value of *k*?

**Exam Questions**

1 The following reaction is second order with respect to NO and first order with respect to $H_2$.

$$2NO_{(g)} + 2H_{2(g)} \rightarrow 2H_2O_{(g)} + N_{2(g)}$$

a) Write a rate equation for the reaction. [2 marks]

b) The rate of the reaction at 800 °C was determined to be 0.00267 mol dm$^{-3}$ s$^{-1}$ when $[H_{2(g)}]$ = 0.0020 mol dm$^{-3}$ and $[NO_{(g)}]$ = 0.0040 mol dm$^{-3}$.

i) Calculate a value for the rate constant at 800 °C, including units. [3 marks]

ii) Predict the effect on the rate constant of decreasing the temperature of the reaction to 600 °C. [1 mark]

2 The ester ethyl ethanoate, $CH_3COOC_2H_5$, is hydrolysed by heating with dilute acid to give ethanol and ethanoic acid. The reaction is first order with respect to the concentration of $H^+$ and the ester.

a) Write the rate equation for the reaction. [1 mark]

b) When the initial concentration of the acid is 2.0 mol dm$^{-3}$ and the ester is 0.25 mol dm$^{-3}$, the initial rate is $2.2 \times 10^{-3}$ mol dm$^{-3}$ s$^{-1}$. Calculate a value for the rate constant at this temperature and give its units. [3 marks]

c) The temperature is kept constant and more solvent is added to the initial mixture so that the volume doubles. Calculate the new initial rate. [2 marks]

3 A reaction between substances X and Y, which is first order with respect to X and Y, has an initial rate of $1.6 \times 10^{-3}$ mol dm$^{-3}$ s$^{-1}$ at 300 K. The reaction rate is doubled when the temperature rises by 10 K (a 3.33% increase).

Which of the following changes, A or B, has a greater effect on the reaction rate? Explain your answer.

A Increasing the temperature by 10 K

B Increasing the concentration of X from 2.00 mol dm$^{-3}$ to 2.06 mol dm$^{-3}$ (a 3.33% increase)? [3 marks]

## *Rate constants are masters of disguise...*

*Here are some of their most common disguises. If you think you've spotted one, heating it will transform it back.*

# Rates and Reaction Mechanisms

*It's a cold, miserable grey day outside, but on the plus side I just had a really nice slice of carrot and ginger cake. Anyway, this page is about the connection between rate equations and reaction mechanisms.*
***These pages are for AQA (Unit 4), OCR A (Unit 5), OCR B (Unit 4) and Edexcel (Unit 4).***

## The **Rate-Determining Step** is the **Slowest Step** in a Multi-Step Reaction

Mechanisms can have **one step** or a **series of steps**. In a series of steps, each step can have a **different rate**. The **overall rate** is decided by the step with the **slowest** rate — the **rate-determining step**.

Otherwise known as the rate-limiting step.

## Reactants in the **Rate Equation** Affect the **Rate**

The rate equation is handy for helping you work out the **mechanism** of a chemical reaction.

You need to be able to pick out which reactants from the chemical equation are involved in the **rate-determining step**. Here are the **rules** for doing this:

> If a reactant appears in the **rate equation**, it must be affecting the **rate**. So this reactant, or something derived from it, must be in the **rate-determining step**.
>
> If a reactant **doesn't** appear in the **rate equation**, then it **won't** be involved in the **rate-determining step** (and neither will anything derived from it).

Catalysts can appear in rate equations, so they can be in rate-determining steps too.

Some **important points** to remember about rate-determining steps and mechanisms are:

1) The rate-determining step **doesn't** have to be the first step in a mechanism.
2) The reaction mechanism **can't** usually be predicted from **just** the chemical equation.

## You Can Predict the **Rate Equation** from the **Rate-Determining Step...**

> The **order of a reaction** with respect to a reactant shows the **number of molecules** of that reactant which are involved in the **rate-determining step**.

So, if a reaction's second order with respect to X, there'll be two molecules of X in the rate-determining step.

For example, the mechanism for the reaction between **chlorine free radicals** and **ozone**, $O_3$, consists of **two steps**:

$$Cl\bullet_{(g)} + O_{3(g)} \rightarrow ClO\bullet_{(g)} + O_{2(g)}$$ — **slow (rate-determining step)**

$$ClO\bullet_{(g)} + O\bullet_{(g)} \rightarrow Cl\bullet_{(g)} + O_{2(g)}$$ — **fast**

$Cl\bullet$ and $O_3$ must both be in the rate equation, so the rate equation is of the form: **rate =** $k[Cl\bullet]^m[O_3]^n$.
There's only **one** $Cl\bullet$ radical and **one** $O_3$ molecule in the rate-determining step, so the **orders**, m and n, are both **1**.
So the rate equation is **rate =** $k[Cl\bullet][O_3]$.

## **...And You Can Predict the Mechanism from the Rate Equation**

Knowing exactly which reactants are in the **rate-determining step** gives you an idea of the reaction **mechanism**.

For example, here are two possible mechanisms for the reaction $(CH_3)_3CBr + OH^- \rightarrow (CH_3)_3COH + Br^-$

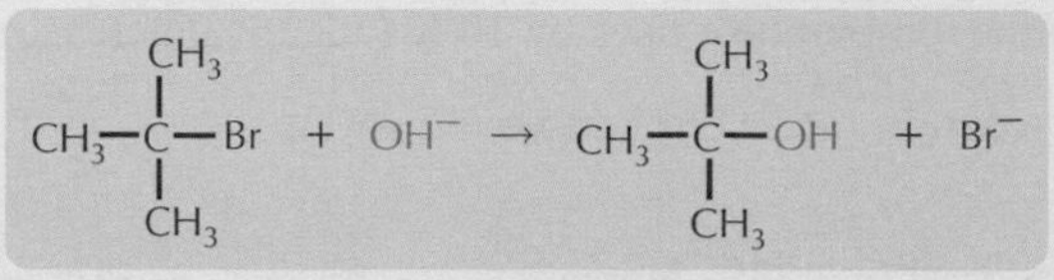

**or**

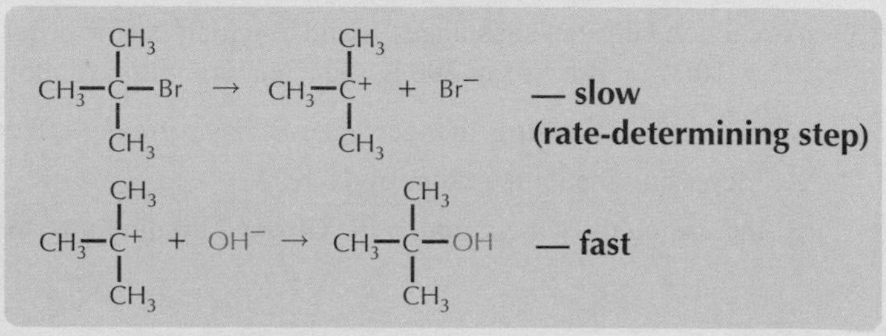

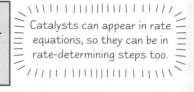

The actual **rate equation** was worked out by rate experiments: **rate =** $k[(CH_3)_3CBr]$
**$OH^-$** isn't in the **rate equation**, so it **can't** be involved in the rate-determining step.
The **second mechanism** is most likely to be correct because $OH^-$ **isn't** in the rate-determining step.

# Rates and Reaction Mechanisms

## You have to Take Care when Suggesting a Mechanism

If you're suggesting a mechanism, **watch out** — things might not always be what they seem.
For example, when nitrogen(V) oxide, $N_2O_5$, decomposes, it forms nitrogen(IV) oxide and oxygen:

$$2N_2O_{5(g)} \rightarrow 4NO_{2(g)} + O_{2(g)}$$

From the chemical equation, it looks like **two** $N_2O_5$ molecules react with each other. So you might predict that the reaction is **second order** with respect to $N_2O_5$ ... but you'd be wrong.

Experimentally, it's been found that the reaction is **first order** with respect to $N_2O_5$ — the rate equation is: **rate = $k[N_2O_5]$**.
This shows that there's only one molecule of $N_2O_5$ in the rate-determining step.

One **possible mechanism** that fits the rate equation is:

Only one molecule of $N_2O_5$ is in the rate-determining step, fitting in with the rate equation.

$N_2O_{5(g)} \rightarrow NO_{2(g)} + NO_{3(g)}$ — **slow (rate-determining step)**

$NO_{3(g)} + N_2O_{5(g)} \rightarrow 3NO_{2(g)} + O_{2(g)}$ — **fast**

The two steps add up to the overall chemical equation. You can cancel the $NO_{3(g)}$ as it appears on both sides.

## Practice Questions

Q1 What is meant by the term 'rate-determining step'?

Q2 Is the rate-determining step the first step in the reaction?

Q3 What is the connection between the rate equation and the rate-determining step?

Q4 How can the rate-determining step help you to understand the mechanism?

**Exam Questions**

1 The following reaction is first order with respect to $H_2$ and first order with respect to ICl.

$$H_{2(g)} + 2ICl_{(g)} \rightarrow I_{2(g)} + 2HCl_{(g)}$$

a) Write the rate equation for this reaction. [1 mark]

b) The mechanism for this reaction consists of two steps.
   i) Identify the molecules that are in the rate-determining step. Justify your answer. [2 marks]
   ii) A chemist suggested the following mechanism for the reaction.

$2ICl_{(g)} \rightarrow I_{2(g)} + Cl_{2(g)}$ slow

$H_{2(g)} + Cl_{2(g)} \rightarrow 2HCl_{(g)}$ fast

   Suggest, with reasons, whether this mechanism is likely to be correct. [2 marks]

2 The reaction between hydrogen bromide and oxygen gas occurs rapidly at 700 K.

It can be represented by the equation $4HBr_{(g)} + O_{2(g)} \rightarrow 2H_2O_{(g)} + 2Br_{2(g)}$

The rate equation found by experiment is Rate = $k[HBr][O_2]$

a) Explain why the reaction cannot be a one-step reaction. [3 marks]

b) Each of the 4 steps of this reaction involves the reaction of 1 molecule of HBr. Two of the steps are the same. The rate-determining step is the first one and results in the formation of $HBrO_2$. Write equations for the full set of 4 reactions. [4 marks]

## *I found rate-determining step aerobics a bit on the slow side...*

*These pages show you how rate equations, orders of reaction and reaction mechanisms all tie together and how each actually means something in the grand scheme of A2 Chemistry. It's all very profound. So get it all learnt and answer the questions and then you'll have plenty of time to practise the quickstep for your Strictly Come Dancing routine.*

# Rate Calculations

***Technically, these pages are only for Edexcel (Unit 4) — but everybody else might find the worked example helpful too.***

## You can **Work Out** Order Of Reaction and Rate Equation by **Experimentation**

The way to solve these kinds of problems is generally the same.

1) Do a series of experiments **monitoring** the **rate of the reaction.**
2) In each separate experiment, **vary** the concentration of **only one reactant**. Keep everything else the same.
3) **Plot** each experiment on a **concentration-time graph** for each experiment and **calculate** the **initial rate of reaction** (gradient at t = 0).
4) Analyse the results to see how changing the concentration affects the rate, and work out the **rate equation**. Once you've got the rate equation, you can try predicting the **reaction mechanism**.

## Worked Example — Reaction of **Propanone** and **Iodine**

The **equation** for this reaction is:

$$CH_3COCH_{3(aq)} + I_{2(aq)} \xrightarrow{H^+_{(aq)}} CH_3COCH_2I_{(aq)} + H^+_{(aq)} + I^-_{(aq)}$$

And from this, you can write the **rate equation**: $\text{Rate} = k\,[CH_3COCH_3]^x\,[H^+]^y\,[I_2]^z$

Now you need to work out the values of x, y and z from the data.

## **Repeat** Experiments **Changing** the Concentration of **Only One** Reactant

You can monitor the reaction by **taking samples** at regular intervals. You need to **stop** the reaction in the sample by adding sodium hydrogencarbonate to neutralise the acid.

**Titrate** the sample solutions against sodium thiosulfate and starch to work out the **concentration of the iodine** (see p42).

Carry out the experiment several times. In each experiment, you should **only** change the concentration of **one reactant**.

| Experiment | 1 | 2 | 3 | 4 | 5 | 6 | 7 |
|---|---|---|---|---|---|---|---|
| [Propanone] (mol dm$^{-3}$) | 0.4 | 0.8 | 1.2 | 0.4 | 0.4 | 0.4 | 0.4 |
| [Iodine] (mol dm$^{-3}$) | 0.002 | 0.002 | 0.002 | 0.004 | 0.006 | 0.002 | 0.002 |
| [H$^+$] (mol dm$^{-3}$) | 0.4 | 0.4 | 0.4 | 0.4 | 0.4 | 0.8 | 1.2 |

## Plot **Concentration-Time** Graphs to Work Out the **Rate of Reaction**

Here is the **table of data** from each of the seven experiments. The volume of sodium thiosulfate is proportional to the concentration of iodine, so the results can be used to draw a series of **concentration-time graphs**. From each graph you can work out the **initial rate of reaction** by **measuring the gradient** at t = 0.

| | Volume of sodium thiosulfate (cm$^{-3}$) | | | | | | |
|---|---|---|---|---|---|---|---|
| Experiment | 1 | 2 | 3 | 4 | 5 | 6 | 7 |
| 0 seconds | 19.0 | 19.0 | 19.0 | 38.0 | 57.0 | 19.0 | 19.0 |
| 60 seconds | 17.0 | 15.3 | 13.5 | 36.0 | 55.0 | 15.5 | 13.4 |
| 120 seconds | 15.0 | 12.1 | 8.7 | 33.9 | 53.3 | 12.0 | 8.6 |
| 180 seconds | 13.0 | 9.2 | 5.1 | 31.9 | 51.6 | 9.0 | 4.9 |
| 240 seconds | 11.0 | 6.7 | 3.0 | 29.8 | 49.9 | 6.5 | 3.1 |

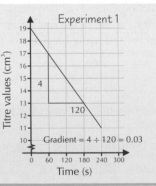

In this experiment the graph is a **straight line**, so it's easy to measure the gradient. If the graph was a **curve**, you'd need to measure the **initial gradient** (gradient at t = 0) to work out the initial rate.

## **Compare** the Results to Determine the **Effect** of **Concentration** on the **Rate**

Once you've worked out the rate for each experiment it's time to make another table. This time it shows how **changing** the concentration of the **reactants** affects the **rates of reaction**.

| Expt | Change compared to Expt 1 | Rate of Reaction | Change |
|---|---|---|---|
| 1 | — | 0.033 | — |
| 2 | [propanone] doubled | 0.062 | Rate doubled |
| 3 | [propanone] trebled | 0.092 | Rate trebled |
| 4 | [iodine] doubled | 0.034 | No change in rate |
| 5 | [iodine] trebled | 0.032 | No change in rate |
| 6 | [H$^+$] doubled | 0.058 | Rate doubled |
| 7 | [H$^+$] trebled | 0.094 | Rate trebled |

# Rate Calculations

## Work Out the **Rate** Equation

From the table at the bottom of page 16, you can say...

1) The **rate is proportional** to [propanone], so the **order is 1** with respect to propanone.
2) The **rate is independent** of [iodine], so the **order is 0** with respect to iodine.
3) The **rate is proportional** to [$H^+$], so the **order is 1** with respect to [$H^+$].

See p8 for how changing the concentration of reactants relates to the rate order.

You can now write the full rate equation...

**Rate = $k[CH_3COCH_3]^1[H^+]^1[I_2]^0 = k[CH_3COCH_3][H^+]$**

You can now see that the rate is independent of [iodine], which is why the graphs of [iodine] vs time are straight lines.

## Use the **Rate Equation** to Come Up with a **Reaction Mechanism**

Using the rules about reaction mechanisms on page 14, here's what you can say about the reaction:

1) Propanone and $H^+$ are **in the rate equation** — so they must be **in the rate-determining step.**
2) Iodine is **not in the rate equation** so it's **not in the rate-determining step.**
3) The **order** of reaction for propanone and $H^+$ is **1** — so the rate determining step must use **1 molecule** of each.
4) $H^+$ is a **catalyst** — so it must be **regenerated** in another step.

And when you put all that together you could come up with a reaction mechanism like this...

Step 1 **only** involves **one** molecule of propanone and **one** of $H^+$.

Iodine is **not** in the rate equation, so **doesn't** appear in the rate-determining step — instead it appears in step three.

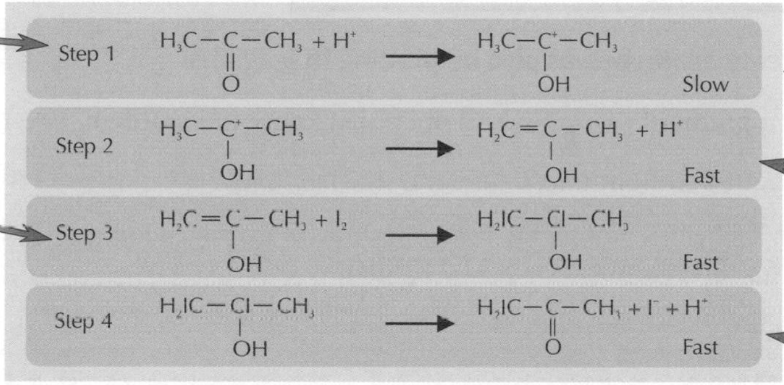

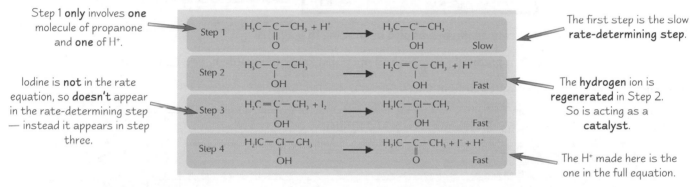

The first step is the slow **rate-determining step**.

The **hydrogen** ion is **regenerated** in Step 2. So is acting as a **catalyst**.

The $H^+$ made here is the one in the full equation.

## Practice Questions

Q1 Why is sodium hydrogencarbonate added to samples from the reaction mixture in this experiment?

Q2 In this investigation, why are the concentration-time graphs straight lines?

Q3 If the graph showed a curve, where would you measure the gradient?

Q4 A reaction is first order with respect to A. How many molecules of A will be involved in the rate-determining step?

**Exam Question**

1 X and Y react together according to the equation: $X_2 + 3Y \rightarrow X_2Y_3$

In a series of experiments carried out at 288 K, the following results were obtained:

| Experiment | initial [$X_2$] (mol $dm^{-3}$) | initial [Y] (mol $dm^{-3}$) | initial rate (mol $dm^{-3}$ $s^{-1}$) |
|---|---|---|---|
| 1 | 0.100 | 0.100 | 0.00198 |
| 2 | 0.100 | 0.300 | 0.01801 |
| 3 | 0.200 | 0.100 | 0.00401 |

a) What is the order of reaction with respect to X? [2 marks]

b) What is the order of reaction with respect to Y? [2 marks]

c) Write the rate equation for the reaction between X and Y. [1 mark]

## The fun just never stops...

*I know experiments like these might not seem the most exciting in the world. But you have got to learn them. Besides once upon a time they were exciting. At some point in history people would have been positively enthusiastic about a titration. They'd love the opportunity to swirl a flask of liquid until the colour changed. Honest...*

# Activation Energy

*It's more maths on this page. But keep going, it'll be over soon.*
***This page is for Edexcel (Unit 4).*** *The rest of you: feel free to go and make a brew.*

## Use the Arrhenius Equation to Calculate the Activation Energy

The **Arrhenius equation** (nasty-looking thing in the blue box) links the **rate constant** ($k$) with **activation energy** ($E_a$, the minimum amount of kinetic energy particles need to react) and **temperature** (T). This is probably the **worst** equation there is in A2 Chemistry. But the good news is, you **don't** have to learn it — you just have to understand what it's showing you. Here it is:

$$k = Ae^{-E_a/RT}$$

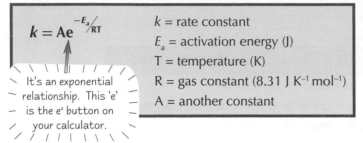

$k$ = rate constant
$E_a$ = activation energy (J)
T = temperature (K)
R = gas constant (8.31 J $K^{-1}$ $mol^{-1}$)
A = another constant

It's an exponential relationship. This 'e' is the $e^x$ button on your calculator.

1) As the activation energy, $E_a$, gets **bigger**, $k$ gets **smaller**. So, a **large $E_a$** will mean a **slow rate**. You can **test** this out by trying **different numbers** for $E_a$ in the equation... ahh go on, be a devil.
2) The equation also shows that as the temperature **rises**, $k$ **increases**. Try this one out too.

Putting the **Arrhenius equation** into **logarithmic form** makes it a bit easier to use.

$$\ln k = \ln A - \frac{E_a}{RT} = (\text{a constant}) - \frac{E_a}{RT}$$

There's a handy 'ln' button on your calculator for this.

You can use this equation to create an **Arrhenius plot** by plotting **ln *k*** against $\frac{1}{T}$.

This will produce a graph with a **gradient** of $\frac{-E_a}{R}$. And once you know the gradient, you can find the **activation energy**.

***Example:***

The graph on the right shows an Arrhenius plot for the decomposition of hydrogen iodide. Calculate the activation energy for this reaction. R = 8.31 J $K^{-1}$ $mol^{-1}$.

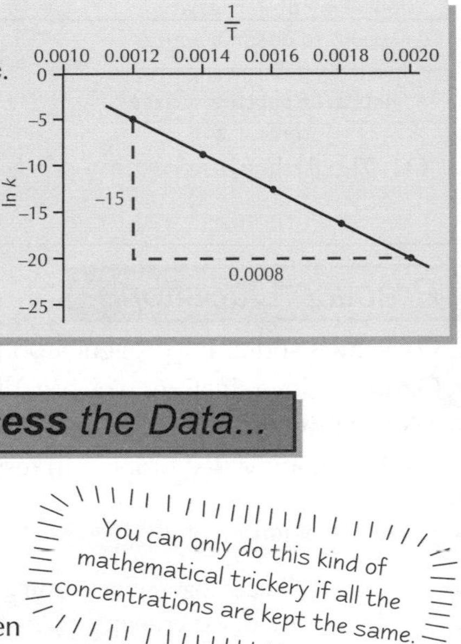


The gradient, $\frac{-E_a}{R} = \frac{-15}{0.0008} = -18\ 750$

So, $E_a = -(-18\ 750 \times 8.31) = 155\ 812.5$ J $mol^{-1}$ ≈ **156 kJ $mol^{-1}$**

## To Calculate the Activation Energy, First Collect and Process the Data...

Here's another example of how to work out the activation energy.

$$S_2O_8{}^{2-}{}_{(aq)} + 2I^-{}_{(aq)} \rightarrow 2SO_4{}^{2-}{}_{(aq)} + I_{2(aq)}$$

You can only do this kind of mathematical trickery if all the concentrations are kept the same.

You can use the **iodine-clock reaction** to monitor when a fixed amount of $I_2$ has been made (see page 10). The **rate of the reaction** is **inversely proportional** to the **time taken** (**t**) for the solution to change colour — a faster rate means a shorter time taken.

So, mathematically speaking, the rate is **proportional** to **1/time**. This means that 1/t can be used instead of $k$ in the Arrhenius equation, which means you can calculate the activation energy. Hurrah!!

| Time, t (s) | Temp, T (K) | 1/t ($s^{-1}$) | ln 1/t | 1/T ($K^{-1}$) |
|---|---|---|---|---|
| 204 | 303 | 0.0049 | −5.32 | 0.00330 |
| 138 | 308 | 0.0072 | −4.93 | 0.00325 |
| 115 | 312 | 0.0087 | −4.74 | 0.00321 |
| 75 | 318 | 0.0133 | −4.32 | 0.00314 |
| 55 | 323 | 0.0182 | −4.01 | 0.00310 |

Here's some collected data for this reaction at different temperatures. The first two columns show the raw data and the other columns show the data that's needed to draw a graph of **ln (1/t)** against **1/T** (see the next page).

# Activation Energy

## ...Then Draw an Arrhenius Plot to Find $E_a$

Here's an **Arrhenius plot** of the data at the bottom of page 18.
The graph will **always** show a **straight line**, which makes it easy to work out the gradient — and once you know the gradient, you can find $E_a$.

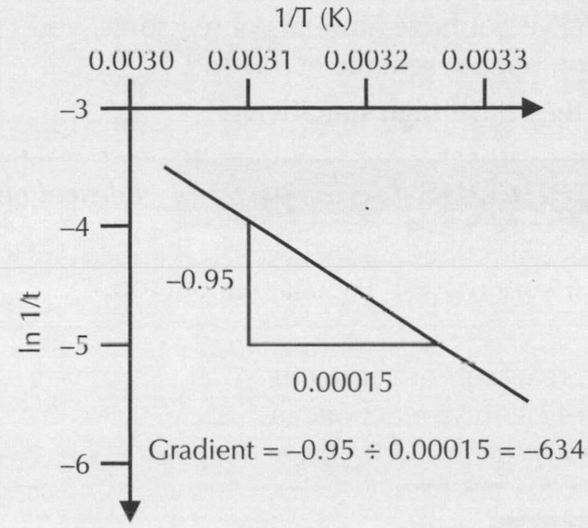

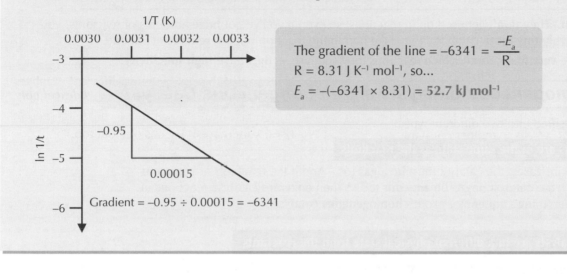

The gradient of the line = −6341 = $\frac{-E_a}{R}$
R = 8.31 J K$^{-1}$ mol$^{-1}$, so...
$E_a$ = −(−6341 × 8.31) = **52.7 kJ mol$^{-1}$**

Looking at the gradient, Steve decided the activation energy needed to walk up the mountain was too high.

## Practice Questions

Q1 The Arrhenius equation can be written as ln $k$ = (a constant) − $E_a$/RT. What do the terms $k$, T and R represent?

Q2 The Arrhenius equation is $k = Ae^{-E_a/RT}$. What happens to $k$ as $E_a$ increases?

Q3 What consideration must you make when using a clock reaction to monitor a reaction?

Q4 How do you work out $E_a$ from a plot of ln (1/t) against 1/T?

**Exam Question**

1 a) Explain what is meant by the term 'activation energy'. [1 mark]

b) The table gives values for the rate constant of the reaction between hydroxide ions and bromoethane at different temperatures.

i) Complete the table and then plot a graph of ln $k$ ($y$ axis) against $\frac{1}{T}$ ($x$ axis). [5 marks]

ii) Calculate the gradient of the straight line produced. [2 marks]

iii) The Arrhenius equation is:

$$\ln k = (\text{a constant}) - \frac{E_a}{RT}$$

Use this equation to calculate the activation energy of the reaction.
(R = 8.31 J K$^{-1}$mol$^{-1}$) [3 marks]

| T | $k$ | 1/T | ln $k$ |
|---|---|---|---|
| 305 | 0.181 | 0.00328 | −1.709 |
| 313 | 0.468 | 0.00319 | −0.759 |
| 321 | 1.34 | 0.00312 | 0.293 |
| 333 | 3.29 | 0.00300 | 1.191 |
| 344 | 10.1 | 0.00291 | 2.313 |
| 353 | 22.7 | 0.00283 | 3.122 |

## Aaaaaaaaaarrrrrrrgggggggggghhhhhhhhhhhhhhh...

*This was my first thought when I saw the Arrhenius equation. A big chocolate-covered marshmallow was my second, but that's not really important. The thing to remember is that they will give you the formula in the exam. So concentrate on learning how to use it — which bits to plot on an Arrhenius graph and what things to calculate to work out the $E_a$.*

# Catalysts

***These pages are for OCR B (Unit 4) and Edexcel (Unit 4).***

## *Catalysts Lower the Activation Energy*

You can use **catalysts** to make chemical reactions happen **faster**. Here's a nice definition for you to learn:

> A **catalyst** increases the **rate** of a reaction by providing an **alternative reaction pathway** with a **lower activation energy**. The catalyst is **chemically unchanged** at the end of the reaction.

1) Catalysts are **great**. They **don't** get used up in reactions, so even if you've got **huge** amounts of reactants, you only need a relatively **tiny bit** of catalyst. They take part in the reaction but are **remade** at the end.
2) Many catalysts are **very fussy** about which reactions they catalyse — they have **high specificity**.

## *There are Homogeneous Catalysts and Heterogeneous Catalysts*

***Edexcel only***

Catalysts can be classified into two different types:

### Homogeneous catalysts are in the same state as the reactants

So, if the reactants are **gases**, the catalyst must be a **gas** too. And if the reactants are **aqueous** (dissolved in water), the catalyst has to be **aqueous** too. When **enzymes** catalyse reactions in your body **cells**, everything's **aqueous** — so it's **homogeneous catalysis**.

### Heterogeneous catalysts are in a different physical state from the reactants

1) **Solid** heterogeneous catalysts provide a **surface** for the reaction to take place on. The catalyst is usually in the form of a **mesh** or a **fine powder** to increase the **surface area**. Alternatively it might be spread over an **inert support**.
2) Heterogeneous catalysts are great because they can be easily separated from the products and leftover reactants.
3) **Heterogeneous catalysts** can be poisoned though. A **poison** is a substance that clings to the catalyst's surface **more strongly** than the reactant does, **preventing** the catalyst from getting involved in the reaction it's meant to be **speeding up**. For instance, **sulfur** can poison the **iron catalyst** used in the **Haber process**.

Here are some examples of heterogeneous catalysts:

- **Vanadium pentoxide** in the **contact process** for making **sulfuric acid**
- **Nickel** in the **hydrogenation of vegetable oils**
- **Platinum** and **rhodium** in **catalytic converters** in cars. Catalytic converters change nasty gases like **nitric oxide** and **carbon monoxide** into less dangerous gases like nitrogen and carbon dioxide.

Transition metals are often used as catalysts — see page 164.

$$2NO_{(g)} + 2CO_{(g)} \xrightarrow{Pt_{(s)} / Rh_{(s)}} N_{2(g)} + 2CO_{2(g)}$$

## *A Catalyst Lowers the Activation Energy of a Reaction*

***Edexcel only***

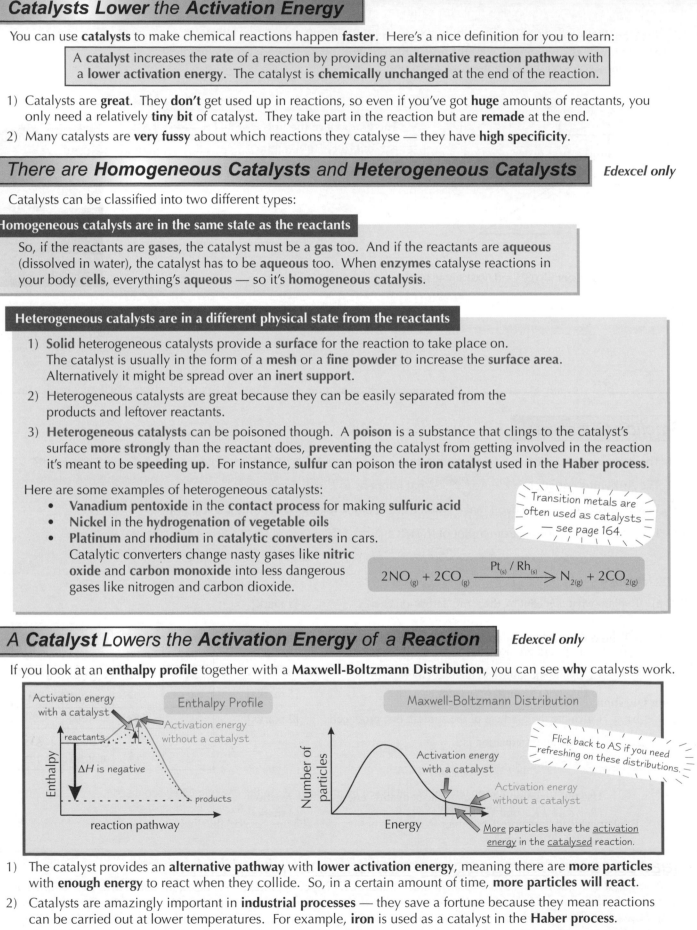

If you look at an **enthalpy profile** together with a **Maxwell-Boltzmann Distribution**, you can see **why** catalysts work.

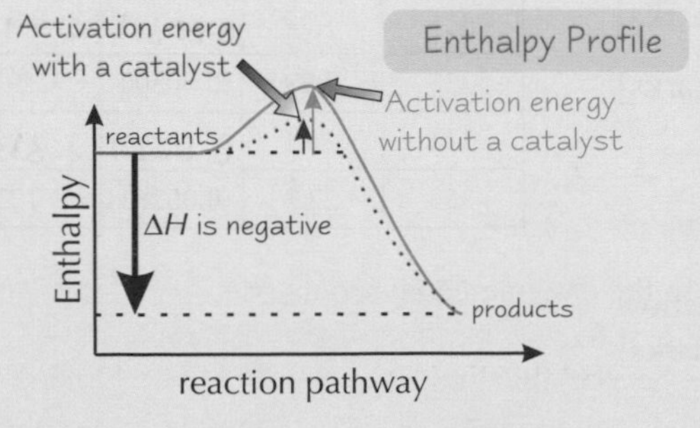


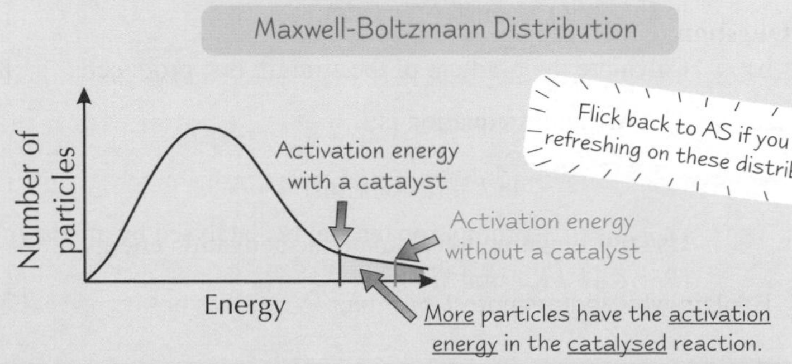


Flick back to AS if you need refreshing on these distributions.

1) The catalyst provides an **alternative pathway** with **lower activation energy**, meaning there are **more particles** with **enough energy** to react when they collide. So, in a certain amount of time, **more particles will react**.
2) Catalysts are amazingly important in **industrial processes** — they save a fortune because they mean reactions can be carried out at lower temperatures. For example, **iron** is used as a catalyst in the **Haber process**.

# Catalysts

## Enzymes are Biological Catalysts

*OCR B only*

There's more about enzymes on page 95.

**Enzymes** are biological molecules that can **catalyse** certain reactions.

1) An enzyme molecule works by joining to a reactant molecule — called a **substrate** — and forming an **enzyme-substrate complex**.
2) The substrate reacts more easily while attached to the enzyme. Once the product is formed, the enzyme **detaches** and goes on to connect to another substrate molecule.

## Enzyme-Catalysed Reactions Don't Behave as You'd Expect

*OCR B only*

1) In a very simple **first order** reaction, a molecule of **substrate, S**, might become a molecule of **product, P**.
2) As the concentration of S **increases**, the reaction **speeds up**. In fact, because it's a first order reaction, doubling the concentration of S should **double** the rate of reaction. If you plotted this as a **rate-concentration graph** it would be a straight line (see below) — showing that rate is **directly proportional** to substrate concentration.
3) But when the above reaction is **catalysed by an enzyme, E**, something odd happens — the graph below shows this...

> 1) The **uncatalysed** reaction is **first order** with respect to S — it's a straight line on the graph.
> 2) The **enzyme-catalysed** reaction starts out as first order (a straight line), but as more substrate is added, the graph levels out — the reaction becomes **zero order** with respect to S.

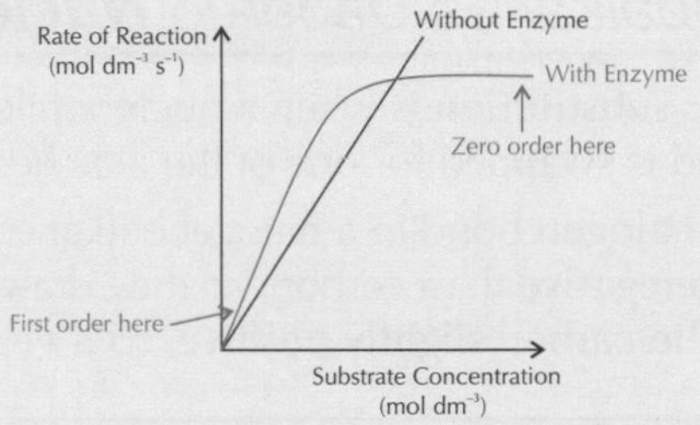


The reason for the change basically involves the **rate-determining step** changing in the **reaction mechanism**...

| | | |
|---|---|---|
| $S + E \rightarrow ES$ | **step 1** | ES = enzyme-substrate complex |
| $ES \rightarrow EP$ | **step 2** | EP = enzyme-product complex |
| $EP \rightarrow E + P$ | **step 3** | |

1) To start with, **step 1** is the **rate-determining step** — so adding more S speeds up step 1, increasing the reaction rate.
2) Eventually, **all** the E is already **being used** in the reaction. At this point, adding more S doesn't speed up step 1 as there's no more E to combine with the extra S.
3) The **rate-determining step** now becomes **step 2** — the rate depends on the speed at which the ES complex can convert into EP. This step **doesn't contain S**, so the order has now become **zero order** with respect to S.

## Practice Questions

Q1 Explain how a catalyst works.
Q2 What's the difference between a heterogeneous catalyst and a homogeneous one?
Q3 Give three examples of heterogeneous catalysts.
Q4 What happens to the order of an enzyme-catalysed reaction as the substrate concentration increases?

**Exam Question**

1 It is known that the hydrolysis of 1-bromopropane occurs according to the following one-step mechanism:

$$CH_3CH_2CH_2Br + OH^- \rightarrow CH_3CH_2CH_2OH + Br^-$$

a) Write a rate equation for the reaction that fits the mechanism and state the overall order of reaction. [4 marks]

b) The hydrolysis of 1-bromopropane can be catalysed by an enzyme. In the enzyme-catalysed reaction there is a limit to how fast the reaction can be made to go by increasing the concentration of the reactants. Explain why adding more 1-bromopropane does not increase the rate beyond this limit. [2 marks]

## Catalysis — splitting stuff with cats...

*Ah, the humble catalyst — one of chemistry's unsung heroes. I propose a national holiday — preferably around my birthday — where we spend all day speeding up reactions and generally having a whale of a time. And it might be a nice idea to give extra presents to anyone whose birthday falls in the same week. A street party would be good too...*

# Halogenoalkanes and Reaction Mechanisms

*'Lean hog on a lake' is an anagram of halogenoalkane. Bet you didn't know that...*
***These pages are only for Edexcel (Unit 4).***

## *Halogenoalkanes can be Hydrolysed by Hydroxide Ions*

There are 3 different types of halogenoalkane:

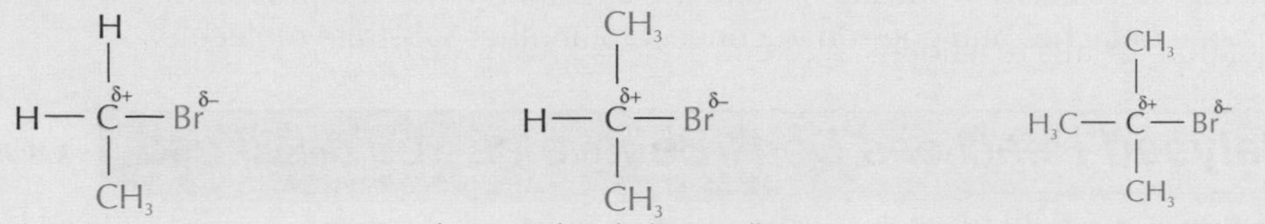

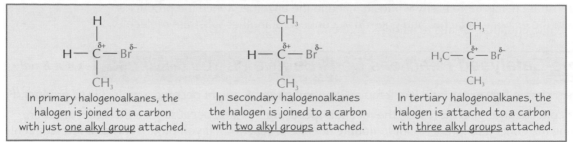

In primary halogenoalkanes, the halogen is joined to a carbon with just one alkyl group attached.

In secondary halogenoalkanes the halogen is joined to a carbon with two alkyl groups attached.

In tertiary halogenoalkanes, the halogen is attached to a carbon with three alkyl groups attached.

All three types can be hydrolysed by heating them with sodium hydroxide — but they react using **different mechanisms**.

## *Halogenoalkanes Undergo Nucleophilic Substitution*

**Nucleophilic substitution** is when a nucleophile attacks another molecule and is **swapped** for one of the attached groups.

The carbon–halogen bond in a halogenoalkane is **polar** — halogens are much more **electronegative** than carbon, so they draw the electrons **towards** themselves. This makes the carbon **slightly positive**, so it's easily attacked by **nucleophiles**.

$C^{\delta+}–Br^{\delta-}$

Nucleophiles are particles that are attracted to positive charge, such as $OH^-$ and $CN^-$.

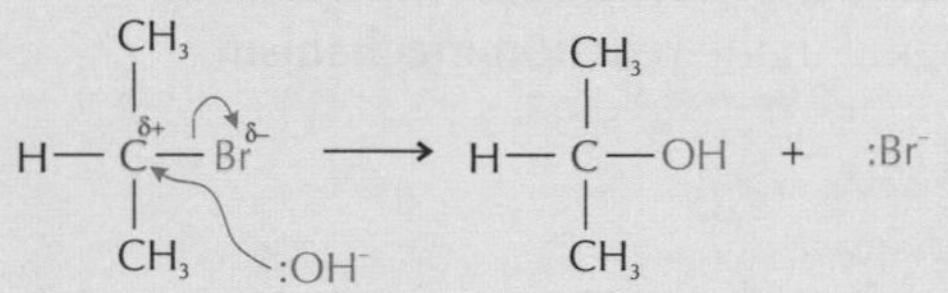

1) $OH^-$ is the **nucleophile** — it provides a pair of electrons for the $C^{\delta+}$.
2) The C–Br bond breaks **heterolytically** — both electrons from the bond are taken by $Br^-$.
3) $Br^-$ comes away and $OH^-$ bonds to the carbon.

There are two different mechanisms for nucleophilic substitution — **$S_N$1** and **$S_N$2**.

$S_N$**1** reactions only involve **1** molecule or ion in the **rate-determining step**.
$S_N$**2** reactions involve **2** molecules, 1 molecule and 1 ion or 2 ions in the **rate-determining step**.

**Primary halogenoalkanes** only react by the **$S_N$2** mechanism.
**Secondary halogenoalkanes** can react by **both** the $S_N$1 and $S_N$2 mechanisms.
**Tertiary halogenoalkanes** only react by the **$S_N$1** mechanism.

## *The **Rate Equation** shows **Primary** Halogenoalkanes Use an **$S_N$2 Mechanism***

The equation for the reaction of the primary halogenoalkane **bromoethane** with **hydroxide ions** is:

$$CH_3CH_2Br + OH^- \rightarrow CH_3CH_2OH + Br^-$$

And the rate equation is: rate = $k[CH_3CH_2Br][OH^-]$

So, the **rate is dependent** on the concentration of **both** the reactants and the **order** with respect to **each** is **1**. This means the **rate-determining** step must include **one** of **each** reactant molecule — which is **two** in total so it's $S_N$2.

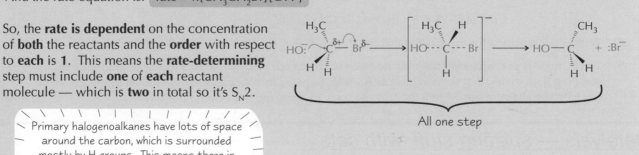

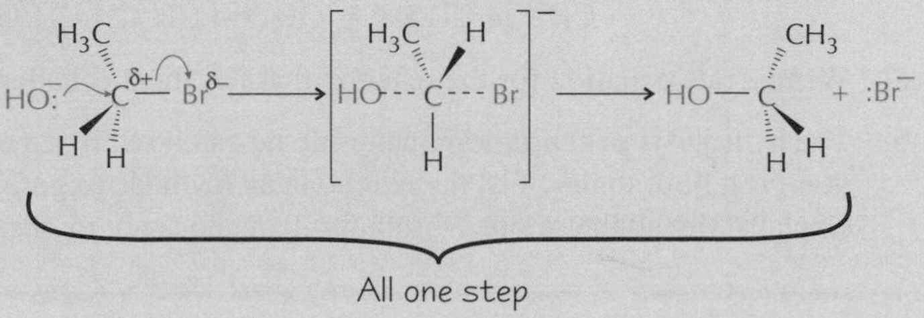

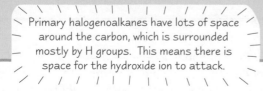

Primary halogenoalkanes have lots of space around the carbon, which is surrounded mostly by H groups. This means there is space for the hydroxide ion to attack.

# Halogenoalkanes and Reaction Mechanisms

## The **Rate Equation** shows **Tertiary** Halogenoalkanes Use $S_N1$

The equation for the reaction of the tertiary halogenoalkane **2-bromo-2-methylpropane** with **hydroxide ions** looks similar to the reaction with bromoethane on the previous page:

$$(CH_3)_3CBr + OH^- \rightarrow (CH_3)_3COH + Br^-$$

But the rate equation for this reaction is different: rate = $k[(CH_3)_3CBr]$

The **rate is only dependent** on the concentration of the **halogenoalkane.** The **order of the reaction** with respect to the halogenoalkane is **1**. So the **rate-determining** step must only include **one** molecule of the halogenoalkane. The reaction happens in two steps. In the first step, the halogen leaves the halogenoalkane. The nucleophile is then able to attack in the second step.

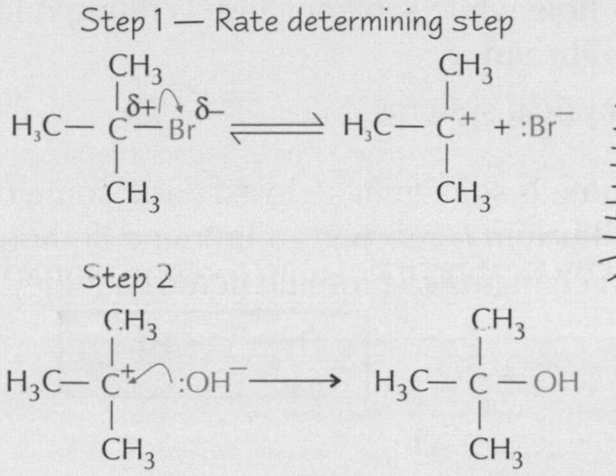

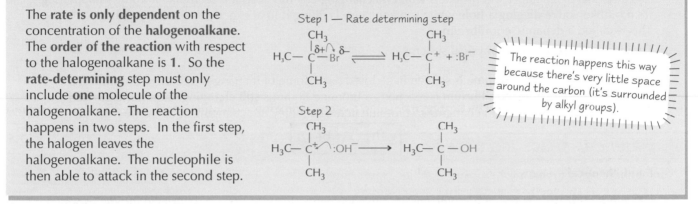

The reaction happens this way because there's very little space around the carbon (it's surrounded by alkyl groups).

## Practice Questions

Q1 Which sort of bromoalkane is 2-bromobutane — primary, secondary or tertiary?

Q2 What sort of agent does the hydroxide ion behave as in the hydrolysis of a halogenoalkane?

Q3 What do the terms $S_N1$ and $S_N2$ mean?

Q4 What is the order of reaction with respect to hydroxide ions in the hydrolysis of a tertiary halogenoalkane?

**Exam Questions**

1 The equation below represents the reaction between sodium hydroxide and 1-chloropropane:

$$CH_3CH_2CH_2Cl + NaOH \rightarrow CH_3CH_2CH_2OH + NaCl$$

The rate equation for this reaction is:

A Rate = $k$ [NaOH] B Rate = $k\,[CH_3CH_2CH_2Cl]$

C Rate = $k\,[CH_3CH_2CH_2Cl]^2$ D Rate = $k\,[CH_3CH_2CH_2Cl][NaOH]$ [1 mark]

2 The hydrolysis of 2-bromo-2-methylpropane by hydroxide ions follows an $S_N1$ mechanism. Which one of the following is the rate-determining step?

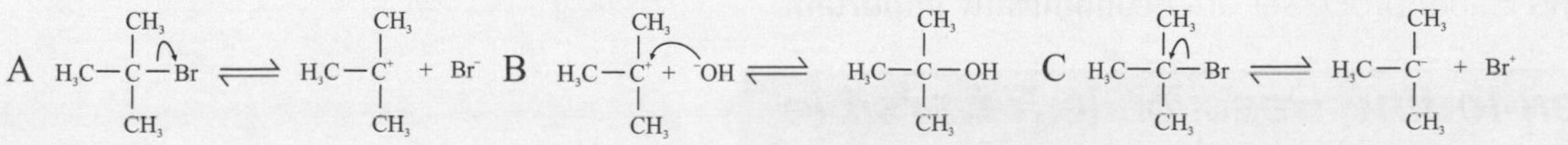

D $OH^- \rightarrow OH^+ + 2e^-$

[1 mark]

3 The following equation shows the hydrolysis of 1-iodobutane by hydroxide ions:

$$CH_3CH_2CH_2CH_2I + OH^- \rightarrow CH_3CH_2CH_2CH_2OH + I^-$$

a) Is 1-iodobutane a primary, secondary or tertiary iodoalkane? [1 mark]

b) Write the rate equation for this reaction. [1 mark]

c) What type of mechanism is involved in this reaction? [2 marks]

d) Draw a detailed mechanism for this reaction. [3 marks]

## Way-hay!!! — it's the curly arrows...

*Seriously, whenever I talk to someone who's done chemistry the one thing they've remembered is curly arrows. They have no idea how they work. But they know they exist. Now it's OK for them 'cos they don't have an exam, but you do — so make sure you understand where the arrows are coming from and going to. Check back to AS to be sure.*

# Dynamic Equilibria

*Dynamic equilibria. Sounds exciting right? I mean James Bond's dynamic isn't he? Well, sorry to disappoint...*
***These pages are for Edexcel (Unit 4) only.***

## At Equilibrium the Amounts of Reactants and Products Stay the Same

1) Lots of changes are **reversible** — they can go **both ways**. To show a change is reversible, you stick in a $\rightleftharpoons$.
2) As the **reactants** get used up, the **forward** reaction **slows down** — and as more **product** is formed, the **reverse** reaction **speeds up**. After a while, the forward reaction will be going at exactly the **same rate** as the backward reaction.
   The amounts of reactants and products **won't be changing** any more, so it'll seem like **nothing's happening**.
   It's a bit like you're **digging a hole** while someone else is **filling it in** at exactly the **same speed**.
   This is called a **dynamic equilibrium**.
3) Equilibria can be set up in **physical** systems...

*Example:* When **liquid bromine** is shaken in a closed flask, some of it changes to orange **bromine gas**. After a while, **equilibrium** is reached — bromine liquid is **still** changing to bromine gas and bromine gas is still changing to bromine liquid, but they are changing at the **same rate**.

$$Br_{2(l)} \rightleftharpoons Br_{2(g)}$$

...and **chemical** systems...

*Example:* If **hydrogen gas** and **iodine gas** are mixed together in a closed flask, **hydrogen iodide** is formed.

$$H_{2(g)} + I_{2(g)} \rightleftharpoons 2HI_{(g)}$$

Imagine that **1.0 mole** of hydrogen gas is mixed with **1.0 mole** of iodine gas at a constant temperature of **640 K**. When this mixture reaches equilibrium, there will be **1.6 moles** of hydrogen iodide and **0.2 moles** of both hydrogen gas and iodine gas. No matter how long you leave them at this temperature, the **equilibrium** amounts **never change**. As with the physical system, it's all a matter of the forward and backward rates **being equal**.

4) A **dynamic equilibrium** can only happen in a **closed system** at a **constant temperature**.

A closed system just means nothing can get in or out.

## Many Important Industrial Reactions Are Reversible

1) The **Contact process** is used to manufacture **sulfuric acid** for use in fertilisers, dyes, medicines and batteries. It is made up of several stages, one of which — the **conversion** of **sulfur dioxide** to **sulfur trioxide**, shown below — is reversible.

$$2SO_{2(g)} + O_{2(g)} \rightleftharpoons 2SO_{3(g)}$$

2) The **Haber process** is used to manufacture **ammonia** for making fertilisers and other nitrogen-containing compounds. It is also reversible:

$$N_{2(g)} + 3H_{2(g)} \rightleftharpoons 2NH_{3(g)}$$

Both the Contact and Haber processes are **economically important**.

## The Hydrogen-Iodine Reaction Is Reversible

The table below shows the results of several experiments that investigate the hydrogen-iodine reaction in a closed system at 763 K.

Square brackets, [ ], mean concentration in mol dm$^{-3}$.

| | Starting Concentrations | | | Equilibrium Concentrations | | |
|---|---|---|---|---|---|---|
| Experiment | $[H_{2(g)}]$ | $[I_{2(g)}]$ | $[HI_{(g)}]$ | $[H_{2(g)}]$ | $[I_{2(g)}]$ | $[HI_{(g)}]$ |
| 1 | 1.0 | 1.0 | 0.0 | 0.228 | 0.228 | 1.544 |
| 2 | 0.0 | 0.0 | 2.0 | 0.228 | 0.228 | 1.544 |
| 3 | 1.0 | 2.0 | 3.0 | 0.316 | 1.316 | 4.368 |

The **equilibrium concentrations** of the **reactants** and **products** depend on the **initial concentrations** of each **element** in the reaction — whichever side of the equilibrium they start off on. When these initial concentrations are **the same**, the equilibrium concentrations of the products and reactants will be the same. **Experiments 1 and 2** both start off with 2 mol dm$^{-1}$ of H atoms and the same of I atoms — and both finish with the same equilibrium concentrations.

# Dynamic Equilibria

## The **Equilibrium Concentrations** of Reactants and Products are **Related**

If you calculate the ratio of **product concentration to reactant concentration** for each of the experiments on the previous page, you will **always** end up with the **same value**.
For the hydrogen-iodine reaction, the **ratio of equilibrium concentrations** can be calculated as:

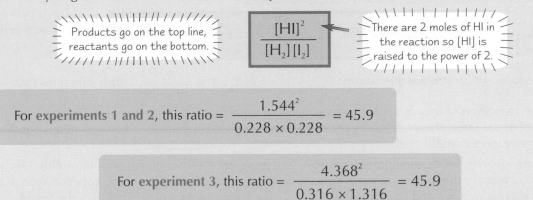

Products go on the top line, reactants go on the bottom.

$$\frac{[HI]^2}{[H_2][I_2]}$$

There are 2 moles of HI in the reaction so [HI] is raised to the power of 2.

For **experiments 1 and 2**, this ratio = $\frac{1.544^2}{0.228 \times 0.228} = 45.9$

For **experiment 3**, this ratio = $\frac{4.368^2}{0.316 \times 1.316} = 45.9$

If you repeated this experiment at 763 K using **different starting concentrations** of $H_2$, $I_2$ or HI, and then plugged the numbers into this same expression, you would **always** end up with a value of 45.9. The value of this ratio is known as the **equilibrium constant, $K_c$**, and it is always **constant** for a particular reaction when measured at the **same temperature**.

## Practice Questions

Q1 If you know that a system is in equilibrium, what does that tell you about the rate of the forward reaction compared to the rate of the reverse reaction?

Q2 What is a 'closed system'?

Q3 Name two industrial processes that involve reversible reactions.

Q4 Under what conditions does the equilibrium constant of a particular reaction remain the same?

**Exam Question**

1 a) What is meant by dynamic equilibrium? [2 marks]

b) At 473 K, the equilibrium constant, $K_c$, for the reaction below has a numerical value of 125.

$$PCl_{3(g)} + Cl_{2(g)} \rightleftharpoons PCl_{5(g)}$$

i) At 473 K, a quantity of $Cl_{2(g)}$ was added to the mixture and equilibrium was re-established. What effect would this have on the value of the equilibrium constant? Explain your answer. [2 marks]

ii) The temperature of the equilibrium mixture was allowed to drop to 423 K. What effect would this have on the value of the equilibrium constant? Explain your answer. [2 marks]

iii) At 473 K, what would be the numerical value of $K_c$ for the reaction below? [2 marks]

$$PCl_{5(g)} \rightleftharpoons PCl_{3(g)} + Cl_{2(g)}$$

## Dynamic equilibria — the movers and shakers of the equilibrium world...

*As those of you who are a bit more on the ball might've guessed from the section title, these next few pages are all about equilibria. This has been quite a nice, gentle introduction I think — compared with what's to come anyway, mwahahahaaa. Take your time getting to grips with it all, then turn over. It'll be fine. Honestly. That mwahahahaa thing was just a joke...*

# Equilibrium Constants

*The equilibrium constant is about to become a constant presence in your life — just you wait and see...*
***These pages are for AQA (Unit 4), OCR A (Unit 5), OCR B (Unit 5) and Edexcel (Unit 4).***

## $K_c$ is the Equilibrium Constant

$K_c$ is calculated from the **ratio** of product concentration to reactant concentration.
This means that if you know the **molar concentration** of each substance **at equilibrium**, you can work out $K_c$.
Your value of $K_c$ will only be true for that particular **temperature**.

The lower-case letters a, b, d and e are the number of moles of each substance.

For the general reaction $aA + bB \rightleftharpoons dD + eE$, $K_c = \frac{[D]^d[E]^e}{[A]^a[B]^b}$ ← Products go on the top line.

So for the reaction $H_{2(g)} + I_{2(g)} \rightleftharpoons 2HI_{(g)}$, $K_c = \frac{[HI]^2}{[H_2]^1[I_2]^1}$. This simplifies to $K_c = \frac{[HI]^2}{[H_2][I_2]}$.

1) Actually this definition of $K_c$ only applies to **homogeneous equilibria**, i.e. ones where all the products and reactants are in the **same phase**. If you've got more than one phase in there — a **heterogeneous equilibrium** — life's slightly more complicated.
2) If the mixture involves **solids and liquids** you use $K_c$ and **leave out** the concentration of the **solids**. For a mix of **solids and gases** you need to use a different term, $K_p$ (see p28-29), but you still leave out the concentration of the **solids**. If you've got a mix of **gases and liquids** you also use $K_p$, but leave out the concentration of the **liquids** instead.

## You Might Need to *Work Out* the *Equilibrium Concentrations*

You might have to figure out some of the **equilibrium concentrations** before you can find $K_c$:

***Example:*** 0.20 moles of phosphorus(V) chloride decomposes at 600 K in a vessel of 5.00 dm³. The equilibrium mixture is found to contain 0.08 moles of chlorine. Write the expression for $K_c$ and calculate its value, including units.

$$PCl_{5(g)} \rightleftharpoons PCl_{3(g)} + Cl_{2(g)}$$

First find out how many moles of $PCl_5$ and $PCl_3$ there are at equilibrium:

The **equation** tells you that when **1 mole of $PCl_5$** decomposes, **1 mole of $PCl_3$** and **1 mole of $Cl_2$** are formed.
So if 0.08 moles of chlorine are produced at equilibrium, then there will be **0.08 moles** of $PCl_3$ as well.
0.08 mol of $PCl_5$ must have decomposed, so there will be (0.2 – 0.08 =) **0.12 moles** left.

Divide each number of moles by the volume of the flask to give the molar concentrations:

$[PCl_3] = [Cl_2] = 0.08 \div 5.00 = \mathbf{0.016\ mol\ dm^{-3}}$ $[PCl_5] = 0.12 \div 5.00 = \mathbf{0.024\ mol\ dm^{-3}}$

Put the concentrations in the expression for $K_c$ and calculate it: $K_c = \frac{[PCl_3][Cl_2]}{[PCl_5]} = \frac{[0.016][0.016]}{[0.024]} = \mathbf{0.011}$

To work out the **units** of $K_c$ put the units in the expression instead of the numbers: $K_c = \frac{(mol\ dm^{-3})(mol\ dm^{-3})}{(mol\ dm^{-3})} = \mathbf{mol\ dm^{-3}}$

So $K_c = \mathbf{0.011\ mol\ dm^{-3}}$

## $K_c$ can be used to Find *Concentrations* in an *Equilibrium Mixture*

***Example:*** When ethanoic acid was allowed to reach equilibrium with ethanol at 25 °C, it was found that the equilibrium mixture contained 2.0 mol dm⁻³ ethanoic acid and 3.5 mol dm⁻³ ethanol. The $K_c$ of the equilibrium is 4.0 at 25 °C. What are the concentrations of the other components?

$$CH_3COOH_{(l)} + C_2H_5OH_{(l)} \rightleftharpoons CH_3COOC_2H_{5(l)} + H_2O_{(l)}$$

Put all the values you know in the $K_c$ expression: $K_c = \frac{[CH_3COOC_2H_5][H_2O]}{[CH_3COOH][C_2H_5OH]} \Rightarrow 4.0 = \frac{[CH_3COOC_2H_5][H_2O]}{2.0 \times 3.5}$

Rearranging this gives: $[CH_3COOC_2H_5][H_2O] = 4.0 \times 2.0 \times 3.5 = 28.0$

From the equation, you know that an equal number of moles of $CH_3COOC_2H_5$ and $H_2O$ will form, so:

$[CH_3COOC_2H_5] = [H_2O] = \sqrt{28} = 5.3\ mol\ dm^{-3}$ **The concentration of $CH_3COOC_2H_5$ and $H_2O$ is 5.3 mol dm⁻³**

# Equilibrium Constants

## The **Equilibrium Constant** Can Be Calculated from **Experimental Data**

**Edexcel only**

A simple experiment that can be carried out in the laboratory involves the following reaction:

$$Fe^{2+}_{(aq)} + Ag^{+}_{(aq)} \rightleftharpoons Fe^{3+}_{(aq)} + Ag_{(s)}$$

1) To carry out this reaction you need to add **500 cm³** of **0.1 mol dm⁻³** silver nitrate solution to **500 cm³** of **0.1 mol dm⁻³** of iron(II) sulfate solution. The **silver nitrate** provides the $Ag^+$ ions and the **iron(II) sulfate** provides the $Fe^{2+}$ ions.
2) If you leave the mixture in a stoppered flask at 298 K, it will eventually reach **equilibrium**. You can then take samples of the equilibrium mixture and **titrate** them — this will let you work out the **equilibrium concentration** of the **$Fe^{2+}$ ions**. From this, you can work out the equilibrium concentrations of the other components.

***Example calculation:***

The **starting concentrations** of $Ag^+$ and $Fe^{2+}$ are the same and equal to **0.05 mol dm⁻³**.

500 cm³ of each solution is diluted to 1000 cm³. The concentration of each reactant is halved.

The **titration result** gives you an **equilibrium concentration** for $Fe^{2+}$ of **0.0439 mol dm⁻³**.

The equation tells you 1 mole of $Fe^{2+}$ reacts with 1 mole of $Ag^+$ to form 1 mole of $Fe^{3+}$ and 1 mole of Ag. In this particular reaction **solid** silver is formed. The concentration of a solid is **constant**, so you **don't** need to include it in the expression for $K_c$.

The equilibrium concentration of **$Ag^+$** will be the same as $Fe^{2+}$, i.e. **0.0439 mol dm⁻³**.
The equilibrium concentration of **$Fe^{3+}$** will be 0.05 – 0.0439 = **0.0061 mol dm⁻³**.

$$\text{So } K_c = \frac{[Fe^{3+}]}{[Fe^{2+}][Ag^+]} = \frac{0.0061}{0.0439 \times 0.0439} = 3.17$$

$$\text{The units of } K_c \text{ are: } \frac{\cancel{mol\ dm^{-3}}}{(\cancel{mol\ dm^{-3}})(mol\ dm^{-3})} = mol^{-1}\ dm^{3}$$

**At 298 K, $K_c$ for this reaction = 3.17 mol⁻¹ dm³**

## Practice Questions

Q1 What do the square brackets, [ ], represent in a $K_c$ expression?

Q2 Write the expression for $K_c$ for the following equilibrium: $2SO_2 + O_2 \rightleftharpoons 2SO_3$

Q3 In the reaction $Cl_{2(g)} + PCl_{3(g)} \rightleftharpoons PCl_{5(g)}$, what are the units of $K_c$?

**Exam Questions**

1 The equilibrium constant for the reaction $2HI_{(g)} \rightleftharpoons H_{2(g)} + I_{2(g)}$ is 0.0167 at 450 °C.
How many moles of hydrogen iodide will be in equilibrium with 2.0 moles of hydrogen and 0.3 moles of iodine at 450 °C in a 1 dm³ vessel? [3 marks]

2 Nitrogen dioxide dissociates according to the equation $2NO_{2(g)} \rightleftharpoons 2NO_{(g)} + O_{2(g)}$.
When 42.5 g of nitrogen dioxide were heated in a vessel of volume 22.8 dm³ at 500 °C, 14.1 g of oxygen were found in the equilibrium mixture.

a) Calculate i) the initial number of moles of nitrogen dioxide. [1 mark]

ii) the number of moles of each gas in the equilibrium mixture. [3 marks]

b) Write an expression for $K_c$ for this reaction. Calculate the value for $K_c$ at 450 °C and give its units. [5 marks]

## As far as I'm concerned, equilibria are a constant pain in the *@?!

*I suppose my issue is... if they were proper constants, you wouldn't have to calculate them all the time would you? I mean, at least when Avogadro said he had a constant he flippin' well meant it. Still, since they're there to be calculated, calculate them you must — and the only way to get good at it is to practise. And then practise again, just to be on the safe side.*

# Gas Equilibria

***These pages are for Edexcel (Unit 4) and OCR B (Unit 5) only.*** *Everyone else can skip merrily along to page 32.*

## The Total Pressure is Equal to the Sum of the Partial Pressures

In a mixture of gases, each individual gas exerts its own pressure — this is called its **partial pressure**.

The **total pressure** of a gas mixture is the **sum** of all the **partial pressures** of the individual gases.

You might have to put this fact to use in pressure calculations:

***Example:*** When 3.0 moles of the gas $PCl_5$ is heated, it decomposes into $PCl_3$ and $Cl_2$.

$$PCl_{5(g)} \rightleftharpoons PCl_{3(g)} + Cl_{2(g)}$$

In a sealed vessel at 500 K, the equilibrium mixture contains chlorine with a partial pressure of 263 kPa. If the total pressure of the mixture is 714 kPa, what is the partial pressure of $PCl_5$?

From the equation you know that $PCl_3$ and $Cl_2$ are produced in equal amounts, so the partial pressures of these two gases are the **same** at equilibrium — they're both 263 kPa.

Total pressure = $p(PCl_5) + p(PCl_3) + p(Cl_2)$

$714 = p(PCl_5) + 263 + 263$

$p$ is often used to mean partial pressure.

So the partial pressure of $PCl_5$ = 714 – 263 – 263 = **188 kPa**

## Partial Pressures can be Worked Out from Mole Fractions

'**Mole fraction**' might sound a bit complicated, but it's just the **proportion** of a gas mixture that is a particular gas. So if you've got four moles of gas in total, and two of them are gas A, the mole fraction of gas A is ½.
There are two formulas you've got to know:

$$\text{Mole fraction of a gas in a mixture} = \frac{\text{number of moles of gas}}{\text{total number of moles of all gases in the mixture}}$$

Partial pressure of a gas = mole fraction of gas × total pressure of the mixture

***Example:*** When 3.0 mol of $PCl_5$ is heated in a sealed vessel as above, the equilibrium mixture contains 1.75 mol of chlorine. If the total pressure of the mixture is 714 kPa, what is the partial pressure of $PCl_5$?

$PCl_3$ and $Cl_2$ are produced in equal amounts, so there'll be **1.75 moles** of $PCl_3$ too.
1.75 moles of $PCl_5$ must have decomposed so (3.0 – 1.75 =) **1.25 moles** of $PCl_5$ must be left at equilibrium.
This means that the total number of moles of gas at equilibrium = 1.75 + 1.75 + 1.25 = **4.75**

So the mole fraction of $PCl_5 = \frac{1.25}{4.75} = \mathbf{0.263}$

The partial pressure of $PCl_5$ = mole fraction × total pressure = 0.263 × 714 = **188 kPa**

## The Equilibrium Constant $K_p$ is Calculated from Partial Pressures

The expression for $K_p$ is just like the one for $K_c$ — except you use partial pressures instead of concentrations.

For the equilibrium $aA_{(g)} + bB_{(g)} \rightleftharpoons dD_{(g)} + eE_{(g)}$: $K_p = \frac{p(D)^d\,p(E)^e}{p(A)^a\,p(B)^b}$

There are no square brackets because they're partial pressures, not molar concentrations.

So to **calculate $K_p$**, it's just a matter of sticking the partial pressures in the expression.
You have to work out the **units** each time though, just like for $K_c$.

***Example:*** Calculate $K_p$ for the decomposition of $PCl_5$ gas at 500 K (as shown above).
The partial pressures of each gas are: $p(PCl_5)$ = 188 kPa, $p(PCl_3)$ = 263 kPa, $p(Cl_2)$ = 263 kPa

$$K_p = \frac{p(Cl_2)\,p(PCl_3)}{p(PCl_5)} = \frac{263 \times 263}{188} = 368$$

The units for $K_p$ are worked out by putting the units into the expression instead of the numbers, and cancelling (like for $K_c$): $K_p = \frac{\text{kPa} \times \text{kPa}}{\text{kPa}} = \text{kPa}$ So, $K_p$ = **368 kPa**

# Gas Equilibria

## $K_p$ can be Used to Find *Partial Pressures*

You might be given the $K_p$ and have to use it to calculate **equilibrium partial pressures**.

***Example:*** An equilibrium exists between ethanoic acid monomers ($CH_3COOH$) and dimers $(CH_3COOH)_2$.
At 160 °C the $K_p$ for the reaction $(CH_3COOH)_{2(g)} \rightleftharpoons 2CH_3COOH_{(g)}$ is 180 kPa.
At this temperature the partial pressure of the dimer, $(CH_3COOH)_2$, is 28.5 kPa.
Calculate the partial pressure of the monomer in this equilibrium and state the total pressure exerted by the equilibrium mixture.

$$K_p = \frac{p(CH_3COOH)^2}{p((CH_3COOH)_2)}$$

This rearranges to give: $p(CH_3COOH)^2 = K_p \times p((CH_3COOH)_2) = 180 \times 28.5 = 5130$

$\Rightarrow p(CH_3COOH) = \sqrt{5130} = \mathbf{71.6\ kPa}$

So the total pressure of the equilibrium mixture = 28.5 + 71.6 = **100.1 kPa**

Add the two partial pressures together to get the total pressure.

## $K_p$ for **Heterogenous** Equilibria Still **Only Includes Gases**

***Edexcel only***

Up until now we've only thought about $K_p$ expressions for **homogeneous equilibria**.
If you're writing an expression for $K_p$ for a **heterogeneous equilibrium**, you don't include **solids** or **liquids**.

E.g. for the **heterogeneous equilibrium** $NH_4HS_{(s)} \rightleftharpoons NH_{3(g)} + H_2S_{(g)}$, $K_p = p(NH_3)\,p(H_2S)$

There's no bottom line as the reactant is a solid.

## Practice Questions

Q1 What is meant by partial pressure?

Q2 How do you work out the mole fraction of a gas?

Q3 Write the expression for $K_p$ for the following equilibrium: $PCl_{5(g)} \rightleftharpoons PCl_{3(g)} + Cl_{2(g)}$

Q4 Write the expression for $K_p$ for the following equilibrium: $H_2O_{(g)} + C_{(s)} \rightleftharpoons H_{2(g)} + CO_{(g)}$

**Exam Questions**

1 At high temperatures sulfuryl chloride, $SO_2Cl_2$, dissociates according to the equation $SO_2Cl_{2(g)} \rightleftharpoons SO_{2(g)} + Cl_{2(g)}$.
When 1.50 moles of $SO_2Cl_2$ dissociates at 700 K, the equilibrium mixture contains $SO_2$ with a partial pressure of 60.2 kPa. The mixture has a total pressure of 141 kPa.

a) Write an expression for $K_p$ for this reaction. [1 mark]

b) Calculate the partial pressure of $Cl_2$ and the partial pressure of $SO_2Cl_2$ in the equilibrium mixture. [3 marks]

c) Calculate a value for $K_p$ for this reaction and give its units. [3 marks]

2 When nitric oxide and oxygen were mixed in a 2:1 mole ratio, an equilibrium was set up at a constant temperature in a sealed flask, according to the equation $2NO_{(g)} + O_{2(g)} \rightleftharpoons 2NO_{2(g)}$.
The partial pressure of the nitric oxide (NO) at equilibrium was 36 kPa and the total pressure in the flask was 99 kPa.

a) Deduce the partial pressure of oxygen in the equilibrium mixture. [2 marks]

b) Calculate the partial pressure of nitrogen dioxide in the equilibrium mixture. [2 marks]

c) Write an expression for the equilibrium constant, $K_p$, for this reaction and calculate its value at this temperature. State its units. [4 marks]

## Baked beans unbalance your gas equilibrium...

*Partial pressures are just like concentrations for gases. The more of a substance you've got in a solution, the higher the concentration, and the more of a gas you've got in a container, the higher the partial pressure. It's all to do with how many molecules you've got crashing into the sides. With gases though, you've got to keep the lid on tight or they'll escape.*

# Equilibrium Constants and Entropy

*I've said this before — the problem with equilibrium constants is, they are constantly turning up...*
***These pages are for Edexcel (Unit 4) only.***

## *Total Entropy Change* is Related to the *Equilibrium Constant, K*

A **spontaneous** reaction produces lots of product so it will have a **high equilibrium constant**. Its spontaneity depends on the **total entropy change** for the reaction, $\Delta S_{total}$ (see page 134). It's not surprising then that there's an equation linking $\Delta S_{total}$ and the **equilibrium constant**, ***K***:

$$\Delta S_{total} = R \ln K$$ (where **R** is the **gas constant, 8.31 J K$^{-1}$ mol$^{-1}$**)

ln = natural log

By substituting in values for $\Delta S_{total}$ you can see how ***K* varies** with **increasing total entropy**.

***Example 1:*** Reaction of barium hydroxide with ammonium chloride:

$Ba(OH)_2.8H_2O_{(s)} + 2NH_4Cl_{(s)} \rightarrow BaCl_{2(s)} + 10H_2O_{(l)} + 2NH_{3(g)}$ $\Delta S_{total} = 50.8$ J K$^{-1}$ mol$^{-1}$

You know $\Delta S_{total}$, so you need to rearrange the equation to find ln*K*: $\ln K = \Delta S_{total} \div R$

Plugging the numbers in, you get: $\ln K = 50.8 \div 8.31 = 6.11$

So, $\ln K = 6.11$
$K = e^{6.11} = 450$

For this calculation you're going to need the exponential button, $e^x$, on your calculator — it's the inverse of natural log, ln. Basically, when $\ln a = b$, $a = e^b$.

***Example 2:*** The burning of hydrogen:

$H_{2(g)} + \frac{1}{2}O_{2(g)} \rightleftharpoons H_2O_{(l)}$ $\Delta S_{total} = 796.2$ J K$^{-1}$ mol$^{-1}$

$\ln K = 796.2 \div 8.31 = 95.81$
$K = e^{95.81} = 4.1 \times 10^{41}$

A small increase in $\Delta S_{total}$ will cause a big increase in ***K***.

## The *Size of K* Tells You *How Far* a Reaction Has *Progressed*

The equilibrium constant is the **ratio** of products against reactants (see p26).

This means that the **higher** the value of ***K***, the **greater** the concentration of **product** compared with reactant and the **further** the forward reaction has progressed.

A **low** value of *K* would mean that very **little product** had been formed.

It's generally accepted by science bods that:

1) A reaction with an equilibrium constant of **less than 10$^{-10}$** does **not** take place.
2) A reaction with an equilibrium constant **greater than 10$^{10}$** goes to **completion**.
3) Reactions with **intermediate values** are **reversible**.

If the total entropy change for a reaction is positive, the reaction will be spontaneous. Because there's a relationship between *K* and $\Delta S_{total}$, you can also look at the **value of $\Delta S_{total}$** to see **how far** a reaction progresses.

| *K* | $\Delta S_{total}$ | Progression of Reaction |
|---|---|---|
| > 10$^{-10}$ | > −191 | Reaction doesn't go |
| > 10$^{-5}$ | > −96 | Reversible reaction with equilibrium pushed well to the **left** |
| 1 | 0 | Reversible reaction **balanced** between product and reactants |
| < 10$^{5}$ | < +96 | Reversible reaction with equilibrium pushed well to the **right** |
| < 10$^{10}$ | < +191 | Reaction complete |

***Examples:***

1) The dissolution of sodium chloride — $\Delta S_{total} = +30.2$ — this is a **reversible reaction** with the equilibrium pushed to the **right**.
2) The dissolution of silver chloride — $\Delta S_{total} = -186.6$ — this reaction is reversible, with the equilibrium pushed **well to the left**. If this value were much lower, the reaction wouldn't go — only a **very small amount** of silver chloride will dissolve in water.
3) The burning of hydrogen — $\Delta S_{total} = +796.2$ — this reaction goes to **completion**.

# Equilibrium Constants and Entropy

## Changing the **Temperature** of a Reaction Affects $\Delta S_{total}$

$$\Delta S_{total} = \Delta S_{system} + \Delta S_{surroundings} \quad \text{and} \quad \Delta S_{surroundings} = -\frac{\Delta H}{T}$$

This means that: $\Delta S_{total} = \Delta S_{system} - \frac{\Delta H}{T}$

When you **increase** the temperature, the value of $\frac{\Delta H}{T}$ **decreases.**

1) For an **endothermic** reaction, **increasing** the temperature will cause an **increase** in $\Delta S_{total}$. For an **exothermic** reaction, increasing the temperature will **decrease** $\Delta S_{total}$.
2) Conversely, **decreasing** in temperature will **decrease** $\Delta S_{total}$ in an **endothermic** reaction and **increase** it in an **exothermic** reaction.

'Apparently, they were trying to increase the entropy when the lab exploded...'

Changing the temperature of a reaction can change its **outcome.**

***Example:*** The thermal decomposition of calcium carbonate:

$$CaCO_{3(s)} \rightleftharpoons CaO_{(s)} + CO_{2(g)} \qquad \Delta H = +178 \text{ kJ mol}^{-1} \qquad \Delta S_{system} = 165.0 \text{ J K}^{-1} \text{mol}^{-1}$$

At 298 K, $\Delta S_{total} = 165.0 - (178\,000 \div 298) = 165.0 - 597.0 = -432 \text{ J K}^{-1} \text{mol}^{-1}$

$\Delta S_{total}$ is **negative**, so the reaction doesn't happen.

To get $\Delta S_{total}$ to a **positive** value and the reaction happen spontaneously, $\Delta S_{surroundings}$ would have to be at least **165 J K⁻¹ mol⁻¹**.

This means raising the **temperature** of the reaction system.

To calculate this temperature you need to rearrange the equation for $\Delta S_{surroundings}$:

$$T = \Delta H / \Delta S_{surroundings} = 178\,000 \div 165 = \mathbf{1080\ K.}$$

This is the sort of temperature found in the lime kilns where this reaction takes place.

## Practice Questions

Q1 Why does a spontaneous reaction have a high equilibrium constant?

Q2 For a particular reaction, what is the value of $K$, at 298 K, when $\Delta S_{total} = 43.5 \text{ J K}^{-1} \text{mol}^{-1}$?

Q3 In terms of the extent of the reaction, how would you classify the reaction in Q2?

Q4 What happens to $\Delta S_{total}$ for an endothermic reaction when its temperature is increased?

**Exam Question**

1 This question relates to the equilibrium:

$$N_2O_{4(g)} \rightleftharpoons 2NO_{2(g)} \qquad \Delta H = +57.2 \text{ kJ mol}^{-1} \quad \Delta S_{system} = 175.8 \text{ J K}^{-1} \text{mol}^{-1}$$

a) Calculate $\Delta S_{total}$ at 60 °C for this reaction. [2 marks]

b) What is the value of $K$ at 60 °C? There is no need to include the units for $K$. [2 marks]

c) Calculate the values of $\Delta S_{total}$ and $K$ at 160 °C. [4 marks]

d) What effect does the increased temperature have on the position of equilibrium? [2 marks]

## I've run out of 'constant' jokes now...The Equilibrium Gardener anyone?

*Entropy and the equilibrium constant — as a double act they're up there with the greats: Morecambe and Wise, Laurel and Hardy, Ant and Dec?? Anyway, what you need to take away from this is that the equilibrium constant, K, and the total entropy change for a reaction are related. You don't need to take my word for it — there's an equation to prove it.*

# Le Chatelier's Principle

*Equilibria are stubborn little things — the moment you change something, they'll start trying to put it back how it was...*
***These pages are for AQA (Unit 4), OCR A (Unit 5), OCR B (Unit 5) and Edexcel (Unit 4).***

## *Le Chatelier's Principle* Predicts what will happen if *Conditions are Changed*

If you **change** the **pressure** or **temperature** of a reversible reaction, you're going to **alter** the **position of equilibrium**. This just means you'll end up with **different amounts** of reactants and products at equilibrium.

If the position of equilibrium moves to the **left**, you'll get more **reactants**.

$$\mathbf{H_{2(g)} + I_{2(g)}} \rightleftharpoons 2HI_{(g)}$$

If the position of equilibrium moves to the **right**, you'll get more **products**.

$$H_{2(g)} + I_{2(g)} \rightleftharpoons \mathbf{2HI_{(g)}}$$

**Le Chatelier's principle** tells you how the **position of equilibrium** will change if a **condition changes**:

If there's a change in **pressure** or **temperature**, the equilibrium will move to help **counteract** the change.

So, basically, if you **raise the temperature**, the position of equilibrium will shift to try to **cool things down**.
And if you **raise the pressure**, the position of equilibrium will shift to try to **reduce it again**.

## *Temperature* Changes Alter $K_c$ and $K_p$ — *Pressure* Changes Don't

**CONCENTRATION** *AQA and OCR A only*

The value of the **equilibrium constant**, $K_c$, is **fixed** at a given temperature. So if the concentration of one thing in the equilibrium mixture **changes** then the concentrations of the others must change to keep the value of $K_c$ the same.

$$CH_3COOH_{(l)} + C_2H_5OH_{(l)} \rightleftharpoons CH_3COOC_2H_{5(l)} + H_2O_{(l)}$$

If you increase the concentration of $CH_3COOH$ then the equilibrium will move to the right to get rid of the extra $CH_3COOH$ — so more $CH_3COOC_2H_5$ and $H_2O$ are produced. This keeps the equilibrium constant the same.

The removal of his dummy was a change that Maxwell always opposed.

**PRESSURE** (changing this only affects **equilibria involving gases**) ***Not AQA***

**Increasing** the pressure shifts the equilibrium to the side with **fewer** gas molecules — this **reduces** the pressure. **Decreasing** the pressure shifts the equilibrium to the side with **more** gas molecules. This **raises** the pressure again. $K_p$ stays the **same**, no matter what you do to the pressure.

There are 3 moles on the left, but only 2 on the right. So an increase in pressure would shift the equilibrium to the right. ⟹ $2SO_{2(g)} + O_{2(g)} \rightleftharpoons 2SO_{3(g)}$

**TEMPERATURE**

1) If you **increase** the temperature, you **add heat**. The equilibrium shifts in the **endothermic (positive $\Delta H$) direction** to absorb this heat.
2) **Decreasing** the temperature **removes heat**. The equilibrium shifts in the **exothermic (negative $\Delta H$) direction** to try to replace the heat.
3) If the forward reaction's **endothermic**, the reverse reaction will be **exothermic**, and vice versa.
4) If the change means **more product** is formed, $K_c$ and $K_p$ will **rise**. If it means **less product** is formed, then $K_c$ and $K_p$ will **decrease**.

The reaction below is exothermic in the forward direction. If you increase the temperature, the equilibrium shifts to the left to absorb the extra heat. This means that less product's formed.

Exothermic ⟹

$$CH_3COOH_{(l)} + C_2H_5OH_{(l)} \rightleftharpoons CH_3COOC_2H_{5(l)} + H_2O_{(l)}$$

⟸ Endothermic $\quad \Delta H = -50\ \text{kJ mol}^{-1}$

$$K_c = \frac{[CH_3COOC_2H_5][H_2O]}{[CH_3COOH][C_2H_5OH]}$$

⟸ There's less product, so $K_c$ decreases.

**Catalysts** have **NO EFFECT** on the **position of equilibrium**.
They **can't** increase **yield** — but they **do** mean equilibrium is approached **faster**.

# Le Chatelier's Principle

## Both **Temperature** and **Pressure** Affect the **Rate of a Reaction** — OCR B and Edexcel

A lot of this depends on the good old **collision theory**. It pretty much says that particles have to **collide** in the right direction and with a minimum amount of **kinetic energy** in order to react.

Changes to temperature and pressure can affect the rate at which equilibrium is reached.

1) If you **increase** the **temperature** of a reaction system, the particles move around more and their average kinetic energy is higher. As a result, they'll collide more often and are more likely to **react** when they do — this'll **speed up** the reaction. A **decrease** in temperature will **slow down** the reaction because particles will move around less and have less energy to react.

2) A change in pressure will only affect the rate of reaction if the reagents are **gases**. If you **increase** the **pressure** of a reaction system, the gas particles will be pushed closer together — this increases the chances of the particles colliding and reacting so the reaction **speeds up**. If you **decrease** the pressure, rate of reaction will **slow down**.

## Practice Questions

Q1 In which direction does the position of equilibrium move to get more products?

Q2 How does an increase in pressure affect $K_p$?

Q3 For an exothermic reaction, in which direction would the equilibrium move when the temperature is decreased?

Q4 How does the presence of a catalyst affect the position of equilibrium?

**Exam Questions**

1 This question relates to the following equilibrium:

$$CO_{(g)} + 2H_{2(g)} \rightleftharpoons CH_3OH_{(g)} \quad \Delta H = -92 \text{ kJ mol}^{-1}$$

Explain what happens to the equilibrium concentration of $CH_3OH_{(g)}$ when:

a) The temperature of the system is increased. [2 marks]

b) The pressure of the system is decreased. [2 marks]

c) A catalyst is added. [2 marks]

2 The following equilibrium was established at temperature $T_1$:

$$2SO_{2(g)} + O_{2(g)} \rightleftharpoons 2SO_{3(g)} \quad \Delta H = -196 \text{ kJ mol}^{-1}.$$

$K_p$ at $T_1$ was found to be 0.67 kPa$^{-1}$.

a) When equilibrium was established at a different temperature, $T_2$, the value of $K_p$ was found to have increased. State which of $T_1$ or $T_2$ is the lower temperature and explain why. [3 marks]

b) The experiment was repeated at $T_1$. It was exactly the same in all respects except a flask of smaller volume was used. How would this change affect the yield of sulfur trioxide and the value of $K_p$? [2 marks]

## *It's just a move to the left — and then a step to the right...*

*The take home point: temperature affects the value of K, concentration, pressure and catalysts don't. Easy. That's really all there is to say. I mean I could waffle on about how the position of equilibrium moves to counteract changes to temperature and pressure and how they both affect rate of reaction, but I won't. Keep it simple. That's my motto.*

# Equilibria in Industrial Processes

*Finally, the light at the end of the tunnel. I spy section 4 approaching...*
***These pages are for OCR B (Unit 5) and Edexcel (Unit 4).***

## The **Haber Process** Combines **Nitrogen** and **Hydrogen** to make **Ammonia**

$$N_{2(g)} + 3H_{2(g)} \rightleftharpoons 2NH_{3(g)} \qquad \Delta H = -92 \text{ kJ mol}^{-1}, \ \Delta S_{system} = -201.8 \text{ J K}^{-1}\text{ mol}^{-1}$$

Businesses using the Haber process want to make **as much** ammonia as they can, as **quickly** and as **cheaply** as possible, so that they make bags of money. To do this, they've had to look carefully at choosing the **best conditions** for the job.

## The **Temperature** Chosen is a **Compromise**

1) Because it's an **exothermic reaction**, **lower** temperatures favour the forward reaction. This means **more** hydrogen and nitrogen is converted to ammonia — you get a better **yield**.
2) The trouble is, **lower temperatures** mean a **slower rate of reaction** — and you'd be **daft** to try to get a **really high yield** of ammonia if it's going to take you 10 years. So the temperature chosen is a **compromise** between **maximum yield** and **a faster reaction**.
3) Another way of looking at this problem is to consider the **entropy changes** involved:

Usually, the Haber process is carried out at about 450 °C and a pressure of around 200 atm — you don't need to learn this though.

***Edexcel only***

You get a **balanced equilibrium** (equal amounts of reactant and product) when $\Delta S_{total} = 0$.

The temperature this happens at is: $\Delta H \div \Delta S_{system} = -92\,000 \div 201.8 = 456$ K (= 183 °C)

Remember: the forward reaction is **exothermic**. If you **increase** the temperature, $\Delta S_{total}$ will **decrease** and the position of equilibrium will shift to the **left** — producing **less ammonia**. The temperature has to be increased though, because the reaction would be too slow at 456 K.

## **High Pressure** Would Give a **Big Yield** — But It'd Be **Expensive**

1) **Higher pressures** favour the **forward reaction**. This is because the equilibrium moves to the side with **fewer molecules**. There are **four molecules** of gas on the reactant side ($N_{2(g)} + 3H_{2(g)}$) to every **two molecules** on the product side ($2NH_{3(g)}$).
2) **Increasing** the **pressure** also **increases** the **rate** of reaction.
3) Cranking up the pressure as high as you can sounds like a great idea so far. **But** very **high pressures** are really **expensive** to produce. You also need **strong pipes** and **containers** to **withstand** the **high pressure**. So the pressure chosen is a **compromise**. In the end, it all comes down to **minimising costs**.

During the **industrial production** of ammonia the reaction **never** actually **reaches equilibrium**. This is because it doesn't take place in a **closed system**. The gas mixture continually leaves the reactor and is liquified so that the **ammonia** can be **removed** — the unreacted nitrogen and hydrogen are then recycled.

The Haber process uses a catalyst, but it doesn't affect how much product is made — it just makes the reaction reach equilibrium much more quickly.

## **Industrial Reactions** are Designed to **Maximise Atom Economy**

***Edexcel only***

$$\% \text{ atom economy} = \frac{\text{mass of atoms in product}}{\text{mass of atoms in reactants}} \times 100$$

The greater the atom economy, the less the waste. There are a couple of ways to increase it:

1) **Recycling** unreacted materials.

Looking at the **Haber process** again, you can see that the atom economy for the conversion of nitrogen and hydrogen to ammonia is **100%** — assuming that the reaction goes to completion. But the reaction is in **equilibrium** with a **conversion rate** of only about **15%** — this means that the atom economy is also 15%. If the **unreacted gases** are continually **recycled**, then the conversion rate and atom economy are **increased** to **98%**.

2) Finding an **alternative route** for synthesis.

**Ibuprofen**, a pain-killer, was patented in the 1960s. It was manufactured in a **6 step process** with an atom economy of **40%**. In the mid-1980s a new company came along and developed an **alternative synthesis**, which converted the same starting materials to ibuprofen in just **three steps** — this increased the atom economy to **77%**.

# Equilibria in Industrial Processes

## Industrial Processes Need to be **Controlled**

***Edexcel only***

If you're developing an industrial process based on a chemical reaction, you'll need to answer a few questions first.

**1) WILL THE REACTION GO?**

Analysis of equilibrium constants and **entropy changes** can answer this question. Reactions with $\Delta S_{total}$ values of **less than –100 J K⁻¹ mol⁻¹** are unlikely to go even with changes to temperature and pressure. Reactions with $\Delta S_{total}$ values **between –100 and 0 J K⁻¹ mol⁻¹** could be made to go with economic and safe changes to temperature and pressure. Given that the product is removed, the equilibrium can be pushed towards better yields. If $\Delta S_{total}$ is **greater than 0 J K⁻¹ mol⁻¹** the reaction should work without interference.

**2) HOW FAST IS THE REACTION?**

Some reactions will occur, but only **very slowly**. This doesn't make the process very **economical**. Changes to temperature and pressure, or the introduction of a catalyst, can **speed up** the rate at which equilibrium is reached.

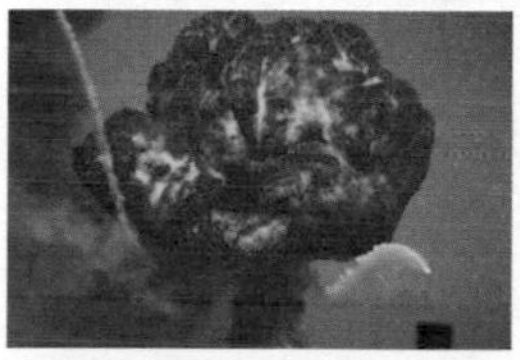

Jill's industrial marshmallow-toaster needed a few tweaks before going on sale.

**3) CAN THE ATOM ECONOMY OF THE PROCESS BE INCREASED?**

This will help **reduce waste** (which is better for the environment) and **keep costs down**.

**4) ARE THERE WAYS OF REDUCING ENERGY CONSUMPTION?**

E.g. by using **heat exchangers**. This will help to keep production **costs** down.

**5) WHAT SAFETY PROCEDURES NEED TO BE PUT IN PLACE?**

If **high pressures or temperatures** are used, there need to be **safeguards** in place to protect the **workforce** and the **environment**. The same is true if the **products** or **waste products** from the reaction are **toxic** or **highly flammable**.

Answering these questions is vital if you're going to control the chemical reactions that form part of the industrial process.

## Practice Questions

Q1 In an exothermic reaction, what sort of temperature favours the reverse reaction?

Q2 Why are the reaction conditions for the Haber process regarded as a compromise?

Q3 Why is it important to maximize the atom economy of an industrial process?

**Exam Question**

1 The following reaction is part of the Contact process, which is used to manufacture sulfuric acid:

$$2SO_{2(g)} + O_{2(g)} \rightleftharpoons 2SO_{3(g)} \quad \Delta H = -57.2\ \text{kJmol}^{-1}$$

a) The reaction takes place at a temperature of 450 °C. Explain why this might be termed a 'compromise temperature'. [3 marks]

b) A vanadium(V) oxide catalyst is used to speed up the reaction. How does this affect the product yield? [1 mark]

c) Suggest how the atom economy of this process might be increased. [1 mark]

d) A new company has decided to start manufacturing sulfuric acid. Suggest and explain two factors that could influence their choice of process. [4 marks]

## *Industrial chemistry — like life, it's all a matter of compromise...*

*These two pages have basically taken everything you've learnt so far and told you how it gets used in the chemical industry — so if you're planning a career as a chemical engineer I'd make sure you've read this properly. To be fair, I'd say read it properly anyway. There is an exam at the end of all this. I reckon they're bound to ask you some questions about it.*

# Acids and Bases

*Remember this stuff? Well, it's all down to Brønsted and Lowry — they've got a lot to answer for...*
***These pages are for AQA (Unit 4), OCR A (Unit 5), OCR B (Units 4 and 5) and Edexcel (Unit 4).***

## An Acid **Releases** Protons — a Base **Accepts** Protons

1) The **scientific definition** of an **acid** has changed over time — originally, the word **acid** just meant something that **tasted sour**.
2) In the late 19th century, the Swedish scientist **Svante Arrhenius** came up with a more scientific definition — he defined an acid as a substance that produces **excess hydrogen ions** when it dissolves in water.
3) In 1923, **Johannes Nicolaus Brønsted** and **Martin Lowry** refined the definition. They said that acids and bases were to do with **donating and accepting protons**. Here's their definition...

**Brønsted-Lowry acids** are **proton donors** — they release **hydrogen ions** ($H^+$) when they're mixed with water. You never get $H^+$ ions by themselves in water though — they're always combined with $H_2O$ to form **hydroxonium ions, $H_3O^+$**.

HA is just any old acid. ⟹ $HA_{(aq)} + H_2O_{(l)} \rightarrow H_3O^+_{(aq)} + A^-_{(aq)}$

**Brønsted-Lowry bases** do the opposite — they're **proton acceptors**.
When they're in solution, they grab **hydrogen ions** from water molecules.

B could be any base. ⟹ $B_{(aq)} + H_2O_{(l)} \rightarrow BH^+_{(aq)} + OH^-_{(aq)}$

## Acids React with **Metals** and **Carbonates**

***OCR A only***

1) **Reactive metals** react with acids releasing **hydrogen gas**.
2) The metal atoms **donate electrons** to the **$H^+$ ions** in the acid solution.
The metal atoms are **oxidised** and the $H^+$ ions are **reduced**.

E.g. $Mg_{(s)} + 2H^+_{(aq)} \rightarrow Mg^{2+}_{(aq)} + H_{2(g)}$

Oxidation Is Loss, Reduction Is Gain (of electrons).

3) **Carbonates** react with acids to produce **carbon dioxide** and **water**.

E.g. $CO_3^{2-}{}_{(aq)} + 2H^+_{(aq)} \rightarrow H_2O_{(l)} + CO_{2(g)}$

## Acids React with **Bases** and **Alkalis** Too

***OCR A only***

1) Acids produce $H^+$ ions when dissolved in water and alkalis produce $OH^-$ ions.
2) Acids and bases **neutralise** each other to form water.
E.g. acids and **alkalis** react like this...

$H^+_{(aq)} + OH^-_{(aq)} \rightarrow H_2O_{(l)}$

Remember — alkalis are bases that dissolve in water.

Most insoluble bases are **metal oxides** and they're neutralised in a similar way.

$2H^+_{(aq)} + O^{2-}{}_{(s)} \rightarrow H_2O_{(l)}$

# Acids and Bases

## Acids and Bases can be *Strong* or *Weak*

*Not OCR B*

1) **Strong acids** dissociate (or ionise) almost completely in water — **nearly all** the $H^+$ ions will be released. E.g. hydrochloric acid is a strong acid:

$$HCl_{(g)} + \text{water} \rightarrow H^+_{(aq)} + Cl^-_{(aq)}$$

2) **Strong bases** ionise almost completely in water too. E.g. sodium hydroxide is a strong base:

$$NaOH_{(s)} + \text{water} \rightarrow Na^+_{(aq)} + OH^-_{(aq)}$$

These are really all reversible reactions, but for strong acids and bases the equilibrium lies extremely far to the right.

3) **Weak acids** (e.g. ethanoic or citric) dissociate only very **slightly** in water — so only small numbers of $H^+$ ions are formed. An **equilibrium** is set up which lies well over to the **left**.

$$\text{E.g. } CH_3COOH_{(aq)} \rightleftharpoons CH_3COO^-_{(aq)} + H^+_{(aq)}$$

4) **Weak bases** (e.g. ammonia) only slightly ionise in water. Just like with weak acids, the **equilibrium** lies well over to the **left**.

$$\text{E.g. } NH_{3(aq)} + H_2O_{(l)} \rightleftharpoons NH_4^+{}_{(aq)} + OH^-_{(aq)}$$

## *Protons* are *Transferred* when *Acids* and *Bases* React

*AQA and Edexcel only*

Acids **can't** just throw away their protons — they can only get rid of them if there's a **base** to accept them. In this reaction the **acid**, HA, **transfers** a proton to the **base**, B: $HA_{(aq)} + B_{(aq)} \rightleftharpoons BH^+_{(aq)} + A^-_{(aq)}$

It's an **equilibrium**, so if you add more **HA** or **B**, the position of equilibrium moves to the **right**. But if you add more **$BH^+$** or **$A^-$**, the equilibrium will move to the **left**. This is all down to **Le Chatelier's principle** (see p32).

When an acid is added to **water**, the water acts as the **base** and accepts the proton:

$$HA_{(aq)} + H_2O_{(l)} \rightleftharpoons H_3O^+_{(aq)} + A^-_{(aq)}$$

The equilibrium's far to the left for weak acids, and far to the right for strong acids.

## Acids and Bases form *Conjugate Pairs*

*Not AQA*

1) When an acid's added to water, the equilibrium shown on the right is set up.
2) In the **forward reaction**, HA acts as an **acid** as it **donates** a proton. In the **reverse reaction**, $A^-$ acts as a **base** and **accepts** a proton from the $H_3O^+$ ion to form HA.
3) HA and $A^-$ are called a **conjugate pair** — HA is the **conjugate acid** of $A^-$ and $A^-$ is the **conjugate base** of the acid, HA. **$H_2O$** and **$H_3O^+$** are a conjugate pair too.

$$HA + H_2O \rightleftharpoons H_3O^+ + A^-$$

acid (HA), base ($H_2O$), acid ($H_3O^+$), base ($A^-$); conjugate pair: $H_2O$ / $H_3O^+$; conjugate pair: HA / $A^-$

4) The acid and base of a conjugate pair can be linked by an **$H^+$**, like this: $HA \rightleftharpoons H^+ + A^-$ or like this: $H^+ + H_2O \rightleftharpoons H_3O^+$

E.g. Here's the equilibrium for aqueous HCl. $Cl^-_{(aq)}$ is the conjugate base of $HCl_{(aq)}$.

$$HCl_{(aq)} + H_2O_{(l)} \rightleftharpoons H_3O^+_{(aq)} + Cl^-_{(aq)}$$

acid ($HCl$), base ($H_2O$), acid ($H_3O^+$), base ($Cl^-$); conjugate pair: $H_2O$ / $H_3O^+$; conjugate pair: $HCl$ / $Cl^-$

5) An equilibrium with **conjugate pairs** is also set up when a **base** dissolves in water. The base B takes a proton from the water to form **$BH^+$** — so B is the **conjugate base** of $BH^+$, and $BH^+$ is the **conjugate acid** of B. $H_2O$ and $OH^-$ also form a **conjugate pair**.

$$B + H_2O \rightleftharpoons BH^+ + OH^-$$

base (B), acid ($H_2O$), acid ($BH^+$), base ($OH^-$); conjugate pair: B / $BH^+$; conjugate pair: $H_2O$ / $OH^-$

# Acids and Bases

## **Water** can Behave as an **Acid AND** a **Base**

***Not OCR B***

Water can act as an **acid** by **donating** a proton — but it can also act as a **base** by accepting a **proton**. So in water there'll always be both **hydroxonium ions** and **hydroxide ions** swimming around at the **same time**.

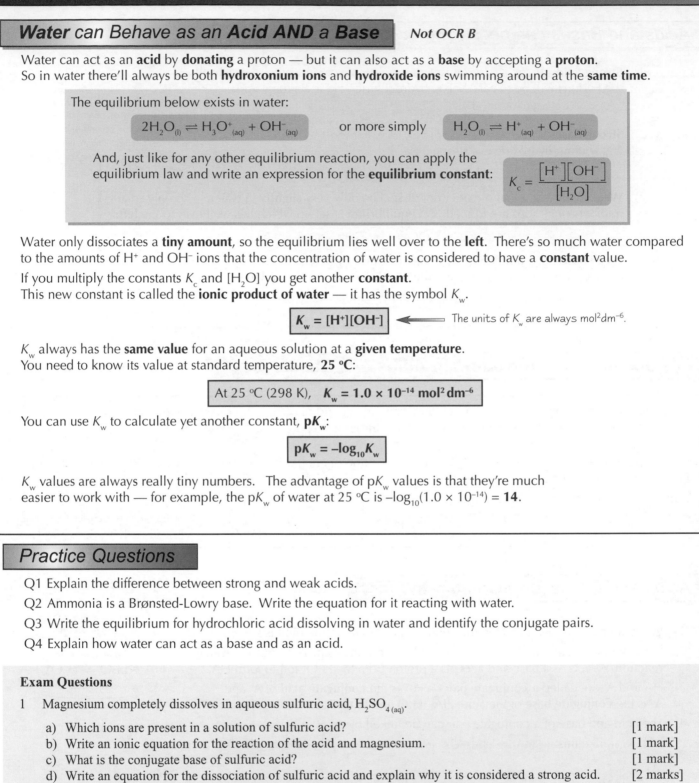

The equilibrium below exists in water:

$$2H_2O_{(l)} \rightleftharpoons H_3O^+_{(aq)} + OH^-_{(aq)} \quad \text{or more simply} \quad H_2O_{(l)} \rightleftharpoons H^+_{(aq)} + OH^-_{(aq)}$$

And, just like for any other equilibrium reaction, you can apply the equilibrium law and write an expression for the **equilibrium constant**:

$$K_c = \frac{[H^+][OH^-]}{[H_2O]}$$

Water only dissociates a **tiny amount**, so the equilibrium lies well over to the **left**. There's so much water compared to the amounts of $H^+$ and $OH^-$ ions that the concentration of water is considered to have a **constant** value.

If you multiply the constants $K_c$ and $[H_2O]$ you get another **constant**.
This new constant is called the **ionic product of water** — it has the symbol $K_w$.

$$\mathbf{K_w = [H^+][OH^-]}$$

The units of $K_w$ are always $mol^2dm^{-6}$.

$K_w$ always has the **same value** for an aqueous solution at a **given temperature**.
You need to know its value at standard temperature, **25 °C**:

$$\text{At 25 °C (298 K),} \quad K_w = 1.0 \times 10^{-14}\ mol^2\ dm^{-6}$$

You can use $K_w$ to calculate yet another constant, $\mathbf{pK_w}$:

$$pK_w = -\log_{10}K_w$$

$K_w$ values are always really tiny numbers. The advantage of $pK_w$ values is that they're much easier to work with — for example, the $pK_w$ of water at 25 °C is $-\log_{10}(1.0 \times 10^{-14})$ = **14**.

## Practice Questions

Q1 Explain the difference between strong and weak acids.

Q2 Ammonia is a Brønsted-Lowry base. Write the equation for it reacting with water.

Q3 Write the equilibrium for hydrochloric acid dissolving in water and identify the conjugate pairs.

Q4 Explain how water can act as a base and as an acid.

**Exam Questions**

1 Magnesium completely dissolves in aqueous sulfuric acid, $H_2SO_{4\,(aq)}$.

a) Which ions are present in a solution of sulfuric acid? [1 mark]
b) Write an ionic equation for the reaction of the acid and magnesium. [1 mark]
c) What is the conjugate base of sulfuric acid? [1 mark]
d) Write an equation for the dissociation of sulfuric acid and explain why it is considered a strong acid. [2 marks]

2 Hydrocyanic acid, HCN, is a weak acid.

a) Write an equation to show the equilibrium set up when it is added to water. [1 mark]
b) Use your equation to explain why HCN is a weak acid. [1 mark]
c) From your equation, identify the two conjugate pairs formed. [2 marks]
d) Which ion links conjugate pairs? [1 mark]

## Acids and bases — the Julie Andrews and Marilyn Manson of the chemistry world...

*Don't confuse strong acids with concentrated acids, or weak acids with dilute acids. Strong and weak are to do with how much an acid ionises, whereas concentrated and dilute are to do with the number of moles of acid you've got per dm³. You can have a dilute strong acid, or a concentrated weak acid. It works the same way with bases too.*

# pH Calculations

*Get those calculators warmed up — especially the log function key.*
***These pages are for AQA (Unit 4), OCR A (Unit 5), OCR B (Unit 5) and Edexcel (Unit 4).***

## The **pH Scale** is a Measure of the **Hydrogen Ion Concentration**

The **concentration of hydrogen ions** can vary enormously. To make them easier to work with, chemists express the concentration using a **logarithmic scale**: $pH = -\log_{10}[H^+]$

The pH scale normally goes from **0** (very acidic) to **14** (very alkaline). **pH 7** is **neutral**.

## For Strong Monoprotic Acids, **Hydrogen Ion Concentration = Acid Concentration**

Hydrochloric acid (HCl) and nitric acid ($HNO_3$) are **strong acids**, so they ionise fully. They're also **monoprotic**, so each mole of acid produces **one mole of hydrogen ions**. This means the $H^+$ concentration is the **same** as the acid concentration.

Here's an example:

Find the pH of 0.05 mol dm$^{-3}$ nitric acid. $[H^+] = 0.05$ mol dm$^{-3}$ $\Rightarrow$ $pH = -\log_{10}(0.05) = \mathbf{1.30}$

You also need to be able to work out **[H⁺]** if you're given the **pH** of a solution.
You do this by finding the **inverse log of –pH**, which is $\mathbf{10^{-pH}}$.

If an acid solution has a pH of 2.45, what is the hydrogen ion concentration, or $[H^+]$, of the acid?

$[H^+] = 10^{-2.45} = \mathbf{3.55 \times 10^{-3}}$ **mol dm$^{-3}$**

## Use $K_w$ to Find the **pH** of a **Base**

Sodium hydroxide (NaOH) and potassium hydroxide (KOH) are **strong bases**, so they **fully ionise** in water.
They each have **one hydroxide ion per molecule**, so they donate **one mole of $OH^-$ ions** per mole of base.
This means that the concentration of $OH^-$ ions is the **same** as the **concentration of the base**.
So for 0.02 mol dm$^{-3}$ sodium hydroxide solution, $[OH^-]$ is also **0.02 mol dm$^{-3}$**.

But to work out the **pH** you need to know **[H⁺]** — luckily this is linked to **[OH⁻]** through the **ionic product of water**, $K_w$:

$$K_w = [H^+][OH^-] = 1.0 \times 10^{-14} \text{ at 298 K}$$

So if you know $K_w$ and $[OH^-]$ for a **strong aqueous base** at a certain temperature, you can work out **[H⁺]** and then the **pH**.

Find the pH of 0.1 mol dm$^{-3}$ NaOH at 298 K.

$[OH^-] = 0.1$ mol dm$^{-3}$ $\Rightarrow [H^+] = \dfrac{K_w}{[OH^-]} = \dfrac{1.0\times10^{-14}}{0.1} = 1.0 \times 10^{-13}$ mol dm$^{-3}$

So $pH = -\log_{10}(1.0 \times 10^{-13}) = \mathbf{13.0}$

## To Find the **pH** of a **Weak Acid** you Use $K_a$ (the **Acid Dissociation Constant**)

Weak acids **don't** ionise fully in solution, so $[H^+]$ **isn't** the same as the acid concentration.
This makes it a **bit trickier** to find their pH. You have to use yet another **equilibrium constant**, $K_a$.

For a weak aqueous acid, HA, you get the following equilibrium: $HA_{(aq)} \rightleftharpoons H^+_{(aq)} + A^-_{(aq)}$

To find the equilibrium constant you have to make a **couple of assumptions**.

1) Only a **tiny amount** of HA dissociates, so you can assume that $[HA_{(aq)}]_{start} = [HA_{(aq)}]_{equilibrium}$.

So if you apply the equilibrium law, you get: $K_a = \dfrac{[H^+][A^-]}{[HA]}$

2) **All** the **$H^+$ ions** come from the **acid**, so $[H^+_{(aq)}] = [A^-_{(aq)}]$... So $K_a = \dfrac{[H^+]^2}{[HA]}$ ← The units of $K_a$ are mol dm$^{-3}$.

Here's an example of how to use $K_a$ to find the **pH** of a weak acid:

Calculate the hydrogen ion concentration and the pH of a 0.02 mol dm$^{-3}$ solution of propanoic acid ($CH_3CH_2COOH$).
$K_a$ for propanoic acid at this temperature is $1.30 \times 10^{-5}$ mol dm$^{-3}$.

$K_a = \dfrac{[H^+]^2}{[CH_3CH_2COOH]}$ $\Rightarrow [H^+]^2 = K_a[CH_3CH_2COOH] = 1.30 \times 10^{-5} \times 0.02 = 2.60 \times 10^{-7}$

$\Rightarrow [H^+] = \sqrt{2.60\times10^{-7}} = \mathbf{5.10 \times 10^{-4}}$ **mol dm$^{-3}$** So $pH = -\log_{10}(5.10 \times 10^{-4}) = \mathbf{3.29}$

# pH Calculations

## You Might Have to Find the Concentration or $K_a$ of a Weak Acid

You don't need to know anything new for this type of calculation. You usually just have to find **[H⁺]** from the pH, then fiddle around with the **$K_a$ expression** to find the missing bit of information.

The pH of an ethanoic acid ($CH_3COOH$) solution was 3.02 at 298 K. Calculate the molar concentration of this solution. The $K_a$ of ethanoic acid is $1.75 \times 10^{-5}$ mol dm⁻³ at 298 K.

$[H^+] = 10^{-pH} = 10^{-3.02} = 9.55 \times 10^{-4}$ mol dm⁻³

$$K_a = \frac{[H^+]^2}{[CH_3COOH]} \Rightarrow [CH_3COOH] = \frac{[H^+]^2}{K_a} = \frac{(9.55\times10^{-4})^2}{1.75\times10^{-5}} = \mathbf{0.0521\ mol\ dm^{-3}}$$

Remember the assumptions you have to make here:
1) Only a tiny amount of HA dissociates.
2) All the H⁺ ions come from the acid.

A solution of 0.162 mol dm⁻³ HCN has a pH of 5.05 at 298 K. What is the value of $K_a$ for HCN at 298 K?

$[H^+] = 10^{-pH} = 10^{-5.05} = 8.91 \times 10^{-6}$ mol dm⁻³

$$K_a = \frac{[H^+]^2}{[HCN]} = \frac{(8.91\times10^{-6})^2}{0.162} = \mathbf{4.90 \times 10^{-10}\ mol\ dm^{-3}}$$

## $pK_a = -\log_{10} K_a$ and $K_a = 10^{-pK_a}$

$pK_a$ is calculated from $K_a$ in exactly the same way as pH is calculated from [H⁺] — and vice versa. So if an acid has a $K_a$ value of $1.50 \times 10^{-7}$, its $\mathbf{pK_a = -\log_{10}(1.50 \times 10^{-7}) = 6.82}$. And if an acid has a $pK_a$ value of 4.32, its $\mathbf{K_a = 10^{-4.32} = 4.79 \times 10^{-5}}$.

Notice how $pK_a$ values aren't annoyingly tiny like $K_a$ values.

Just to make things that bit more complicated, there might be a **$pK_a$** value in a question. If so, you need to convert it to $K_a$ so that you can use the **$K_a$ expression**.

Methanoic acid, HCOOH, has a $pK_a$ of 3.75 at 298 K. Calculate the pH of 0.050 mol dm⁻³ methanoic acid at 298 K.

First convert the $pK_a$ to $K_a$: $K_a = 10^{-pK_a} = 10^{-3.75} = 1.78 \times 10^{-4}$ mol dm⁻³

$$K_a = \frac{[H^+]^2}{[HCOOH]} \Rightarrow [H^+]^2 = K_a[HCOOH] = 1.78 \times 10^{-4} \times 0.050 = 8.9 \times 10^{-6}$$

$$\Rightarrow [H^+] = \sqrt{8.9\times10^{-6}} = 2.98 \times 10^{-3}\ mol\ dm^{-3}$$

pH = $-\log(2.98 \times 10^{-3})$ = **2.53**

Sometimes you have to give your answer as a **$pK_a$** value. In this case, you just work out the $K_a$ value as usual and then convert it to **$pK_a$** — and Bob's your pet hamster.

## The pH of Equimolar Solutions can give you Information about the Substances

You can learn quite a lot about the nature of a chemical just by looking at its **pH**.

***Edexcel only***

| Substance | pH |
|---|---|
| 1 mol dm⁻³ HCl | 0 |
| 1 mol dm⁻³ $C_2H_5COOH$ | 2.44 |
| 1 mol dm⁻³ NaCl | 7 |
| 1 mol dm⁻³ $NH_3$ | 10.62 |
| 1 mol dm⁻³ NaOH | 14 |

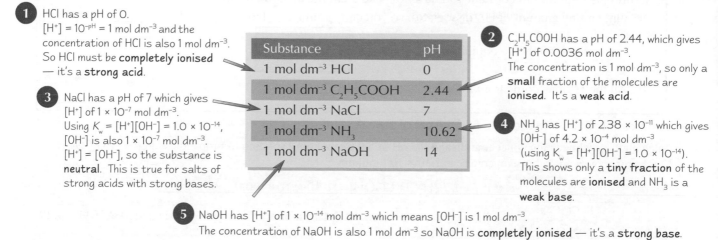

1. HCl has a pH of 0. $[H^+] = 10^{-pH} = 1$ mol dm⁻³ and the concentration of HCl is also 1 mol dm⁻³. So HCl must be **completely ionised** — it's a **strong acid**.
2. $C_2H_5COOH$ has a pH of 2.44, which gives [H⁺] of 0.0036 mol dm⁻³. The concentration is 1 mol dm⁻³, so only a **small** fraction of the molecules are **ionised**. It's a **weak acid**.
3. NaCl has a pH of 7 which gives [H⁺] of $1 \times 10^{-7}$ mol dm⁻³. Using $K_w = [H^+][OH^-] = 1.0 \times 10^{-14}$, [OH⁻] is also $1 \times 10^{-7}$ mol dm⁻³. [H⁺] = [OH⁻], so the substance is **neutral**. This is true for salts of strong acids with strong bases.
4. $NH_3$ has [H⁺] of $2.38 \times 10^{-11}$ which gives [OH⁻] of $4.2 \times 10^{-4}$ mol dm⁻³ (using $K_w = [H^+][OH^-] = 1.0 \times 10^{-14}$). This shows only a **tiny fraction** of the molecules are **ionised** and $NH_3$ is a **weak base**.
5. NaOH has [H⁺] of $1 \times 10^{-14}$ mol dm⁻³ which means [OH⁻] is 1 mol dm⁻³. The concentration of NaOH is also 1 mol dm⁻³ so NaOH is **completely ionised** — it's a **strong base**.

# pH Calculations

## When Acids are Diluted their pH Changes

*Edexcel only*

If you measure the **pH** of a strong and a weak acid at **different concentrations** you get a set of results that looks something like this.

| Concentration of Solution | HCl pH at 298 K | $C_2H_5COOH$ pH at 298 K |
|---|---|---|
| 1 mol dm$^{-3}$ | 0 | 2.44 |
| 0.1 mol dm$^{-3}$ | 1 | 2.94 |
| 0.01 mol dm$^{-3}$ | 2 | 3.44 |
| 0.001 mol dm$^{-3}$ | 3 | 3.94 |

When you **dilute** an acid the **concentration** of $H^+$ ions **changes**. So the **pH changes** too.

### Strong Acid — HCl

A strong acid is completely ionised in solution. So the **[H⁺] is equal** to the **acid concentration**. As you **dilute** the **acid** by a factor of 10 the **[H⁺]** is also **reduced** by a factor of 10. This will **increase pH** by 1.

### Weak Acid — Propanoic acid

The **pH of the weak acid increases** by 0.5 each time it's **diluted** by a factor of 10. You can show this by calculating the [H⁺] at each of the concentrations using the formula on page 39.

$$K_a = [H^+]^2 \div [C_2H_5COOH] \quad \Rightarrow \quad [H^+] = \sqrt{K_a[C_2H_5COOH]}$$

The $K_a$ of propanoic acid at 298 K is $1.31 \times 10^{-5}$.

If $[C_2H_5COOH] = 1$ mol dm$^{-3}$ then $[H^+] = 3.62 \times 10^{-3}$ = pH 2.44

If $[C_2H_5COOH] = 0.1$ mol dm$^{-3}$ then $[H^+]$ is $1.14 \times 10^{-3}$ = pH 2.94

The pH will always change by **0.5** for a **weak acid** if it is diluted by a factor of **10**.

## Practice Questions

Q1 Explain how to find the pH of a strong acid.

Q2 How do you find the pH of a strong base?

Q3 Explain how to find the pH of a weak acid.

Q4 The pH of a 1 mol dm$^{-3}$ solution of nitric acid is 0 at 298 K. What does this tell you about nitric acid?

**Exam Questions**

1 The value of $K_a$ for the weak acid HA, at 298 K, is $5.60 \times 10^{-4}$ mol dm$^{-3}$.

a) Write an expression for $K_a$ for the weak acid HA. [1 mark]

b) Calculate the pH of a 0.280 mol dm$^{-3}$ solution of HA at 298 K. [3 marks]

2 The pH of a 0.150 mol dm$^{-3}$ solution of a weak monoprotic acid, HX, is 2.65 at 298 K. Calculate the value of $K_a$ for the acid HX at 298 K. [4 marks]

3 The pH of a 0.1 mol dm$^{-3}$ solution of the weak acid benzoic acid, $C_6H_5COOH$, is 2.60 at 298 K.

a) Calculate the value of $K_a$ for benzoic acid at this temperature. [4 marks]

b) Use your answer to part (a) to find the [H⁺] of a 0.01 mol dm$^{-3}$ solution of this acid at 298 K. [2 marks]

c) Calculate the pH of the 0.01 solution of acid at 298 K. [1 mark]

d) Show that the pH of a 1 mol dm$^{-3}$ solution is 2.1. [2 marks]

e) What rule can you suggest for the effect of tenfold dilutions on the pH of this acid? [1 mark]

## My mate had a red Ka — but she drove it into a lamppost...

*Strong acids have high $K_a$ values and weak acids have low $K_a$ values. For $pK_a$ values, it's the other way round — the stronger the acid, the lower the $pK_a$. If something's got p in front of it, like pH, $pK_w$ or $pK_a$, it tends to mean $-\log_{10}$ of whatever. Not all calculators work the same way, so make sure you know how to work logs out on your calculator.*

# pH Curves, Titrations and Indicators

***These pages are for AQA (Unit 4), OCR A (Unit 5), OCR B (Unit 4) and Edexcel (Unit 4).***

## Use *Titration* to Find the *Concentration* of an *Acid* or *Alkali*

**Titrations** allow you to find out **exactly** how much alkali is needed to **neutralise** a quantity of acid.

1) You measure out some **acid** of known concentration using a pipette and put it in a flask, along with some **appropriate indicator**.
2) First do a rough titration — add the **alkali** to the acid using a **burette** fairly quickly to get an approximate idea where the solution changes colour (the **end point**). Give the flask a regular **swirl**.
3) Now do an **accurate** titration. Run the alkali in to within 2 $cm^3$ of the end point, then add it **drop by drop**. If you don't notice exactly when the solution changes colour you've **overshot** and your result won't be accurate.
4) **Record** the amount of alkali needed to **neutralise** the acid. It's best to **repeat** this process a few times, making sure you get very similar answers each time (within about 0.2 $cm^3$ of each other).

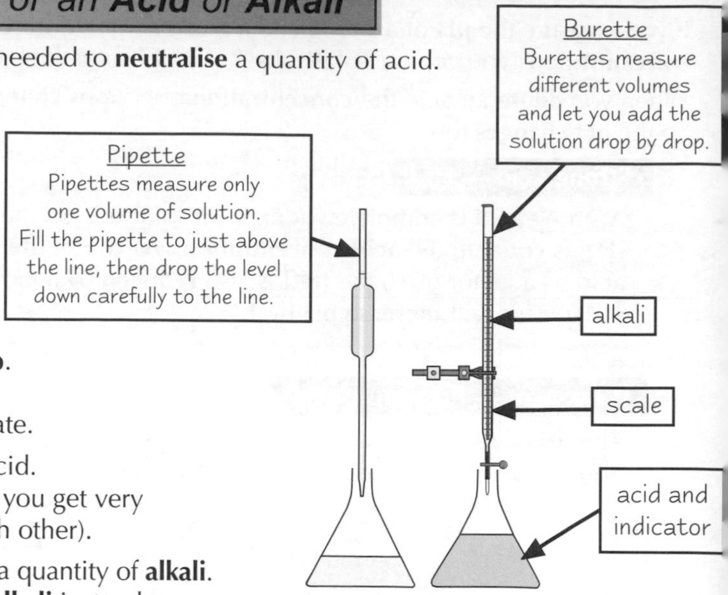


You can also find out how much **acid** is needed to neutralise a quantity of **alkali**. It's exactly the same process as above, but you add **acid to alkali** instead.

Remember — an alkali is just a base that dissolves in water.

## *pH Curves* Plot *pH* Against *Volume* of *Acid* or *Base* Added

The graphs below show the pH curves for the **different combinations** of **strong and weak** monoprotic acids and bases.

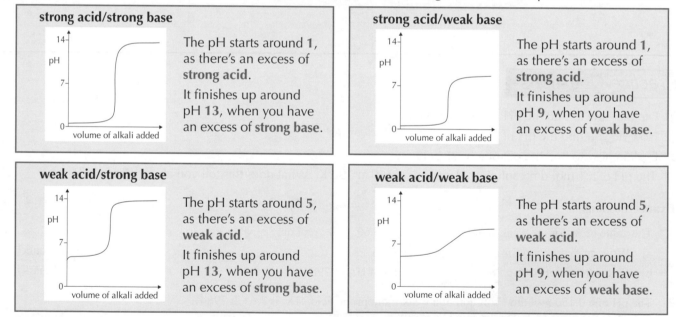

**strong acid/strong base**

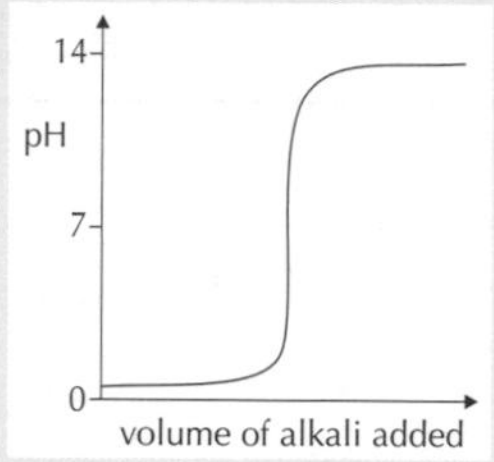


The pH starts around **1**, as there's an excess of **strong acid**.

It finishes up around pH **13**, when you have an excess of **strong base**.

**strong acid/weak base**

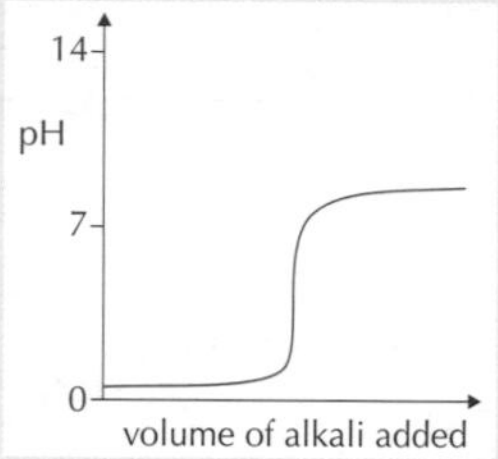


The pH starts around **1**, as there's an excess of **strong acid**.

It finishes up around pH **9**, when you have an excess of **weak base**.

**weak acid/strong base**

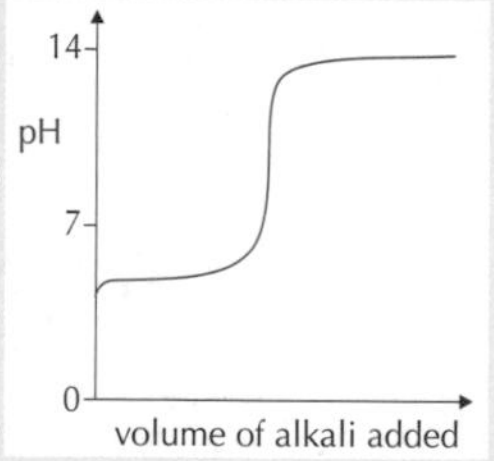


The pH starts around **5**, as there's an excess of **weak acid**.

It finishes up around pH **13**, when you have an excess of **strong base**.

**weak acid/weak base**

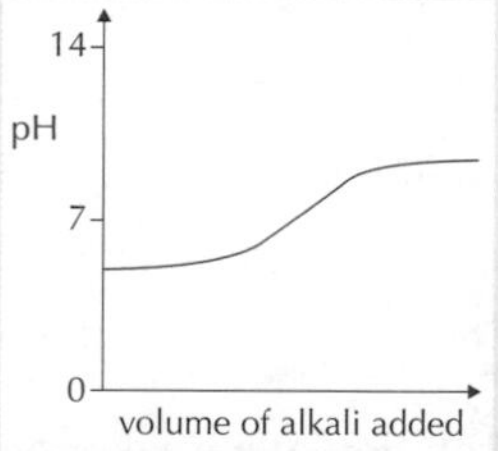


The pH starts around **5**, as there's an excess of **weak acid**.

It finishes up around pH **9**, when you have an excess of **weak base**.

All the graphs apart from the weak acid/weak base graph have a bit that's almost vertical — this is the **equivalence point** or **end point**. At this point, a tiny amount of base causes a sudden, big change in pH — it's here that all the acid is just **neutralised**.

You don't get such a sharp change in a **weak acid/weak base** titration. If you used an indicator for this type of titration, its colour would change very **gradually**, and it would be very tricky to see the exact end point. So you're usually better off using a **pH meter** for this type of titration.

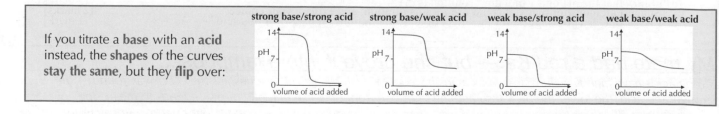

If you titrate a **base** with an **acid** instead, the **shapes** of the curves **stay the same**, but they **flip** over:

**strong base/strong acid**

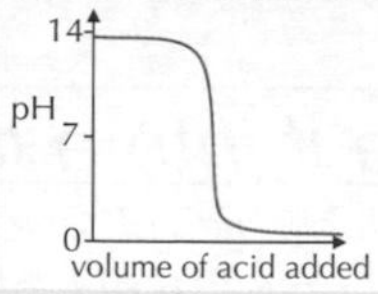


**strong base/weak acid**

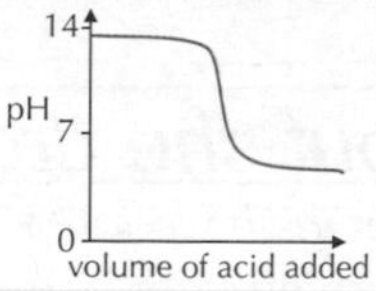


**weak base/strong acid**

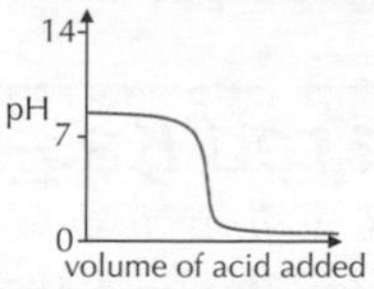


**weak base/weak acid**

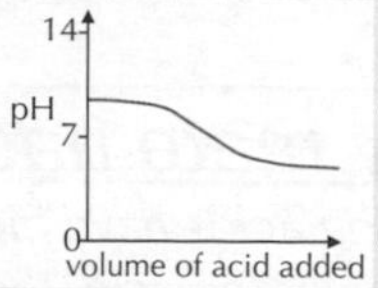

# pH Curves, Titrations and Indicators

## *pH Curves can Help you Decide which Indicator to Use*

When you use an **indicator**, you need it to change colour exactly at the **end point** of your titration. So you need to pick one that changes colour over a **narrow pH range** that lies **entirely** on the **vertical part** of the **pH curve**.

So for this titration you'd want an indicator that changed colour somewhere between pH 7 and pH 11.

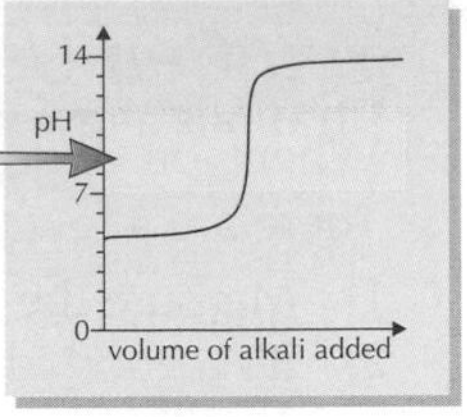


**Methyl orange** and **phenolphthalein** are **indicators** that are often used for acid-base titrations. They each change colour over a **different pH range**:

| Name of indicator | Colour at low pH | Approx. pH of colour change | Colour at high pH |
|---|---|---|---|
| Methyl orange | red | 3.1 – 4.4 | yellow |
| Phenolphthalein | colourless | 8.3 – 10 | pink |

For a **strong acid/strong alkali** titration, you can use **either** of these indicators — there's a rapid pH change over the range for **both** indicators.

For a **strong acid/weak alkali** titration only **methyl orange** will do. The pH changes rapidly across the range for methyl orange, but not for phenolphthalein.

For a **weak acid/strong alkali** titration, **phenolphthalein** is the stuff to use. The pH changes rapidly over phenolphthalein's range, but not over methyl orange's.

For **weak acid/weak alkali** titrations there's no sharp pH change, so **no** indicators will work.

## *Practice Questions*

Q1 Explain what 'equivalence point' means.

Q2 Why are indicators not used for weak acid/weak alkali titrations?

Q3 What indicator could you use for a weak acid/strong alkali titration?

Q4 Sketch the pH curve for a strong acid/weak alkali titration.

**Exam Questions**

1 A known volume of acid is titrated with a known volume of alkali.
The pH of the solution is followed throughout the titration using a pH meter.

a) Suggest an acid and an alkali that may have been used in this titration. [2 marks]

b) Suggest a suitable indicator for use in this titration. [1 mark]

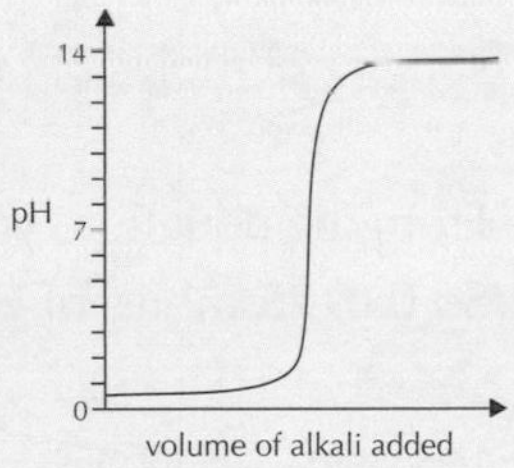


2 a) Sketch a graph to show the shape of the pH curve for the titration of a weak acid with a weak base.
Assume that both solutions have a concentration of 0.1 mol $dm^{-3}$. [2 marks]

b) What will the pH of the solution be at the equivalence point? [1 mark]

3 Look at the three pH curves below labelled X, Y and Z.

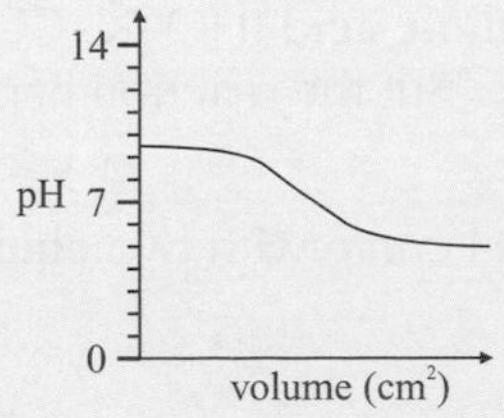


X

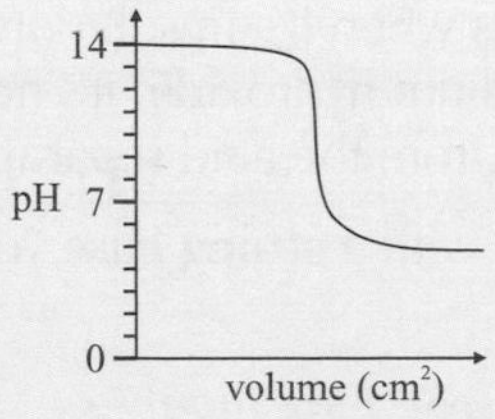


Y

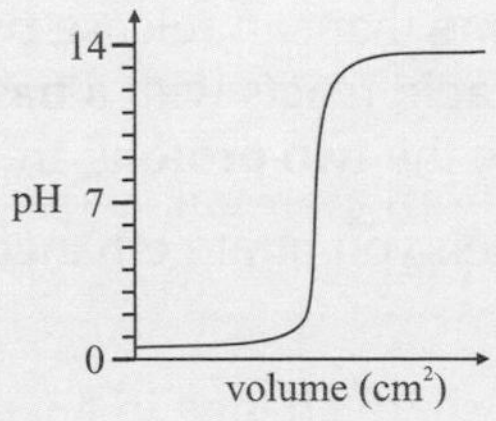


Z

a) Which of these curves could represent the titration of sodium hydroxide with ethanoic acid? [1 mark]

b) Write an equation for the reaction between sodium hydroxide and ethanoic acid. [2 marks]

c) Suggest an indicator that you could use for this titration, and explain your choice. [2 marks]

## *Try learning this stuff drop by drop...*

*Titrations involve playing with big bits of glassware that you're told not to break as they're really expensive — so you instantly become really clumsy. If you manage not to smash the burette, you'll find it easier to get accurate results if you use a dilute acid or alkali — drops of dilute acid and alkali contain fewer particles so you're less likely to overshoot.*

# Titration Calculations

*Now you know how to do a titration, here's what you can do with the results...*
***These pages are for AQA (Unit 4) only.***

## You Can Use **Titration Results** to Calculate **Concentrations**

When you've done a titration, you can use your results to calculate the **concentration** of your acid or base.
There are a few things you can do to make sure your titration **results** are as **accurate** as possible:

1) Measure the neutralisation volume as closely as you possibly can. This will usually be to the **nearest 0.05 cm³**.
2) It's a good idea to **repeat** the titration at least three times and take a **mean average** titre value. That'll help you to make sure your answer is **reliable**.
3) Don't use any **anomalous** (unusual) results — as a rough guide, all your results should be within 0.2 cm³ of each other.

If you use a **pH meter** rather than an indicator, you can draw a pH curve of the titration and use it to work out how much acid or base is needed for neutralisation. You do this by finding the **equivalence point** (the mid-point of the line of rapid pH change) and drawing a **vertical line downwards** until it meets the x-axis. The value at this point on the x-axis is the volume of acid or base needed.

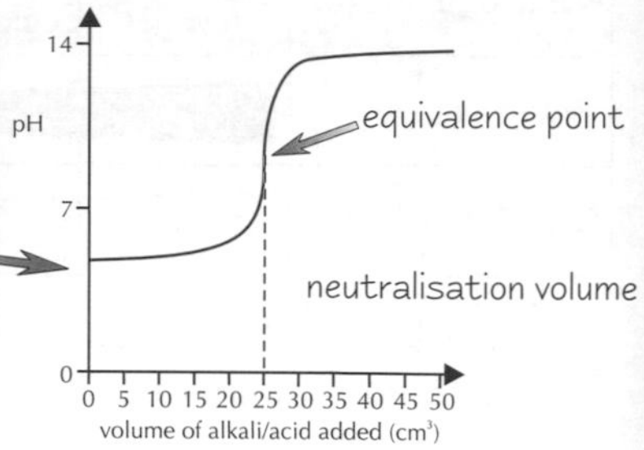

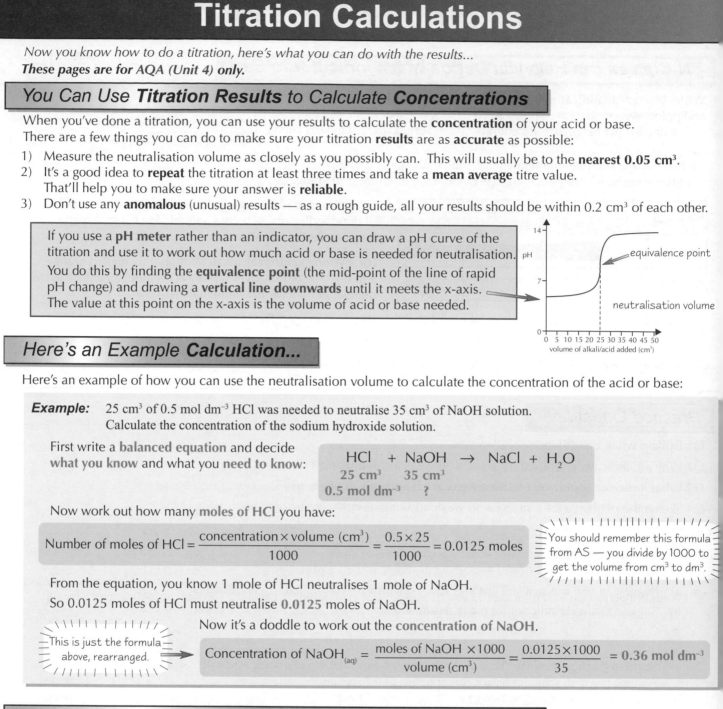

## Here's an Example **Calculation...**

Here's an example of how you can use the neutralisation volume to calculate the concentration of the acid or base:

***Example:*** 25 cm³ of 0.5 mol dm⁻³ HCl was needed to neutralise 35 cm³ of NaOH solution. Calculate the concentration of the sodium hydroxide solution.

First write a **balanced equation** and decide **what you know** and what you **need to know**:

| HCl | + NaOH | → | NaCl + $H_2O$ |
|---|---|---|---|
| **25 cm³** | **35 cm³** | | |
| **0.5 mol dm⁻³** | **?** | | |

Now work out how many **moles of HCl** you have:

$$\text{Number of moles of HCl} = \frac{\text{concentration} \times \text{volume (cm}^3)}{1000} = \frac{0.5 \times 25}{1000} = 0.0125 \text{ moles}$$

You should remember this formula from AS — you divide by 1000 to get the volume from cm³ to dm³.

From the equation, you know 1 mole of HCl neutralises 1 mole of NaOH.
So 0.0125 moles of HCl must neutralise **0.0125** moles of NaOH.

Now it's a doddle to work out the **concentration of NaOH**.

This is just the formula above, rearranged.

$$\text{Concentration of NaOH}_{(aq)} = \frac{\text{moles of NaOH} \times 1000}{\text{volume (cm}^3)} = \frac{0.0125 \times 1000}{35} = \mathbf{0.36 \text{ mol dm}^{-3}}$$

## A **Diprotic Acid** Releases **Two Protons** When it Dissociates

A **diprotic acid** is one that can release **two protons** when it's in solution. **Ethanedioic acid** (HOOC-COOH) is diprotic. When ethanedioic acid reacts with a **base** like sodium hydroxide, it's **neutralised**. But the reaction happens in **two stages**, because the **two protons** are removed from the acid **separately**.

This means that when you titrate **ethanedioic acid** with a **strong base** you get a pH curve with two **equivalence points**:

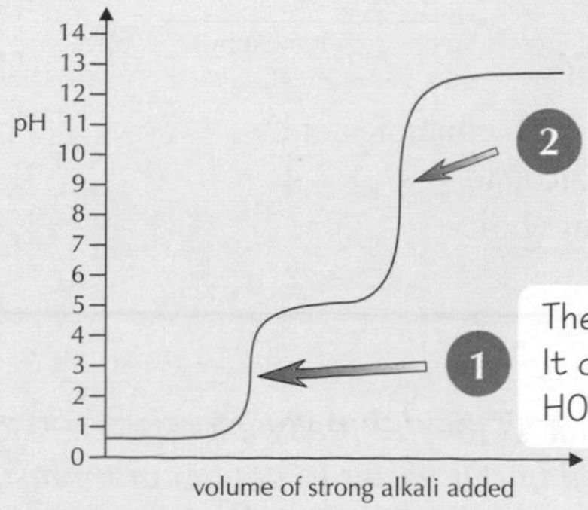

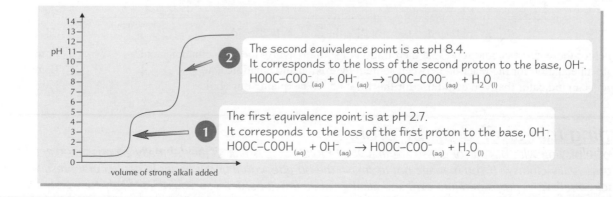

**2** The second equivalence point is at pH 8.4.
It corresponds to the loss of the second proton to the base, $OH^-$.
$HOOC{-}COO^-_{(aq)} + OH^-_{(aq)} \rightarrow {}^-OOC{-}COO^-_{(aq)} + H_2O_{(l)}$

**1** The first equivalence point is at pH 2.7.
It corresponds to the loss of the first proton to the base, $OH^-$.
$HOOC{-}COOH_{(aq)} + OH^-_{(aq)} \rightarrow HOOC{-}COO^-_{(aq)} + H_2O_{(l)}$

# Titration Calculations

## You Can Find the **Concentration** of a **Diprotic Acid** From Titration Results Too

You can calculate the concentration of a **diprotic** acid from titration data in the same way as you did for a monoprotic acid.

***Example:*** 25 $cm^3$ of the ethanedioic acid, $C_2H_2O_4$, was neutralised by 20 $cm^3$ of 0.1 mol $dm^{-3}$ NaOH solution. Calculate the concentration of the ethanedioic acid solution.

Write a **balanced equation** and decide **what you know** and what you **need to know**:

| $C_2H_2O_4$ | + | 2NaOH | → | $Na_2C_2O_4$ | + | $2H_2O$ |
|---|---|---|---|---|---|---|
| **25 $cm^3$** | | **20 $cm^3$** | | | | |
| **?** | | **0.1 mol $dm^{-3}$** | | | | |

Because it's a diprotic acid, you need twice as many moles of base as moles of acid.

Now work out how many **moles of NaOH** you have:

$$\text{Number of moles of NaOH} = \frac{\text{concentration} \times \text{volume (cm}^3)}{1000} = \frac{0.1 \times 20}{1000} = 0.002 \text{ moles}$$

You know from the equation that you need 2 moles of NaOH to neutralise 1 mole of $C_2H_2O_4$.
So 0.002 moles of NaOH must neutralise (0.002 ÷ 2) = **0.001 moles of $C_2H_2O_4$**.

Now find the **concentration of $C_2H_2O_4$**.

$$\text{Concentration of } C_2H_2O_4 = \frac{\text{moles of } C_2H_2O_4 \times 1000}{\text{volume (cm}^3)} = \frac{0.001 \times 1000}{25} = \mathbf{0.04 \text{ mol dm}^{-3}}$$

## Practice Questions

Q1 Write a balanced equation for the reaction between the strong monoprotic acid $HNO_3$ and NaOH.

Q2 How many moles of NaOH would you need to neutralise one mole of a monoprotic acid?

Q3 What is a diprotic acid?

Q4 How many moles of NaOH would you need to neutralise one mole of a diprotic acid?

**Exam Questions**

1 A student performed a titration with 25 $cm^3$ of hydrochloric acid, adding 0.1 mol $dm^{-3}$ sodium hydroxide from a burette. The student's results are shown in the table below.

| | Titration 1 | Titration 2 | Titration 3 |
|---|---|---|---|
| Titre Volume ($cm^3$ of NaOH) | 25.6 | 25.65 | 25.55 |

a) Write an equation for the reaction. [1 mark]

b) i) Calculate the average titre of sodium hydroxide that was needed to neutralise the hydrochloric acid. [1 mark]

ii) Use this to find the number of moles of sodium hydroxide that were needed to neutralise the acid. [2 marks]

c) Find the concentration of the hydrochloric acid. [2 marks]

2 Sulphuric acid is a diprotic acid. 25 $cm^3$ of this acid is needed to neutralise 35.65 $cm^3$ of 0.1 mol $dm^{-3}$ sodium hydroxide.

a) Write an equation for the reaction. [1 mark]

b) Calculate:

i) The moles of sodium hydroxide present in the 35.65 $cm^3$ sample. [2 marks]

ii) The moles of sulphuric acid needed to neutralise the sodium hydroxide. [1 mark]

iii) The concentration of the sulphuric acid used. [2 marks]

3 What volume of 0.1 mol $dm^{-3}$ hydrochloric acid would be needed to neutralise 10 $cm^3$ of 0.25 mol $dm^{-3}$ sodium hydroxide? [6 marks]

## Diprotic acids — twice the titration fun...

*And that's a whole lot of calculation-based merriment. Don't forget, if it's a diprotic acid that you're using, you need twice as many moles of NaOH to neutralise it as you would a monoprotic acid. But when it comes down to it, it's the same story as any other chemistry calculation — write out the equation, compare the number of moles, and put the values into the right formula.*

# Buffer Action

*These pages are for AQA (Unit 4), OCR A (Unit 5), OCR B (Unit 5) and Edexcel (Unit 4).*

## *Buffers* Resist Changes in *pH*

A **buffer** is a solution that **resists** changes in pH when **small** amounts of acid or alkali are added.

A buffer **doesn't** stop the pH from changing completely — it does make the changes **very slight** though.
Buffers only work for small amounts of acid or alkali — put too much in and they'll go "Waah" and not be able to cope.

## *Acidic Buffers* are Made from a *Weak Acid* and one of its *Salts*

**Acidic buffers** have a pH of less than 7 — they're made by mixing a **weak acid** with one of its **salts**.
**Ethanoic acid** and **sodium ethanoate** is a good example:

The salt **fully** dissociates into its ions when it dissolves: $CH_3COO^-Na^+_{(aq)} \rightarrow CH_3COO^-_{(aq)} + Na^+_{(aq)}$

The ethanoic acid is a **weak acid**, so it only **slightly** dissociates: $CH_3COOH_{(aq)} \rightleftharpoons H^+_{(aq)} + CH_3COO^-_{(aq)}$

In the solution you've got heaps of **ethanoate ions** from the salt, and heaps of **undissociated ethanoic acid molecules**.

**Le Chatelier's principle** (see p 32) explains how buffers work:

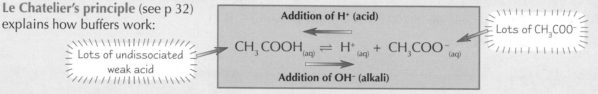

Addition of $H^+$ (acid) ← 

Lots of undissociated weak acid → $CH_3COOH_{(aq)} \rightleftharpoons H^+_{(aq)} + CH_3COO^-_{(aq)}$ ← Lots of $CH_3COO^-$

→ Addition of $OH^-$ (alkali)

If you add a **small** amount of **acid** the **$H^+$ concentration** increases. Most of the extra $H^+$ ions combine with $CH_3COO^-$ ions to form $CH_3COOH$. This shifts the equilibrium to the **left**, using up the $H^+$ — so the **pH** doesn't change much.

If a **small** amount of **alkali** (e.g. NaOH) is added, the **$OH^-$ concentration** increases. Most of the extra $OH^-$ ions react with $H^+$ ions to form water — removing $H^+$ ions from the solution. This causes more $CH_3COOH$ to **dissociate** to form $H^+$ ions — shifting the equilibrium to the **right**. The $H^+$ concentration increases again so the **pH** doesn't change much.

## *Basic Buffers* are Made from a *Weak Base* and one of its *Salts*

*AQA and Edexcel only*

**Basic buffers** have a pH greater than 7 — and they're made by mixing a **weak base** with one of its **salts**.
A solution of **ammonia** ($NH_3$, a weak base) and **ammonium chloride** ($NH_4Cl$, a salt of ammonia) acts as a **basic** buffer.

So the solution will contain loads of **ammonium ions** ($NH_4^+$), and lots of **ammonia** molecules too.

The **equilibrium position** of this reaction can move to **counteract** changes in pH:

Addition of $H^+$ (acid) →

Lots of weak base → $NH_{3\,(aq)} + H_2O_{(l)} \rightleftharpoons NH^+_{4\,(aq)} + OH^-_{(aq)}$ ← Lots of $NH_4^+$

← Addition of $OH^-$ (base)

1) If a small amount of **base** is added, the $OH^-$ concentration **increases**, making the solution more **alkaline**. Most of the extra $OH^-$ ions will react with the $NH_4^+$ ions, to form $NH_3$ and $H_2O$. So the equilibrium will shift to the **left**, removing $OH^-$ ions from the solution, and stopping the pH from changing much.
2) If a small amount of **acid** is added, the $H^+$ concentration **increases**, making the solution more **acidic**.
   - Some of the $H^+$ ions react with **$OH^-$** ions to make **$H_2O$**. When this happens the equilibrium position **moves to the right** to replace the $OH^-$ ions that have been used up.
   - Some of the $H^+$ ions react with **$NH_3$** molecules to form $NH_4^+$: $NH_3 + H^+ \rightleftharpoons NH_4^+$

   These reactions will **remove** most of the extra $H^+$ ions that were added — so the pH **won't** change much.

## *Buffer* Action Can Be Seen on a *Titration Curve*

*Edexcel only*

The **titration curves** for weak acids with strong bases, and strong acids with weak bases, have a **distinctive shape** due to the formation of **buffer solutions** as the reaction proceeds.

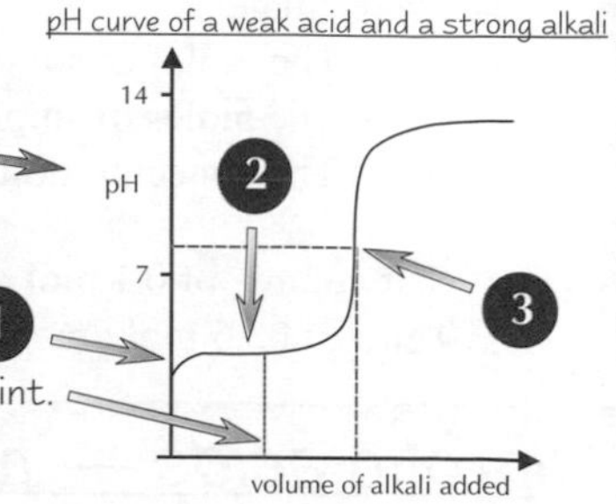


You can work out $K_a$ of a weak acid using the **half-equivalence point** on a pH curve for a **weak acid/strong base titration**.
The half-equivalence point is when **half the alkali** needed to reach the equivalence point has been added — at this point **half the acid** has been **neutralised**. The upshot of this is the **p$K_a$** is **equal** to the **pH** (don't worry about where this comes from). Just read off the pH to find the p$K_a$ and convert it to $K_a$ using the formula on page 40.

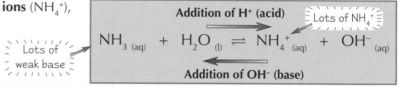

1) The pH starts by changing quickly because the alkali is strong.
2) Then the curve levels off because a buffer solution is formed.
3) Eventually the equivalence point is reached.

# Buffer Action

## Here's How to Calculate the **pH** of a **Buffer Solution**

Calculating the **pH** of an acidic buffer isn't too tricky. You just need to know the $\boldsymbol{K_a}$ of the weak acid and the **concentrations** of the weak acid and its salt. Here's how to go about it:

***Example:*** A buffer solution contains 0.40 mol dm$^{-3}$ methanoic acid, HCOOH, and 0.6 mol dm$^{-3}$ sodium methanoate, $HCOO^-Na^+$. For methanoic acid, $K_a = 1.6 \times 10^{-4}$ mol dm$^{-3}$. What is the pH of this buffer?

Firstly, write the expression for $K_a$ of the weak acid:

$$HCOOH_{(aq)} \rightleftharpoons H^+_{(aq)} + HCOO^-_{(aq)} \Rightarrow K_a = \frac{[H^+_{(aq)}] \times [HCOO^-_{(aq)}]}{[HCOOH_{(aq)}]}$$

Remember — these all have to be equilibrium concentrations.

You have to make a **few assumptions** here:
- $HCOO^-Na^+$ is fully dissociated, so assume that the equilibrium concentration of $HCOO^-$ is the same as the initial concentration of $HCOO^-Na^+$.
- HCOOH is only slightly dissociated, so assume that its equilibrium concentration is the same as its initial concentration.

Then rearrange the expression and stick in the data to calculate $[H^+_{(aq)}]$:

$$[H^+_{(aq)}] = K_a \times \frac{[HCOOH_{(aq)}]}{[HCOO^-_{(aq)}]} = 1.6 \times 10^{-4} \times \frac{0.4}{0.6} = 1.07 \times 10^{-4} \text{ mol dm}^{-3}$$

Finally, convert $[H^+_{(aq)}]$ to pH: $pH = -\log_{10}[H^+_{(aq)}] = -\log_{10}(1.07 \times 10^{-4}) = \mathbf{3.97}$ And that's your answer.

## **Buffer** Solutions are Important in **Biological Environments**

1) **Cells** need a constant pH to allow the **biochemical reactions** to take place. The pH is controlled by a buffer based on the equilibrium between **dihydrogen phosphate** and **hydrogen phosphate**.

$$H_2PO_4^- \rightleftharpoons H^+ + HPO_4^{2-}$$

2) **Blood** needs to be kept at pH 7.4.
It's buffered using carbonic acid ($H_2CO_3$).
The levels of $\mathbf{H_2CO_3}$ are **controlled** by the body.

$$H_2CO_{3(aq)} \rightleftharpoons H^+_{(aq)} + HCO_{3\,(aq)}^-$$
and
$$H_2CO_{3(aq)} \rightleftharpoons H_2O_{(l)} + CO_{2(aq)}$$

By **breathing out** $\mathbf{CO_2}$ the level of $H_2CO_3$ is reduced as it moves this **equilibrium** to the **right**. The levels of $HCO_3^-$ are controlled by the **kidneys** with excess being **excreted** in the urine.

3) Buffers are used in **food products** to control the pH. Changes in pH can be caused by **bacteria** and **fungi** and cause food to **deteriorate**. A common buffer is **sodium citrate**, which sets up an equilibrium between citrate ions and citric acid. **Phosphoric acid/phosphate ions** and **benzoic acid/benzoate ions** are also used as buffers.

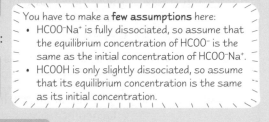

Nobody's gonna change my pH.

Acids and alkalis didn't mess with Jeff after he became buffer.

## Practice Questions

Q1 What's a buffer solution?
Q2 How can a mixture of ethanoic acid and sodium ethanoate act as a buffer?
Q3 Describe how to make an alkaline buffer.

**Exam Questions**

1 A buffer solution contains 0.40 mol dm$^{-3}$ benzoic acid, $C_6H_5COOH$, and 0.20 mol dm$^{-3}$ sodium benzoate, $C_6H_5COO^-Na^+$. At 25 °C, $K_a$ for benzoic acid is $6.4 \times 10^{-5}$ mol dm$^{-3}$.
  a) Calculate the pH of the buffer solution. [3 marks]
  b) Explain the effect on the buffer of adding a small quantity of dilute sulfuric acid. [3 marks]

2 A buffer was prepared by mixing solutions of butanoic acid, $CH_3(CH_2)_2COOH$, and sodium butanoate, $CH_3(CH_2)_2COO^-Na^+$, so that they had the same concentration.
  a) Write an equation to show butanoic acid acting as a weak acid. [1 mark]
  b) Given that $K_a$ for butanoic acid is $1.5 \times 10^{-5}$ mol dm$^{-3}$, calculate the pH of the buffer solution. [3 marks]

## Old buffers are often resistant to change...

*So that's how buffers work. There's a pleasing simplicity and neatness about it that I find rather elegant. Like a fine wine with a nose of berry and undertones of... OK, I'll shut up now.*

# Formulas and Isomers

*This page is all about how a molecule's atoms are actually arranged, and how you can represent its shape on paper.*
***These pages are for AQA (Unit 4), OCR A (Unit 4), OCR B (Unit 4) and Edexcel (Unit 4).***

## There are **Loads of Ways** of **Representing** Organic Compounds

| TYPE OF FORMULA | WHAT IT SHOWS YOU | FORMULA FOR BUTAN-1-OL |
|---|---|---|
| General formula | An algebraic formula that can describe **any member** of a family of compounds. | $C_nH_{2n+1}OH$ (for all alcohols) |
| Empirical formula | The **simplest ratio** of atoms of each element in a compound (cancel the numbers down if possible). (So ethane, $C_2H_6$, has the empirical formula $CH_3$.) | $C_4H_{10}O$ |
| Molecular formula | The **actual** number of atoms of each element in a molecule, with any **functional groups** indicated. | $C_4H_9OH$ |
| Structural formula | Shows the atoms **carbon by carbon**, with the attached hydrogens and functional groups. | $CH_3CH_2CH_2CH_2OH$ |
| Displayed formula | Shows how all the atoms are **arranged**, and all the bonds between them. | 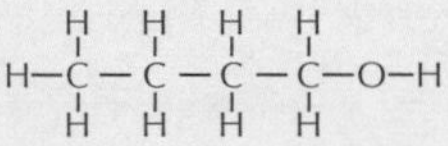 |
| Skeletal formula | Shows the **bonds** of the carbon skeleton **only**, with any functional groups. The H and C atoms aren't shown. This is used to draw big, complicated structures, like cyclic molecules. | 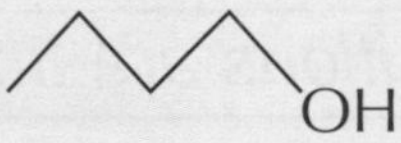 |

A functional group is a reactive part of a molecule — it gives it most of its chemical properties.

A **homologous series** is a bunch of organic compounds which have the **same general formula**. **Alkanes** are a homologous series. Each member of a homologous series differs by **$-CH_2-$**.

## ***Structural Isomers** have Different **Structural Arrangements** of Atoms*

In structural isomers, the atoms are **connected** in different ways. But they still have the **same molecular formula**. There are **three types** of structural isomer:

**CHAIN ISOMERS**
Chain isomers have different arrangements of the **carbon skeleton**. Some are **straight chains** and others are **branched** in different ways.

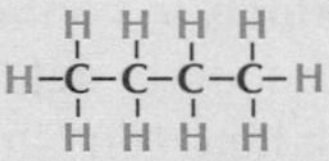
butane

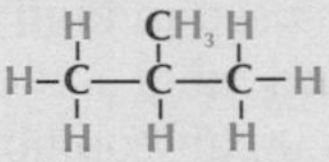
methylpropane

**POSITIONAL ISOMERS**
Positional isomers have the **same skeleton** with the **same groups of atoms** attached. The difference is that the **functional group** is attached to a **different carbon atom**.

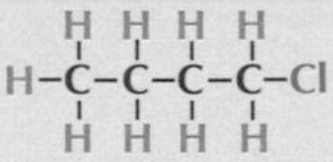
1-chlorobutane

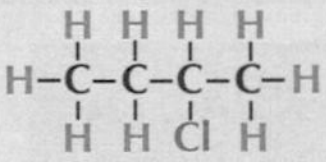
2-chlorobutane

**FUNCTIONAL GROUP ISOMERS**
Functional group isomers have the same atoms arranged into **different functional groups**.

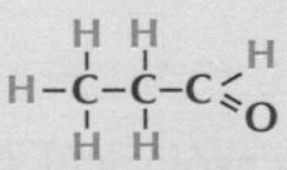
propanal

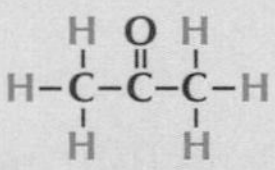
propanone

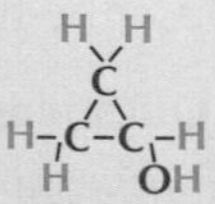
cyclopropanol

## ***Single-Bonded Carbon Atoms** have their Bonds Arranged Like a **Tetrahedron***

1) When a carbon atom makes four single bonds (as in alkanes), the atoms around the carbon form a **tetrahedral shape**.

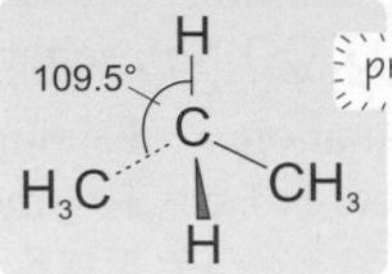


propane

This is all because electron pairs repel each other and try to get as far apart as possible.

2) This **tetrahedral** shape around each carbon atom means that single-bonded carbon chains containing three or more carbon atoms form a 'wiggly line'.

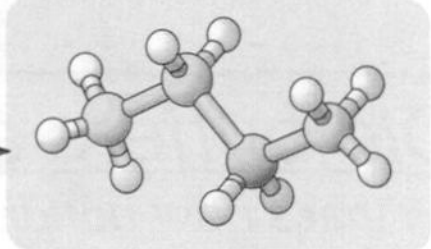

# Formulas and Isomers

## Atoms Around a **Double-Bonded** Carbon form an **Equilateral Triangle**

When there's a **double-bond** involved, the situation is different.

1) The C=C double bond and the atoms bonded to these carbons are **planar** (flat).
2) Each double-bonded carbon and the atoms attached to it are **trigonal planar** — the attached atoms are at the corners of an imaginary **equilateral triangle**, and all of the bond angles are 120°.

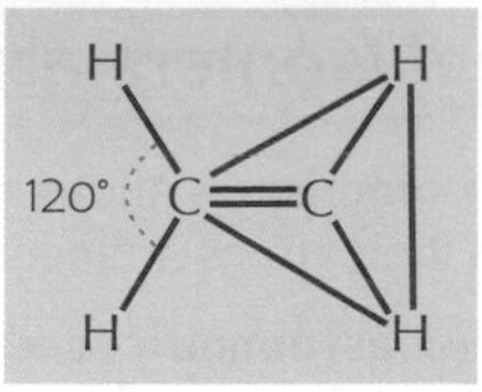


## *E/Z Isomerism* is a Type of *Stereoisomerism*

1) **Stereoisomers** have the same structural formula, but a **different arrangement** in space. (Just bear with me for a moment... that will become clearer, I promise.)
2) You can **twist** and **rotate** a molecule any way you like around a **single bond**. But a **double bond** has a **fixed position** — you **can't** rotate the rest of the molecule around it.
3) Because of the **lack of rotation** around the double bond, some **alkenes** have stereoisomers.
4) Stereoisomers only happen when each double-bonded carbon atom has two **different atoms** or **groups** attached to it. Then you get an '**E-isomer**' and a '**Z-isomer**'.

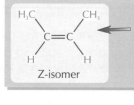

The astronauts liked to arrange things differently in space.

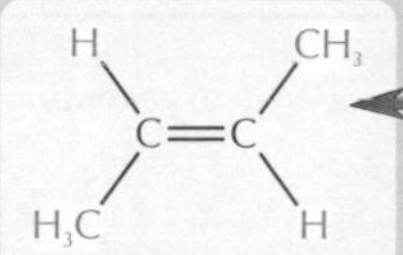

E-isomer

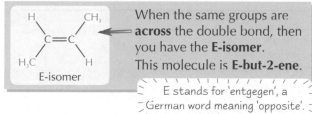

When the same groups are **across** the double bond, then you have the **E-isomer**. This molecule is **E-but-2-ene**.

E stands for 'entgegen', a German word meaning 'opposite'.

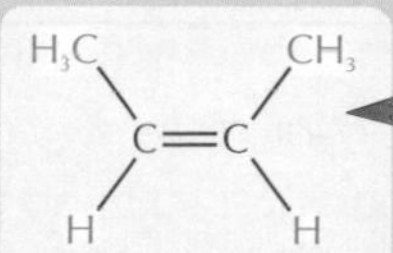

Z-isomer

When the same groups are **both above** or **both below** the double bond, it's the Z-isomer. This molecule is **Z-but-2-ene**.

Z stands for 'zusammen', the German for 'together'.

E/Z isomerism is also known as **cis-trans isomerism**, where '**cis**' is the **Z-isomer**, and '**trans**' is the **E-isomer**. So the two molecules above would be trans-but-2-ene (on the left), and cis-but-2-ene (on the right).

## *Practice Questions*

Q1 Explain what the term 'general formula' means.

Q2 Give both the empirical formula and the molecular formula of propanal.

Q3 Explain why 1,1-dichloropropane and 1,2-dichloropropane are positional isomers.

Q4 Draw the Z-isomer of 1,2-dichloroethene, $C_2H_2Cl_2$.

**Exam Questions**

1 A chemist has samples of three chemicals, labelled A, B and C.

a) Chemical A is a straight-chain alcohol with the molecular formula $C_5H_{11}OH$. Give the names of two positional isomers that fit this description. [2 marks]

b) Chemical B is an alkene with the molecular formula $C_5H_{10}$. Give the names of a pair of stereoisomers with this molecular formula. [2 marks]

c) Chemical C is a hydrocarbon with the molecular formula $C_3H_6$. Give the names of two functional group isomers with this molecular formula. [2 marks]

2 There are sixteen possible structural isomers of the compound $C_3H_6O_2$, four of which show stereoisomerism.

a) Explain the meaning of the term *stereoisomerism*. [2 marks]

b) Draw a pair of E/Z isomers of $C_3H_6O_2$, with hydroxyl groups. Label them E and Z. [3 marks]

## *Human structural isomers...*

# Optical Isomerism and Chirality

*As if E/Z isomerism wasn't exciting enough, take a deep breath and prepare for stereoisomerism part two — optical isomerism...*
***This page is for AQA (Unit 4), OCR A (Unit 4), OCR B (Unit 4) and Edexcel (Unit 4).***

## Optical Isomers are Mirror Images of Each Other

**Optical isomerism** is another type of stereoisomerism. Stereoisomers have the **same structural formula**, but have their atoms arranged differently in **space**.

A **chiral** (or **asymmetric**) carbon atom is one that has **four different groups** attached to it. It's possible to arrange the groups in two different ways around the carbon atom so that two different molecules are made — these molecules are called **enantiomers** or **optical isomers**.

The enantiomers are **mirror images** and no matter which way you turn them, they can't be **superimposed**.

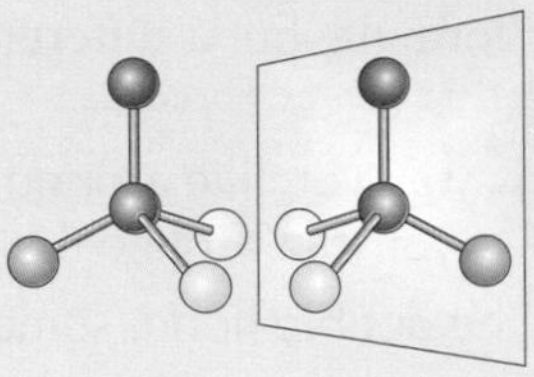

If the molecules can be superimposed, they're achiral — and there's no optical isomerism.

You have to be able to draw optical isomers. But first you have to identify the chiral centre...

Example

Locating the chiral centre:
Look for the carbon atom with four different groups attached. Here it's the carbon with the four groups H, OH, CHO and $CH_3$ attached.

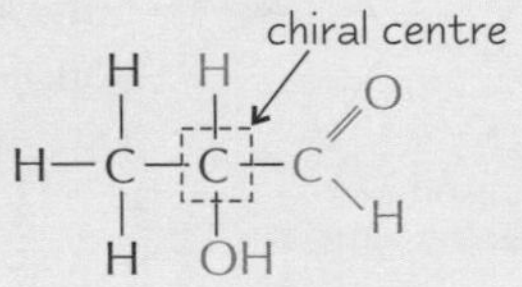


2-hydroxypropanoic acid

Drawing isomers:
Once you know the chiral carbon, draw one enantiomer in a tetrahedral shape. Don't try to draw the full structure of each group — it gets confusing. Then draw a mirror image beside it.

enantiomers of 2-hydroxypropanoic acid

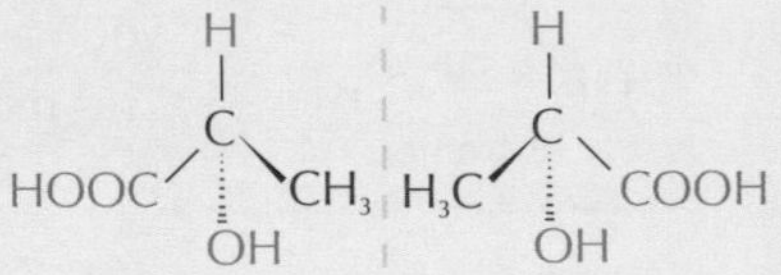


A **solid wedge** means that a bond is coming out of the page **towards** you. A **dotted line** means that it's going into the page **away** from you.

## Optical Isomers Rotate Plane-Polarised Light

Optical isomers are **optically active** — they **rotate plane-polarised light**. One enantiomer rotates it in a **clockwise** direction, and the other rotates it in an **anticlockwise** direction.

Normal light vibrates in all directions, but plane-polarised light only vibrates in one direction.

## A Racemate is a Mixture of Both Optical Isomers

***AQA and Edexcel only***

A **racemate** (or **racemic mixture**) contains **equal quantities** of each enantiomer of an optically active compound.

Racemates **don't** show any optical activity — the two enantiomers **cancel** each other's light-rotating effect.
Chemists often react two **achiral** things together and get a **racemic** mixture of a **chiral** product.
This is because when two molecules react there's an **equal chance** of forming each of the enantiomers.

Look at the reaction between butane and chlorine:

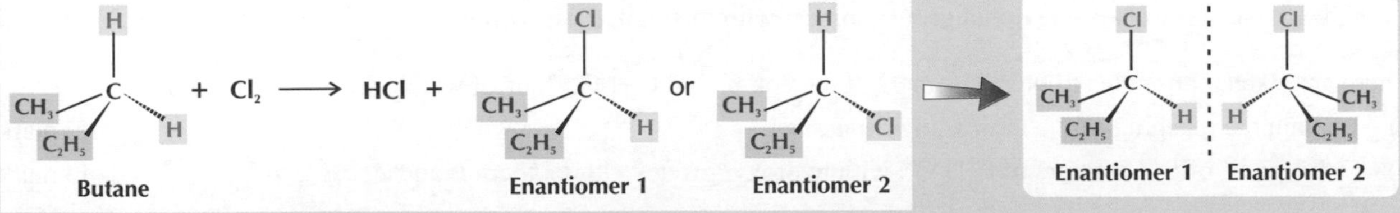

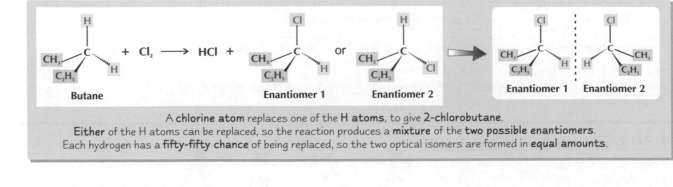

A **chlorine atom** replaces one of the H **atoms**, to give **2-chlorobutane**.
**Either** of the H atoms can be replaced, so the reaction produces a **mixture** of the **two possible enantiomers**.
Each hydrogen has a **fifty-fifty chance** of being replaced, so the two optical isomers are formed in **equal amounts**.

# Optical Isomerism and Chirality

## You Can Use Optical Activity to Work Out a Reaction Mechanism

**Edexcel only**

Optical activity can give you some insight into how the **mechanism** of a reaction works.
For example, **nucleophilic substitution** (see page 22) can take place by one of two mechanisms.

### $S_N1$ mechanism

If it's an $S_N1$ mechanism and you start with a **single enantiomer** reactant, the product will be a **racemic mixture** of **two optical isomers** of each other.

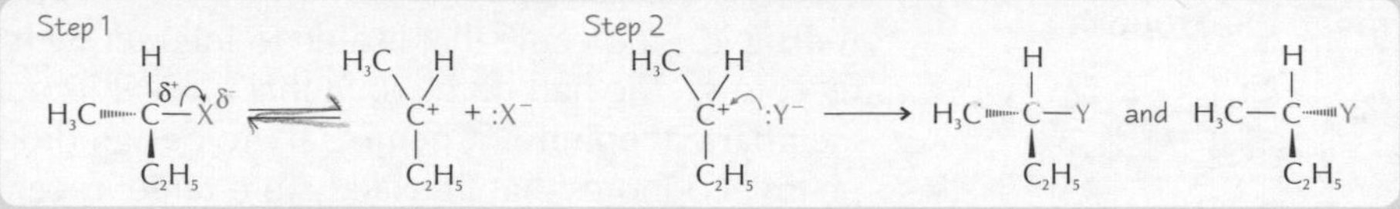

In step 1, a leaving group breaks off, leaving a **planar** (flat) ion.
In step 2, the planar ion can be **attacked** by a nucleophile from **either side** — this results in two optical isomers.

### $S_N2$ mechanism

In an $S_N2$ mechanism, a **single enantiomer** reactant produces a **single enantiomer** product.

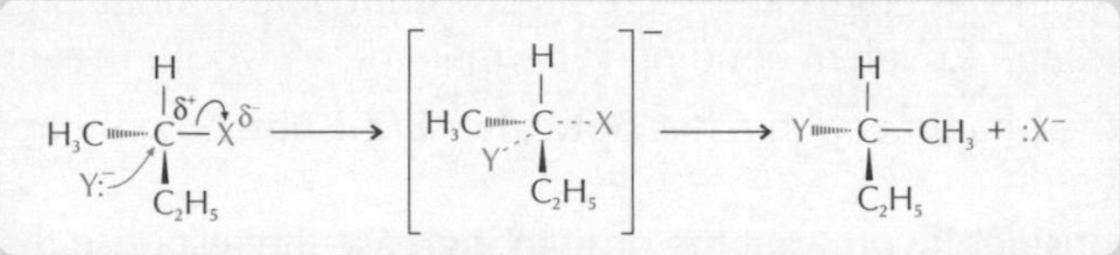

There's only **one step** in this mechanism — the nucleophile always attacks the **opposite side** to the leaving group, so only **one product** is produced. During the reaction, the molecule is **flipped** inside out which causes the product to rotate polarised light in the **opposite direction** from the reactant.

So if you know the **optical activity** of the **reactant** and **products**, you can sometimes work out the reaction **mechanism**.

## Practice Questions

Q1 What's an optical isomer?

Q2 What's a racemic mixture?

Q3 The displayed formula of 2-methylbutan-1-al is shown on the right. Explain why the carbon atom marked with a * is a chiral centre.

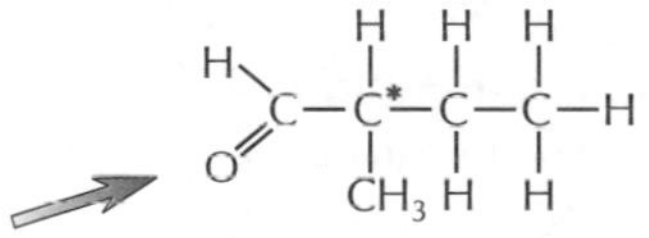

**Exam Questions**

1 The molecule 1-chloroethanol, $CH_3CHClOH$, is chiral.

a) Draw both enantiomers of 1-chloroethanol. [2 marks]

b) What structural feature of the molecules you have drawn gives rise to optical isomerism? [1 mark]

c) Chiral molecules are optically active. Explain what the term 'optically active' means. [1 mark]

2 The molecule 2-bromobutane, shown on the right, displays optical isomerism.

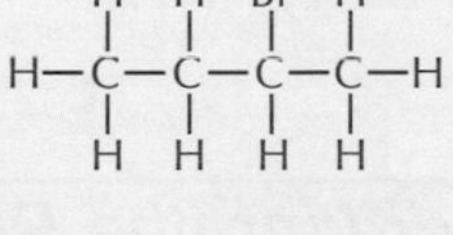

a) Mark the chiral centre of the molecule on the diagram. [1 mark]

A sample of a single, pure enantiomer of 2-bromobutane is dissolved in an ethanol and water solvent and mixed with dilute sodium hydroxide solution. This mixture is gently heated under reflux. The product of the reaction is a racemic mixture of butan-2-ol.

b) Explain why the butan-2-ol solution produced will not rotate plane-polarised light. [2 marks]

c) Has the substitution reaction proceeded via an $S_N1$ mechanism or an $S_N2$ mechanism? Explain your answer. [2 marks]

## Time for some quiet reflection...

*This optical isomer stuff's not all bad — you get to draw pretty little pictures of molecules. If you're having difficulty picturing them as 3D shapes, you could always make some models with matchsticks and clay. It's easier to see the mirror image structure with a solid version in front of you. And if you become a famous artist, you can sell them for millions...*

# Pharmaceutical Synthesis

*A spoonful of sugar helps the medicine section to sink in — but a chocolate biscuit is even better...*
***These pages are for AQA (Unit 4), OCR A (Unit 4), OCR B (Unit 4) and Edexcel (Unit 5).***

## Medicines Contain **Pharmacophores**

In virtually every cell of your body there are things called **receptors**. Some chemicals fit into these receptors and temporarily bond with them, which triggers a series of **biochemical reactions**. The chemicals have to be exactly the right **size and shape** to fit the receptor otherwise they don't bond and nothing happens.

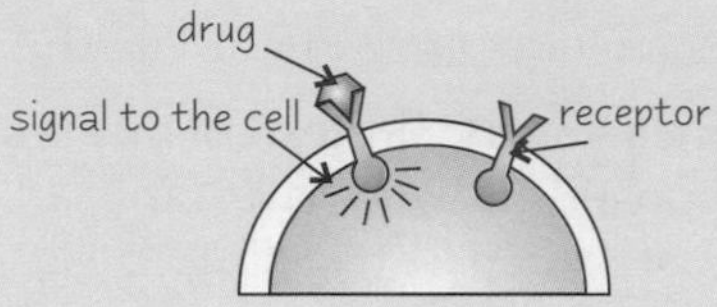


A **drug** is a molecule that is able to interact with one of these receptors. The part of the drug that gives it its activity is called the **pharmacophore**. Chemists try to design drugs with pharmacophores that fit exactly into target **receptors**.

The 'fit' of a **pharmacophore** into a **receptor site** depends on:

1) **Size** and **shape** — it's got to have a particular structure that will fit into the receptor site.
2) **Bond formation** — functional groups in the pharmacophore form **temporary bonds** with functional groups in the receptor. These are mostly **ionic** interactions or **intermolecular** forces e.g. hydrogen bonding. Covalent bonding is permanent, so would irreversibly block the receptor.
3) **Orientation** — if the pharmacophore has **optical** or **E/Z isomers**, only one of the isomers will fit.

To design a drug you need to consider if you want the drug to **increase** the response that happens naturally, or **decrease** it.

1) If you want a drug to increase the natural response you use an **agonistic** drug. This binds to the receptor and **triggers** a **response**.
2) If you want to decrease the response you use an **antagonistic** drug. This binds to the receptor and **blocks** it.

## Chemists are Responsible for the **Design** and **Synthesis** of **New Drugs**

***OCR B only***

Here are some of the things chemists think about when they're trying to make a new drug to treat a disease:

**Is there a natural compound already used to treat the disease?**
Years ago foxglove leaves were used to treat heart failure — the drug's now been isolated and it's still used today.

**Is there a compound in the body that's involved in the process?**
This could give you a good starting point.

**Molecule screening**
This is where loads of molecules are tested to see if any of them bind to the target receptor.

→ **Modifying the Compound**
Now you've got something that interacts with the receptor site, you can modify its structure to make it fit better. This is where functional groups are added, removed or changed.

→ **Testing the Compound**
Once it's modified, you've got to test it to see if it works. This often happens again and again to make the best, safest drug possible.

→ **Drug**

## **Modifying** the **Pharmacophore** Changes the **Pharmacological Activity**

***OCR B only***

Once you know that part of a molecule is a **pharmacophore** you can change bits of it to make a drug **more effective** or to reduce its side effects. For example, **noradrenaline** is naturally found in the body and has been modified to treat different disorders.

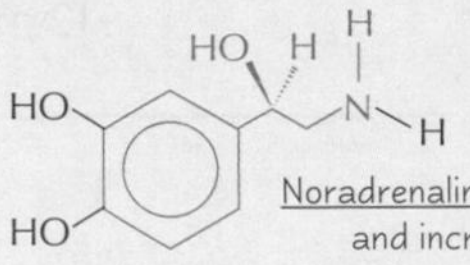

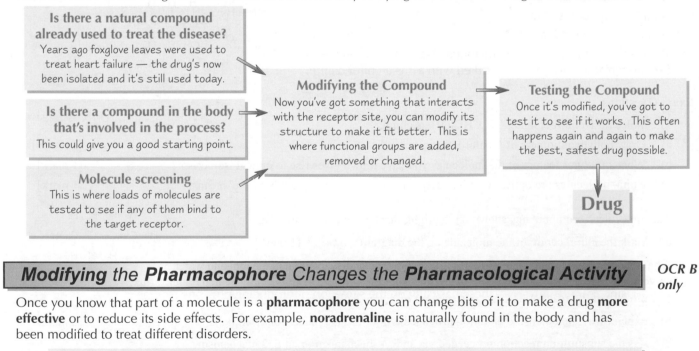

Noradrenaline — expands airways and increases your heart rate and blood pressure

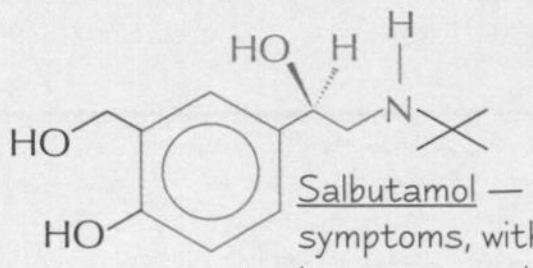

Salbutamol — treats asthma symptoms, without the raised heart rate and blood pressure

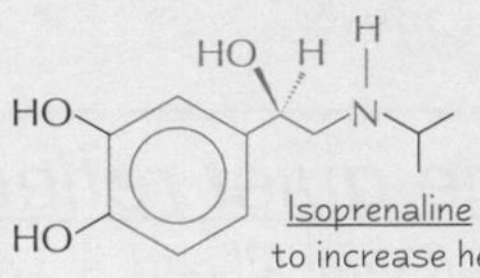

Isoprenaline — used to increase heart rate for some heart problems

# Pharmaceutical Synthesis

## Today **Large Numbers** Of Similar Molecules are Made and Tested

*OCR B and Edexcel*

1) Developing a new medicine is all about finding a molecule that contains the **pharmacophore** that you're interested in, but that isn't going to have **adverse effects** on the body.
2) One way of doing this is to test a load of **similar compounds** to find one that has the **most powerful medicinal properties** and the **least nasty side effects**.
3) When pharmaceutical companies develop modern drugs, they usually have to test a **huge** number of compounds before they find one that might just work as a new medicine.
4) Chemists finding new medicines in the past would prepare one compound at a time for testing — this took ages.
5) To speed things up, modern chemists use a technique called **combinatorial chemistry**. Instead of making compounds one at a time, they make **hundreds** of similar ones at once. This set of compounds is called a **library**. All of the compounds in the library are tested in the hope that one of them will be a safe and effective drug.

One way to quickly produce a large **library** of compounds is to pass a range of different **reactants** over **reagents** that are bonded to **polymer beads**. You end up with lots of **similar small molecules** still bonded to their polymer supports. Then you can **split** your beads up into groups, and expose each group to more different reactants.

## **Computer Modelling** Techniques **Speed Up** Drug Design

*OCR B only*

Testing the library to find a molecule that fits a receptor takes time and is expensive. It's sped up by screening compounds in batches, but this still takes **ages**, and there's no guarantee you'll find something that works.

**Computer 3D modelling** can speed things up. **Databases** of 3D models of compounds can be searched to find compounds that may fit a **3D model of the target receptor site**, or to find ones containing particular structures and functional groups. This cuts down the number of compounds you need to test in the lab.

## **Pharmaceutical Drugs** Tend to Contain **One Optical Isomer**

*Not OCR B*

1) If **enzymes** in a **living cell** are involved in producing a chiral molecule, they will usually only make one **enantiomer**.
2) If you prepare the same compound synthetically in a lab, it will contain an **equal split** of enantiomers instead — a **racemic** mixture (see page 50). This creates problems when producing **pharmaceutical drugs**.
3) Drugs work by binding to **receptor molecules** in the body and **changing** chemical reactions. So a drug must be **exactly** the right **shape** to fit the receptor — only **one enantiomer** will do. The other enantiomer might fit another receptor, and may have **no effect** at all, or cause **harmful side-effects**.
4) Synthetic chiral drugs usually have to be made so that they only contain **one enantiomer**. This has the **benefit** that only half the dose is needed. It also reduces the risk of the drug companies being sued over side effects.
5) The problem is that optical isomers are very **tricky to separate** — producing single-enantiomer drugs is **expensive**.

*OCR A only*

Methods for producing single-enantiomer drugs include (often in combination):

- Using natural **enzymes** or **bacteria** in the process which tend to produce only one isomer.
- Using **naturally-occuring** single optical isomer compounds as starting materials, e.g. sugars, amino acids.
- Using **chemical chiral synthesis** — this involves using carefully chosen reagents and conditions that will ensure only one isomer is produced.

  Chemical chiral synthesis methods usually rely on chemically **modifying** the reagent molecule in a way that **physically blocks** most approaches to it, so that it can only be 'attacked' from **one side**. For example, you could turn your reagent into a **cyclic molecule**, or **bond** your reagent molecules to a **polymer support** and let the other reactants flow over them.

- Using **chiral catalysts** — these basically do the same job of producing only one isomer, but have the advantage that only a small amount is needed because they're reused in the reaction. (But you have to start with either achiral or single-enantiomer reactants, which can be very expensive.)

*Edexcel only*

If you want to make a particular **chiral drug molecule**, it's important to know the **mechanisms** of all the reactions involved.

This can help you plan a reaction scheme that **only** gives the enantiomer you want.

For example: if the reaction involves an **$S_N2$ nucleophilic substitution**, it's important to know that during this type of reaction, chiral molecules **invert** (see p51). So if your reactant molecules are **all** one **enantiomer**, your product will be composed entirely of the **other enantiomer**.

# Pharmaceutical Synthesis

## Medicines Go Through **A Lot of Testing** Before They Can Be Sold

***OCR B only***

Before a drug is licensed to be sold, or prescribed by a doctor, it has to go through a lengthy series of tests. The tests are designed to answer three questions:

1. **Is it safe?**
If the drug's found to be toxic or to have damaging side effects it's removed from the trials at this stage.

2. **Does it work?**
If it doesn't have the medicinal effects that the trials are looking for then a chemical will be rejected.

3. **Is it better than anything currently available?**
If a chemical is safe and works, researchers then compare it to other medicines that are available. It's only worth marketing a new drug if it offers something that other medicines don't — such as curing problems more quickly, or with fewer side effects.

The drug testing process must also be **ethical**.

1) In the UK, all new drugs are tested on **animals** by law. This is a controversial issue — some people think that animal testing is **wrong** because of the suffering that the animals are put through. Others would say that using animals is absolutely **necessary** to ensure that drugs are safe for human use.
2) New drugs also go through a series of **human trials** before being approved. In some trials, healthy volunteers are sought through adverts with money being offered as an incentive. But could this be seen as seeking out poor people who **need the money** to take the risks for others...
3) Some people think that **pharmaceutical companies** have too much **influence** over the drug approval process. They claim that test results can be easily **skewed** to obtain the desired result and that **marketing tricks** may be used by companies to push their products to market.

## **High Atom Economy Reactions** are More Environmentally Friendly

***OCR B only***

1) Medicine production can be damaging to the environment if it uses **lots of natural resources** or produces **large amounts of waste chemicals** that have to be disposed of.
2) To avoid these environmental problems it's important to try to find reactions with a **high atom economy** (see page 34).

## Practice Questions

Q1 Why do pharmaceutical companies make large numbers of similar molecules when they are developing new drugs?

Q2 Give two techniques that you could use to produce a single-enantiomer drug.

Q3 Give two reasons why a drug may be rejected during its testing stage.

**Exam Questions**

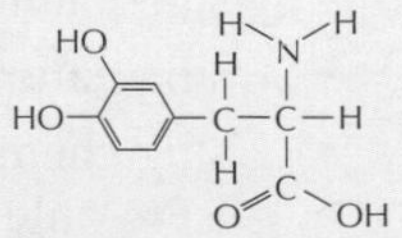


1 Parkinson's disease involves a deficiency of dopamine. It is treated by giving patients a single pure enantiomer of DOPA (dihydroxyphenylalanine), a naturally occurring amino acid, which is converted to dopamine in the brain.

a) DOPA is a chiral molecule. Its structure is shown above on the right. Mark the structure's chiral centre. [1 mark]

b) A DOPA racemic mixture was synthesised in 1911, but today a natural form of the pure DOPA enantiomer is isolated from fava beans for use as a pharmaceutical.

i) Why is it potentially dangerous to use the racemic mixture as a pharmaceutical drug? [2 marks]

ii) Suggest another reason for using the pure DOPA enantiomer instead of the racemic mixture. [1 mark]

2 Combinatorial chemistry is used by pharmaceutical companies.

a) Explain what the term 'combinatorial chemistry' means. [2 marks]

b) How does combinatorial chemistry help chemists when they are looking for new drugs? [2 marks]

## *I isolated it from some fava beans and a nice Chianti...*

*Developing a new medicine can take years — not only do they have to find suitable molecules, but with some serious diseases, it can take years to find out if the drug is successful. Before clinical trials start, the drugs are tested on animals. But even if they don't seem to do any harm to animals, there's always a risk that they'll act differently in humans...*

# Aldehydes and Ketones

*Aldehydes and ketones are both carbonyl compounds. They've got their carbonyl groups in different positions though.*
***These pages are for AQA (Unit 4), OCR A (Unit 4), OCR B (Unit 4) and Edexcel (Unit 4).***

## ***Aldehydes*** *and* ***Ketones*** *contain a* ***Carbonyl Group***

Aldehydes and ketones are **carbonyl compounds** — they contain the **carbonyl** functional group, **C=O**.

'R' represents a carbon chain of any length.

**Aldehydes** have their carbonyl group at the **end** of the carbon chain. Their names end in **–al**.

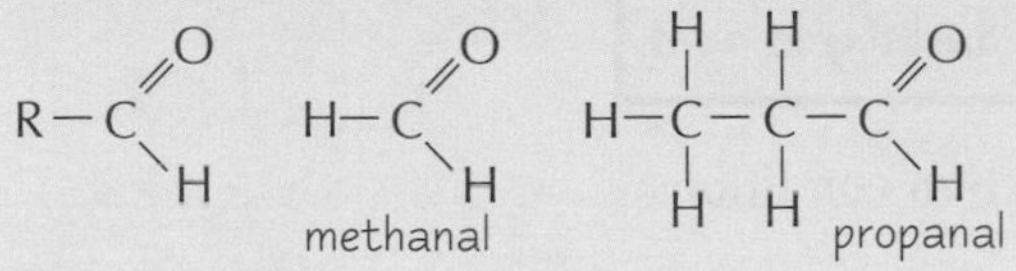


**Ketones** have their carbonyl group in the middle of the carbon chain. Their names end in **–one**, and often have a number to show which **carbon** the carbonyl group is on.

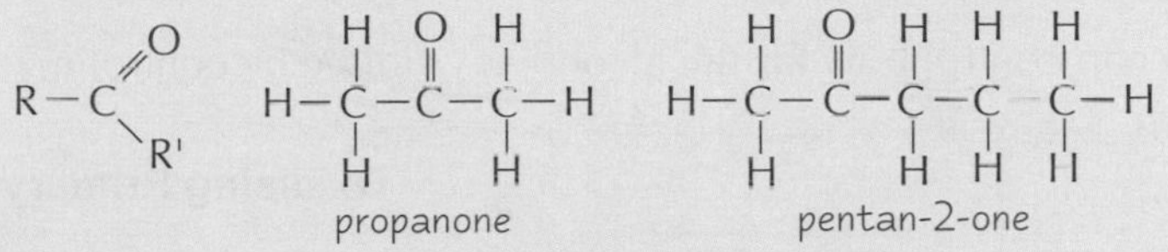


## *Aldehydes and Ketones* ***Don't Hydrogen Bond*** *with* ***Themselves...***

***Edexcel only***

Aldehydes and ketones **don't** have a **polar** $\overset{\delta-}{\text{O}}$–$\overset{\delta+}{\text{H}}$ **bond**, so they can't form **hydrogen bonds** with other aldehyde or ketone molecules.

This lack of hydrogen bonding means **solutions** of aldehydes and ketones have **lower boiling points** than their equivalent alcohols (which **can** form hydrogen bonds because they **do** have a polar O–H bond).

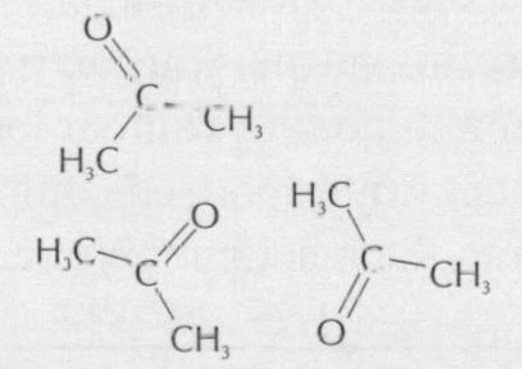

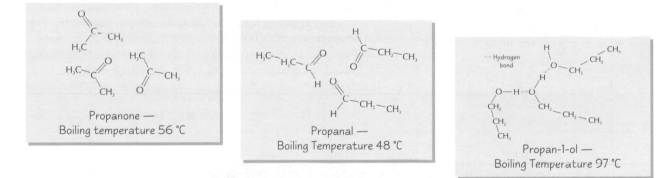

Propanone —
Boiling temperature 56 °C

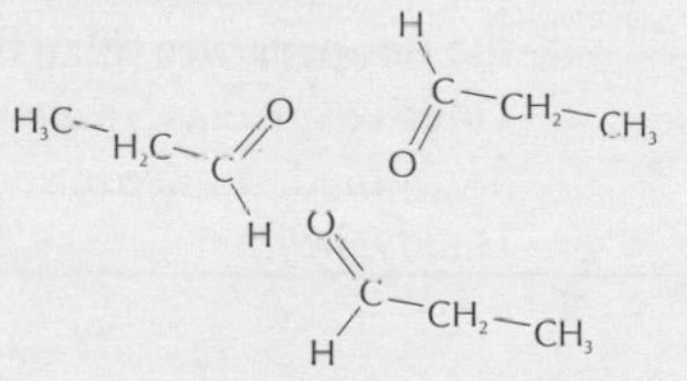

Propanal —
Boiling Temperature 48 °C

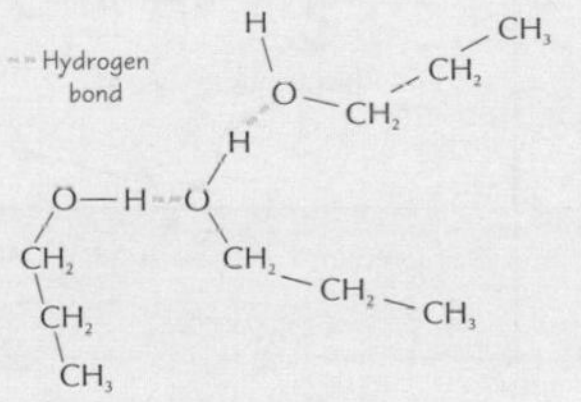


Propan-1-ol —
Boiling Temperature 97 °C

## *...****But*** *Aldehydes and Ketones can* ***Hydrogen Bond*** *with* ***Water***

***Edexcel only***

Although aldehydes and ketones don't have polar OH groups, they do have a **polar** $\overset{\delta+}{\text{C}}$=$\overset{\delta-}{\text{O}}$ **bond**.

This polarity means that the oxygen can use its lone pairs to form **hydrogen bonds** with $H^{\delta+}$ atoms on **water** molecules. So **small** aldehydes and ketones will **dissolve** in water.

Large aldehydes and ketones have **long** carbon chains. The intermolecular forces between these long chains are relatively large. So if an aldehyde or ketone is **large enough**, the intermolecular forces will be stronger than the hydrogen bonds that could form and the compound **won't dissolve**.

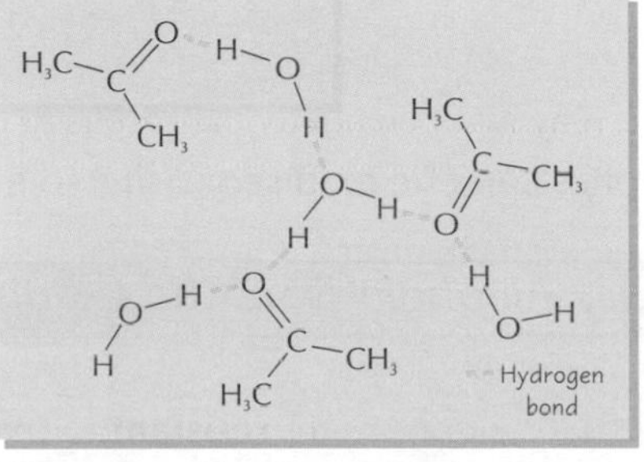


Look back at pages 6-7 if you're a bit rusty on polar bonds, intermolecular forces or hydrogen bonding.

# Aldehydes and Ketones

## *Aldehydes* and *Carboxylic Acids* are made by Oxidising *Primary Alcohols*

You can use **acidified dichromate(VI) ions** ($Cr_2O_7^{2-}$) to **mildly** oxidise alcohols.
Acidified **potassium dichromate(VI)** ($K_2Cr_2O_7$ / $H_2SO_4$) is often used.

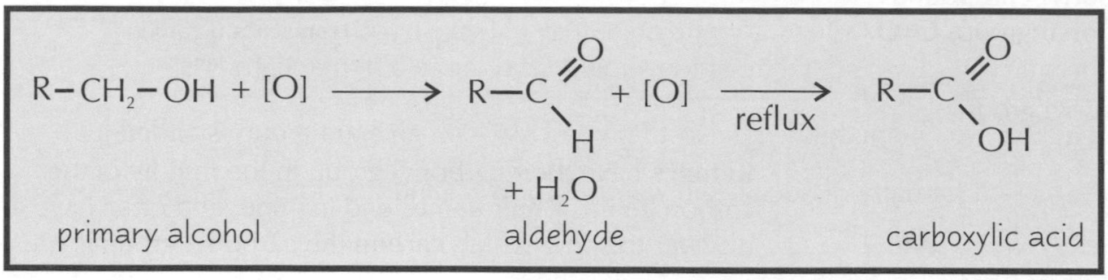


[O] = oxidising agent

The orange dichromate(VI) ion is reduced to the green chromium(III) ion, $Cr^{3+}$.

You can control how **far** the alcohol is oxidised by controlling the **reaction conditions**:

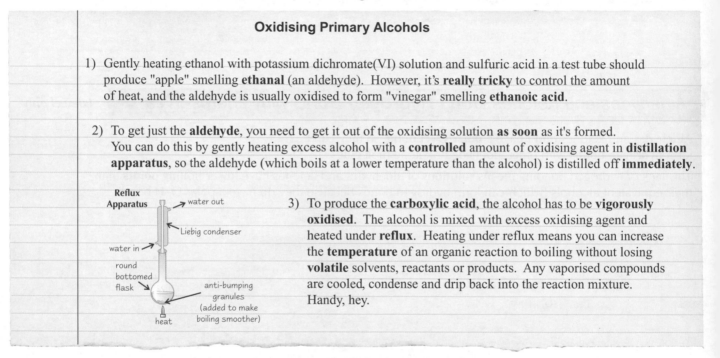

### Oxidising Primary Alcohols

1) Gently heating ethanol with potassium dichromate(VI) solution and sulfuric acid in a test tube should produce "apple" smelling **ethanal** (an aldehyde). However, it's **really tricky** to control the amount of heat, and the aldehyde is usually oxidised to form "vinegar" smelling **ethanoic acid**.

2) To get just the **aldehyde**, you need to get it out of the oxidising solution **as soon** as it's formed. You can do this by gently heating excess alcohol with a **controlled** amount of oxidising agent in **distillation apparatus**, so the aldehyde (which boils at a lower temperature than the alcohol) is distilled off **immediately**.

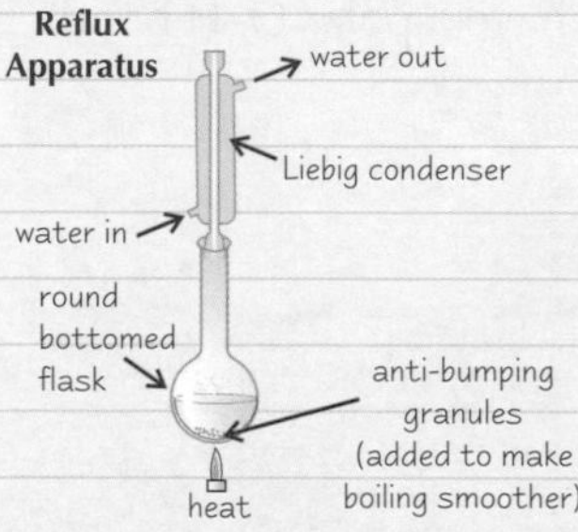


3) To produce the **carboxylic acid**, the alcohol has to be **vigorously oxidised**. The alcohol is mixed with excess oxidising agent and heated under **reflux**. Heating under reflux means you can increase the **temperature** of an organic reaction to boiling without losing **volatile** solvents, reactants or products. Any vaporised compounds are cooled, condense and drip back into the reaction mixture. Handy, hey.

## *Ketones* are made by Oxidising *Secondary Alcohols*

1) Refluxing a secondary alcohol, e.g. propan-2-ol, with acidified dichromate(VI) will produce a **ketone**.

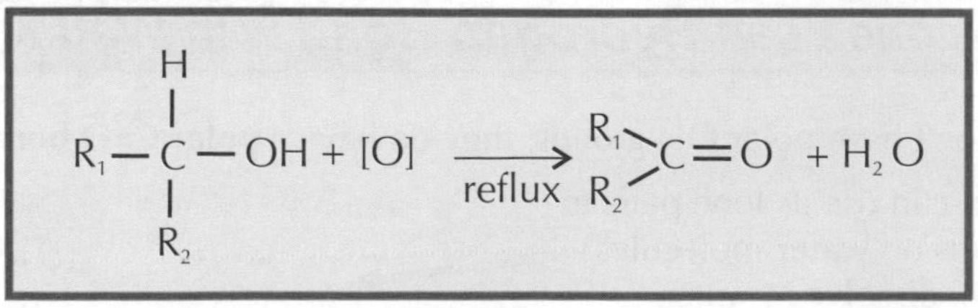


2) Ketones can't be oxidised easily, so even prolonged refluxing won't produce anything more.

## *Tertiary Alcohols* **Can't** *be Oxidised Easily*

Tertiary alcohols are **resistant** to oxidation.
They **don't react** with potassium dichromate(VI) at all — the solution stays orange.

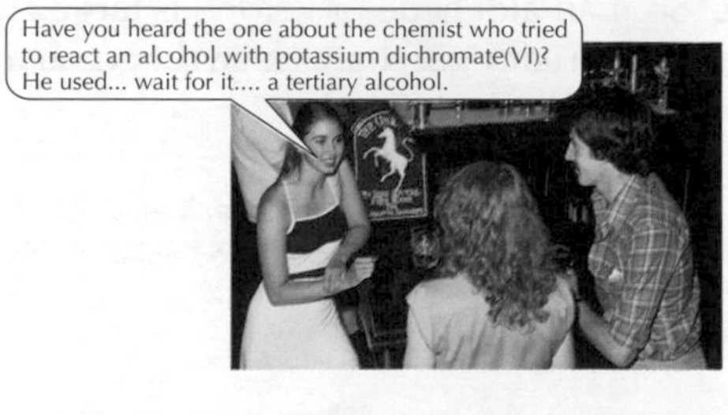
Have you heard the one about the chemist who tried to react an alcohol with potassium dichromate(VI)? He used... wait for it.... a tertiary alcohol.

# Aldehydes and Ketones

## Hydrogen Cyanide will React with Carbonyls by Nucleophilic Addition

**Not OCR A**

Hydrogen cyanide reacts with carbonyl compounds to produce **hydroxynitriles**.
(Hydroxynitriles are molecules that contain both a CN and an OH group).

> **Hydrogen cyanide** is a **highly toxic** gas. When this reaction is done in the laboratory, a solution of **acidified potassium cyanide** ($KCN_{(aq)}$) is used instead, to reduce the risk. The **cyanide ions** needed for the reaction are formed in the solution. Even so, the reaction should be done in a **fume cupboard**.

This is a **nucleophilic addition reaction** — a **nucleophile** attacks the molecule, and an extra group is **added** to it.

Hydrogen cyanide is a **weak acid** — it partially dissociates in water to form $H^+$ and $CN^-$ ions. $HCN \rightleftharpoons H^+ + CN^-$

1) The $CN^-$ group **attacks** the slightly positive carbon atom and **donates** a pair of electrons to it. Both electrons from the double bond transfer to the oxygen.
2) $H^+$ (from either hydrogen cyanide or water) bonds to the oxygen to form the **hydroxyl group** (OH).

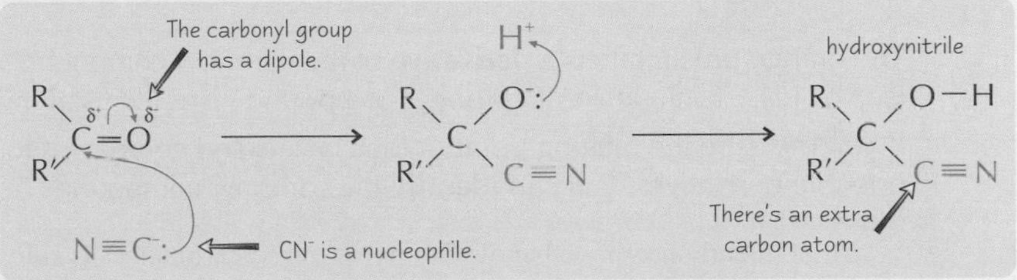


You can use information about the optical activity of the **hydroxynitrile** product to provide **evidence** that the reaction proceeds by the mechanism shown above.

*Edexcel only*

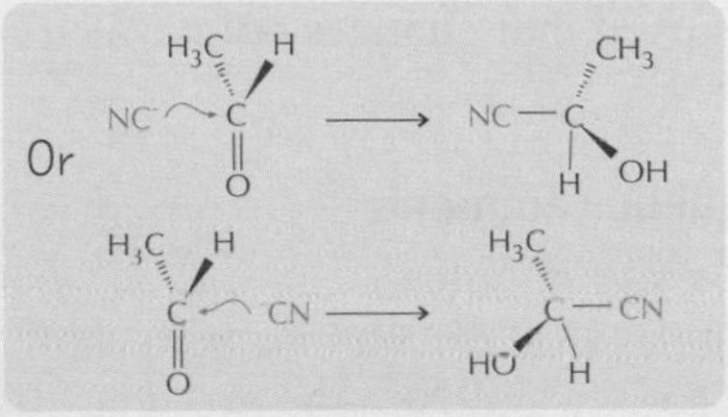


The carbonyl group in a ketone or aldehyde is **planar**. The nucleophile ($CN^-$ ion) can attack it from **either side**.

When you react **an** aldehyde or (asymmetric) ketone with $CN^-$, you get a **racemic mixture** of **two optical isomers**. This is exactly what you'd expect from the mechanism — the carbonyl group gets attacked equally from **each side**, producing **equal amounts** of the two products, which are optical isomers.

## Practice Questions

Q1 What is the difference between an aldehyde and a ketone?

Q2 Why do aldehydes and ketones have lower boiling points than their equivalent alcohols?

Q3 Name the mechanism by which a $CN^-$ ion reacts with an aldehyde or ketone.

**Exam Questions**

1 Ethanol is heated with acidified potassium dichromate(VI).
As soon as the product forms it is removed from the reaction mixture by distillation.

a) Name the type of reaction that is occurring. [1 mark]

b) Name the product and the functional group that it contains. [2 marks]

c) i) Explain why it is important that the product is not left in the reaction mixture when it forms. [2 marks]

ii) Why is this not a problem when the same reaction is performed with propan-2-ol in place of ethanol? [2 marks]

2 An alcohol, **X**, is refluxed with an oxidising agent to form compound **Y**, which when reacted with HCN forms 2-hydroxy-2-methylbutanenitrile (shown right). Give the names of **X** and **Y** and draw their displayed formulas. [6 marks]

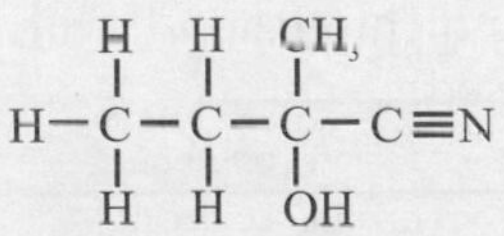

## There ain't nobody nowhere gonna oxidise me...

*You've got to be a dab hand at recognising functional groups from a mile off. Make sure that you know how aldehydes differ from ketones, how to name them, and what you get when you oxidise them. And don't forget to learn the mechanism for the reaction with HCN — it might look a bit nasty, but just remember where the curly arrows go, and you'll be fine.*

# More on Aldehydes and Ketones

*Knowing what an aldehyde and a ketone look like isn't going to help you tell them apart in the lab. Unless the bottle is labelled with a picture of them. But if it's not labelled, which is quite likely, you're going to need to know these tests...*
***These pages are for AQA (Unit 4), OCR A (Unit4), and Edexcel (Unit 4).***

## ***Brady's Reagent*** *Tests for a* ***Carbonyl Group***

***OCR A and Edexcel***

**Brady's reagent** is **2,4-dinitrophenylhydrazine** (2,4-DNPH) dissolved in methanol and concentrated sulfuric acid.
The **2,4-dinitrophenylhydrazine** forms a **bright orange precipitate** if a carbonyl group is present.
This only happens with **C=O groups**, not with more complicated ones like COOH, so it only tests for **aldehydes** and **ketones**.

### *The* ***Melting Point*** *of the Precipitate* ***Identifies*** *the Carbonyl Compound*

The orange precipitate is a **derivative** of the carbonyl compound which can be purified by **recrystallisation** (see p112). Each different carbonyl compound gives a crystalline derivative with a **different melting point**.
If you measure the melting point of the crystals and compare it to a table of **known** melting points of the possible derivatives, you can **identify** the carbonyl compound.

## *And There are a Few Ways of Testing for* ***Aldehydes***

These tests let you distinguish between an aldehyde and a ketone.
They all work on the idea that an **aldehyde** can be **easily oxidised** to a carboxylic acid, but a ketone can't.
As an aldehyde is oxidised, another compound is **reduced** — so a reagent is used that **changes colour** as it's reduced.

### Tollens' Reagent

Tollens' reagent is a **colourless** solution of **silver nitrate** dissolved in **aqueous ammonia**.
If it's heated in a test tube with an aldehyde, a **silver mirror** forms after a few minutes.

You shouldn't heat the test tube directly over a flame — most organic compounds are flammable. Use a water bath or heating mantle instead.

colourless → silver

$$Ag(NH_3)_2{}^+{}_{(aq)} + e^- \longrightarrow Ag_{(s)} + 2NH_{3(aq)}$$

### Fehling's solution or Benedict's solution

Fehling's solution is a **blue** solution of complexed **copper(II) ions** dissolved in **sodium hydroxide**.
If it's heated with an aldehyde the copper(II) ions are reduced to a **brick-red precipitate** of **copper(I) oxide**.

blue → brick-red

$$Cu^{2+}{}_{(aq)} + e^- \longrightarrow Cu^+{}_{(s)}$$

(Don't forget — heat the test tube in a water bath or heating mantle)

Benedict's solution is exactly the same as Fehling's solution except the copper(II) ions are dissolved in **sodium carbonate** instead. You still get a **brick-red precipitate** of copper(I) oxide though.

## *Aldehydes* ***Oxidise*** *to* ***Carboxylic Acids*** *— Ketones* ***Don't***

1) If you **heat** an **aldehyde** with the **acidified dichromate(VI) ions** you get a carboxylic acid.
The **dichromate(VI) ions** are the oxidising agent [O].
Potassium dichromate(VI) with dilute sulfuric acid is often used.
(During this reaction you should see the solution change colour — from orange to green.)

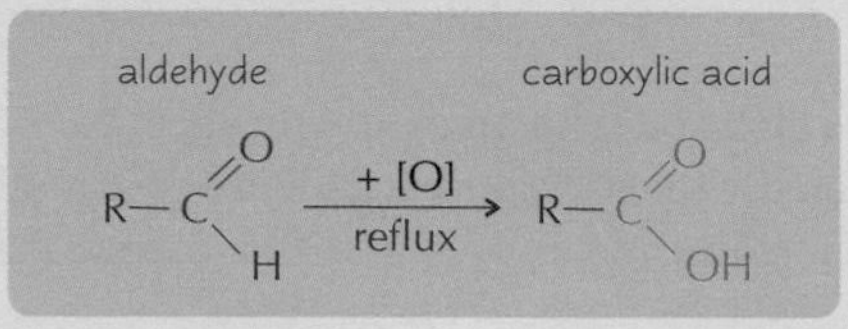


2) Ketones won't oxidise with acidified **dichromate(VI) ions**.
It's not a strong enough oxidising agent.

# More on Aldehydes and Ketones

## You can Reduce Aldehydes and Ketones Back to Alcohols

Using a **reducing agent** [H] you can:

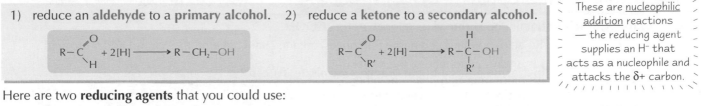

1) reduce an **aldehyde** to a **primary alcohol**. 2) reduce a **ketone** to a **secondary alcohol**.

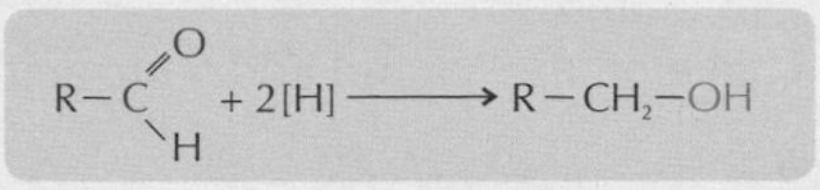

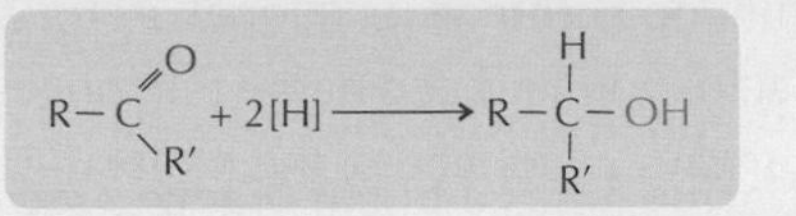

These are nucleophilic addition reactions — the reducing agent supplies an $H^-$ that acts as a nucleophile and attacks the δ+ carbon.

Here are two **reducing agents** that you could use:

1) **$LiAlH_4$** (lithium tetrahydridoaluminate(III) or lithium aluminium hydride) in **dry diethyl ether**. This will do the job easily — it's a very powerful reducing agent, which reacts violently with water, bursting into flames. Eeek.
2) **$NaBH_4$** (sodium tetrahydridoborate(III) or sodium borohydride) dissolved in water with methanol. This is less powerful, but it's what you'd usually use in a lab, as it's pretty harmless.

*AQA and OCR A*

This is the mechanism for the reaction of $NaBH_4$ with a carbonyl group:

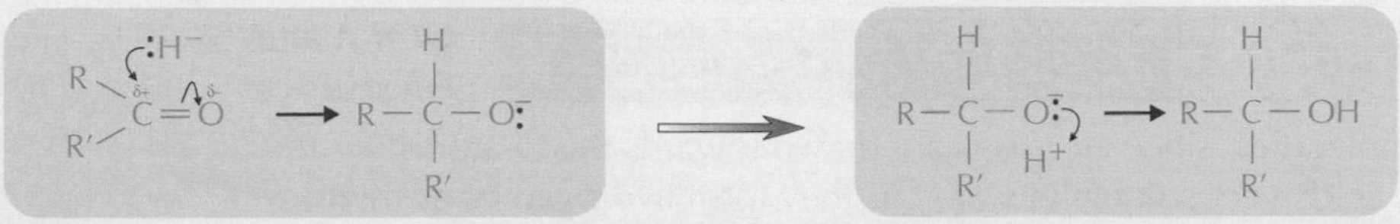

The $NaBH_4$ supplies hydride ions, $H^-$. The pair of electrons on $H^-$ make it a nucleophile, so it attacks the $\delta^+$ carbon on the carbonyl group.

Then you add some acid to supply $H^+$ ions, and you end up with an alcohol.

## Some Carbonyls will React with Iodine

*Edexcel only*

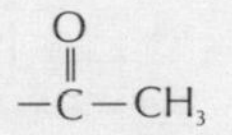

This is a methyl carbonyl group.

Carbonyls that contain a **methyl carbonyl** group react when heated with **iodine** in the presence of an alkali. If there's a methyl carbonyl group you'll get a **straw-yellow precipitate** and an antiseptic smell.

If something contains a methyl carbonyl group, it must be: Ethanal

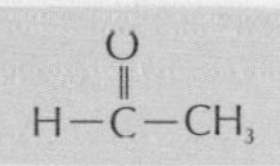

or A ketone with at least one methyl group

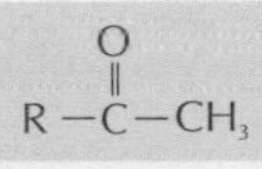

## Practice Questions

Q1 Describe the use of Brady's reagent.

Q2 Describe the use of Tollens' reagent.

Q3 Describe how to convert an aldehyde into an alcohol.

**Exam Questions**

1 There are two straight-chain carbonyl compounds with the molecular formula $C_4H_8O$.

a) Name the two compounds. [2 marks]

b) Name a reagent that you could use to distinguish between the isomers. Give the expected result with each. [3 marks]

c) When you react one of the isomers with a mild oxidising agent, it is converted to a carboxylic acid. Name the organic product of this reaction. [1 mark]

2 Substance Q gives an orange precipitate with Brady's reagent. It has no reaction when warmed with Tollens' reagent. It reacts with iodine to give a yellow precipitate. The formula of Q is $C_7H_{14}O$.

a) Use the information to draw a structure for Q. Explain how each piece of information is used. [4 marks]

b) Explain how Brady's reagent could be used to confirm your suggested structure. [2 marks]

c) Draw the structure of the substance produced when Q reacts with $NaBH_4$. [1 mark]

## It's all crystal clear — unless it's a precipitate or a silver mirror...

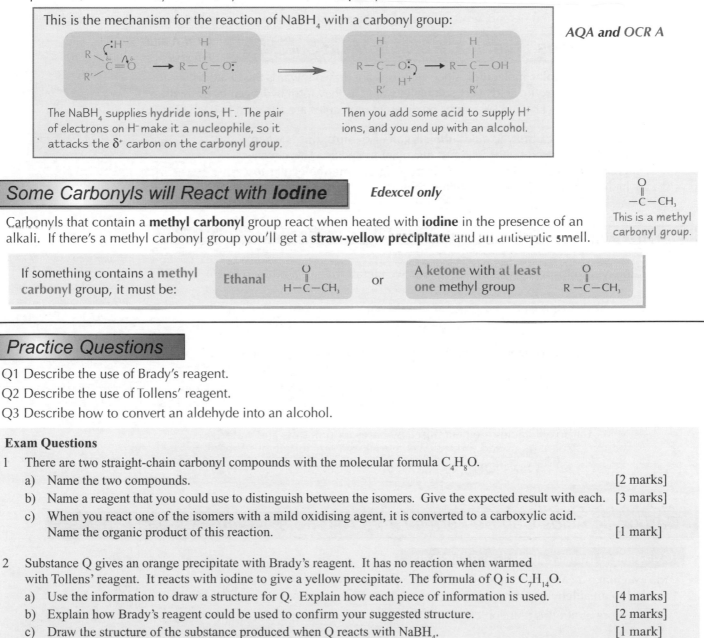

*I wonder what it's like to have a reagent named after you. Could be a great conversation starter at parties. 'So Professor Brady, what do you do?' — 'Well I make scientific reagents.' — '......' — 'My most famous one tests for carbonyl groups.' — '......' — 'It turns orange' — 'Oooo... orange is my favourite, both the colour and the fruit, which is much nicer than celery.'*

# Carboxylic Acids

*Carboxylic acids are more interesting than cardboard boxes — as you're about to discover...*
***These pages are for AQA (Unit 4), OCR A (Unit 4), OCR B (Unit 4) and Edexcel (Unit 4).***

## Carboxylic Acids Contain –COOH Groups

A carboxyl group contains a carbonyl group and a hydroxyl group.

1) **Carboxylic acids** contain the **carboxyl** functional group **–COOH**.
2) To name a carboxylic acid, you find and name the longest alkane chain, take off the 'e' and add **'–oic acid'**.
3) The carboxyl group is always at the **end** of the molecule and when naming it's more important than any other functional groups — so all the other functional groups in the molecule are numbered starting from this carbon.

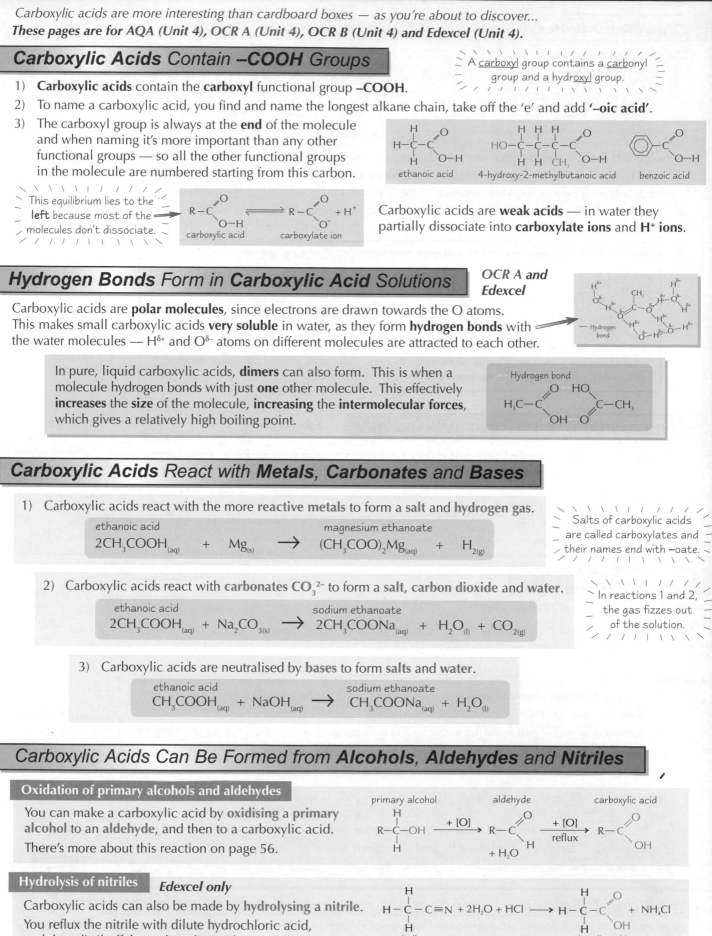

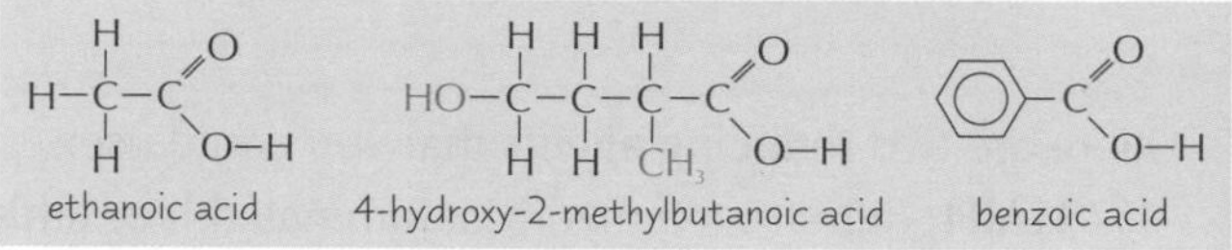


This equilibrium lies to the **left** because most of the molecules don't dissociate.

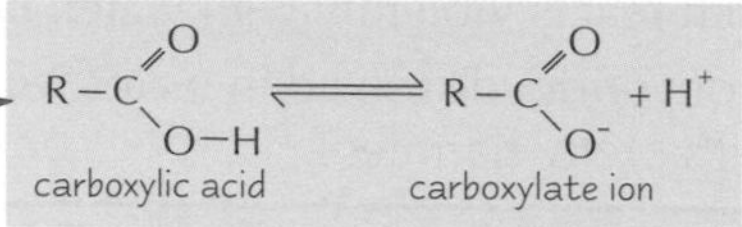


Carboxylic acids are **weak acids** — in water they partially dissociate into **carboxylate ions** and **$H^+$ ions**.

## Hydrogen Bonds Form in Carboxylic Acid Solutions

***OCR A and Edexcel***

Carboxylic acids are **polar molecules**, since electrons are drawn towards the O atoms. This makes small carboxylic acids **very soluble** in water, as they form **hydrogen bonds** with the water molecules — $H^{\delta+}$ and $O^{\delta-}$ atoms on different molecules are attracted to each other.

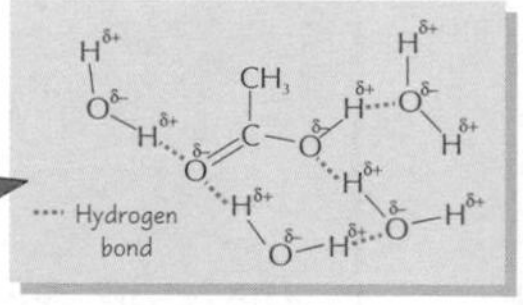


In pure, liquid carboxylic acids, **dimers** can also form. This is when a molecule hydrogen bonds with just **one** other molecule. This effectively **increases** the **size** of the molecule, **increasing** the **intermolecular forces**, which gives a relatively high boiling point.

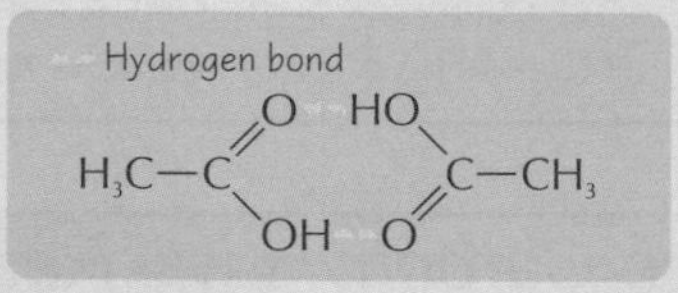


## Carboxylic Acids React with Metals, Carbonates and Bases

1) Carboxylic acids react with the more **reactive metals** to form a **salt** and **hydrogen gas**.

ethanoic acid → magnesium ethanoate

$$2CH_3COOH_{(aq)} + Mg_{(s)} \rightarrow (CH_3COO)_2Mg_{(aq)} + H_{2(g)}$$

Salts of carboxylic acids are called carboxylates and their names end with –oate.

2) Carboxylic acids react with **carbonates $CO_3^{2-}$** to form a **salt**, **carbon dioxide** and **water**.

ethanoic acid → sodium ethanoate

$$2CH_3COOH_{(aq)} + Na_2CO_{3(s)} \rightarrow 2CH_3COONa_{(aq)} + H_2O_{(l)} + CO_{2(g)}$$

In reactions 1 and 2, the gas fizzes out of the solution.

3) Carboxylic acids are neutralised by **bases** to form **salts** and **water**.

ethanoic acid → sodium ethanoate

$$CH_3COOH_{(aq)} + NaOH_{(aq)} \rightarrow CH_3COONa_{(aq)} + H_2O_{(l)}$$

## Carboxylic Acids Can Be Formed from Alcohols, Aldehydes and Nitriles

### Oxidation of primary alcohols and aldehydes

You can make a carboxylic acid by **oxidising** a **primary alcohol** to an **aldehyde**, and then to a carboxylic acid.
There's more about this reaction on page 56.

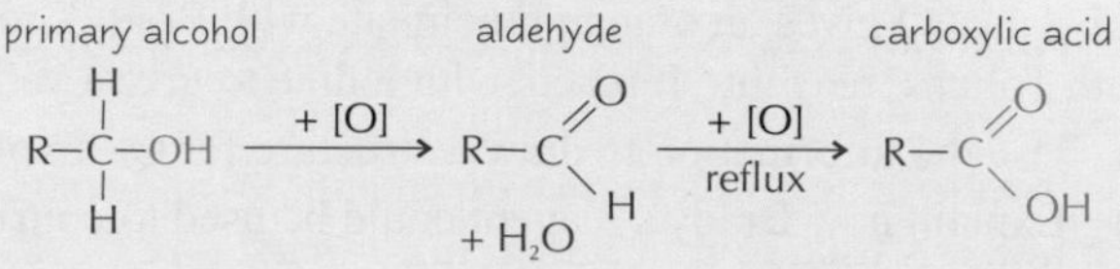


### Hydrolysis of nitriles

***Edexcel only***

Carboxylic acids can also be made by **hydrolysing** a **nitrile**. You reflux the nitrile with dilute hydrochloric acid, and then distil off the carboxylic acid .

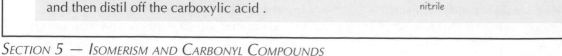

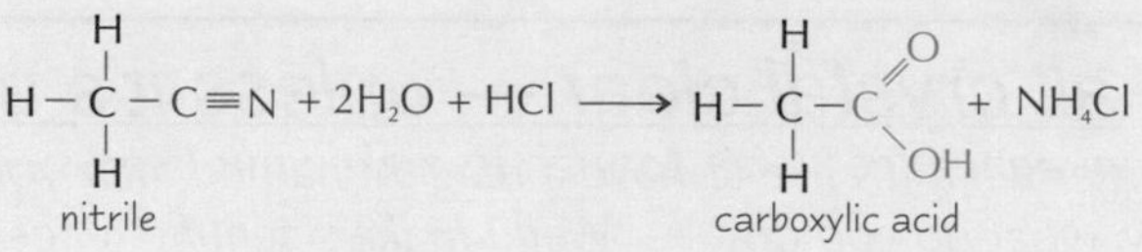

# Carboxylic Acids

## *Other Reactions You'll Need to Know* **Edexcel only**

It's quite **hard** to reduce a carboxylic acid, so you have to use a **powerful reducing agent** like **$LiAlH_4$** in **dry diethyl ether**. It reduces the carboxylic acid right down to an **alcohol** in one go — you can't get the reduction to stop at the aldehyde.

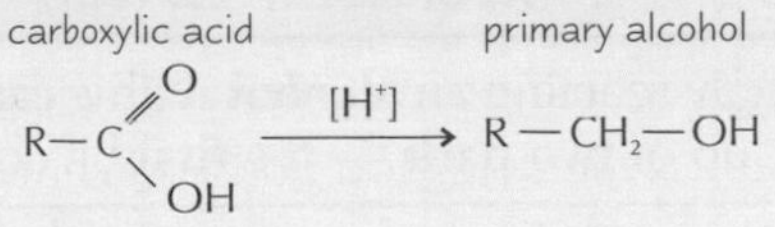

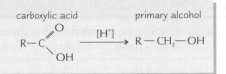

Acyl chlorides are covered on pages 68-69.

Mix a carboxylic acid with **phosphorus(V) chloride** and you'll get an **acyl chloride**.

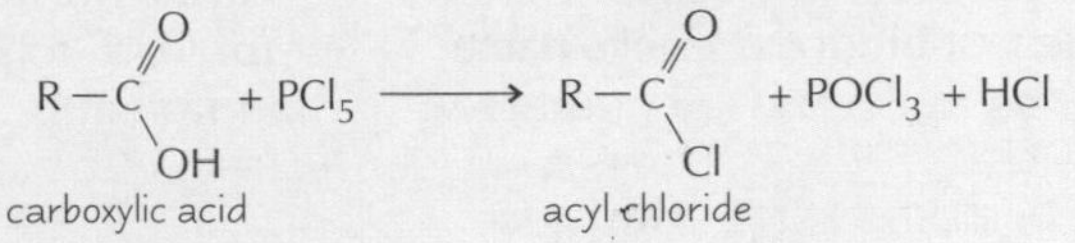

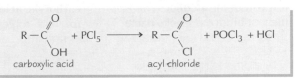

## *Alcohols React with Carboxylic Acids to form Esters*

If you heat a **carboxylic acid** with an **alcohol** in the presence of an **acid catalyst**, you get an **ester** (see page 62). It's called an **esterification** reaction. Concentrated sulfuric acid is usually used as the acid catalyst.

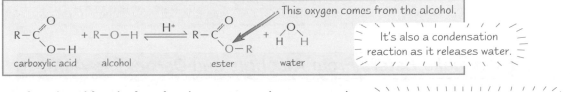

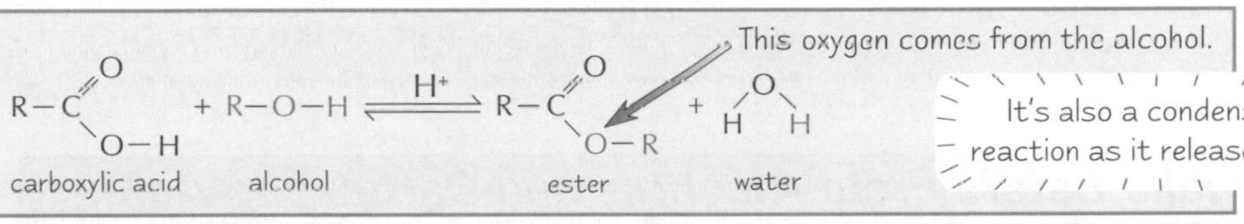


It's also a condensation reaction as it releases water.

For example, if you reflux **ethanoic acid** and **ethanol** in the presence of concentrated sulfuric acid, you get the ester **ethyl ethanoate**. You can see this reaction on page 62.

Ethyl ethanoate is used as a solvent and a pineapple flavouring.

## *Practice Questions*

Q1 Draw the structures of ethanoic and propanoic acids.

Q2 Explain the relatively high boiling points of carboxylic acids.

Q3 Describe two ways of preparing carboxylic acids.

Q4 How can you make an acyl chloride from a carboxylic acid?

**Exam Questions**

1 A primary alcohol is heated with acidified potassium dichromate(VI) solution. Compound X, shown on the right, is produced.

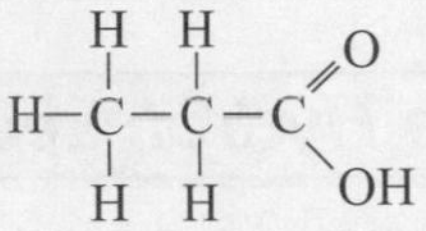

**X**

a) Name compound X. [1 mark]

b) Name the alcohol used to produce compound X. [1 mark]

c) Write a balanced equation for the reaction of compound X with potassium hydroxide solution, KOH. [1 mark]

2 Isovaleric acid is a carboxylic acid that is found in a wide variety of plant essential oils.

a) Its systematic name is 3-methylbutanoic acid. Draw its structure. [1 mark]

b) If solid sodium carbonate, $Na_2CO_3$, is added to a solution of isovaleric acid, the mixture will fizz. Write a balanced equation for the reaction that occurs. [2 marks]

c) Draw and name the structure of the compound formed if isovaleric acid is reduced. Suggest a reducing agent for the reaction. [3 marks]

d) Isovaleric acid will react with ethanol to produce the compound ethyl 3-methylbutanoate, which is used in fruit flavourings. What type of reaction is this? [1 mark]

## Alright, so maybe cardboard boxes do have the edge after all...

*So many reactions — it's enough to make your head swim. When you think about it though, the reactions with metals, bases, and carbonates are just the same as they would be for any old acid. And learning the last section about how to make an ester will really put you ahead of the curve for the next page. Guess what it's about... no, go on, guess...*

# Esters

*If you've ever wondered how they make soap, margarine or pear drops, this is the page for you...*
***These pages are for AQA (Unit 4), OCR A (Unit 4), OCR B (Unit 4) and Edexcel (Unit 4).***

## *Esters have the Functional Group –COO–*

An **ester** is made by reacting an **alcohol** with a **carboxylic acid** — just like you saw on the last page. So the **name** of an **ester** is made up of **two parts** — the **first** bit comes from the **alcohol**, and the **second** bit from the **carboxylic acid**.

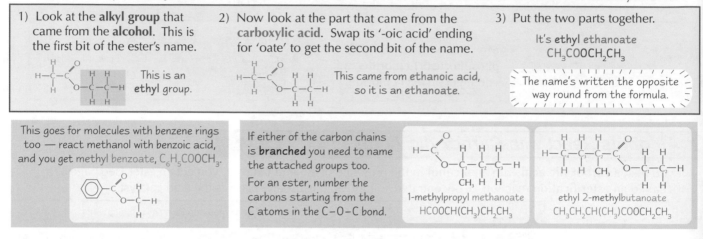

1) Look at the **alkyl group** that came from the **alcohol**. This is the first bit of the ester's name.

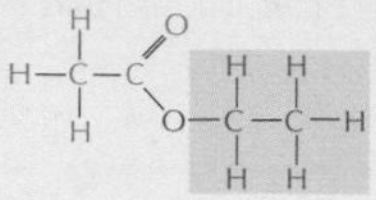

This is an ethyl group.

2) Now look at the part that came from the **carboxylic acid**. Swap its '-oic acid' ending for 'oate' to get the second bit of the name.

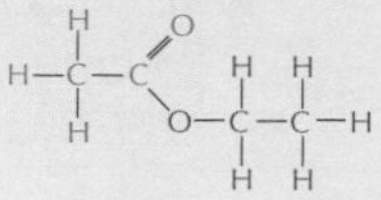

This came from ethanoic acid, so it is an ethanoate.

3) Put the two parts together.

It's ethyl ethanoate
$CH_3COOCH_2CH_3$

The name's written the opposite way round from the formula.

This goes for molecules with benzene rings too — react methanol with benzoic acid, and you get methyl benzoate, $C_6H_5COOCH_3$.

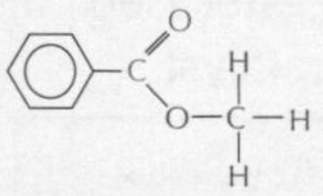

If either of the carbon chains is **branched** you need to name the attached groups too.
For an ester, number the carbons starting from the C atoms in the C–O–C bond.

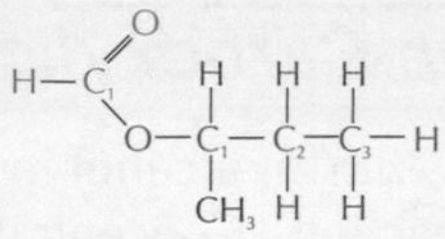

1-methylpropyl methanoate
$HCOOCH(CH_3)CH_2CH_3$

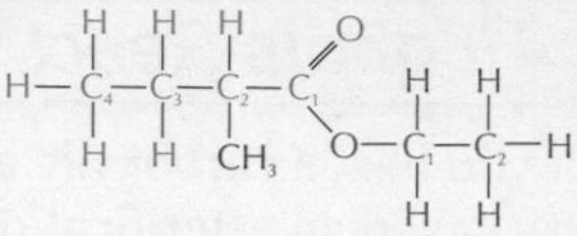

ethyl 2-methylbutanoate
$CH_3CH_2CH(CH_3)COOCH_2CH_3$

## *You can make **Esters** From **Alcohols** and **Carboxylic Acids***

1) If you heat a **carboxylic acid** with an **alcohol** in the presence of an **acid catalyst**, you get an ester.
2) Concentrated sulfuric acid is usually used as the acid catalyst. It's called an **esterification** reaction. This is the carboxylic acid + alcohol ⇌ ester + water reaction that you saw on the last page.
3) For example, to make the ester ethyl ethanoate, you reflux ethanoic acid with ethanol and an acid catalyst:

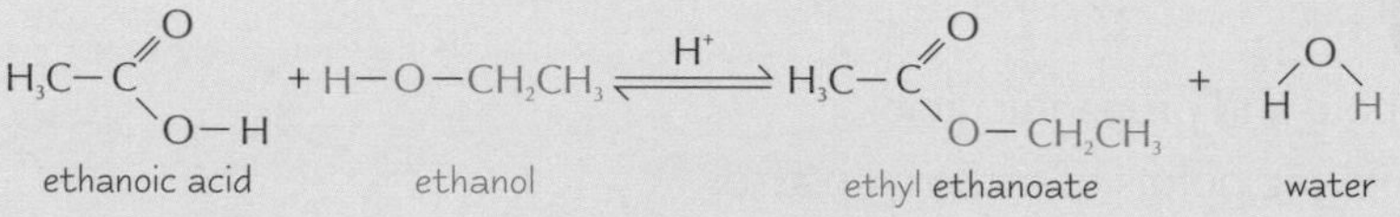


4) The reaction is **reversible**, so you need to separate out the product **as it's formed**.
(For small esters, you can just warm the mixture and **distil off** the ester, because it's more **volatile** than the other compounds. Large esters are harder to form so it's best to heat them under **reflux** and use **fractional distillation** to separate out the ester.)

## *Esters are **Hydrolysed** to Form **Alcohols***

There are two types of hydrolysis of esters — **acid hydrolysis** and **base hydrolysis**. With both types you get an **alcohol**, but the second product in each case is different.

As it's a reversible reaction, you need to use lots of water to push the equilibrium over to the right.

**Acid Hydrolysis**

**Acid hydrolysis** splits the ester into an **acid** and an **alcohol** — it's just the **reverse** of the condensation reaction on page 61. You have to **reflux** the ester with a **dilute acid**, such as hydrochloric or sulfuric.

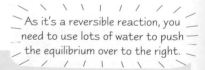

For example:

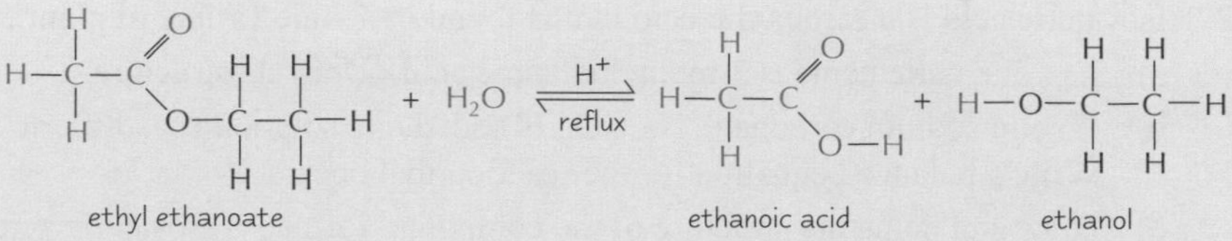


**Base Hydrolysis**

If you **reflux** the ester with a **dilute alkali**, such as sodium hydroxide, then you'll get a **carboxylate salt** and an **alcohol** instead.

For example:

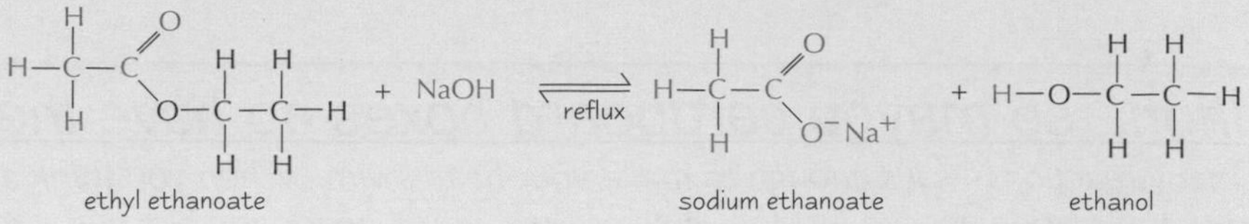

# Esters

## Esters are Used as **Flavourings**, **Perfumes**, **Solvents** and **Plasticisers**

***AQA and OCR A***

1) Esters have a **sweet smell** — it varies from gluey sweet for smaller esters to a fruity 'pear drop' smell for the larger ones. This makes them useful in perfumes.
2) The fragrances and flavours of lots of flowers and fruits come from **naturally-occurring** esters. The **food industry** uses artificial esters to flavour things like drinks and sweets too.
3) Esters are **polar** liquids so lots of **polar organic compounds** will dissolve in them. They've also got quite **low boiling points**, so they **evaporate easily** from mixtures. This makes them good solvents in **glues** and **printing inks**.
4) Esters are used as **plasticisers** — they're added to plastics during polymerisation to make the plastic more **flexible** (see page 101).

Jon enjoyed the naturally-occurring fragrances and flavours of Esther.

## Esters React With **Alcohols** to Make **New Esters**

***Edexcel only***

You can react an **ester** with an **alcohol** to get a **new ester** in a process called **transesterification**. It allows you to **swap** a different alcohol for the alcohol part of the ester.

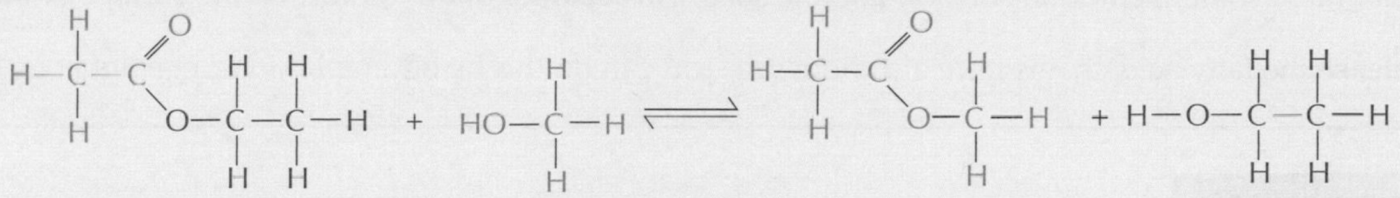

ethyl ethanoate + methanol ⇌ methyl ethanoate + ethanol

This reaction comes in handy for a couple of things:

**Making biodiesel from vegetable oils**

1) Vegetable oils are **esters** of **glycerol** (see p64). If you react these esters with **methanol** it **swaps places** with the glycerol to produce **methyl esters** and free glycerol. This is a **transesterification** reaction.
2) The **methyl esters** can be used as **biodiesel**. There's more about biodiesel on page 67.

**Making low fat spreads to replace butter**

1) **Saturated** fats have **no double bonds** in their fatty acid chains. **Unsaturated** fats have at least one **double bond** in their fatty acid chains (see page 65 for more on fatty acids).
2) **Saturated** fats have a **higher** melting temperature than unsaturated fats because their molecules pack together more easily, **increasing** the **van der Waals** forces between molecules.
3) Low fat spreads used to be made using a process called **hydrogenation**. **Unsaturated** vegetable oils were reacted with **hydrogen** to **remove** its double bonds, giving a **solid** fat that spreads like butter. But this method produces some **trans** isomers of the fatty acids — and the **trans** isomers are associated with various **diseases**.
4) Now manufacturers are using **transesterification** to convert the esters in vegetable oils into **different** esters that have higher melting temperatures but **don't** contain the trans isomers.

# Esters

## Base Hydrolysis of Esters is Used to Make Soaps

*AQA and Edexcel*

**Vegetable oils and animal fats** are made from **glycerol**. Each of the three glycerol OH groups is replaced with a **long chain carboxylic acid** (a 'fatty acid') joined to the molecule by an ester bond. This is covered in more detail on the next page.

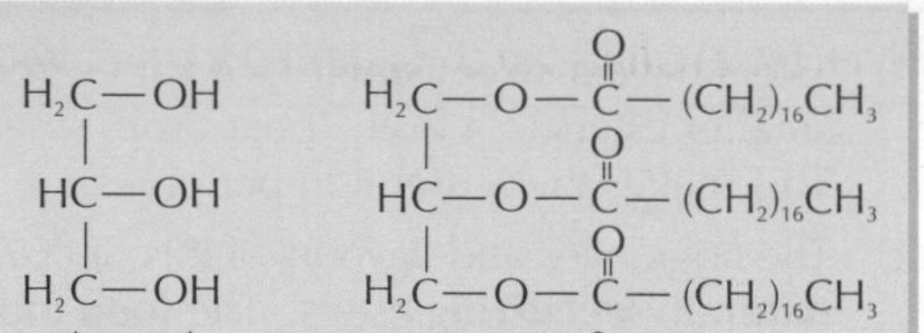

glycerol fat

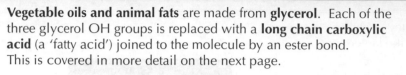

Like any other ester, you can **hydrolyse** fats and oils by heating them with sodium hydroxide. The sodium salt that you make is a **soap**:

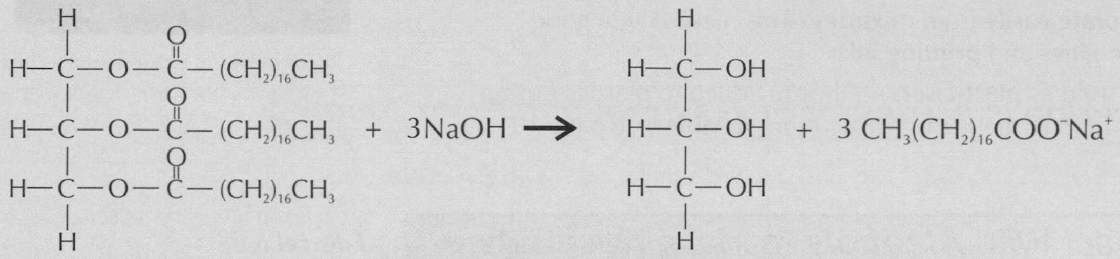

fat glycerol sodium salt (soap)

To make the soap you just **heat** the fat or oil with a **concentrated** solution of **sodium hydroxide**, and allow it to **cool**. Then add some saturated sodium chloride solution and the soap will **separate** out as a crust on the **surface** of the liquid.

If you want to **release** the fatty acid chains from a sodium salt, you can do this by adding $H^+$ ions, e.g. aqueous HCl.

## Practice Questions

Q1 Draw the structure of 2-methylpropyl ethanoate.

Q2 Name the products formed when methyl ethanoate undergoes acid hydrolysis.

Q3 What is meant by transesterification?

Q4 Give two common uses of esters.

Q5 Describe how to make a soap from a vegetable oil.

**Exam Questions**

1 3-methylbutyl ethanoate is the ester responsible for the odour of pear essence.

a) Write an equation for the formation of this ester from an alcohol and a carboxylic acid. [2 marks]

b) Name the carboxylic acid used. [1 mark]

c) What conditions would be needed for this reaction? [2 marks]

**C**

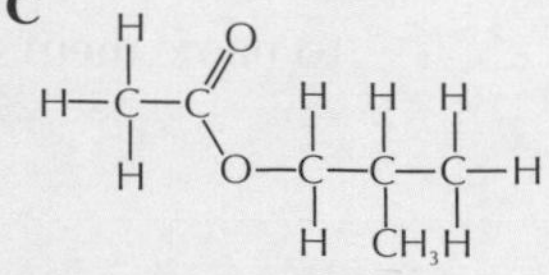

2 Compound C, shown on the right, is a small ester that is found in raspberries.

a) Name compound C. [1 mark]

b) Suggest a possible use for compound C. [1 mark]

c) Draw and name the structures of the products formed when compound C is refluxed with dilute sulfuric acid. What kind of reaction is this? [5 marks]

d) If compound C is refluxed with excess sodium hydroxide, a similar reaction occurs. Give a difference between the products of this reaction and those of the reaction described in part (c). [1 mark]

## Take time to stop and smell the cis-3,7-dimethyl-2,6-octadien-1-yl ethanoate...

*So, your apple flavoured sweets have probably never been anywhere near a nice rosy apple — it's all the work of esters. The low fat spread melting lusciously on your morning toast — more ester magic there too. And if you couldn't hydrolyse esters, you couldn't make soap. So learn the reactions, remember the uses, and go and make some toast. Mmm, ester-y...*

# Fatty Acids and Fats

*OK, brace yourself — you're about to experience three solid pages of pure, unadulterated fat...*
***These pages are for AQA (Unit 4), OCR A (Unit 4), OCR B (Unit 5) and Edexcel (Unit 4).***

## Fatty Acids are Carboxylic Acids

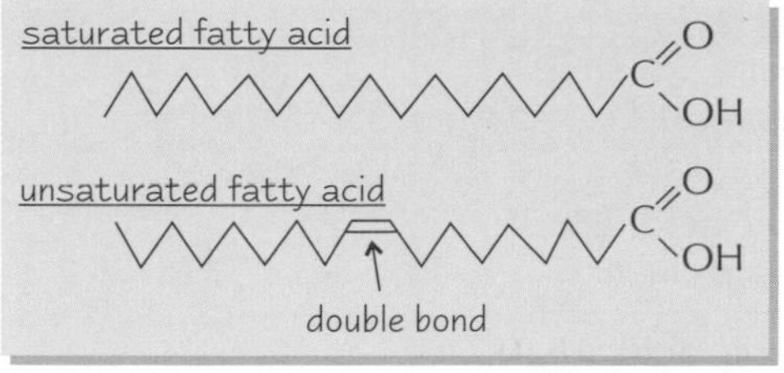


Fatty acids have a long hydrocarbon chain with a **carboxylic acid** group at the end. If the hydrocarbon chain contains **no double bonds** then the fatty acid is **saturated**, but if it contains one or more double bonds then it's **unsaturated**.

Fatty acids can also be written like this where 'R' is a hydrocarbon chain.

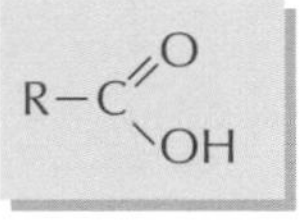


## A Triglyceride is a Triester of Glycerol and Fatty Acids

1) The **animal** and **vegetable fats** and **oils** we eat are mainly **triglycerides**.
2) Triglycerides contain the ester functional group –COO– three times — they are **triglyceryl esters**. They're made by reacting **glycerol** (**propane-1,2,3-triol**) with **fatty acids**.
3) The **three -OH groups** on the glycerol molecules link up to **fatty acids** to produce triglyceride molecules. Water is eliminated, so it's a type of **condensation** reaction.

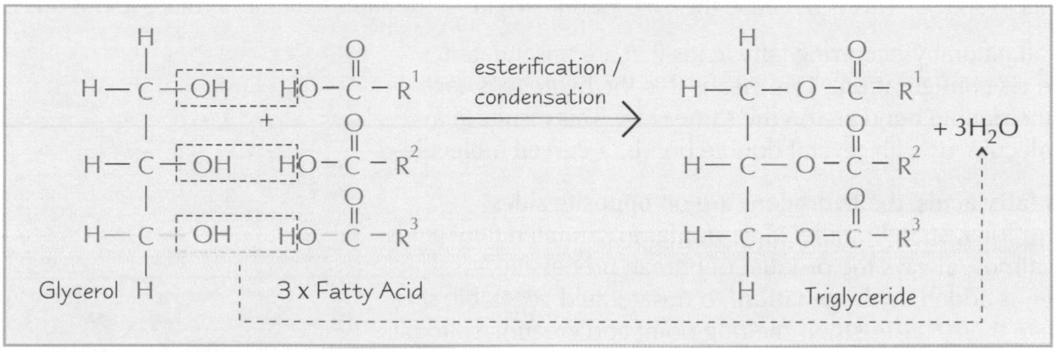


## Systematic Names are used for Complex Molecules...

*OCR A only*

## ...like Fatty Acids

Saturated and unsaturated fats and fatty acids are pretty **complex molecules**, which means describing their structure clearly without having to draw them can become slightly nightmarish.
The best way is by using their **systematic names** which you need to know a few conventions for.

1) Fatty acids are long hydrocarbon chains with a COOH group at the end.
2) To name them systematically, you need to add numbers to say:
   – **how many carbon atoms** there are.
   – **how many double bonds** there are.
   – **where** the double bonds are (count the carbons from the COOH group end).
3) A **fatty acid** with **14** carbon atoms and **0** double bonds (i.e. it's saturated) would be **tetradecanoic acid, 14, 0** (chemical formula $CH_3(CH_2)_{12}COOH$).
4) One with **16** carbon atoms and **1** double bond (i.e. unsaturated) between the **9th and 10th** carbon atoms, would be **hexadec-9-enoic acid, 16, 1(9)** (chemical formula $CH_3(CH_2)_5CH{=}CH(CH_2)_7COOH$).
5) If it has **18** carbon atoms and **2** double bonds (i.e. unsaturated) in positions **9 and 12**, it'd be **octadec-9,12-dienoic acid, 18, 2(9, 12)** (chemical formula $CH_3(CH_2)_4CH{=}CHCH_2CH{=}CH(CH_2)_7COOH$).

tetra means 4
hexa means 6
octa means 8
deca means 10

Most of these chemicals also have a common name, e.g. 'oleic acid' but they're no help if you want to know about the structure.

# Fatty Acids and Fats

***This whole page is just for people doing OCR A.***

## ...and Triglycerides

**Triglycerides** are named by showing **which carbon** from the glycerol molecule has **which fatty acid** attached. For example:

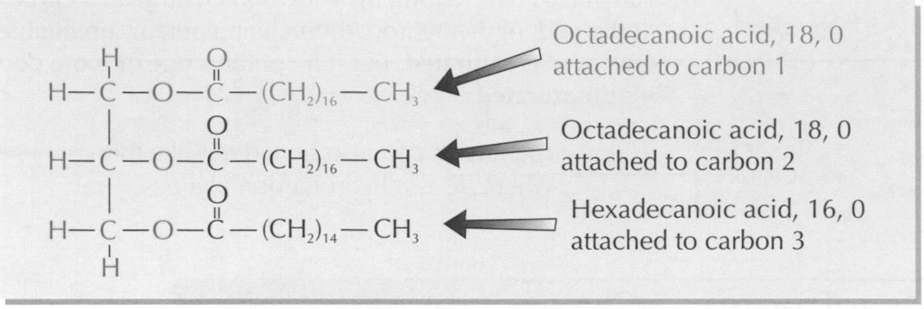


So this triglyceride could be named **propane-1,2-dioctadecanoic acid, 18,0 -3-hexadecanoic acid, 16,0.**
(So that's simple enough.... NOT.) Don't panic though — you won't get anything this complicated in the exam.

## *Fatty Acids* come in *Cis* and *Trans* Forms

Fatty acids can exist as **stereoisomers** — molecules with the same structural formula but different arrangements in space. This is because the C=C bond is **rigid** — the molecule can't rotate about this bond.

1) Almost all naturally-occurring fatty acids that are unsaturated have the **cis configuration**. This means that the hydrogens each side of the double bond are on the same side. This results in a **bent molecule**, or with several double bonds, a **curved molecule**.
2) In **trans fatty acids**, the **hydrogens** are on **opposite sides**. This gives long, straight molecules, similar to saturated fatty acids. They're almost always the product of human processing — hydrogen is added (**hydrogenation**) to unsaturated vegetable oils to saturate them, raising their melting point and creating solid fats.

See page 49 for more on cis-trans isomerism.

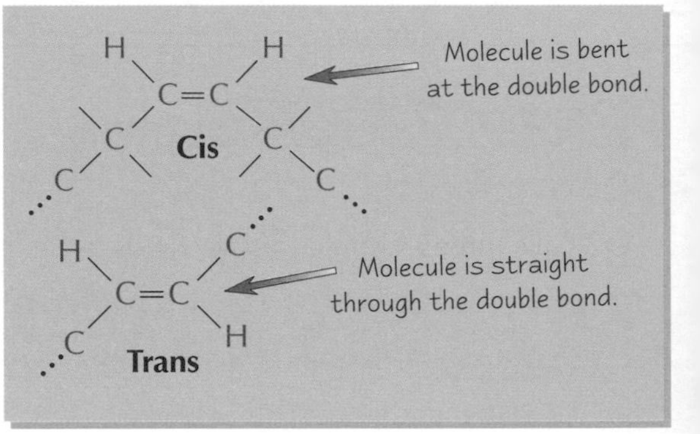


## Fats *Aren't Always* Bad (but they Often Are)

1) **Cholesterol** is a soft, waxy material found in cell membranes and transported in your blood stream. It is partly produced by your body and partly absorbed from animal products that you eat, e.g., eggs, meat, dairy products.
2) There are **two types** of cholesterol — 'good' cholesterol and 'bad' cholesterol.
3) **Bad cholesterol** can clog blood vessels, which increases the risk of heart attacks and strokes.
4) **Good cholesterol** removes bad cholesterol, taking it to the liver to be destroyed. So high levels of good cholesterol can give protection from heart disease.
5) Recent research has shown that **trans fats increase** the amount of bad cholesterol and decrease the amount of good cholesterol.
6) Trans fats are **triglycerides** made from trans fatty acids. They are almost all man-made and are used in many foods such as biscuits, cakes, chips and crisps. Because of recent health concerns, there have been moves to **reduce their use** and more **clearly label** foods that contain them.
7) Bad cholesterol is also increased by eating **saturated fats** (made from fatty acids with no double bonds). They occur in animal products but much less so in plants.
8) Plant oils such as olive and sunflower oils contain **unsaturated fats**. These can be **polyunsaturated** (several double bonds) or **monounsaturated** (one double bond per chain). Polyunsaturated oils have been shown to reduce "bad" cholesterol and are actually a good thing to eat in moderation to prevent heart disease.

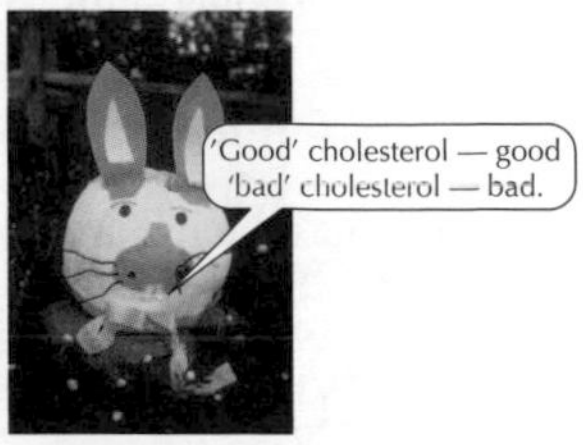


Revision Bunny can help if you're struggling with the key point here.

# Fatty Acids and Fats

## Fats can be Used to make Biodiesel

**Not OCR B**

Biodiesel is a renewable fuel made from **vegetable oil** or **animal fats** that can be used in diesel engines.
It is gaining popularity as an alternative to crude-oil based diesel.

1) Biodiesel is mainly a mixture of methyl and ethyl **esters of fatty acids**.
2) It's made by reacting **triglycerides** (oils or fats) with **methanol** or **ethanol**.

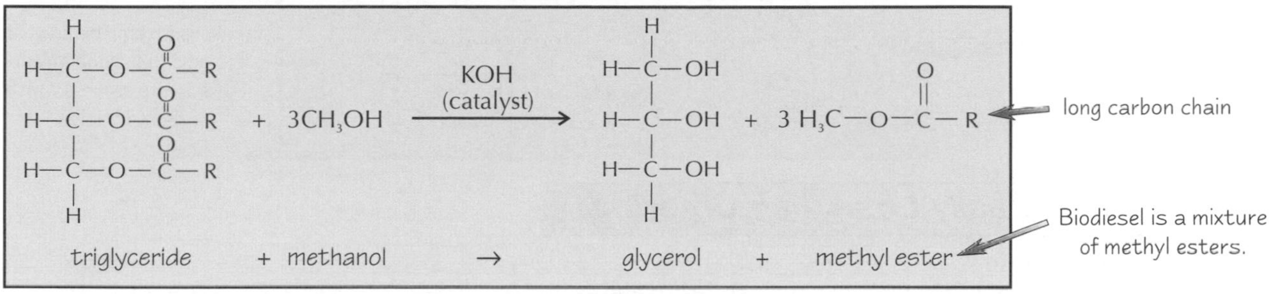


3) The **vegetable oils** used in the process can be **new**, **low grade oil** or **waste oil** from chip shops and restaurants. **Animal fats** that can be used include chicken fat, waste fish oil and lard from meat processing.
4) At present, biodiesel is mainly used **mixed with conventional diesel**, rather than in pure form. **B20 fuel** contains 20% biodiesel and 80% conventional diesel.
5) There is debate about how feasible **large-scale use** of biodiesel is — to produce significant quantities would mean devoting **huge areas of land** to growing biodiesel crops (e.g. rapeseed and soy beans) rather than **food crops**.

## Practice Questions

Q1 What is a fatty acid? How are saturated and unsaturated fatty acids different?

Q2 Give three examples of fatty acids using their systematic names and chemical formulas.

Q3 Write the systematic name of the triester that could be formed from these acids.

Q4 Explain how cis and trans fatty acids are different.

Q5 Give one advantage and one disadvantage of biodiesel over conventional diesel.

**Exam Questions**

1 Stearic acid is the common name for a fatty acid found in many animal fats.
Stearic acid is used in candle making. Its chemical name is octadecanoic acid,18,0.

a) What is the chemical formula of stearic acid? [1 mark]

b) Glycerol (propane-1,2,3-triol) forms a triester with stearic acid.
This triester is widely used in shampoos and cosmetics to give a pearly effect.

i) What name is given to triesters formed from glycerol and fatty acids? [1 mark]

ii) Is the triester formed saturated or unsaturated? Explain how you know. [1 mark]

2 Cis fatty acids are considered to be more healthy than trans fatty acids.

a) A major constituent of olive oil is a cis fatty acid called oleic acid.
What does the term 'cis' tell you about its structure? [1 mark]

b) Explain why trans fatty acids are harmful to human health. [2 marks]

## Altogether now... 'Lard, lard, lard'... 'Lard, Lard, Lard'... 'Lard Lard Lard Lard'...

*If you're struggling to remember everything, have a go at writing down the key facts like this: Fatty acid = carboxylic acid, triglyceride = triester = "fat". If you're still struggling, as a last resort you could summon Revision Bunny by standing on one leg and saying his name three times. Word of warning though, he's a bit loco ding dong. Don't blame me if things get ugly...*

# Acylation

*Acyl chlorides are easy to make and are good starting points for making other types of molecule.*
***These pages are for AQA (Unit 4) and Edexcel (Unit 4).***

## *Acyl Chlorides have the Functional Group –COCl*

**Acyl (or acid) chlorides** have the functional group **COCl** — their general formula is $\mathbf{C_nH_{2n-1}OCl}$.
All their names end in **–oyl chloride**.

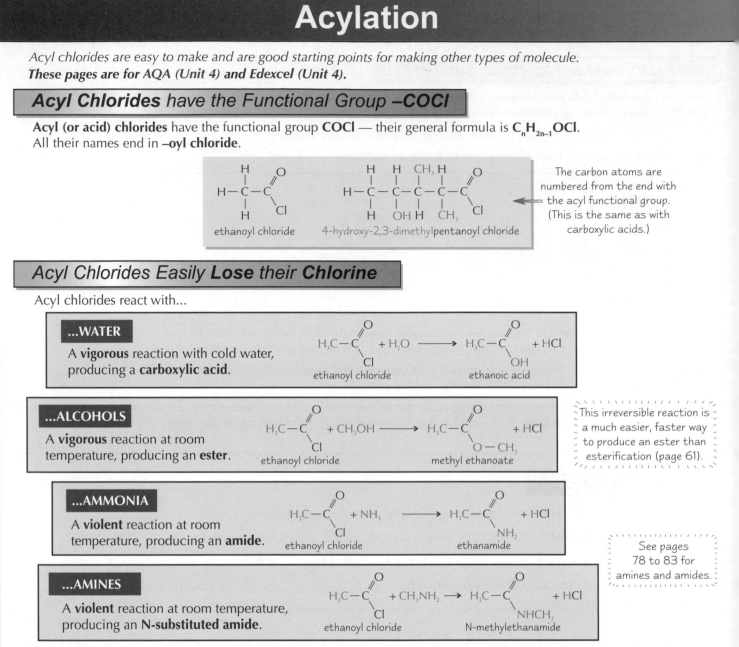

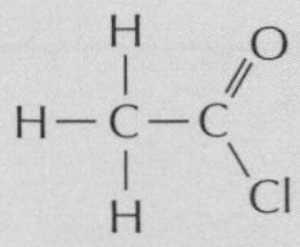

ethanoyl chloride

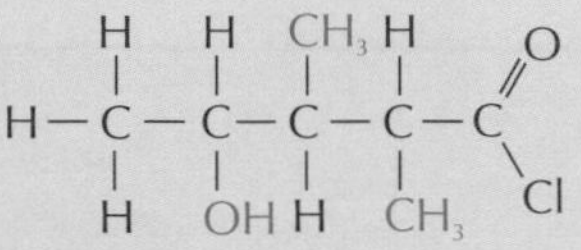

4-hydroxy-2,3-dimethylpentanoyl chloride

The carbon atoms are numbered from the end with the acyl functional group. (This is the same as with carboxylic acids.)

## *Acyl Chlorides Easily **Lose** their **Chlorine***

Acyl chlorides react with...

**...WATER**

A **vigorous** reaction with cold water, producing a **carboxylic acid**.

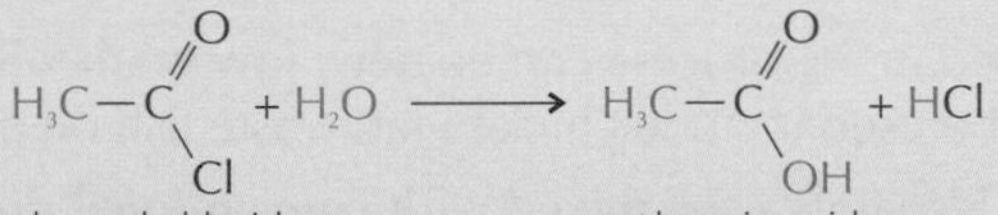

ethanoyl chloride → ethanoic acid

**...ALCOHOLS**

A **vigorous** reaction at room temperature, producing an **ester**.

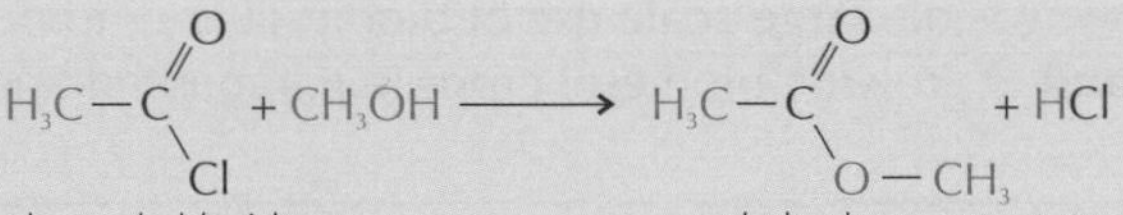

ethanoyl chloride → methyl ethanoate

This irreversible reaction is a much easier, faster way to produce an ester than esterification (page 61).

**...AMMONIA**

A **violent** reaction at room temperature, producing an **amide**.

ethanoyl chloride → ethanamide

See pages 78 to 83 for amines and amides.

**...AMINES**

A **violent** reaction at room temperature, producing an **N-substituted amide**.

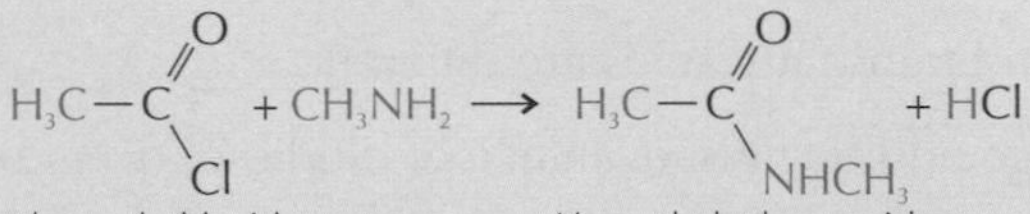

ethanoyl chloride → N-methylethanamide

Each time, **Cl** is **substituted** by an oxygen or nitrogen group and misty fumes of **hydrogen chloride** are given off.

## *Acyl Chlorides and **Acid Anhydrides** React in the Same Way*

***AQA only***

An **acid anhydride** is made from two identical carboxylic acid molecules. If you know the name of the carboxylic acid, they're easy to name — just take away '**acid**' and add '**anhydride**'.

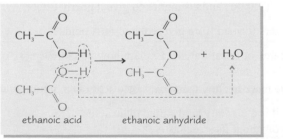

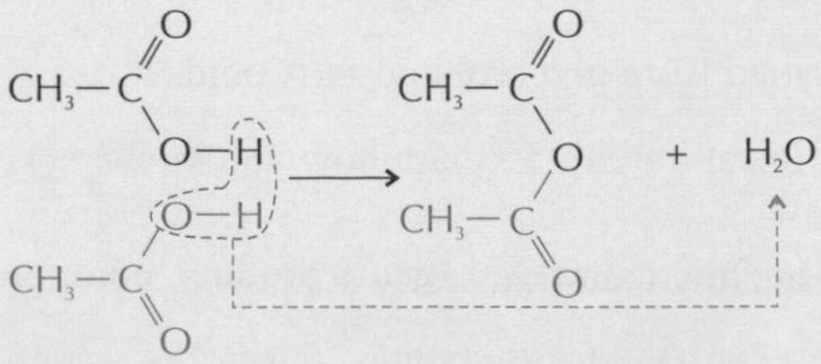

ethanoic acid → ethanoic anhydride

You need to know the reactions of **water**, **alcohol**, **ammonia** and **amines** with acid anhydrides.
Luckily, they're almost the same as those of acyl chlorides — the reactions are just **less vigorous**, and you get a **carboxylic acid** formed instead of HCl:

$$(CH_3CO)_2O_{(l)} + H_2O_{(l)} \rightarrow 2CH_3COOH_{(aq)}$$
ethanoic anhydride + water → 2 × ethanoic acid

$$(CH_3CH_2CO)_2O_{(l)} + NH_{3(aq)} \rightarrow CH_3CH_2CONH_{2(aq)} + CH_3CH_2COOH_{(aq)}$$
propanoic anhydride + ammonia → propanamide + propanoic acid

# Acylation

## Acyl Chloride Reactions are Nucleophilic Addition-Elimination

*AQA only*

In acyl chlorides, both the chlorine and the oxygen atoms draw electrons **towards** themselves, so the carbon has a slight **positive** charge — meaning it's easily attacked by **nucleophiles**.

Here's the mechanism for a **nucleophilic addition-elimination** reaction between ethanoyl chloride and methanol:

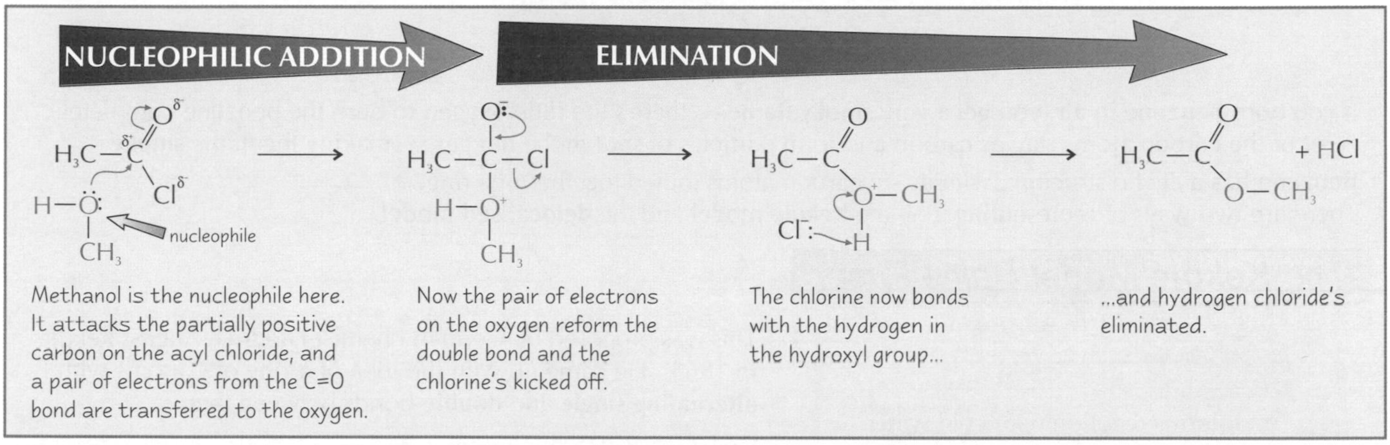

NUCLEOPHILIC ADDITION
ELIMINATION
nucleophile
Methanol is the nucleophile here. It attacks the partially positive carbon on the acyl chloride, and a pair of electrons from the C=O bond are transferred to the oxygen.
Now the pair of electrons on the oxygen reform the double bond and the chlorine's kicked off.
The chlorine now bonds with the hydrogen in the hydroxyl group...
...and hydrogen chloride's eliminated.


The other reactions of acyl chlorides that you need to know all work in exactly the same way.

You just need to change the nucleophile to water ($H_2O$:), ammonia ($\ddot{N}H_3$) or an amine (e.g. $CH_3\ddot{N}H_2$).

## Ethanoic Anhydride is Used for the Manufacture of Aspirin

*AQA only*

**Aspirin** is an **ester** — it's made by reacting **salicylic acid** (which has an alcohol group) with **ethanoic anhydride** or **ethanoyl chloride**.

Ethanoic anhydride is used in industry because:

- it's **cheaper** than ethanoyl chloride.
- it's **safer** to use than ethanoyl chloride as it's **less corrosive**, reacts **more slowly** with water, and **doesn't** produce dangerous **hydrogen chloride** fumes.

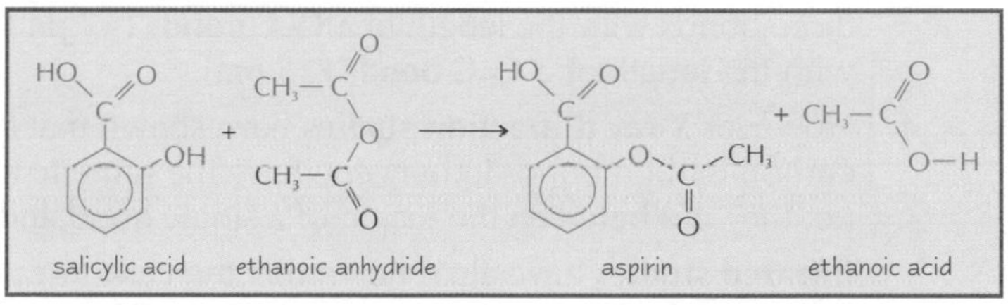

salicylic acid
ethanoic anhydride
aspirin
ethanoic acid


## Practice Questions

Q1 Write the equation for the reaction between ethanoyl chloride and water.

Q2 Write the equation for the reaction between ethanoyl chloride and ammonia.

Q3 Draw the structure of ethanoic anhydride.

Q4 Give two reasons why ethanoic anhydride is preferred to ethanoyl chloride when producing aspirin.

**Exam Questions**

1 Ethanoyl chloride, $CH_3COCl$, and ethylamine, $CH_3CH_2NH_2$, react together at room temperature.

a) Write a balanced equation for this reaction. [1 mark]

b) Draw a mechanism for this reaction. [4 marks]

2 Propanoyl chloride will react vigorously with ethanol at room temperature.

a) Write a balanced equation for this reaction, and name the organic product, compound A, that is formed. [3 marks]

b) Compound A can also be prepared by reacting propanoic acid with ethanol.
Give one advantage of using propanoyl chloride rather than propanoic acid to make compound A. [1 mark]

c) You can also make compound A by reacting propanoic anhydride with ethanol.
Name the other product that is formed during this reaction. [1 mark]

## Why's there no aspirin in the jungle? The paracetamol...

*I could easily lose my mind doing this stuff, let alone a little chlorine particle, and what's worse is I think that all those hydrogen chloride fumes are starting to get to me... I'm feeling kind of dizzy... my head hurts... and all I want to do is lie down and sleep... can't... seem... to... keep... my... eyes... open... zzzzzzzzzzzzzzzzzzzzzzzzzzzzzzzzzzzzzzzzzzzzzzzzz...*

# Benzene

*Yep, it's another section of organic chemistry, I'm afraid — and it kicks off with the beautiful benzene ring.*
***These pages are for AQA (Unit 4), OCR A (Unit 4), OCR B (Unit 5) and Edexcel (Unit 5).***

## Benzene Burns with a **Smoky Flame**

Benzene has the formula $C_6H_6$. It's a **hydrocarbon**, so it burns in oxygen to give carbon dioxide and water:

$$2C_6H_6 + 15O_2 \rightarrow 12CO_2 + 6H_2O$$

If you burn benzene in **air**, you get a very **smoky flame** — there's too little oxygen to burn the benzene completely. A lot of the carbon atoms stay as carbon and form particles of **soot** in the hot gas — making the flame **smoke**.

Benzene has a cyclic structure, with its six carbon atoms joined together in a ring.
There are two ways of representing it — the **Kekulé model** and the **delocalised model**.

## The **Kekulé Model** Came First

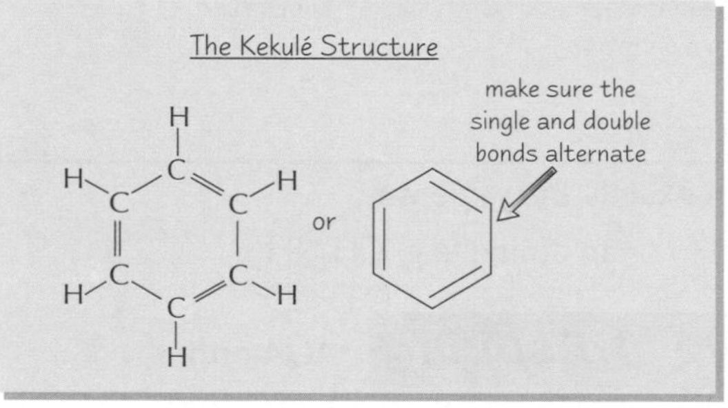


1) This was proposed by German chemist Friedrich August Kekulé in 1865. He came up with the idea of a **ring** of C atoms with **alternating single** and **double** bonds between them.
2) He later adapted the model to say that the benzene molecule was constantly **flipping** between two forms (**isomers**) by switching over the double and single bonds.

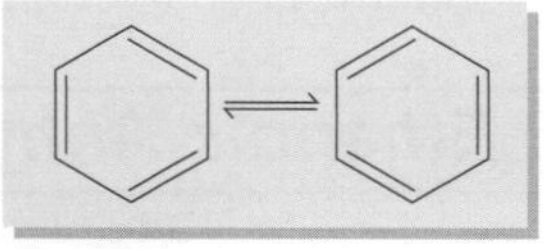

3) If the Kekulé model was correct, you'd expect there to always be three bonds with the length of a **C–C bond** (147 pm) and three bonds with the length of a **C=C bond** (135 pm).
4) However **X-ray diffraction studies** have shown that all the carbon-carbon bonds in benzene have the **same length** of 140 pm — i.e. they are **between** the length of a single bond and a double bond.
   **Infrared studies** have also shown that the carbon-carbon bonds in benzene **aren't** normal double or single bonds because they absorb energy at a **different frequency**.
5) So the Kekulé structure **can't** be completely right, but it's still used today as it's useful for drawing reaction mechanisms.

Apparently Kekulé imagined benzene as a snake catching its own tail. So here's a picture of a man charming some snakes.

## The **Delocalised Model** Replaced Kekulé's Model

The bond-length observations are explained with the delocalised model.

1) The delocalised model says that the **p-orbitals** of all six carbon atoms **overlap** to create **$\pi$-bonds**.
2) This creates two **ring-shaped** clouds of electrons — one above and one below the plane of the six carbon atoms.
3) All the bonds in the ring are the **same length** because all the bonds are the same.
4) The electrons in the rings are said to be **delocalised** because they don't belong to a specific carbon atom. They are represented as a circle inside the ring of carbons rather than as double or single bonds.

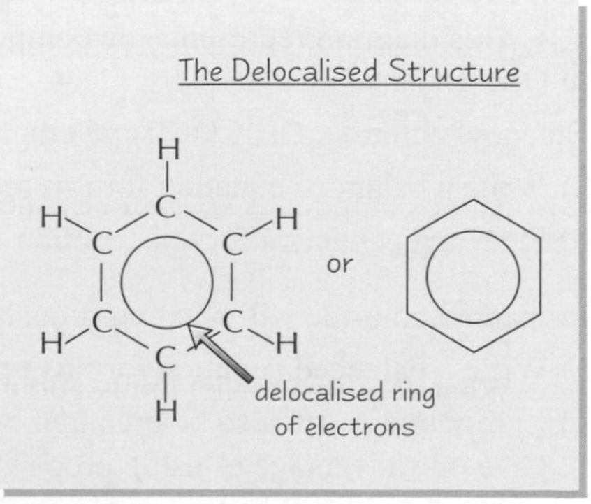


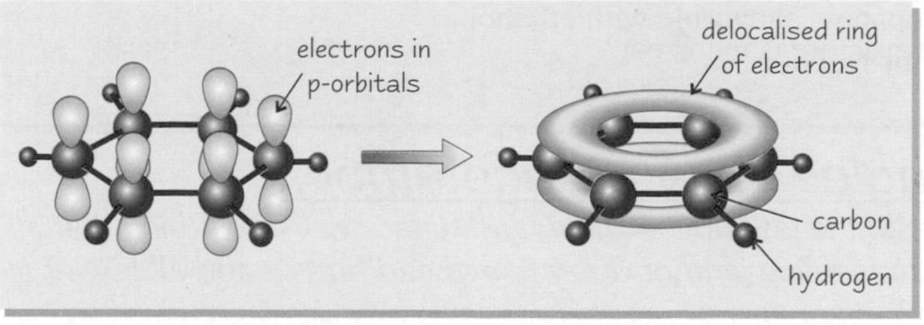


Benzene is a planar (flat) molecule — it's got a ring of carbon atoms with their hydrogens sticking out all on a flat plane.

# Benzene

## Enthalpy Changes Give More Evidence for Delocalisation

1) Cyclohexene has **one** double bond. When it's hydrogenated, the enthalpy change is **–120 kJmol⁻¹**. If benzene had three double bonds (as in the Kekulé structure), you'd expect it to have an enthalpy of hydrogenation of –360 kJmol⁻¹.
2) But the **experimental** enthalpy of hydrogenation of benzene is **–208 kJmol⁻¹** — far **less exothermic** than expected.
3) Energy is put in to break bonds and released when bonds are made. So **more energy** must have been put in to break the bonds in benzene than would be needed to break the bonds in the Kekulé structure.
4) This difference indicates that benzene is **more stable** than the Kekulé structure would be. This is thought to be due to the **delocalised ring of electrons**.

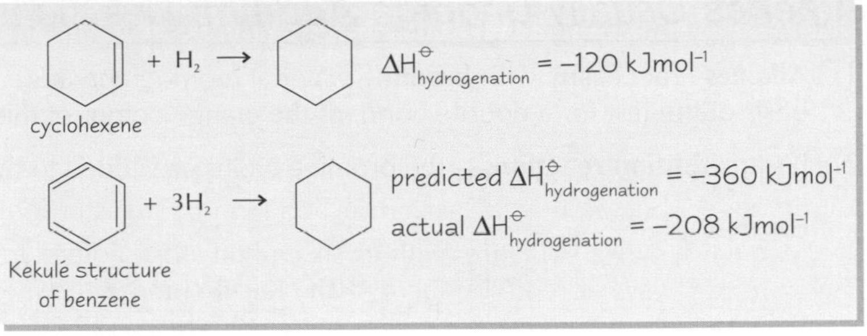


See pages 128-129 for more about enthalpy changes.

## Aromatic Compounds are Derived from Benzene

Compounds containing a **benzene ring** are called **arenes** or **'aromatic compounds'**. Don't be confused by the term 'aromatic' — although some of them are smelly, it's really just a term for compounds that have this structure.
Arenes are **named** in two ways. There's no easy rule — you just have to learn these examples:

Some are named as substituted benzene rings...

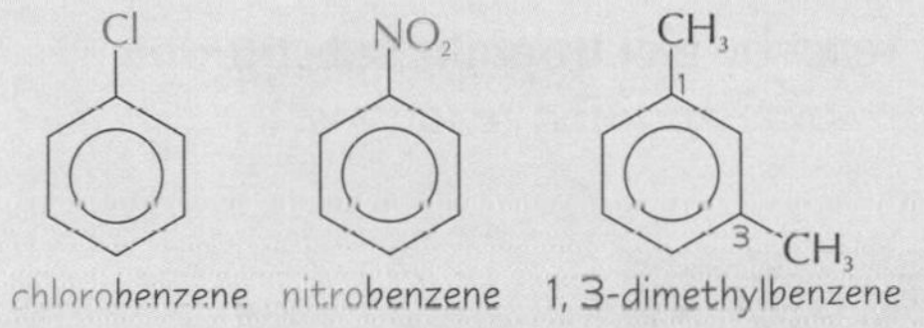


...while others are named as compounds with a phenyl group ($C_6H_5$) attached.

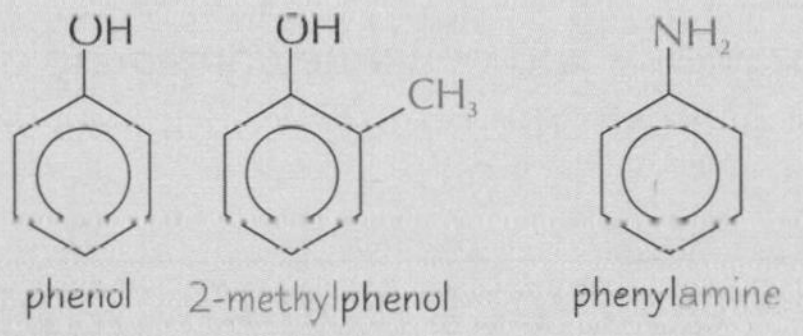


## Practice Questions

Q1 Draw the Kekulé and delocalised models of benzene.

Q2 Give two pieces of evidence for the delocalised electron ring in benzene.

Q3 What type of bonds exist between C atoms in the delocalised model?

**Exam Questions**

1 a) This diagram represents the compound methylbenzene. What is its chemical formula? [1 mark]

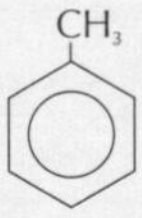


b) What name is given to compounds that contain a ring like this? [1 mark]

c) Name compounds A, B and C, shown on the right. [3 marks]

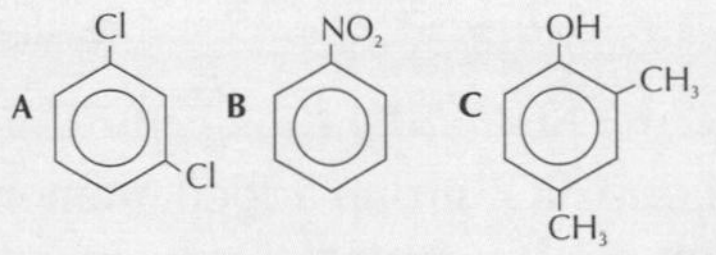

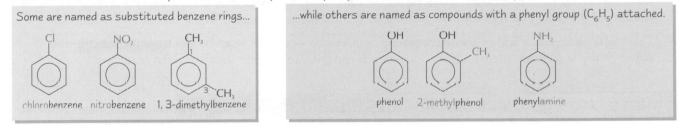

2 a) In 1865, Friedrich Kekulé proposed the structure shown on the right for a benzene molecule. What does this model imply about the carbon-carbon bond lengths in the molecule? [1 mark]

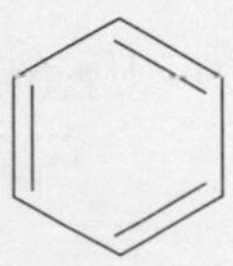

b) What technique has been used to show that the bond lengths suggested by the Kekulé structure are incorrect? [1 mark]

c) How does this technique show that Kekulé's structure is incorrect? [1 mark]

## Everyone needs a bit of stability in their life...

*The structure of benzene is bizarre — even top scientists struggled to find out what its molecular structure looked like. Make sure you can draw all the different representations of benzene given on these pages, including the ones showing the Cs and Hs. Yes, and don't forget that there's a hydrogen at every point on the ring — it's easy to forget they're there.*

# Reactions of Benzene

*Benzene is an alkene but it often doesn't behave like one — whenever this is the case, you can pretty much guarantee that our kooky friend Mr Delocalised Electron Ring is up to his old tricks again...*
***These pages are for AQA (Unit 4), OCR A (Unit 4), OCR B (Unit 5) and Edexcel (Unit 5).***

## *Alkenes* Usually Undergo **Addition** Reactions, but **Benzene's Different**

***OCR A and Edexcel***

1) **Alkenes** react **easily** with **bromine** water at room temperature. The reaction is the basis of the test for a double bond, as the orange colour of the bromine water is lost.
2) It's an **addition reaction** — the bromine atoms are added to the alkene.

   For example:

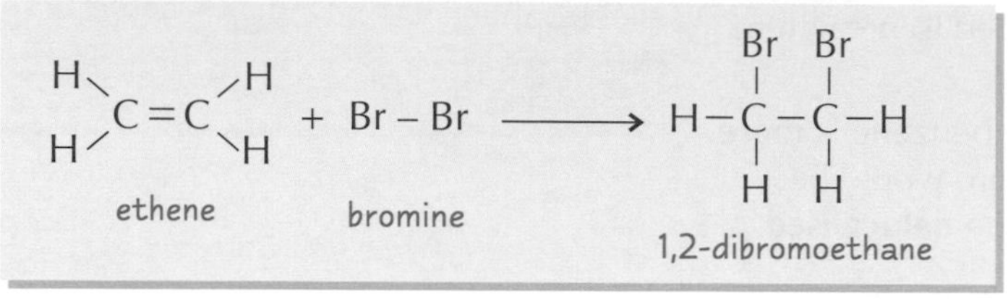

ethene
bromine
1,2-dibromoethane

3) If the Kekulé structure (see page 70) were correct, you'd expect a **similar reaction** between benzene and bromine. In fact, to make it happen you need **hot benzene** and **ultraviolet light** — and it's still a real **struggle**.
4) This difference between benzene and other alkenes is explained by the **delocalised electron rings** above and below the plane of carbon atoms. They make the benzene ring very **stable** by **spreading out** the electrons' negative charge.
5) An addition reaction would need to take electrons from the stable delocalised ring to form **new bonds**. Substitution reactions **don't** do this — a hydrogen atom just gets swapped for something else and the **stability** of the delocalised electrons is preserved. Which makes benzene a happy bunny...
6) That's why benzene — and benzene containing compounds — usually react by **electrophilic substitution**, although if you use extreme enough conditions you can get it to perform some addition reactions.

## Arenes Undergo **Electrophilic Substitution** Reactions...

### ...with **Nitronium Ions** as the Electrophile

When you warm **benzene** with **concentrated nitric** and **sulfuric acids**, you get **nitrobenzene**.
Sulfuric acid's a **catalyst** — it helps to make the nitronium ion, $NO_2^+$, which is the **electrophile**.

$$HNO_3 + H_2SO_4 \rightarrow H_2NO_3^+ + HSO_4^- \Longrightarrow H_2NO_3^+ \rightarrow NO_2^+ + H_2O$$

Remember, **electrophiles** are positively charged ions or polar molecules that are **attracted** to areas of negative charge.

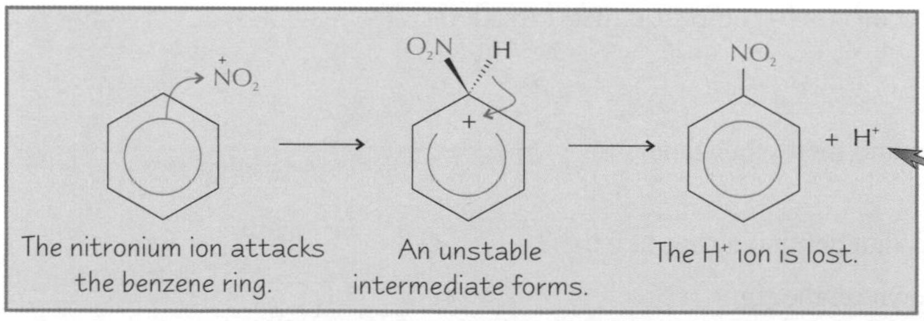

The nitronium ion attacks the benzene ring.
An unstable intermediate forms.
The H⁺ ion is lost.

This $H^+$ ion reacts with $HSO_4^-$ to reform the catalyst, $H_2SO_4$.

If you only want one $NO_2$ group added (**mononitration**), you need to keep the temperature **below 55 °C**. Above this temperature you'll get lots of substitutions.

**Nitration reactions are really useful**

1) Nitro compounds can be **reduced** to form **aromatic amines** (see page 80). These are used to manufacture **dyes** (see page 81) and **pharmaceuticals**.
2) Nitro compounds **decompose violently** when burnt, so they are used as **explosives** — such as 2,4,6-trinitromethylbenzene (**tri**nitro**tol**uene — TNT).

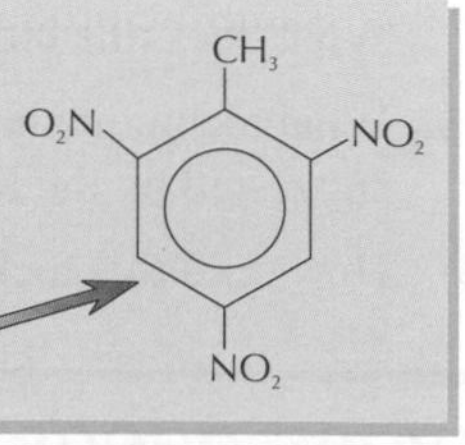

# Reactions of Benzene

## ...and with **Sulfur Trioxide Molecules** as the Electrophile *OCR B and Edexcel*

If you wanted to make **benzenesulfonic acid** (and you never know, one day you might...), you could either:

1) Reflux benzene with **concentrated sulfuric acid** for several hours, or...
2) ...warm benzene to 40 °C with **fuming sulfuric acid** for half an hour.

The electrophile in the reaction is **sulfur trioxide, $SO_3$**...

- Conc. sulfuric acid contains $SO_3$ because it breaks up like this... $H_2SO_4 \rightarrow H_2O + SO_3$
- Fuming sulfuric acid is basically a lot of $SO_3$ molecules dissolved in sulfuric acid. It's much richer in $SO_3$ than conc. sulfuric acid which is why the reaction is quicker and needs less heating.

The mechanism is similar to the one with the $NO_2^+$ electrophile.

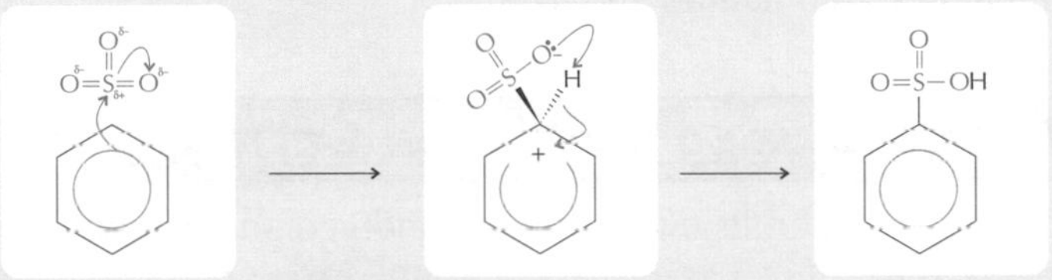

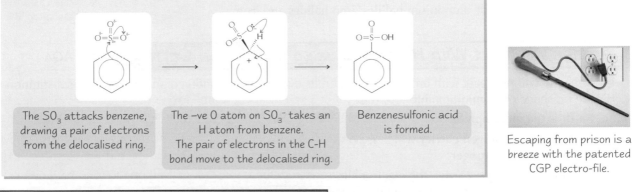

The $SO_3$ attacks benzene, drawing a pair of electrons from the delocalised ring.

The −ve O atom on $SO_3^-$ takes an H atom from benzene. The pair of electrons in the C-H bond move to the delocalised ring.

Benzenesulfonic acid is formed.

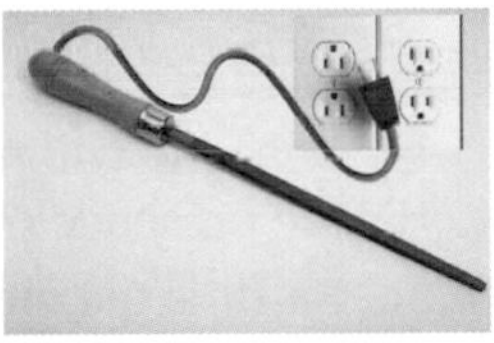

Escaping from prison is a breeze with the patented CGP electro-file.

## Benzene Will Do Some **Addition Reactions** *Edexcel only*

It is possible to add groups to benzene but you have to use really harsh conditions to break that stable delocalised electron system.

1) Benzene reacts with **hydrogen** in the presence of a **Raney nickel catalyst** at **150 °C** to form **cyclohexane**.
2) Benzene reacts with **chlorine** in **ultraviolet light** to form **1,2,3,4,5,6-hexachlorocyclohexane**.

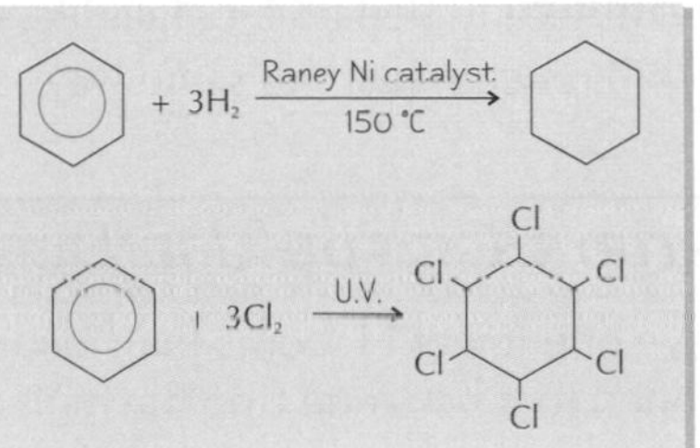


A Raney nickel catalyst has an extremely high surface area.

## Practice Questions

Q1 What type of reaction does benzene prefer to undergo? Explain your answer.

Q2 Name the electrophile formed when sulfuric and nitric acids are mixed.

Q3 What conditions are needed for the hydrogenation of benzene?

### Exam Questions

1 Two electrophilic substitution reactions of benzene are summarised in the diagram:

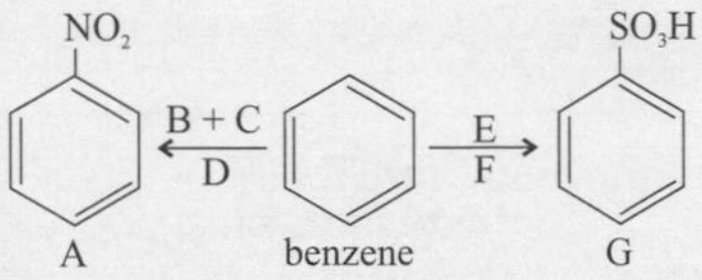


a) i) Name the product A, and the reagents B and C, and give the conditions D. [4 marks]
ii) Outline a mechanism for this reaction. [3 marks]
iii) Write equations to show the formation of the electrophile. [2 marks]

b) i) Name the product G, and the reagent E, and give the conditions F. [3 marks]
ii) What is the electrophile in this reaction? [1 mark]

## One ring to rule them all...

*Arenes really like their delocalised electron ring — it makes them nice and stable, and they don't want to give it up for anything. They much prefer to be involved in electrophilic substitution reactions, as these let them keep their ring intact. But use harsh enough conditions and you can get some things, such as hydrogen and chlorine, added on.*

# More Reactions of Benzene

*If you need a poor electrophile to react with benzene you can turbo boost it with a halogen carrier.*
***These pages are for AQA (Unit 4), OCR A (Unit 4), OCR B (Unit 5) and Edexcel (Unit 5).***

## *Halogen Carriers* Help to Make *Good Electrophiles*

An electrophile has to have a pretty strong **positive charge** to be able to attack the stable benzene ring. Most compounds just **aren't polarised enough** — but some can be made into **stronger electrophiles** using a catalyst called a **halogen carrier**.

A halogen carrier accepts a **lone pair of electrons** from a polar molecule containing a halogen — the electrophile. As the lone pair of electrons is pulled away, the **polarisation** in the electrophile **increases** and sometimes a **carbocation** forms (a carbocation is an organic ion with a positively charged carbon atom). This makes the electrophile loads stronger. Halogen carriers include **aluminium halides**, **iron halides** and **iron**.

$$\overset{\delta+}{R}-\overset{\delta-}{Cl}\!:\dashrightarrow AlCl_3 \longrightarrow R^+ \; AlCl_4^-$$

haloalkane — halogen carrier — carbocation

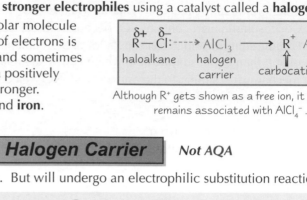

Although $R^+$ gets shown as a free ion, it probably remains associated with $AlCl_4^-$.

## *Arenes will react With* Halogens *using a* Halogen Carrier

***Not AQA***

1) Benzene will not react with bromine, Br–Br, on its own. But will undergo an electrophilic substitution reaction in the presence of aluminium chloride, $AlCl_3$.
2) Br–Br is the **electrophile**.
3) $AlCl_3$ acts as a **halogen carrier** which makes the **electrophile stronger**.
   Without the halogen carrier, the electrophile doesn't have a strong enough positive charge to attack the stable benzene ring.
4) A Br atom is **substituted** in place of a H atom.
5) Chlorine Cl–Cl will react in just the same way.

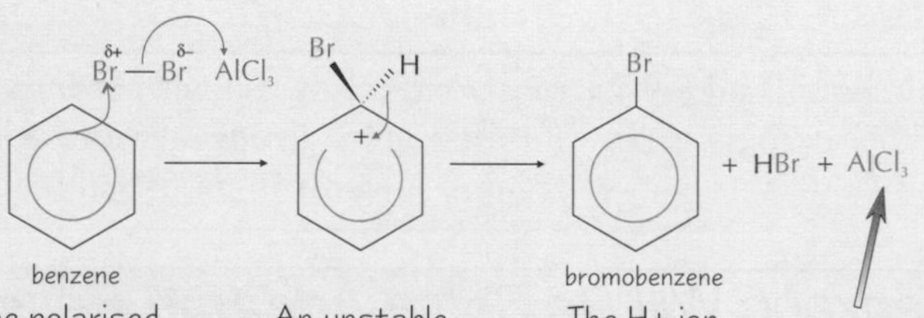

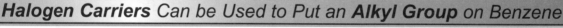

The polarised Br–Br attacks the benzene ring. → An unstable intermediate forms. → The H+ ion is lost. The catalyst is reformed.

## *Halogen Carriers* Can be Used to Put an *Alkyl Group* on Benzene

***OCR B and Edexcel***

1) **Alkyl groups** have one fewer H atoms than alkane molecules, e.g. $CH_3$ is a 'methyl group' — when it's bonded to a benzene ring the molecule is called 'methyl benzene'.
2) Alkyl groups can be substituted for H atoms on benzene rings by refluxing (see page 112) a **chloroalkane** and **benzene** with a **halogen carrier** such as $\mathbf{AlCl_3}$.
   This is how methylbenzene can be made:

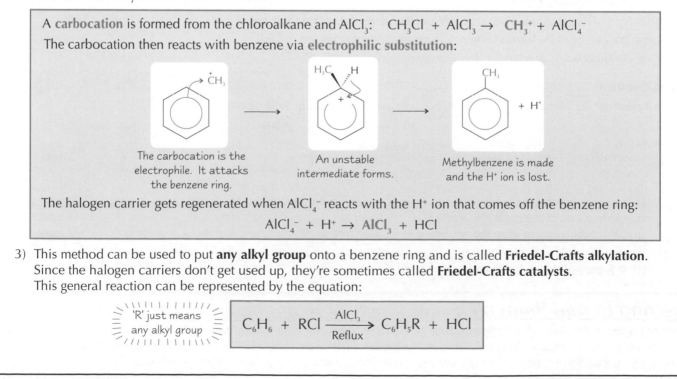

A **carbocation** is formed from the chloroalkane and $AlCl_3$: $CH_3Cl + AlCl_3 \rightarrow CH_3^+ + AlCl_4^-$

The carbocation then reacts with benzene via **electrophilic substitution**:

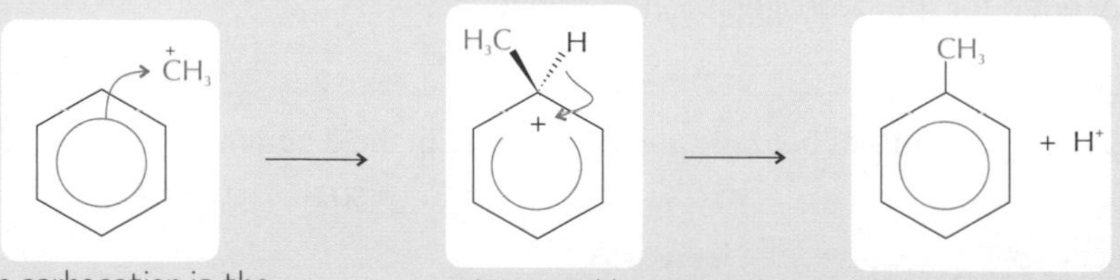


The carbocation is the electrophile. It attacks the benzene ring. → An unstable intermediate forms. → Methylbenzene is made and the $H^+$ ion is lost.

The halogen carrier gets regenerated when $AlCl_4^-$ reacts with the $H^+$ ion that comes off the benzene ring:

$$AlCl_4^- + H^+ \rightarrow AlCl_3 + HCl$$

3) This method can be used to put **any alkyl group** onto a benzene ring and is called **Friedel-Crafts alkylation**. Since the halogen carriers don't get used up, they're sometimes called **Friedel-Crafts catalysts**.
   This general reaction can be represented by the equation:

'R' just means any alkyl group

$$C_6H_6 + RCl \xrightarrow[\text{Reflux}]{AlCl_3} C_6H_5R + HCl$$

# More Reactions of Benzene

## *Halogen Carriers* Can Also Put an *Acyl Group* on Benzene

*Not OCR A*

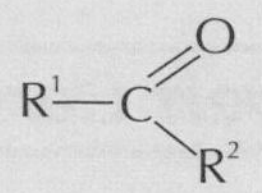

An acyl group. In an acyl chloride, R[1] = Cl.

1) **Acyl groups** contain a **C=O** double bond. They can be substituted for H atoms on benzene using the **Friedel-Crafts** technique — this time by refluxing benzene with an **acyl chloride** instead of a chloroalkane. This produces **phenylketones** (unless R = H, in which case an aldehyde called benzenecarbaldehyde, or benzaldehyde, is formed).
2) There's a different electrophile, but the mechanism is the same as in alkylation:

An **acylium ion** is formed from the acyl chloride and $AlCl_3$: $CH_3COCl + AlCl_3 \rightarrow$ **$CH_3CO^+$** $+ AlCl_4^-$
The acylium ion acts as the **electrophile** and goes on to react with benzene:

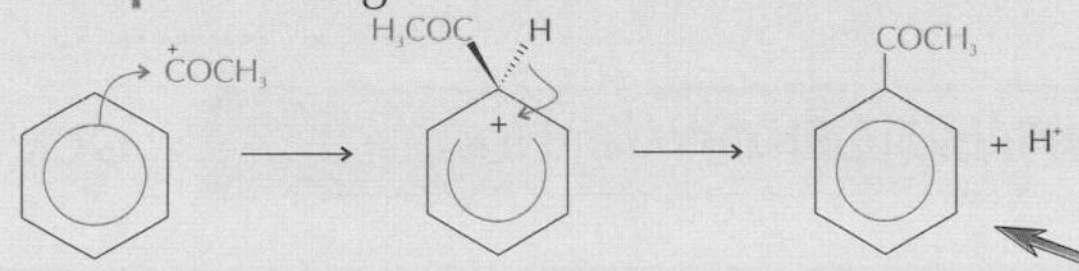

Phenylethanone.

As in the alkylation reaction, $AlCl_3$ then gets regenerated.

## *Ionic Liquids* Can Be Used as an *Alternative* to *Traditional Solvents*

*OCR B only*

**Ionic liquids** are ionic compounds with relatively **low melting points** — usually less than 100 °C. Sometimes, their melting point is so low, they're liquid at **room temperature**. Recently a lot of research has been done on using ionic liquids instead of **organic solvents** in industrial reactions because they have many **environmental advantages**:

- They are **less volatile** and so release **less vapour**.
- They are **less flammable** and often **less toxic**.
- They are easier to re-use and so **reduce waste**.

**Friedel-Crafts** reactions can be performed with ionic liquids called dialkylimidazolium chlorides (don't worry, you don't need to remember this name). $AlCl_3$ is added to form a catalyst-solvent system, which allows reactions to be performed at **lower temperatures** than using traditional solvents, **saving fuel** as well as reducing **pollution**.

## Practice Questions

Q1 Why do compounds such as $AlCl_3$ and $FeBr_3$ help benzene to react with halogens (e.g. $Cl_2$, $Br_2$)?
Q2 What catalysts are used in Friedel-Crafts reactions?
Q3 What could you react benzene with to form methylbenzene?

**Exam Questions**

1 Look at the following synthesis route for manufacturing polystyrene:

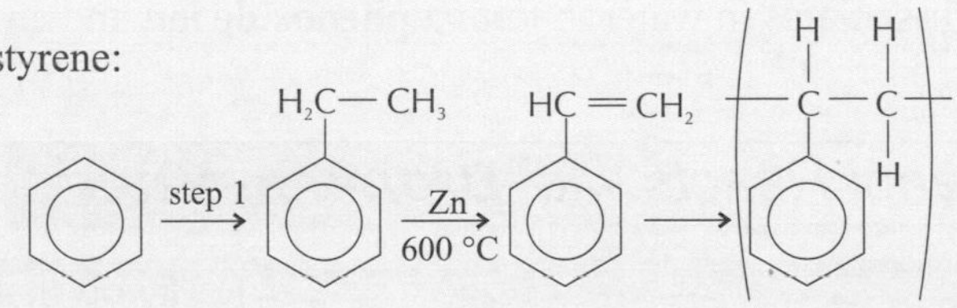


For step 1,
a) Identify the reagent(s) and catalyst(s) required. [2 marks]
b) Outline a mechanism for the reaction, including an equation to show the formation of the electrophile. [4 marks]
c) Explain the role of the catalyst(s) in the reaction. [3 marks]

2 $AlCl_3$ is used as a catalyst in the acylation reaction between benzene and ethanoyl chloride.
a) Draw the structure of the electrophile. [1 mark]
b) Draw a dot-cross diagram of the aluminium chloride molecule, $AlCl_3$. [1 mark]
c) What feature of the molecule makes it possible for $AlCl_3$ to accept $Cl^-$? [1 mark]

## *Sniff, sniff* — is that the sweet smell of exam success?

*OK, lots of reactions here. Sugar-coating it never helped anyone (except perhaps the almond) so I'm just gonna give it to you straight — you do need to know 'em. Fortunately the mechanisms are pretty much along the same lines. I'd make sure you get your head around all that Friedel-Crafts malarkey especially. And be nice to your mum. Two tips for a trouble-free life there.*

# Phenols

*A phenol is the aromatic version of an alcohol. Don't drink them though — they'd get your insides a bit too clean.*
***These pages are for OCR A (Unit 4), OCR B (Unit 4) and Edexcel (Unit 5).***

## Phenols Have Benzene Rings with –OH Groups Attached

Phenol has the formula $C_6H_5OH$.
Other phenols have various groups attached to the benzene ring:

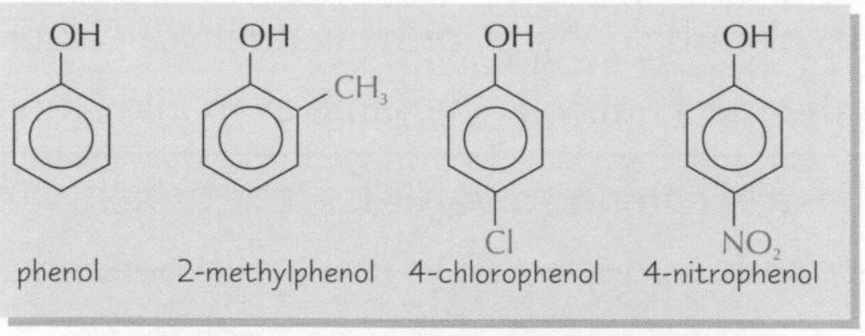


Number the carbons starting from the one with the –OH group.

## Test for Phenols Using Iron(III) Chloride Solution

***OCR B only***

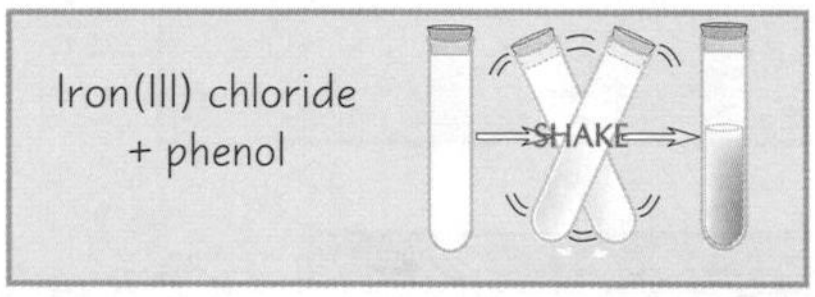


If you add phenol to **iron(III) chloride solution** and shake, you get a **purple** solution. Other phenols give other colours. Great stuff.

## Phenol Reacts with Bases and Sodium to Form Salts

***OCR A and OCR B only***

1) Phenol reacts with **sodium hydroxide solution** at room temperature to form **sodium phenoxide** and **water**.
2) Phenol **doesn't react** with **sodium carbonate** solution though — sodium carbonate is not a strong enough base.
3) **Sodium phenoxide** is also formed when **sodium** metal is added to liquid phenol. **Hydrogen gas** fizzes off this time.

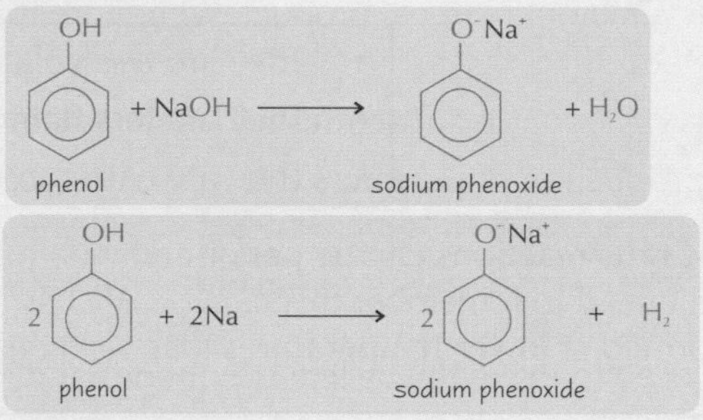


## Phenol Dissolves to Form a Weakly Acidic Solution

***OCR B only***

1) Phenol dissolves a little bit in water, as the hydroxyl group's able to form **hydrogen bonds** with water molecules.
2) The solution formed is **weakly acidic** because phenol dissociates in water to form a **phenoxide ion** and an **$H^+$ ion**:

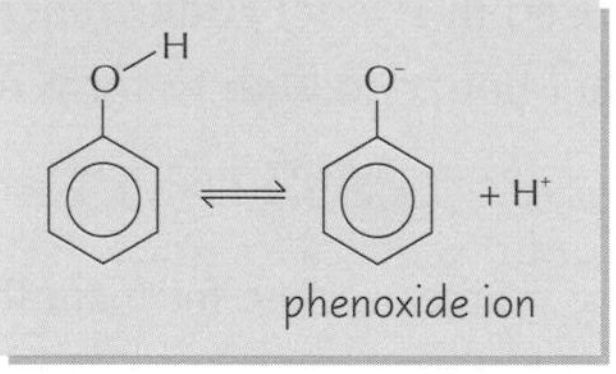


## Phenol Reacts with Bromine Water

***OCR A and Edexcel only***

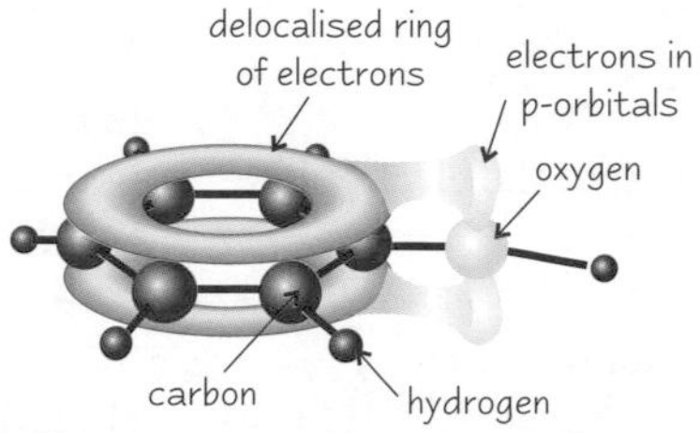


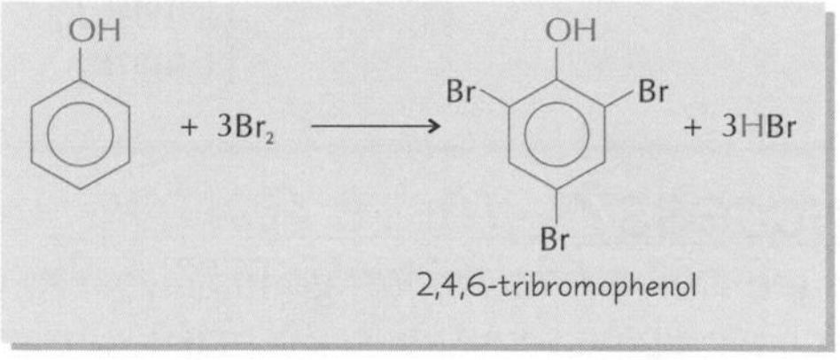

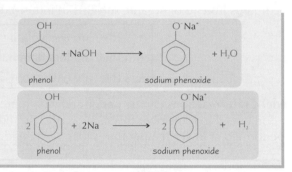

1) If you shake phenol with orange bromine water, it will **react**, **decolorising** it.
2) Benzene **doesn't** react with bromine water (see page 72), so phenol's reaction must be to do with the **OH group**.
3) One of the pairs of electrons in a **p-orbital** of the oxygen atom **overlaps** with the delocalised ring of electrons in the benzene ring.
4) This increases the **electron density** of the ring, especially at positions 2, 4 and 6 (for reasons you don't need to know), making it more likely to be attacked by the bromine molecule in these positions.
5) The hydrogen atoms at 2, 4 and 6 are substituted by bromine atoms — it's an **electrophilic substitution** reaction. The product is called 2,4,6-tribromophenol — it's insoluble in water and **precipitates** out of the mixture. It smells of antiseptic.

# Phenols

## Phenol Can be **Nitrated** Using **Dilute Nitric Acid**

***Edexcel only***

1) Phenol will react with **dilute nitric acid** to give two isomers of nitrophenol, and water.
2) Nitrating phenol is much **easier** than nitrating benzene — that requires **concentrated** nitric and sulfuric acids.
3) The difference is due to the effect of the **OH group** again — which is why you're most likely to get $NO_2$ groups at positions 2 and 4 on the carbon ring.

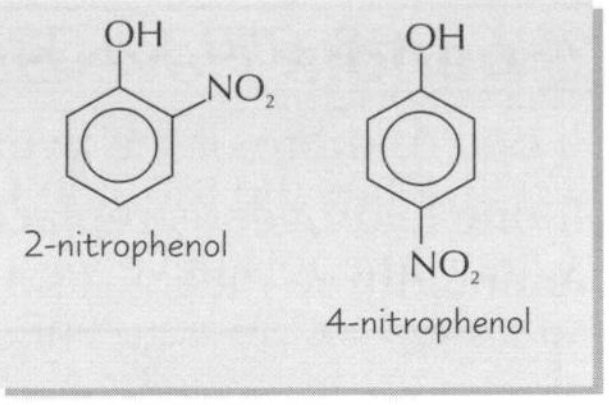


## **Acyl Chlorides** React with Phenols to Form **Esters**

***OCR B only***

The usual way of making an **ester** is to react an alcohol with a carboxylic acid (see page 61).
Phenols react **very** slowly with carboxylic acids though, so it's faster to use an **acyl chloride**, such as ethanoyl chloride.

**Ethanoyl chloride** reacts slowly with phenol at room temperature, producing the ester **phenyl ethanoate** and **hydrogen chloride** gas.

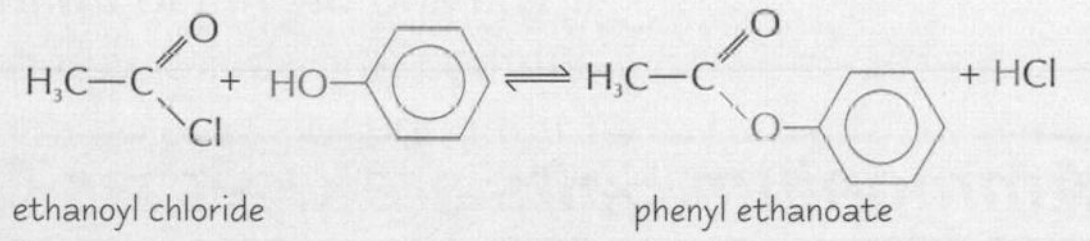

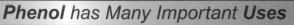

## **Phenol** has Many Important **Uses**

***OCR A only***

Phenol is a major chemical product, with more than 8 million tonnes being produced each year. It's used for:

- the production of **antiseptics** and **disinfectants** such as TCP™.
- the production of **polymers** e.g. KEVLAR® (see page 98) and polycarbonate, which is used in things like bottles, spectacle lenses and CDs.
- the production of **plastics**. **Bakelite**™ was a very early plastic that is a polymer of phenol and formaldehyde. It has good insulating properties and was used to make things like telephones and radio casings.
- Bisphenol A is used in the manufacture of resins called **epoxies**. These have a variety of important uses including **adhesives** and **paints**.

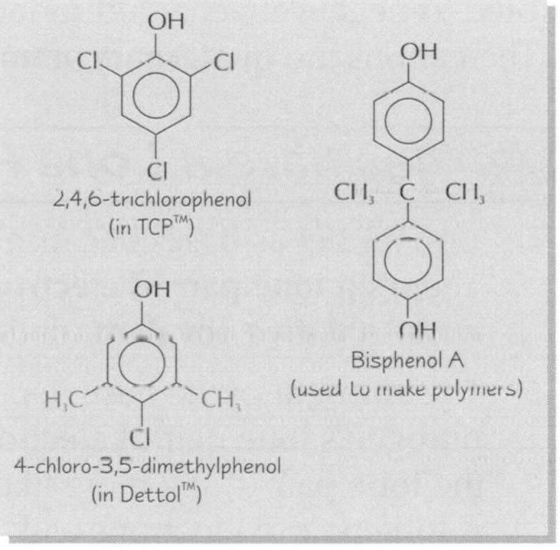


## Practice Questions

Q1 Draw the structures of phenol, 4-chlorophenol and 4-nitrophenol.
Q2 Write a balanced equation for the reaction between phenol and sodium hydroxide solution.
Q3 Write a balanced equation for the reaction between phenol and bromine.
Q4 Give three uses of phenol.

**Exam Questions**

1 a) Draw the structure of 2-methylphenol. [1 mark]
b) Write an equation for the reaction of 2-methylphenol with sodium. [1 mark]
c) 1 mole of gas occupies 24 $dm^3$ at room temperature and pressure.
What mass of 2-methylphenol would you need to produce 4.8 $dm^3$ of hydrogen, at room temperature and pressure, by reaction with excess sodium? [3 marks]

2 a) Bromine water can be used to distinguish between benzene and phenol.
Describe what you would observe in each case. [2 marks]
b) Name the product formed when phenol reacts with bromine water. [1 mark]
c) Explain why phenol reacts differently from benzene. [2 marks]
d) What type of reaction occurs between phenol and bromine? [1 mark]

## Phenol Destination 4 — more chemicals, more equations, more horror...

*You might not like this phenol stuff, but if you were a germ, you'd like it even less. If you're ever looking for TCP™ in the supermarket, try asking for a bottle of 2,4,6-trichlorophenol and see what you get — probably a funny look. Anyway, no time for shopping — you've got to get these pages learned. If you can do all the questions above, you're well on your way.*

# Amines

*If, like me, you thought an amine was a type of Japanese cartoon it's not – it's a nitrogen containing functional group.*
***These pages are for AQA (Unit 4), OCR A (Unit 4), OCR B (Unit 4) and Edexcel (Unit 5).***

## Amines are Organic Derivatives of **Ammonia**

If one or more of the **hydrogens** in **ammonia** ($NH_3$) is replaced with an organic group, you get an **amine**.
If **one** hydrogen is **replaced** with an organic group, you get a **primary amine** — if **two** are replaced, it's a **secondary amine**, **three** means it's a **tertiary amine** and if all **four** are replaced it's called a **quaternary ammonium ion.**

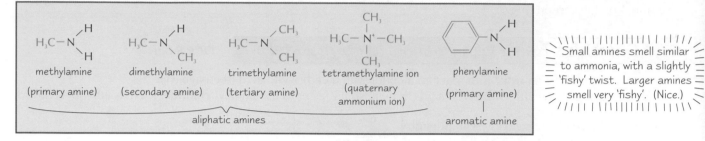

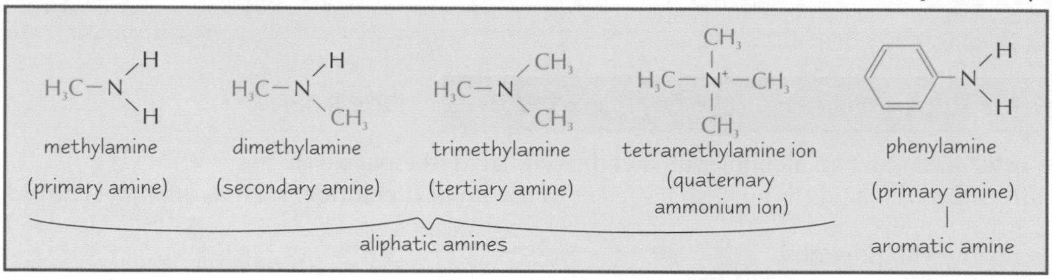


Small amines smell similar to ammonia, with a slightly 'fishy' twist. Larger amines smell very 'fishy'. (Nice.)

## **Quaternary Ammonium Salts** are Used as **Cationic Surfactants**

***AQA only***

**Quaternary ammonium salts** are used in things like fabric conditioner and hair products as **cationic surfactants** — they contain cations (positive ions) which bind to negatively charged surfaces such as hair and fibre, getting rid of **static**. The cations are **quaternary ammonium ions** with long hydrocarbon chains.

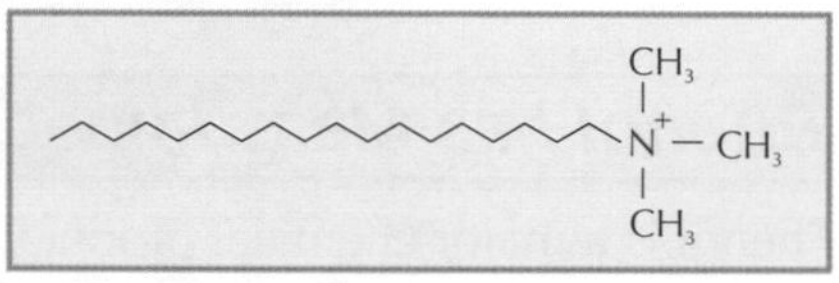

## Amines have a **Lone Pair of Electrons** that can Form **Dative Covalent Bonds**

***AQA and OCR A***

1) Amines act as **bases** because they **accept protons**. There's a **lone pair of electrons** on the **nitrogen** atom that forms a **dative covalent (coordinate) bond** with an $H^+$ ion.

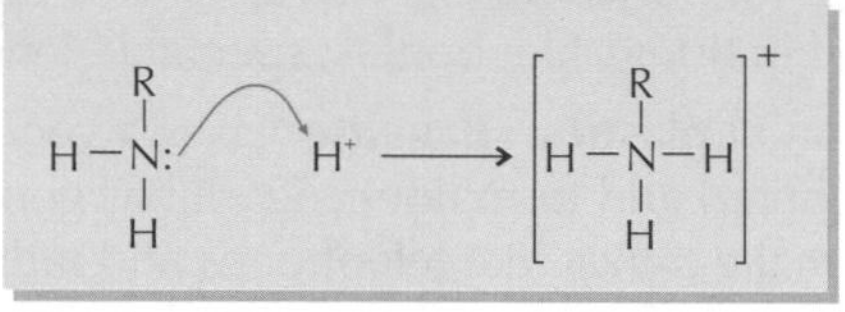

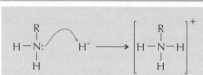

2) The **strength** of the **base** depends on how **available** the nitrogen's lone pair of electrons is. The more **available** the **lone pair** is, the more likely the amine is to **accept a proton**, and the **stronger** a base it will be. A **lone pair** of electrons will be **more available** if its **electron density** is **higher**.
3) **Primary aliphatic amines** are **stronger** bases than **ammonia**, which is a **stronger** base than **aromatic amines**.

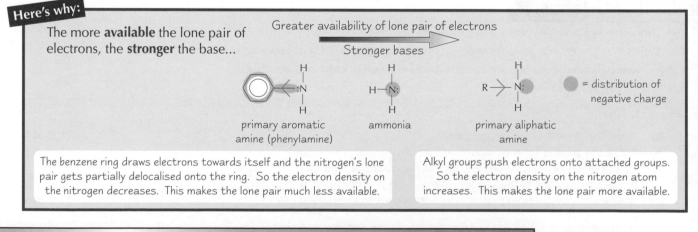

**Here's why:**

The more **available** the lone pair of electrons, the **stronger** the base...

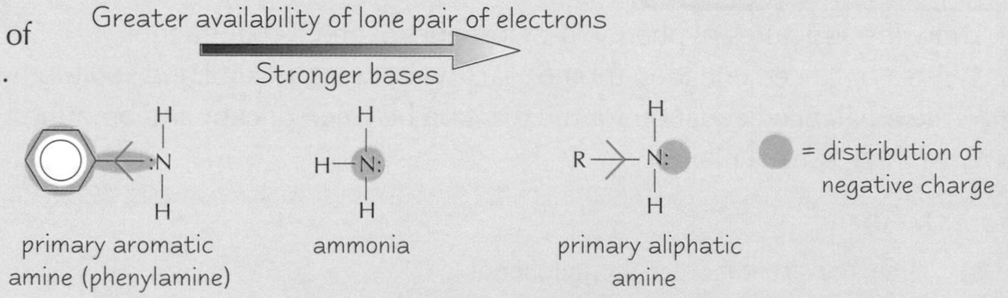


The benzene ring draws electrons towards itself and the nitrogen's lone pair gets partially delocalised onto the ring. So the electron density on the nitrogen decreases. This makes the lone pair much less available.

Alkyl groups push electrons onto attached groups. So the electron density on the nitrogen atom increases. This makes the lone pair more available.

## Small Amines **Dissolve** in Water to form an **Alkaline** Solution

***Edexcel only***

1) Small amines are **soluble in water** — the amine group forms **hydrogen bonds** with the water molecules. The **bigger** the amine, the **greater** the **van der Waals** forces between the amine molecules, and the less soluble it is.

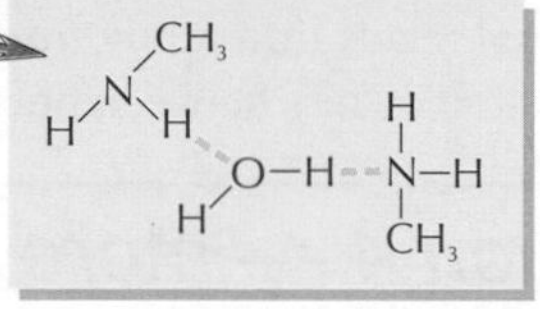

2) If they do dissolve, they form **alkaline** solutions — a hydrogen is taken from water, forming **alkyl ammonium ions** and **hydroxide ions**.

$$CH_3CH_2NH_{2(aq)} + H_2O_{(l)} \rightleftharpoons CH_3CH_2NH_3^+{}_{(aq)} + OH^-_{(aq)}$$

# Amines

## ***Aliphatic Amines** are made from **Haloalkanes** or **Nitriles***

*AQA and OCR A*

There are **two** ways to produce aliphatic amines — either from **haloalkanes** or by **reducing nitriles**. The method for producing **aromatic amines** is different again — as you'll see on the next page.

### YOU CAN HEAT A HALOALKANE WITH AMMONIA

Amines can be made by heating a **haloalkane** with **ammonia**.

E.g.

$$NH_3 + CH_3CH_2Br \longrightarrow CH_3CH_2NH_2 + HBr$$

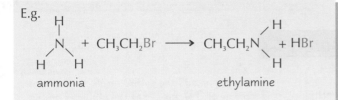

ammonia → ethylamine

You'll get a **mixture** of primary, secondary and tertiary amines, and quaternary ammonium salts, as more than one hydrogen is likely to be substituted.

You can separate the products using **fractional distillation**.

You need to know the mechanism for this reaction:

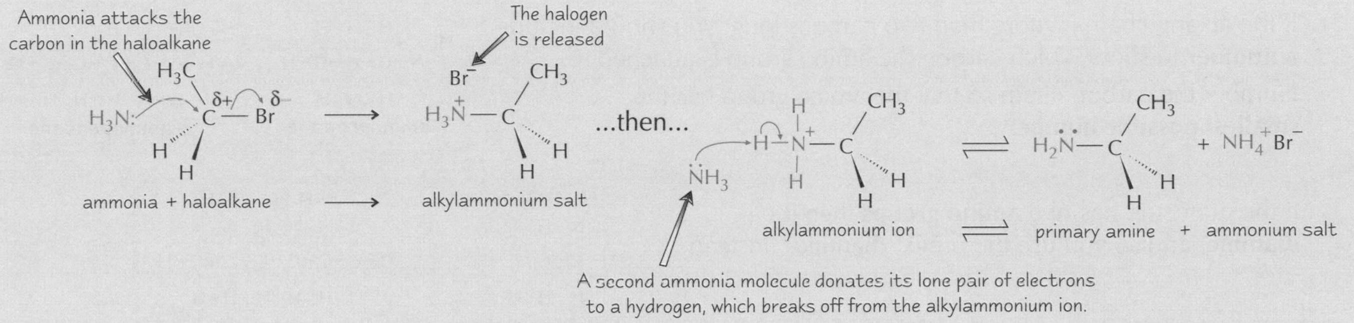


As long as there's some more of the haloalkane, **further substitutions** can take place. They keep happening until you get a **quaternary ammonium salt**, which can't react any further as it has no lone pair of electrons.

Amines undergo the same mechanism as ammonia (see above).

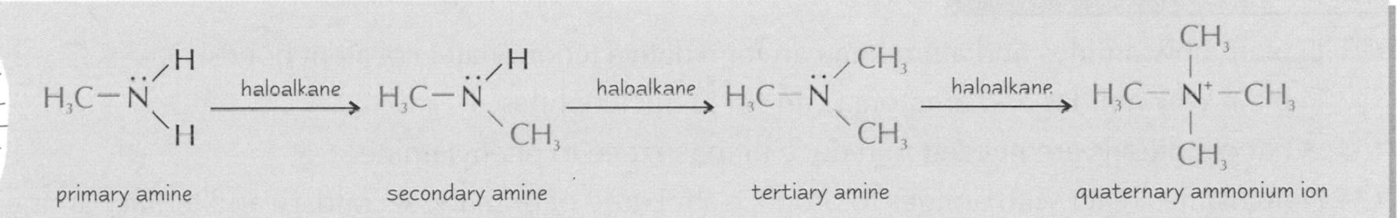


### OR YOU CAN REDUCE A NITRILE

*AQA only*

You can reduce a nitrile to an amine using $LiAlH_4$ in **dry diethyl ether**, followed by some **dilute acid**. Another way is to reflux the nitrile with **sodium** metal and **ethanol**.

E.g.

$$CH_3C{\equiv}N + 4[H] \xrightarrow[\text{(2) dilute acid}]{\text{(1) } LiAlH_4\text{, dry diethyl ether}} CH_3CH_2NH_2$$

ethanenitrile → ethylamine

Becky was reduced to tears by lithium aluminium hydride.

These are great in the lab, but $LiAlH_4$ and sodium are too **expensive** for industrial use.

Industry uses a **metal catalyst** such as platinum or nickel at a high temperature and pressure — it's called **catalytic hydrogenation**.

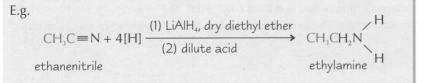

$$CH_3C{\equiv}N + 2H_2 \xrightarrow[\text{high temp. \& pressure}]{\text{Ni}} CH_3CH_2NH_2$$

ethanenitrile → ethylamine

# Amines

## *Aromatic* Amines are made by *Reducing* a *Nitro Compound*

**Not OCR B**

Aromatic amines are produced by **reducing** a nitro compound e.g. **nitrobenzene**. There are **two steps** to the method:

1) First you need to heat a mixture of a **nitro compound**, **tin metal** and **concentrated hydrochloric acid** under **reflux** — this makes a salt. For example, if you use nitrobenzene, the salt formed is $C_6H_5NH_3^+Cl^-$.
2) Then to turn the salt into an **aromatic amine**, you need to add an alkali, such as **sodium hydroxide** solution.

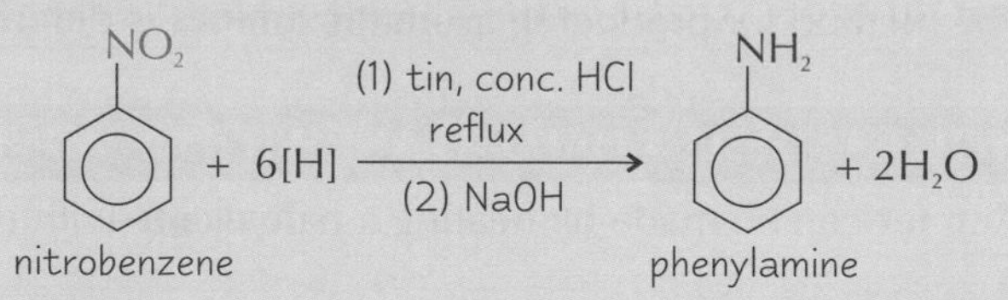

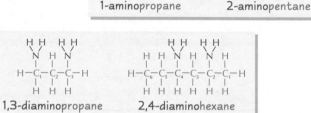

## You Can *Name Amines* Using the Prefix *'Amino-'*

1) To name a **primary amine** all you need to do is find and name the **longest alkane chain** in the molecule, and add '**amino-**' to the front.

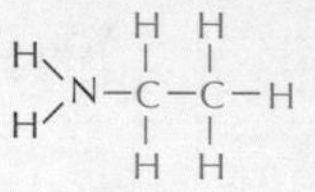

aminoethane

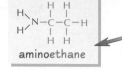

Or you can add the suffix '-amine' to the name of the alkyl group — see the examples on the previous two pages. So this is also ethylamine.

2) If the alkane chain is more than two carbons long, you should include a **number** to show which carbon the amino group is attached to. Number the carbon chain so that the amino group has the **smallest possible number**.

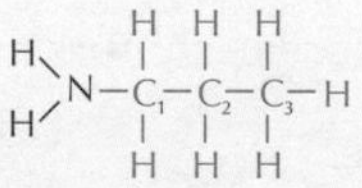

1-aminopropane

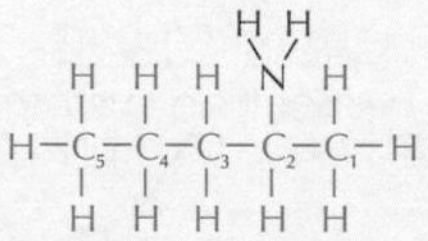

2-aminopentane

3) If the molecule has **two amino groups** then it's a **diamine**, and so you use the prefix '**diamino-**' instead.

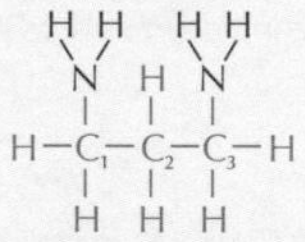

1,3-diaminopropane

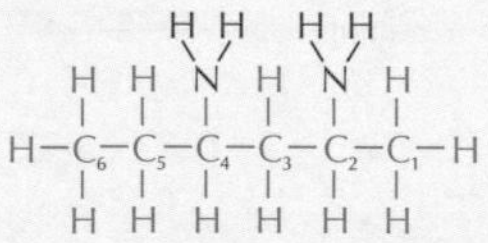

2,4-diaminohexane

## Practice Questions

Q1 Explain how amines and ammonia can form dative (coordinate) covalent bonds.

Q2 Explain why amines and ammonia can act as nucleophiles.

Q3 What conditions are needed to reduce nitrobenzene to phenylamine?

Q4 Haloalkanes react with amines to produce a mixture of primary, secondary and tertiary amines. How can they be separated?

**Exam Questions**

1 a) Explain how methylamine, $CH_3NH_2$, can act like a base. [1 mark]

b) Methylamine is a stronger base than ammonia, $NH_3$. However, phenylamine, $C_6H_5NH_2$, is a weaker base than ammonia. Explain these differences in base strength. [4 marks]

2 The reaction between an amine and a haloalkane produces a mixture of products.

a) Write an equation for the formation of a quaternary ammonium salt from ethylamine and bromomethane. [2 marks]

b) What condition would help to ensure that the quaternary ammonium salt would be a major product? [1 mark]

c) Name a use for quaternary ammonium salts. [1 mark]

3 a) Propylamine can be synthesised from bromopropane. Suggest a disadvantage of this synthesis route. [1 mark]

b) Propylamine can also be synthesised from propanenitrile.

i) Suggest suitable reagents for its preparation in a laboratory. [2 marks]

ii) Why is this method not suitable for industrial use? [1 mark]

iii) What reagents and conditions are used in industry? [2 marks]

## You've got to learn it — amine it might come up in your exam...

*Rotting fish smells so bad because the flesh releases diamines as it decomposes. Is it fish that smells of amines or amines that smell of fish — it's one of those chicken or egg things that no one can answer. Well, enough philosophical pondering — we all know the answer to the meaning of life. It's A2 chemistry. Now make sure you can do all the questions above.*

# Reactions of Amines

*If you're not sure what you can do with an amine once you've got one, the next few pages should help.*
***These pages are for OCR A (Unit 4), OCR B (Units 4 and 5) and Edexcel (Unit 5).***

## Amines React with **Acids** to Form **Salts**

Amines are **neutralised** by **acids** to make an **ammonium salt**.
For example, **ethylamine** reacts with **hydrochloric** acid to form ethylammonium chloride:

$$CH_3CH_2NH_2 + HCl \rightarrow CH_3CH_2NH_3^+Cl^-$$

## **Aromatic Amines** are Used to Make **Azo Dyes**

1) Azo dyes are man-made dyes that contain the **azo group**, **–N=N–**.
2) In most azo dyes, the azo group links **two aromatic groups**.
3) Having two aromatic groups creates a very **stable molecule** — the azo group becomes part of the **delocalised electron system**.
4) The **colours** are the result of **light absorption** by the delocalised electron system. Different **colours** are made by combining different phenols and amines (see below).

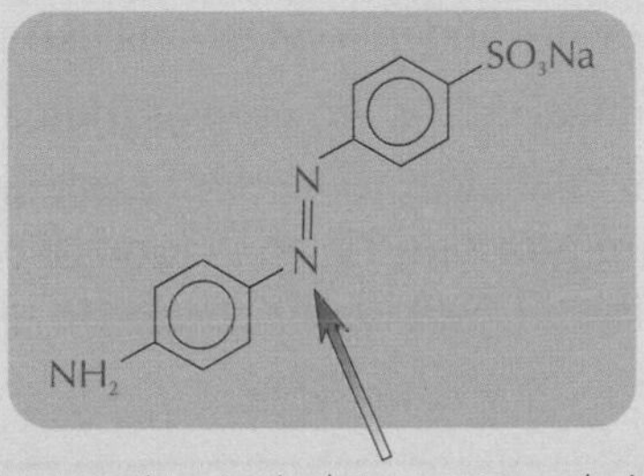

Methyl orange is a typical azo compound with the azo group **-N=N-** linking **two aromatic groups**.

## **Azo Dyes** can be made in a **Coupling** Reaction

The first step in creating an azo dye is to make a **diazonium salt** — diazonium compounds contain the group $-\overset{+}{N}\equiv N-$.
The **azo dye** is then made by **coupling** the diazonium salt with an **aromatic** compound that is susceptible to **electrophilic attack** — like a **phenol**.

Here's the method for creating a yellow-orange azo dye:

### React **Phenylamine** with **Nitrous Acid** to make a **Diazonium Salt**

1) **Nitrous acid ($HNO_2$)** is **unstable**, so it has to be made ***in situ*** from sodium nitrite and hydrochloric acid.

'in situ' means 'in the reaction'

$$NaNO_2 + HCl \rightarrow HNO_2 + NaCl$$

2) **Nitrous acid** reacts with **phenylamine** and **hydrochloric acid** to form **benzenediazonium chloride**. The temperature **must** be below **10 °C** to prevent a phenol forming instead.

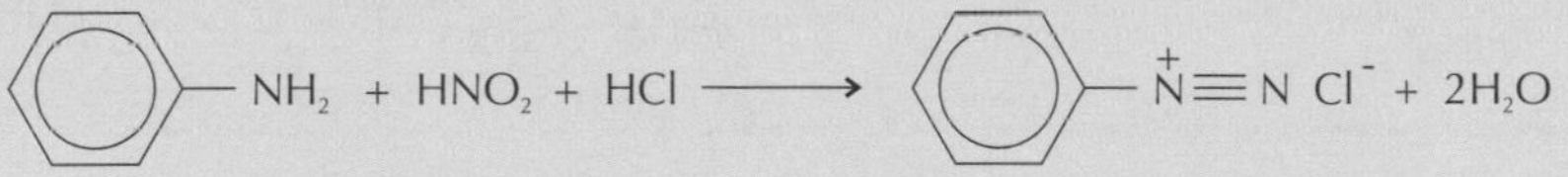

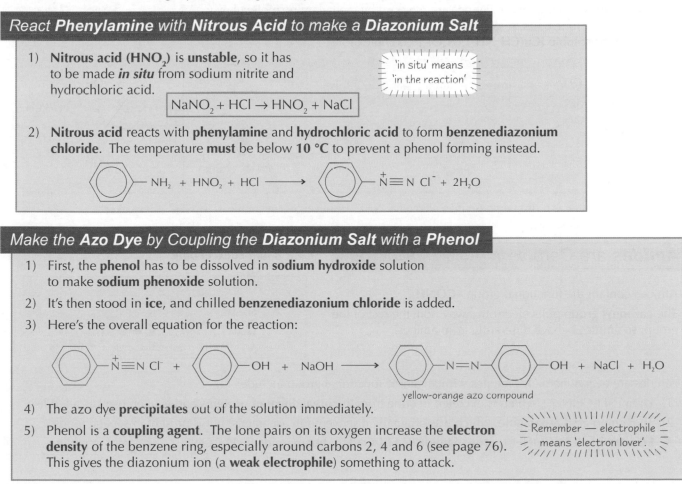

### Make the **Azo Dye** by Coupling the **Diazonium Salt** with a **Phenol**

1) First, the **phenol** has to be dissolved in **sodium hydroxide** solution to make **sodium phenoxide** solution.
2) It's then stood in **ice**, and chilled **benzenediazonium chloride** is added.
3) Here's the overall equation for the reaction:

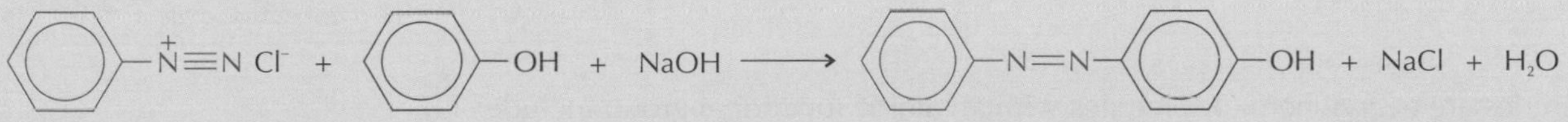

yellow-orange azo compound

4) The azo dye **precipitates** out of the solution immediately.
5) Phenol is a **coupling agent**. The lone pairs on its oxygen increase the **electron density** of the benzene ring, especially around carbons 2, 4 and 6 (see page 76). This gives the diazonium ion (a **weak electrophile**) something to attack.

Remember — electrophile means 'electron lover'.

# Reactions of Amines

## Azo Dyes are used in Food, Textiles and Paints

Some azo dyes have been linked to the condition "clown child".

1) Azo dyes produce **bright**, **vivid** colours, most of them in the **yellow** to **red spectrum**, though many other colours are possible too. Azo dyes make up about 70% of all dyes used in food and textiles.
2) Many azo dyes are used as **food colourings** (and have corresponding E numbers). Examples include tartrazine (E102), yellow 2G (E107), allura red (E129) and brilliant black BN (E151), but there are many, many more.
3) Because the molecules are very **stable**, azo dyes provide **lightfast** (i.e. strong light won't fade them), **permanent** colours for clothing.
4) They are added to materials like clay to produce **paint pigments**.
5) Some azo dyes are used as **indicators**, e.g. methyl orange, because they change colour at different pHs.
6) In recent years there has been **concern** about the use of **artificial additives** in food. Some azo compounds that were previously used in foods have since been **banned** for health reasons — enzymes in the body can break some of them down to produce **toxic** or **carcinogenic** compounds. Others have been linked to **hyperactivity** in children.

## Amines will Form a Complex Ion with Copper(II) Ions

***Edexcel only***

Complex ions are covered in detail on page 156.

1) In **copper(II) sulfate** solution, the $Cu^{2+}$ ions form $\mathbf{[Cu(H_2O)_6]^{2+}}$ complexes with water. The solution is **blue**.
2) If you add a **small** amount of **methylamine solution** to copper(II) sulfate solution you get a **pale blue precipitate** — the amine acts as a **Brønsted-Lowry base** (proton acceptor) and takes two $\mathbf{H^+}$ ions from the complex. This leaves copper hydroxide, $\mathbf{[Cu(H_2O)_4(OH)_2]}$, which is insoluble.
3) Add more methylamine solution, and the **precipitate dissolves** to form a beautiful **deep blue solution**. Some of the ligands are replaced by methylamine molecules, which donate their lone pairs to form dative covalent (coordinate) bonds with the $Cu^{2+}$ ion. This forms soluble $\mathbf{[Cu(CH_3NH_2)_4(H_2O)_2]^{2+}}$ complex ions.

See page 177 for more on ligand exchange reactions.

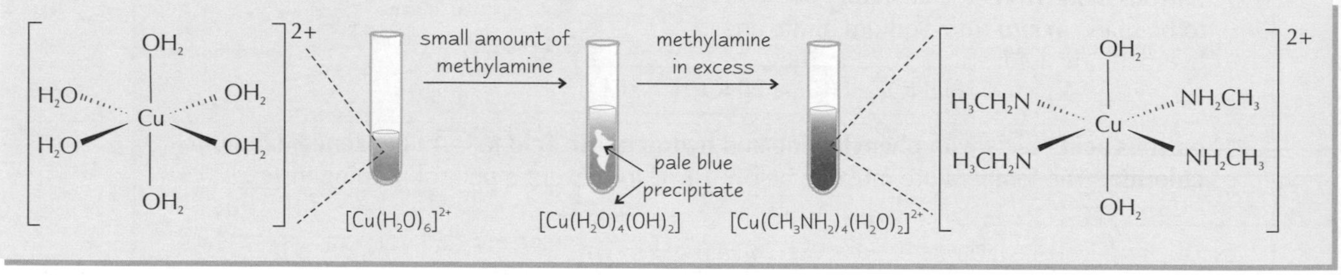


## Amides are Carboxylic Acid Derivatives

***OCR B and Edexcel only***

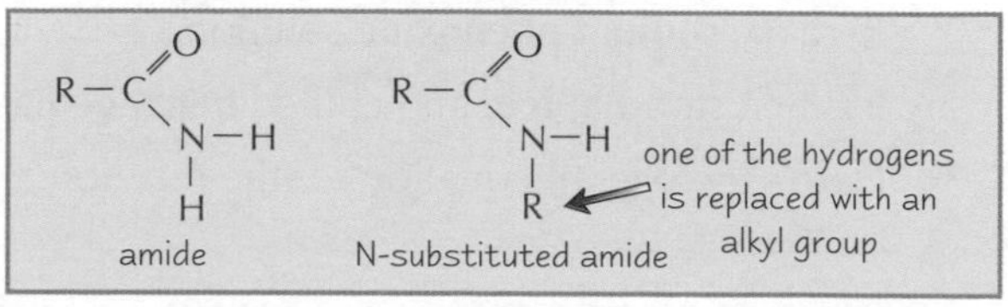


Amides contain the functional group **–CONH₂**.

The **carbonyl group** pulls electrons away from the rest of the group, so amides behave differently from amines.

Amides are everywhere. Molecules with an amide functional group include:

1) **Urea** ($NH_2CONH_2$), which is excreted in urine from the **breakdown of proteins** and is often used as a fertiliser.
2) The amino acid **asparagine**, which was originally discovered in asparagus, but is present in several foods.
3) **Ethanamide** ($CH_3CONH_2$), **propanamide** ($C_2H_5CONH_2$), **butanamide** ($C_3H_7CONH_2$)... you get the picture.

# Reactions of Amines

## Amines can be *Acylated* to form *N-substituted Amides*

***OCR B and Edexcel only***

When amines react with acyl chlorides, a **H atom** on the amine is swapped for the **acyl group** R–C(=O) to produce an **N-substituted amide** and **HCl**. The HCl can then react with another molecule of the amine to produce a salt (page 81).

1) In the case of **butylamine** ($C_4H_9NH_2$), the reactions are:

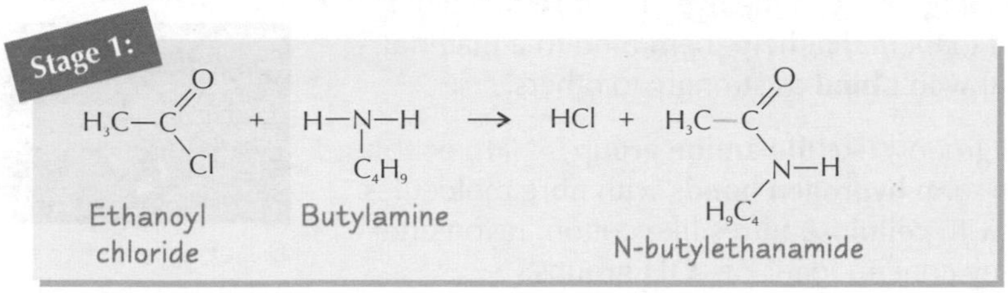


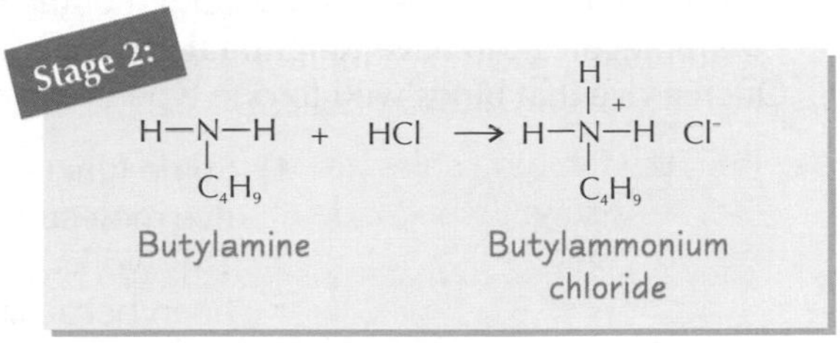


To carry out this reaction, ethanoyl chloride is added to a **concentrated aqueous solution** of the amine. A violent reaction occurs, which produces a **solid, white mixture** of the products.

2) **Phenylamine** ($C_6H_5NH_2$) also reacts with ethanoyl chloride in the same way:

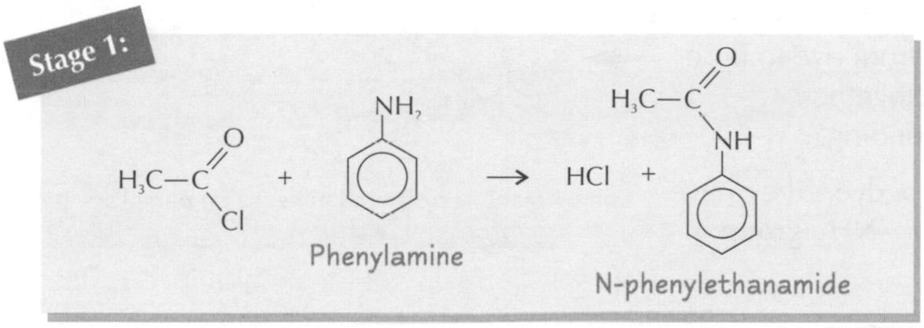


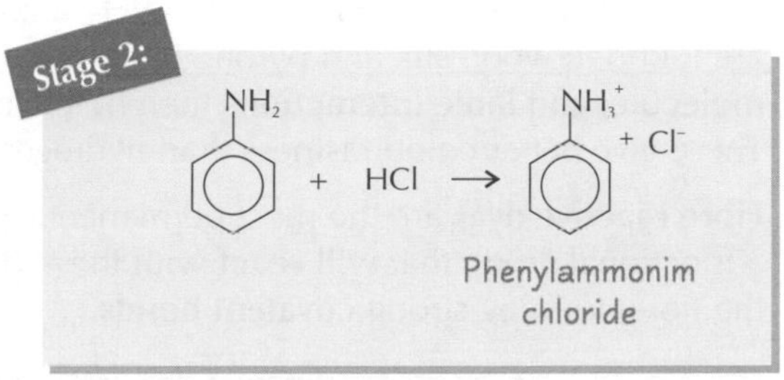


Although the **solid products** of this reaction should be white, they are usually **stained brown** with unreacted phenylamine.

***Edexcel only***

**Paracetamol** can be made by a very similar reaction starting from **p-aminophenol.**

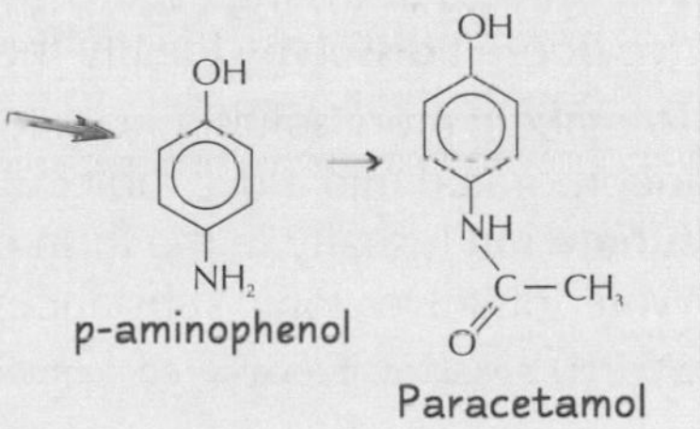


The '**p**' in **p-aminophenol** stands for '**para**'. It means that the two functional groups are directly **opposite** each other on the benzene ring.

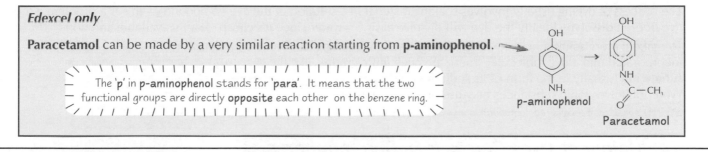

## Practice Questions

Q1 Describe how you would make a diazonium salt.

Q2 What is formed when a diazonium salt reacts with a phenol?

Q3 Describe the reaction of amines with copper(II) ions.

Q4 Describe the preparation of butylammonium chloride.

**Exam Question**

1 Sunset Yellow (E110) is a yellow dye used in orange squash and many foodstuffs.
It has been withdrawn from use in many countries as it has been connected to hyperactivity in children.

a) Which class of dyes does it belong to? [1 mark]

b) Which part of its structure indicates this? [1 mark]

c) Draw the structures of two organic compounds that could be used to produce Sunset Yellow. [2 marks]

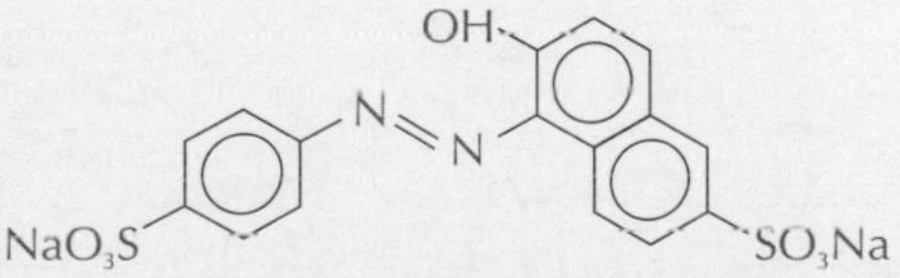

## *I asked Van Gogh if he wanted a drink — He said, "Nah, I've got one ear"...*

*Ok. I realise you might be feeling a little overwhelmed at the prospect of learning all these reactions, but er... don't be. Just break it down into sections and keep going over stuff until you're happy with it — or at least until you've stopped cursing me, the exam board and the good name of amines everywhere. Perhaps you should go and get a biscuit too.*

# More About Azo Dyes

*I'm sure you're dying to read this... ha ha haa. Ah dear. At least I amuse myself.*
***These pages are for OCR B (Unit 5).***

## Dyes have to **Attach** Themselves to Fibres

A good dye has got to be **colourfast** — it can't **wash out** too easily or **fade** in the light. Colourfastness depends on the strength of the **bonding** between the **dye** and **fibre** molecules. Dye molecules can have **functional groups** added to them that help them bind to a material. Often a dye that binds well to one type of material **won't bind** as strongly to others.

Di's attachment to fibre was getting out of hand.

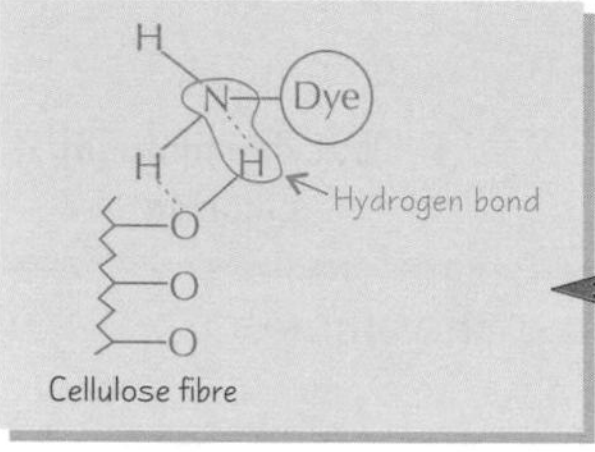


1) Some functional groups, like the **amine group** ($-NH_2$) enable dye molecules to form **hydrogen bonds** with fibre molecules. This works well with **cellulose fibres** like cotton, rayon and linen because they contain loads of **–OH groups**.
   These dyes aren't particularly colourfast because the hydrogen bonds just aren't strong enough.
2) Acidic groups like **carboxylic acid** (–COOH) or **sulfonic acid** ($-SO_3H$) help dyes bind to alkaline **–NH– links** in fibres — these links are found in wool, silk and nylon. **$H^+$ ions** move from dye to fibre molecule, and **ionic interactions** then hold them together. These give better colourfastness than hydrogen bonding.

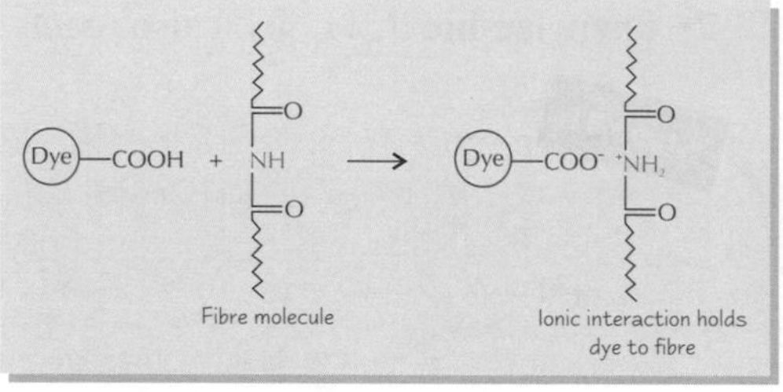


3) **Fibre reactive dyes** are the most permanent type of dye. They have a functional group that will **react** with the **–OH** or **–NH– group** in the fibre, forming strong **covalent bonds**.

## Many Dyes Need to be **Water Soluble**

The process of dyeing usually involves soaking material in a solution of the dye compound — this is a problem if the dye doesn't **dissolve**. Ideally the dye will dissolve easily in **water** since it's cheap, readily available and non-toxic.

To make it more soluble in water, **solubilising functional groups** can be incorporated into a dye molecule. These are often **ionic groups**, like the **sulfate ion** (usually in the form of its **sodium salt**) shown on the right. Water dissolves ionic substances because of its **polar nature**.

Strictly speaking, if a coloured compound is insoluble it's a pigment rather than a dye.

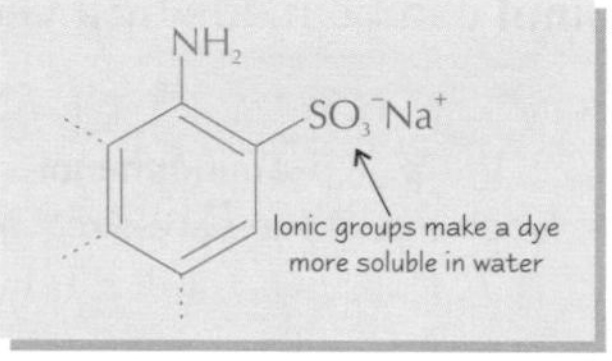


## The **Colour** of Dyes Comes from **Chromophores**

1) The structures in molecules that give them their colour are called **chromophores**.
2) When **light** hits a chromophore, certain wavelengths are **absorbed** by the electrons in it. **Visible wavelengths** not absorbed will be seen as a particular **colour**.
3) Chromophores tend to contain **double or triple bonds** (like C=C or N=N), **lone pairs** of electrons, or **benzene rings**. Usually, these components form part of a **delocalised electron system** across a large section of the molecule.
4) Functional groups containing **O** or **N atoms** with **lone pairs of electrons** can be added to a chromophore to adjust the colour of a dye molecule. They do this because the lone pair of electrons becomes **part of** the delocalised system responsible for **absorbing light**.
5) **Modifying** the chromophore changes the **frequency** of light it absorbs, and so changes the **colour** of the molecule.

How the chromophore absorbs light is explained on the next page.

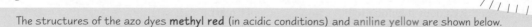

The structures of the azo dyes **methyl red** (in acidic conditions) and **aniline yellow** are shown below.

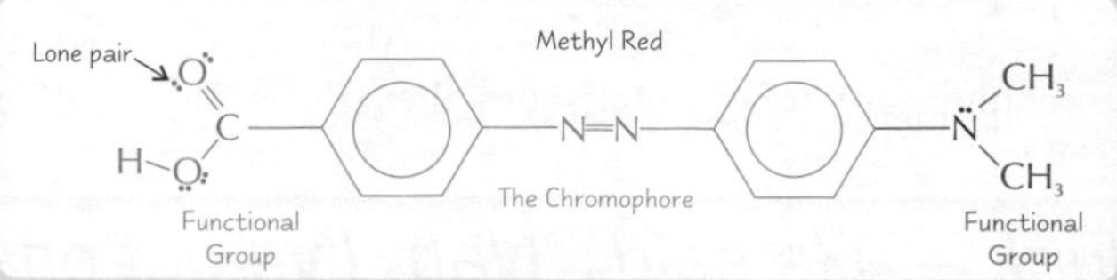


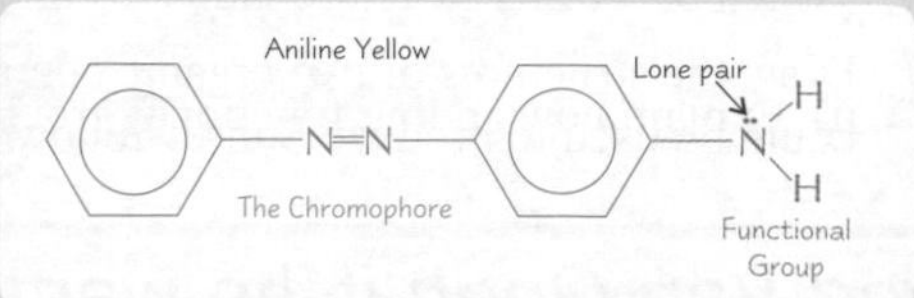

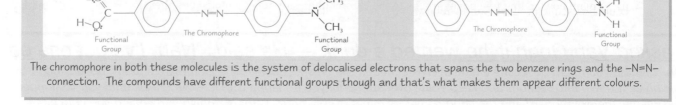

The chromophore in both these molecules is the system of delocalised electrons that spans the two benzene rings and the –N=N– connection. The compounds have different functional groups though and that's what makes them appear different colours.

# More About Azo Dyes

## *Electronic Transitions* in the Chromophore Produce the *Colour*

To understand how chromophores give **colour** you need to understand how **electrons** absorb light.

1) Covalent bonds in molecules are made up of **molecular orbitals** with different energy levels. Not all these orbitals will contain electrons. Electrons normally occupy the lowest energy orbitals.
2) When light of a **particular frequency** is absorbed, electrons become excited and move up to higher energy orbitals. These are called **electronic transitions** — the frequencies absorbed correspond to the **energy gaps** between orbitals.
3) In a **single** covalent bond, there are only **two molecular orbitals** and the energy gap between them is **very large.** So it takes **high-frequency** UV to excite the electrons. These bonds don't produce colour because only UV light is absorbed — all visible light frequencies are transmitted.
4) In **delocalised** electron systems, **many molecular orbitals** are formed. The energy gaps between them are **relatively small**, so **low frequency UV** or even **visible light** can produce electronic transitions.
5) In pure **benzene**, low frequency UV is absorbed, but not visible light, so it appears **colourless.**
6) In the more complex delocalised systems that exist in **chromophores**, the energy gaps are small enough for **visible frequencies** to be absorbed. The other visible frequencies are transmitted, making the molecule **coloured.**
7) **Increasing** the delocalisation in a chromophore produces more molecular orbitals with smaller energy gaps, so the **frequency of light** absorbed **drops.** This is why functional groups that **extend the delocalisation** in chromophores change the colour of the molecules.

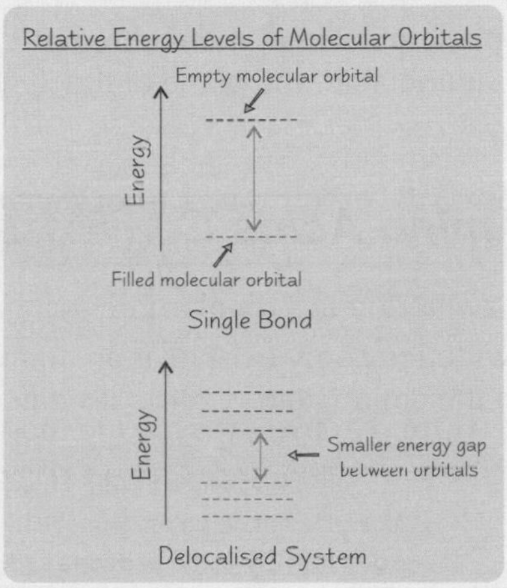


## *Practice Questions*

Q1 What functional group could be added to a dye to make it bind to a protein such as wool?

Q2 What's a chromophore? What happens when you change it?

Q3 What effect does delocalisation have on energy levels in a compound? How does increasing delocalisation change the colour of a molecule?

**Exam Questions**

1 The compound shown on the right is the dye 'Acid Orange 6'.

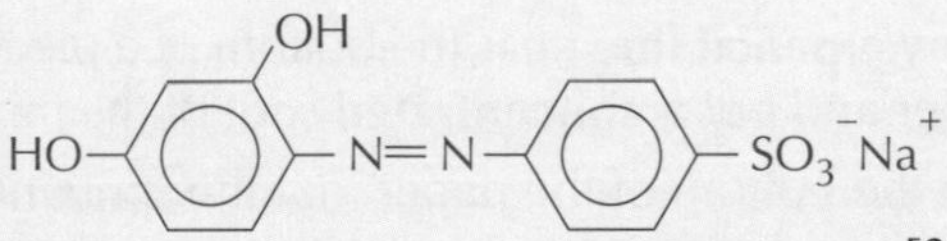


a) Which molecular feature(s) may:

i) be chromophores? [3 marks]

ii) make the dye more soluble? [1 mark]

b) Explain how Acid Orange 6 would bond to silk proteins. [3 marks]

2 Benzene is a liquid that absorbs only UV light.

a) What colour is benzene? [1 mark]

b) Benzene contains a ring of delocalised electrons which often form part of a chromophore in organic molecules.

i) Explain how delocalised systems can produce coloured organic molecules. [2 marks]

ii) Explain how adding functional groups to the chromophores of organic molecules alters their colour. [2 marks]

## *Take it to another level...*

*Electrons, eh? I'm telling you, the world would be a very dull place without those little blighters getting excited and zipping about the place. Remember though, electrons can't just do what they like — they have to absorb a set amount of energy to move between orbitals and only certain movements are allowed. As your teacher might say — organised fun is best.*

# Amino Acids and Proteins

*And now we hurtle headlong into the world of biochemistry. First up, it's proteins...*
***These pages are for AQA (Unit 4), OCR A (Unit 4), OCR B (Unit 4) and Edexcel (Unit 5).***

## Amino Acids have an **Amino Group** and a **Carboxyl** Group

An amino acid has a **basic amino group** ($NH_2$) and an **acidic carboxyl group** (COOH). This makes amino acids **amphoteric** — they've got both acidic and basic properties.

**α–amino acids** have both groups attached to the same carbon atom – the 'α carbon'. The general formula of an α–amino acid is **$RCH(NH_2)COOH$**.

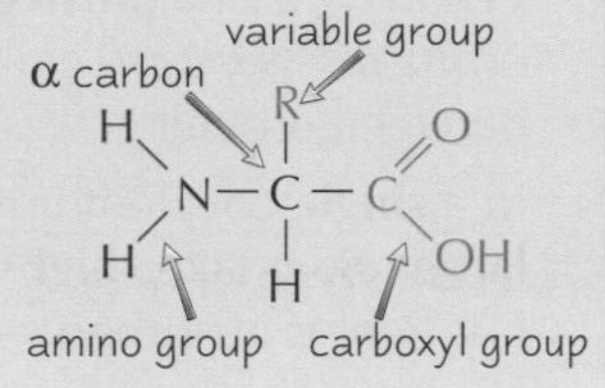


There are usually **four** different groups attached to the central (α) carbon, which means that amino acids are **chiral** molecules and have two **optical isomers** (see page 50).

If **plane-polarised**, **monochromatic light** is shone through an aqueous solution of an α–amino acid, the plane of the light gets **rotated** because of the **chiral carbon**.

## **Amino Acids** Can Exist As **Zwitterions**

A zwitterion is a **dipolar ion** — it has both a **positive** and a **negative charge** in different parts of the molecule. Zwitterions only exist near an amino acid's **isoelectric point**. This is the **pH** where the **average overall charge** on the amino acid is zero. It's different for different acids — in α–amino acids it depends on the R-group.

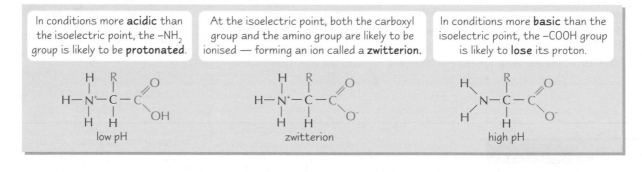

In conditions more **acidic** than the isoelectric point, the $-NH_2$ group is likely to be **protonated**.

At the isoelectric point, both the carboxyl group and the amino group are likely to be ionised — forming an ion called a **zwitterion**.

In conditions more **basic** than the isoelectric point, the –COOH group is likely to **lose** its proton.

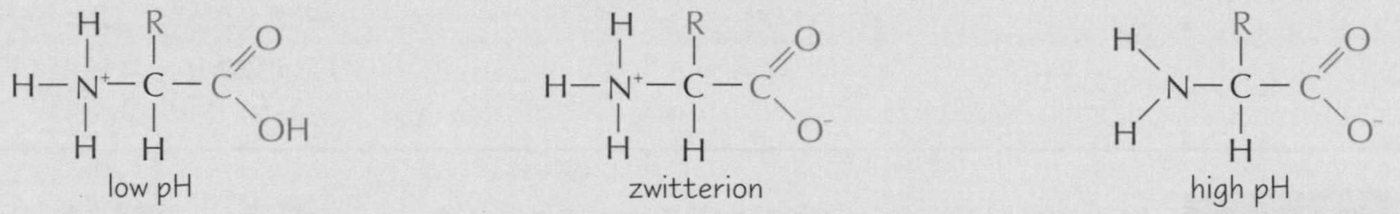


## **Paper Chromatography** is used to **Identify Unknown** Amino Acids

***Not OCR A***

You can easily identify amino acids in a mixture using a simple paper chromatography experiment. Here's how:

1) Draw a **pencil line** near the bottom of a piece of chromatography paper and put a **concentrated spot** of the mixture of amino acids on it.
2) Dip the bottom of the paper (not the spot) into a solvent.
3) As the solvent spreads up the paper, the different amino acids move with it, but at **different rates**, so they separate out.
4) When the solvent's **nearly** reached the top, take the paper out and **mark** the **solvent front** with pencil.
5) Amino acids aren't coloured — so you have to spray **ninhydrin solution** on the paper to turn them purple.
6) You can work out the **$R_f$ values** of the amino acids using this formula:

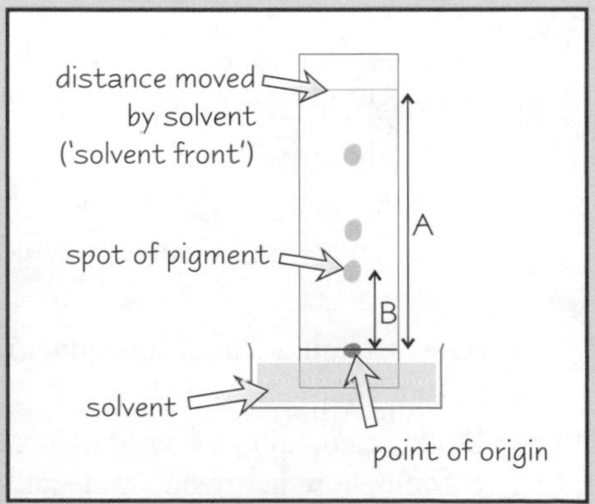


$$R_f \text{ value of amino acid} = \frac{B}{A} = \frac{\text{distance travelled by spot}}{\text{distance travelled by solvent}}$$

Now you can use a **table of known amino acid $R_f$ values** to identify the amino acids in the mixture.

# Amino Acids and Proteins

## Amino Acids can be Detected with Ninhydrin

*Edexcel only*

So, amino acids that have been separated by chromatography can be detected by spraying with a solution of **ninhydrin**.

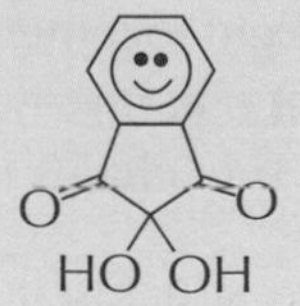


This is a scientifically accurate picture of ninhydrin — with a smiley face.

This molecule reacts with **most amino acids** to produce **ammonia**, an aldehyde, carbon dioxide and a substance called **hydrindantin**. Hydrindantin reacts with the ammonia and more ninhydrin to give a **purple pigment**, called Ruhemann's purple.

Ninhydrin is also used by the police to detect **fingerprints**, which contain traces of amino acids.

## Polypeptides are Condensation Polymers of Amino Acids

Amino acids are joined together in a **condensation** reaction.

When you join two amino acids together you make a dipeptide and between them is a **peptide bond**. When **lots** of amino acids get joined together you get a **polypeptide** or a **protein**. Every time an amino acid is joined on to the chain a **water molecule is lost**.

Peptide bonds are the same as amide links (see p98), but they're called 'peptide' when you're joining amino acids.

Here's how two amino acids join together:

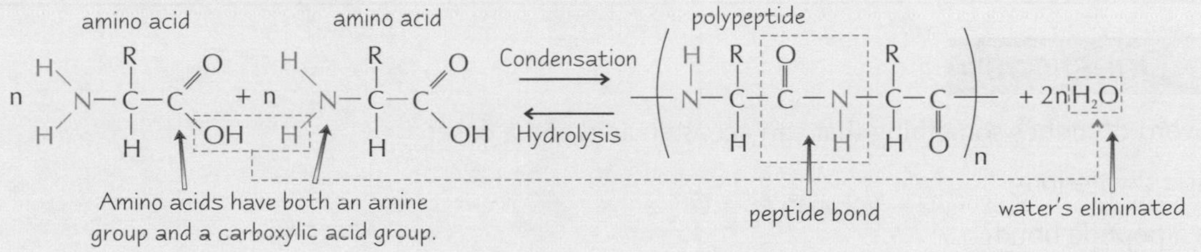


It's possible to take apart (**hydrolyse**) a protein back into amino acids using an acid. **Hot aqueous 6 mol dm$^{-3}$ hydrochloric acid** is added, and the mixture's heated under reflux for 24 hours. The final mixture is then neutralised.

Hydrolysis can also be carried out using alkalis, but in this case the hydrogen in the –COOH group is replaced by a metal to form a **carboxylate salt** of the amino acid, e.g. **$RCH(NH_2)COO^-Na^+$**.

There's more on acid and base hydrolysis on page 99

## Proteins have Different Levels of Structure

*AQA and OCR B*

Proteins are **big**, **complicated** molecules. They're easier to explain if you describe their structure in four 'levels'. These levels are called the **primary**, **secondary**, **tertiary** and **quaternary** structures. You only need to know about the first three though.

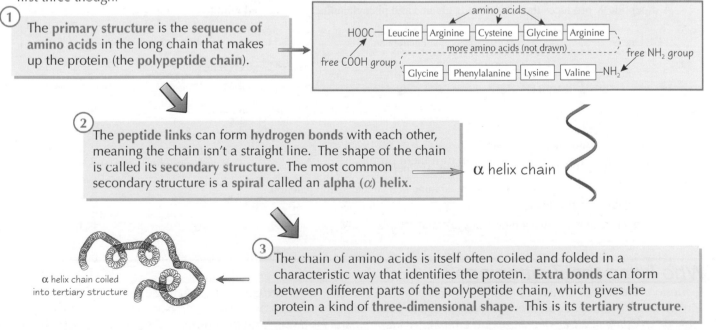

1. The **primary structure** is the **sequence of amino acids** in the long chain that makes up the protein (the **polypeptide chain**).

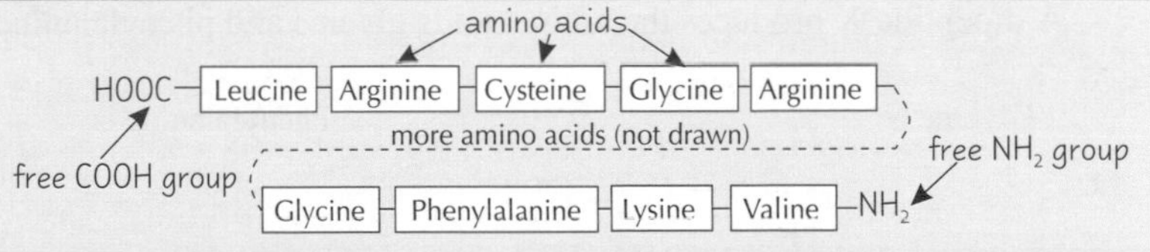


2. The **peptide links** can form **hydrogen bonds** with each other, meaning the chain isn't a straight line. The shape of the chain is called its **secondary structure**. The most common secondary structure is a **spiral** called an **alpha (α) helix**.

α helix chain

3. The chain of amino acids is itself often coiled and folded in a characteristic way that identifies the protein. **Extra bonds** can form between different parts of the polypeptide chain, which gives the protein a kind of **three-dimensional shape**. This is its **tertiary structure**.

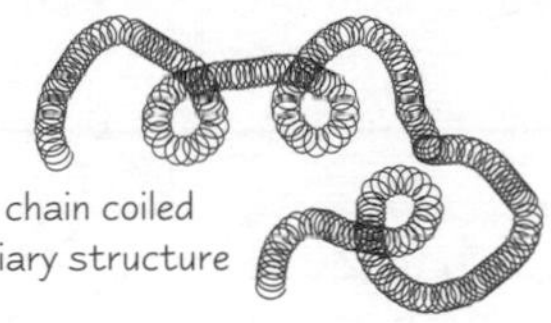

α helix chain coiled into tertiary structure

# Amino Acids and Proteins

## Different Bonds Hold Proteins Together

***OCR B only***

The **secondary** structure is held together by **hydrogen bonds** between the peptide links.
The **tertiary** structure is **held together** by quite a few different types of force.
These all exist between the **side chains** (R-groups) of the amino acids.

These forces hold the tertiary structure together:

1) **Instantaneous dipole-induced dipole** forces — weak attractions between two **non-polar** side groups, e.g. $CH_3$.
2) **Ionic interactions** between **charged** side groups, like $CO_2^-$ and $NH_3^+$.
3) **Hydrogen bonding** — between groups such as –OH and $-NH_2$.
4) **Disulfide bridge** — a covalent bond between two sulfur-containing side groups (–SH). This type of bond is stronger than the others.

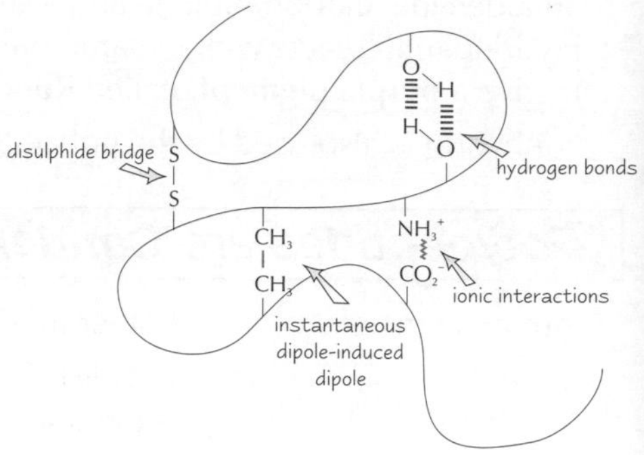


It's the **three-dimensional structure** that gives proteins their properties.
So these intermolecular bonds are really important — because they're what causes the three-dimensional structure.

## Practice Questions

Q1 What word describes something that can act as an acid and a base?

Q2 What is a zwitterion?

Q3 What's a peptide bond?

Q4 Name the four types of intermolecular force that are involved in holding together the tertiary structures of proteins.

**Exam Questions**

1 Alanine is an α-amino acid found in many foods. It has the molecular formula $C_3H_7NO_2$.

a) What is meant by an α-amino acid? [1 mark]

b) Draw the structure of alanine. [1 mark]

c) Which part of this molecule will be different in other α-amino acids? [1 mark]

d) Draw the structure of the zwitterion produced by alanine. [1 mark]

2 A dipeptide X produces the amino acids glycine and phenylalanine when heated with hydrochloric acid.

Glycine is:

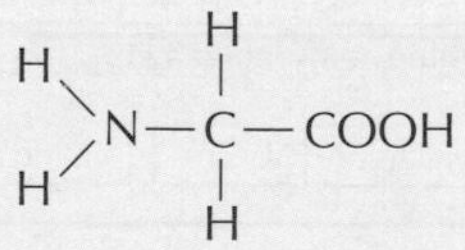

Phenylalanine is:

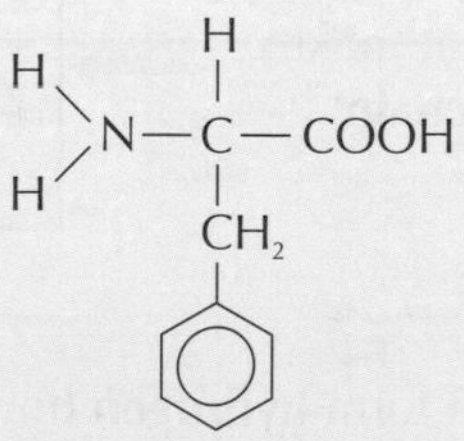

a) What is meant by a dipeptide? [1 mark]

b) Draw one of the two possible structures of dipeptide X. [1 mark]

c) X is formed from glycine and phenylalanine in a condensation reaction.
Explain what this means. [1 mark]

d) Only one of these two amino acids is chiral. Explain why. [1 mark]

## Who killed the Zwittonians?

*Zwitterions are actually the last physical remains of a race of highly advanced beings known as Zwittonians from the galaxy I Zwiky 19. It is thought that they lived approximately 9.75 billion years ago before evolving beyond the need for physical bodies, exploding in a ball of energy and emitting zwitterion particles throughout the cosmos. Fascinating.... Also untrue.*

# DNA

*DNA — the molecule of life. And unfortunately, just like life, it's complicated.* ***These pages are for OCR B (Unit 4) only.***

## *DNA* is a *Polymer* of *Nucleotides*

DNA, DeoxyriboNucleic Acid, contains all the genetic information of an organism.

DNA is made up from lots of **monomers** called **nucleotides**.
Nucleotides are made from the following:

1) **A phosphate group**.
2) **A pentose sugar** — a five-carbon sugar. It's deoxyribose in DNA.
3) **A base** — one of four different bases. In DNA they are **adenine** (A), **cytosine** (C), **guanine** (G) and **thymine** (T).

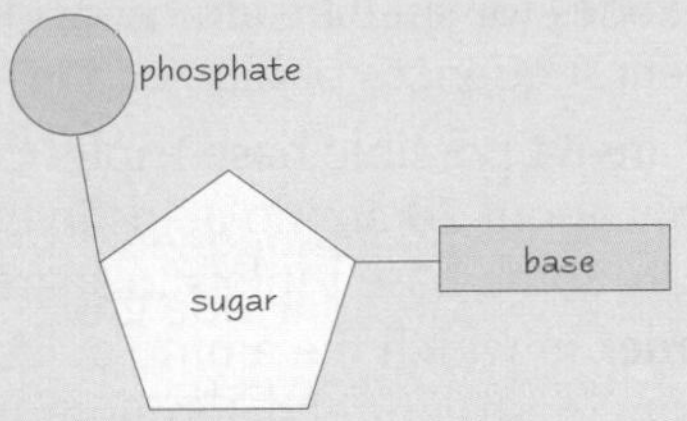


The nucleotides join together to form a **polynucleotide chain**. The bond between each pair of nucleotides forms between the phosphate group of one nucleotide and the sugar of another. This makes what's called a **sugar-phosphate backbone**.

The bases can be in any order, and it's the order of them that holds all the information.

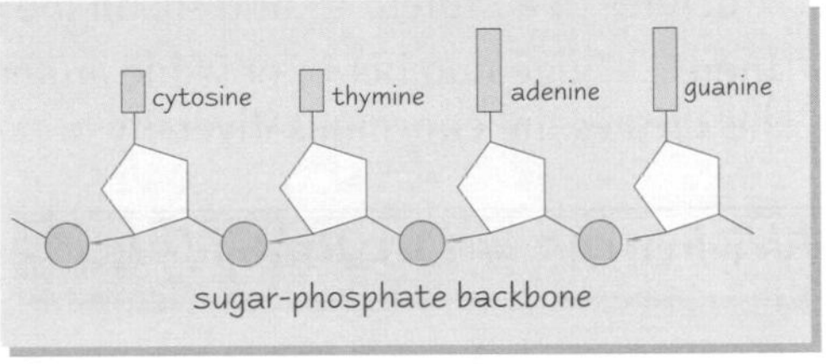


## *DNA* Forms by *Condensation Polymerisation*

The **sugar-phosphate backbone** is formed by condensation polymerisation. The diagram below shows you how:

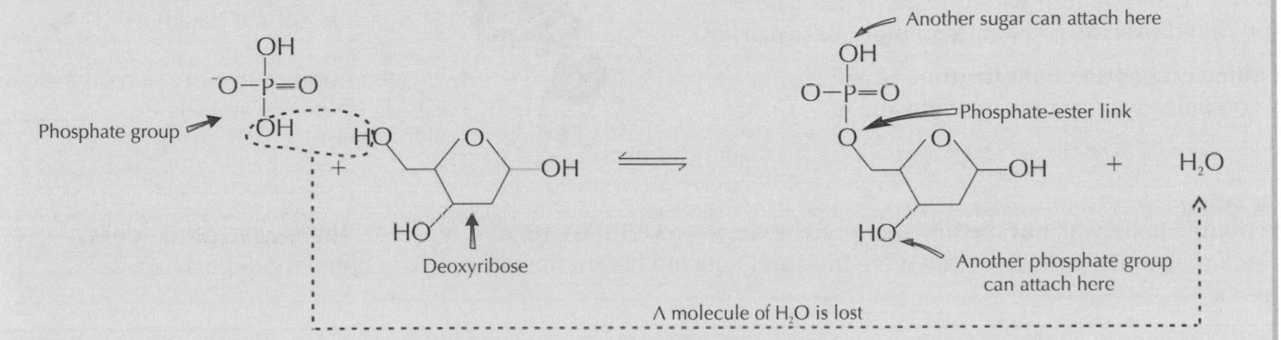


1) The lone pair of electrons on an oxygen atom in the deoxyribose sugar molecule makes a **dative covalent bond** with the phosphorus atom in a phosphate group.
2) A molecule of water is lost and a **phosphate-ester link** is formed.
3) There are still OH groups in the phosphate-ester, so further ester links can be formed. This allows the molecule to grow and make a polymer.

## *DNA* *Bases* Join to the *Sugar* Via a *Condensation* Reaction too

It is also a **condensation reaction** that connects **base molecules** (like **adenine**, shown below) to sugars in the sugar-phosphate backbone. All of the bases have an **NH group** somewhere in their structure. It's the N atom of the NH group that bonds to deoxyribose — eliminating an OH group from the sugar and H from the NH group to form water.

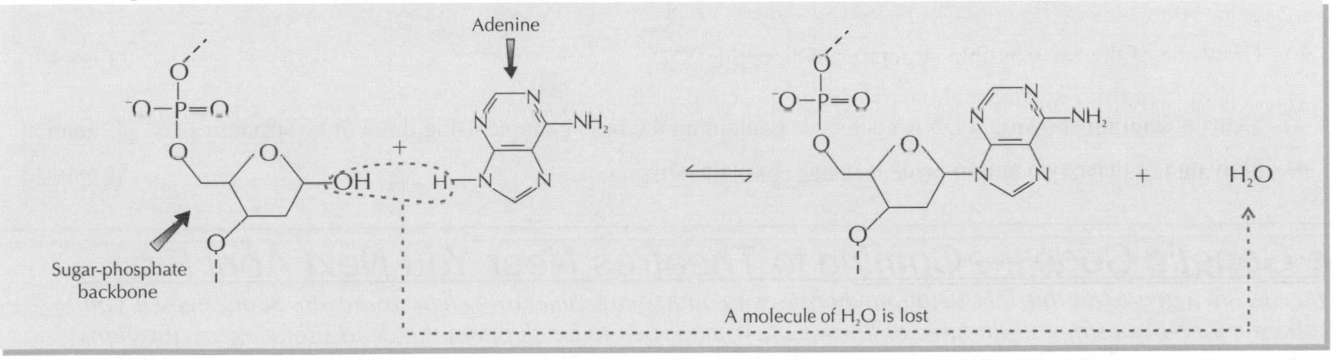

# DNA

## DNA Contains the Basis of the Genetic Code

The **sequence** of bases **determines** the sequence of **amino acids** in a protein. The way that DNA codes for it is called the **genetic code**.

A section of DNA coding for a protein, is called a gene.

1) DNA codes for specific amino acids with sequences of three bases, called **base triplets**. Different sequences of bases code for different amino acids.
2) There are **64** possible **base triplet combinations**, but only about **20** amino acids in human proteins so there are some base triplets to spare. These aren't wasted though:
   - some amino acids are coded for by more than one base triplet.
   - some base triplets act as 'punctuation' to stop and start production of an amino acid chain.
3) The **order** in which the amino acids are connected together (the primary structure) determines the secondary and tertiary structures of a protein — and so, all the **properties** of the protein.
4) There's a huge number of possible arrangements of amino acids and this creates the **enormous diversity** of proteins in living organisms.

## DNA Forms a Double Helix

**DNA** is made of **two polynucleotide strands**.

The two strands spiral together to form a **double helix** structure, which is held together by **hydrogen bonds** between the bases.

Each base can only join with one particular partner — this is called **specific** or **complementary base pairing**.

**Adenine** always pairs with **thymine** (**A – T**) and **guanine** always pairs with **cytosine** (**G – C**).

There's more on this on the next page.

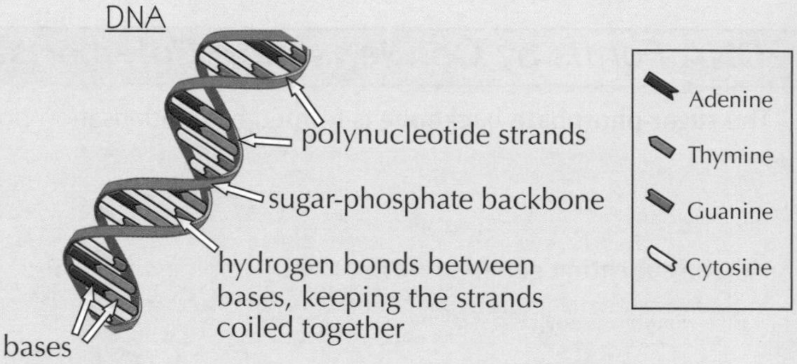


The double helix was **not** the first model to be suggested for the structure of DNA. There were other ideas — including a triple helix — that were tried and rejected before the currently accepted model was arrived at.

## Practice Questions

Q1 What are the monomers that make up DNA called?

Q2 What are the three components of these monomers?

Q3 Name the reaction by which these components connect together.

Q4 Which type of intermolecular force holds the two strands of DNA together in a double helix?

**Exam Question**

1 A phosphate group, the base guanine and the sugar deoxyribose are shown below.

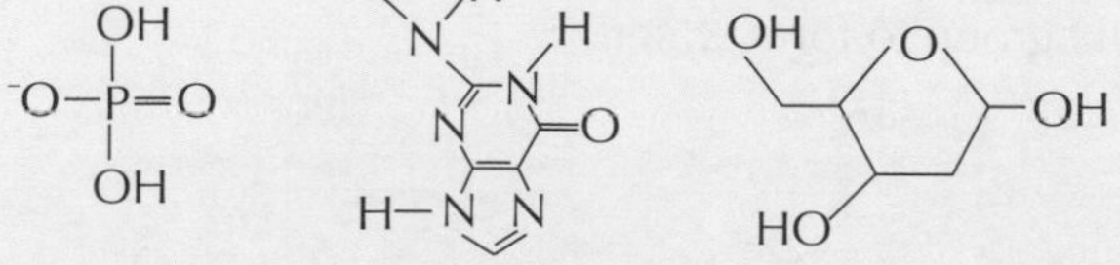

a) Draw a diagram showing a DNA nucleotide containing the base guanine using these three structures. [2 marks]

b) Explain how DNA codes for proteins using bases like guanine. [2 marks]

## The Genetic Code — Coming to Theatres Near You Next April First...

*Let's face it, I'm a geek, but this DNA stuff never ceases to amaze me. It's just so flippin' clever. Sadly, even if you don't share my enthusiasm, you do have to know it. If you happen to be skipping the dead useful exam questions (naughty, naughty), then have a go at this one. Seriously, try it. You can have a biscuit afterwards.*

# More DNA

*Yup, still on DNA I'm afraid...* ***These pages are for OCR B (Unit 4) only.***

## Hydrogen Bonding Causes the Bases to Form Specific Pairs

You saw on the last page that in the DNA double helix, opposite bases always pair up **adenine (A) to thymine (T)** and **guanine (G) to cytosine (C)**. This is called **complementary base pairing**. It happens because of the arrangement of atoms in the base molecules that are capable of forming **hydrogen bonds**.

A **hydrogen bond** forms between a polar positive **H atom** (that's an H attached to anything highly electronegative like N) and a lone pair of electrons on a nearby **O**, **N** or **F atom**. To bond, the two atoms have to be the **right distance apart**.

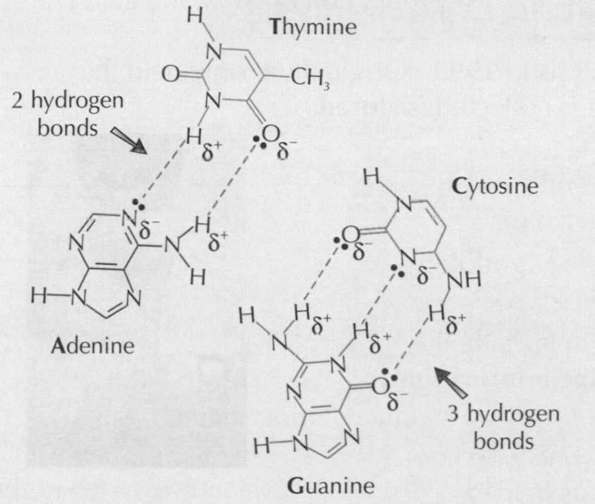


1) A and T have the right atoms — in the right places — to each form **2 hydrogen bonds**. This allows them to pair up. G and C can each form **3 hydrogen bonds**, so they pair up as well.
2) These are the **only** possible base combinations. Other base pairings would put the partially charged atoms too close together (they'd repel each other), or too far apart. In others, the bonding atoms just wouldn't line up properly.
3) The DNA helix has to twist so that the bases are in the **right alignment** and at the **right distance** apart for the complementary base pairs to form.

When **replicating genetic information**, complementary base pairing makes sure that the **order** of bases is copied **accurately**.

## DNA can Copy Itself — Self-Replication

**DNA** has to be able to **copy itself** before **cell division** can take place, which is essential for growth and reproduction — pretty important stuff.

This is how it's done:

1) The hydrogen bonds break and the DNA double helix starts to split into two single strands — a bit like a zip.
2) Bases on **free-floating nucleotides** in the cytoplasm now pair up with the complementary bases on the nucleotides in the DNA. **Complementary base pairing** makes sure the correct nucleotide joins in the correct place.
3) An enzyme called **DNA polymerase** joins the new nucleotides together to form a polynucleotide chain.
4) This happens on each of the strands to make an **exact copy** of what was on the other strand. The result is **two molecules** of DNA **identical** to the **original molecule** of DNA.

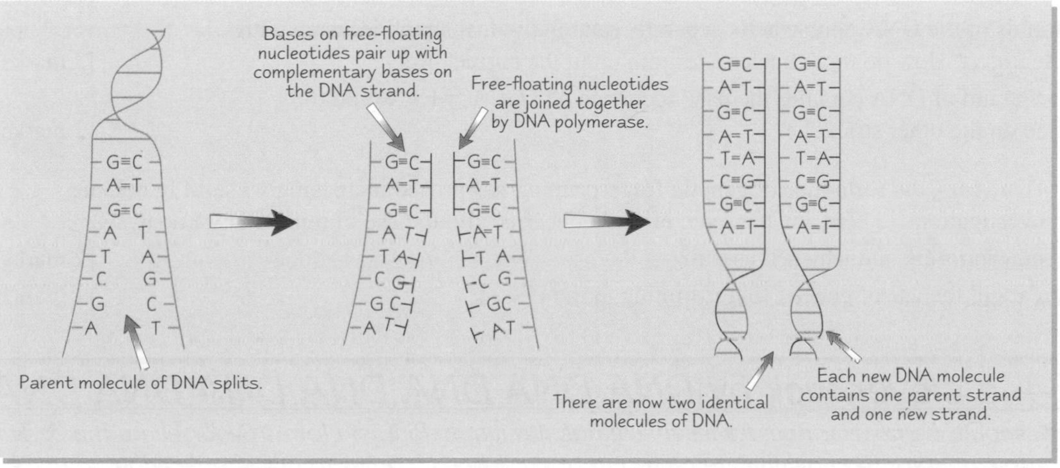

The hospital offered a complementary baby pairing facility.

# More DNA

## Our **DNA** is **Unique** and can be Used to **Identify** Us

Although many parts of the DNA found in human cells are the same, there are sections of the molecule that **vary** from person to person. **Genetic fingerprinting** breaks down DNA and examines the sequences of bases in these sections. The technique is used to **identify people** based on samples of their DNA — which can be collected from a wide variety of fluid or tissue.

## There is an **Ethical Debate** About the Use of Human DNA Analysis

Britain set up a **database** to store data collected from human DNA analysis in **1995**. Originally it only held the DNA profiles of **convicted criminals**, but since 2004 **all** DNA data that is collected is **stored**.

1) There are over a million UK citizens who have never been found guilty of any crime, but who have information about their DNA stored in the database.
2) Some people believe this information should be destroyed because it is adding innocent people to a list of criminals.
3) **Civil rights campaigners** argue that people should be able to ask to have their profiles removed — there are concerns about who could **access the information** and what it could be used for.
4) Others believe that the database should include the DNA of everyone who lives in Britain because the information is so **useful** to the police and has helped **solve many crimes**.

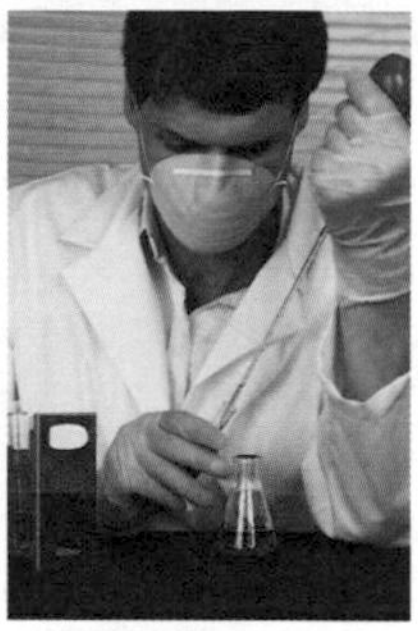

Just as soon as he was done analysing Simon's DNA, Harold was going to prove who stole his Take That CD.

## Practice Questions

Q1 Name the intermolecular forces between bases on different strands of DNA.

Q3 Why are these forces important in DNA replication?

Q2 What is the name of the enzyme that joins nucleotides together?

Q4 How can our DNA be used to identify us?

**Exam Questions**

1 One of the vital features of DNA is that it is able to make exact copies of itself. If this were not possible then cells could not reproduce themselves. The process of copying begins with the double helix separating into two strands, which then turn into two identical DNA molecules.

a) How are the two strands of DNA held together? [2 marks]

b) When the two strands of the DNA double helix separate, each individual strand joins up with free floating nucleotides. How do these nucleotides join up in the correct order? [2 marks]

c) If a section of one strand of DNA contains the base sequence ATTGCA, what would the matching sequence on the other strand be? [2 marks]

2 Over the past twenty-five years, the technique of genetic fingerprinting has proved increasingly useful in helping the police with their investigations. There are, however, ethical concerns with the use of human DNA analysis.

a) What is genetic fingerprinting and why is it useful? [2 marks]

b) Give one concern about the use of genetic fingerprinting in the UK. [1 mark]

## Self-replication — a clever trick by DNA DNA DNA DNA DNA DNA DNA...

*This hydrogen bonding lark should be familiar from AS level — if not, it might help if you refresh yourself on the basics. Hydrogen bonding and complementary base pairing are really important when it comes to DNA replication, so make sure you get how they fit together. That's it for DNA folks. Hold onto your hats, it's about to get really exciting...*

# RNA and Protein Synthesis

*You've met DNA, now here comes its partner in crime — that little rascal RNA...* ***These pages are for OCR B (Unit 4) only.***

## DNA and RNA are Very Similar Molecules

1) RNA is a **polymer of nucleotides**, with a series of bases attached to a sugar-phosphate backbone, just like DNA.
2) But RNA nucleotides have a different sugar. In **DNA** nucleotides the sugar is **deoxyribose** — in **RNA** nucleotides it's **ribose**.
3) The other important difference is that RNA has the base **uracil** instead of **thymine**.

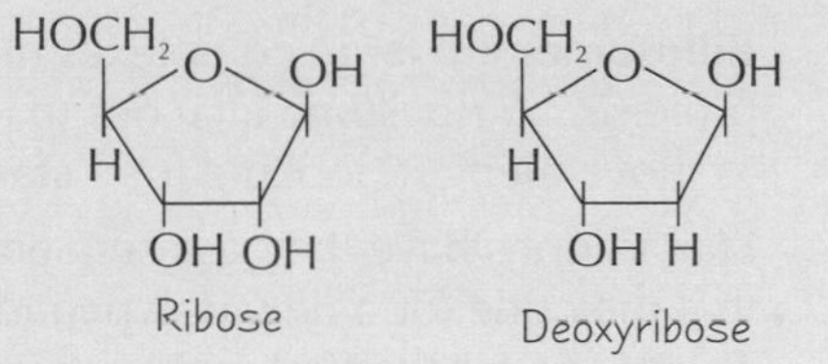


## mRNA, tRNA and rRNA are Different Types of RNA

There are **three types** of RNA and they're all involved in **making proteins**.

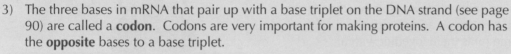

**Messenger RNA (mRNA)**

1) **mRNA** is a **single polynucleotide strand**.
2) It's an exact **reverse copy** of a section of DNA — except thymine's replaced by uracil.
3) The three bases in mRNA that pair up with a base triplet on the DNA strand (see page 90) are called a **codon**. Codons are very important for making proteins. A codon has the **opposite** bases to a base triplet.

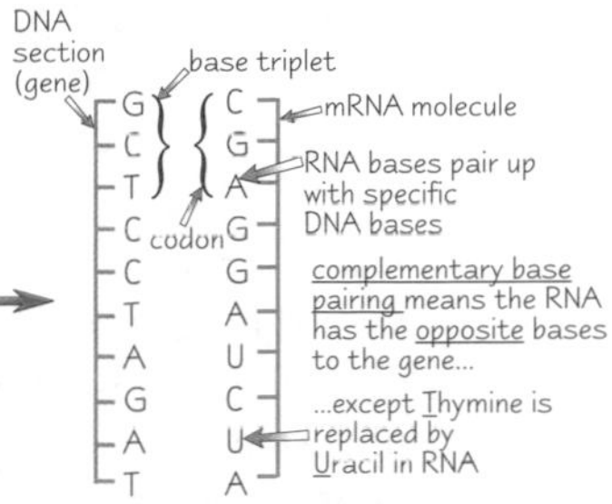


**Transfer RNA (tRNA)**

1) **tRNA** is a **single polynucleotide strand** that's folded into a **clover shape**.
2) Every tRNA has a **binding site** at one end, where a specific **amino acid** attaches.
3) Each tRNA molecule also has a specific sequence of **three bases**, called an **anticodon**.

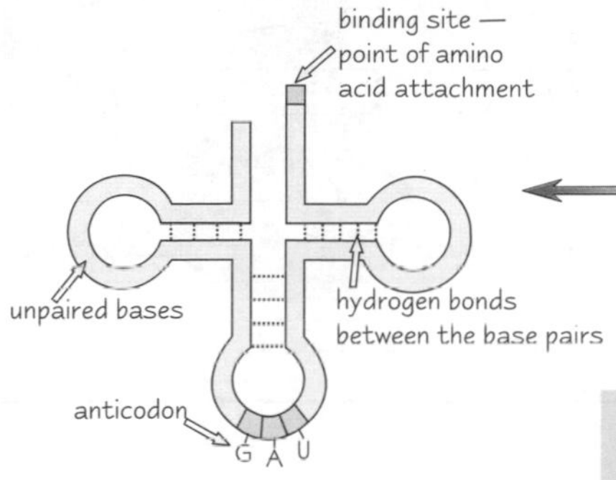


**Ribosomal RNA (rRNA)**

rRNA is made up of polynucleotide strands that are attached to proteins to make things called **ribosomes** (see page 94). It's the largest type of RNA.

## mRNA is needed For Protein Synthesis

Messenger RNA (mRNA) is made using DNA as a **template**, in a similar way to DNA replication. The process is called **transcription**.

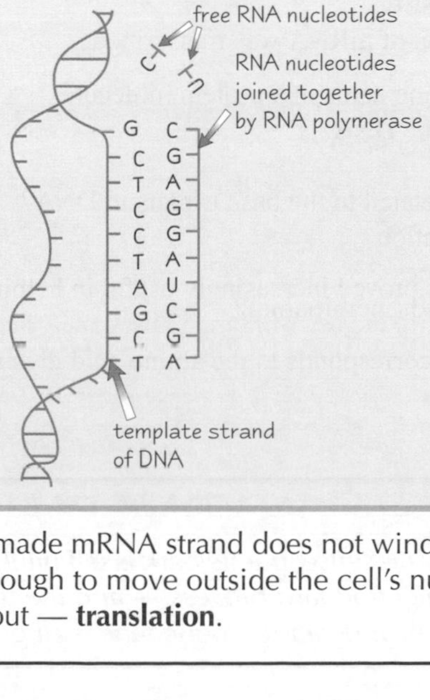

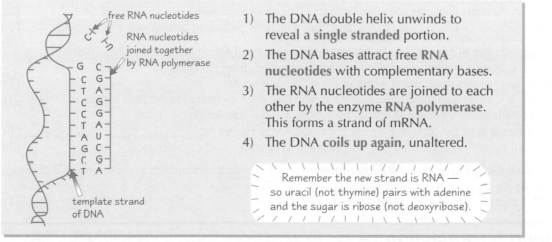

1) The DNA double helix unwinds to reveal a **single stranded** portion.
2) The DNA bases attract free **RNA nucleotides** with complementary bases.
3) The RNA nucleotides are joined to each other by the enzyme **RNA polymerase**. This forms a strand of mRNA.
4) The DNA **coils up again**, unaltered.

Remember the new strand is RNA — so uracil (not thymine) pairs with adenine and the sugar is ribose (not deoxyribose).

The newly made mRNA strand does not wind up with the DNA — it's **released** and is free to **move around** the cell. It's small enough to move outside the cell's nucleus into the cytoplasm, where it's used in the next process you've got to learn about — **translation**.

# RNA and Protein Synthesis

## *Proteins are Made During Translation*

In **translation**, amino acids are joined together to make a **polypeptide** chain.

1) **Ribosomes** are large complexes made from rRNA and proteins. A **ribosome** attaches to the **mRNA**, and starts to move along it, looking for a **start codon**.
   Start codons have the base sequence **AUG** and indicate that the code for a new polypeptide chain is beginning. They code for the **first** amino acid in the chain (so it's always the same one — methionine).
2) Once it's found a start codon, the ribosome temporarily pauses, until a **tRNA** with the correct **anticodon bases** pairs with the AUG codon inside the ribosome.
   The tRNA has an amino acid attached to it.
3) The ribosome then moves three bases forward, and waits for a different tRNA to bring another amino acid into the ribosome. Now there are two amino acids inside the ribosome and the ribosome joins them together with a **peptide bond**.
4) The ribosome moves forwards again. The first tRNA now **leaves** the ribosome and breaks away from its amino acid. A new tRNA brings in the third amino acid of the chain.
5) The process continues in this way until a **stop codon** is reached.
   The stop codon **doesn't** code for an amino acid.
   The ribosome **releases** the polypeptide chain at this point.

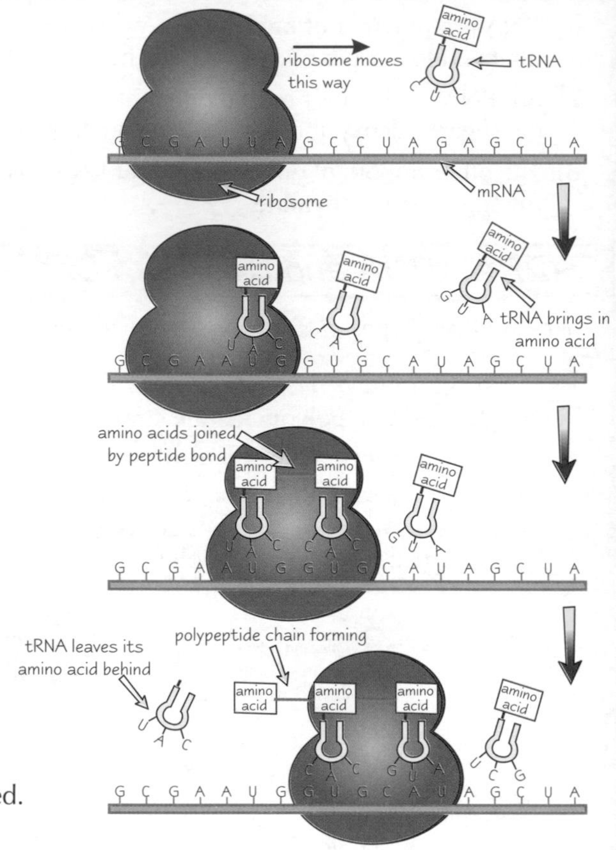


## *Practice Questions*

Q1 What's made during transcription?

Q2 What base does RNA have that DNA doesn't?

**Exam Questions**

1 The sequence of bases in a small portion of mRNA is as follows: –AAGGUGCAUCGA–
   a) Why couldn't the sequence be from a portion of DNA? [1 mark]
   b) How many amino acids does this sequence code for? Explain your answer. [2 marks]
   c) Write the sequence of bases for the DNA strand from which the portion of mRNA was transcribed. [2 marks]

2 DNA contains a sequence of base triplets that represents a sequence of amino acids in a protein molecule.
   The first stage in making a protein is to make a molecule of mRNA from the DNA.
   a) What is the name of this process and where in the cell does it occur? [2 marks]
   b) What is the name of a set of three bases in mRNA, and how are they related to the base triplets in DNA? [2 marks]
   c) A protein is made using the bases in mRNA by a process called translation.
      i) What is the name of the protein-RNA complex involved in this process? [1 mark]
      ii) Why do all proteins made in this way start with the same amino acid (methionine)? [2 marks]

3 A codon on a section of mRNA has the sequence of bases –GGU–, which corresponds to the amino acid glycine.
   The mRNA codes for a polypeptide which contains 73 amino acids.
   Explain how this glycine molecule is inserted into the polypeptide. [4 marks]

## *Help — I need a translation...*

*When you first start looking at protein synthesis it might make approximately no sense, but its bark is definitely worse than its bite, I promise. All those strange words disguise what is really quite a straightforward process — and the diagrams are really handy for getting to grips with it all. Keep drawing them out yourself, 'til you can reproduce them all perfectly.*

# Enzymes

*Ah enzymes. Where would we be without them? I wouldn't be eating this delicious chocolatey oaty biscuit that's for sure...*
***These pages are for OCR B (Unit 4) only.***

## *Enzymes are Biological Catalysts*

**Enzymes** speed up chemical reactions by acting as biological catalysts.

1) They catalyse every **metabolic reaction** in the bodies of living organisms.
2) Enzymes are **proteins**. Some also have **non-protein components**.
3) Every enzyme has an area called its **active site**. This is the part that the **substrate** fits into so that it can interact with the enzyme. The active site is three-dimensional — it's part of the **tertiary structure** of the enzyme protein (see page 87).

Substrates are the molecules that enzymes act on to speed up reactions.

## *Enzymes have High Specificity*

1) Enzymes are a bit picky. They only work with **specific substrates** — usually only one.
2) This is because, for the enzyme to work, the substrate has to **fit** into the **active site**. If the substrate's shape doesn't match the active site's shape, then the reaction won't be catalysed. This is called the '**lock and key**' model.

The substrate fits into the enzyme the same way a key fits into a lock.

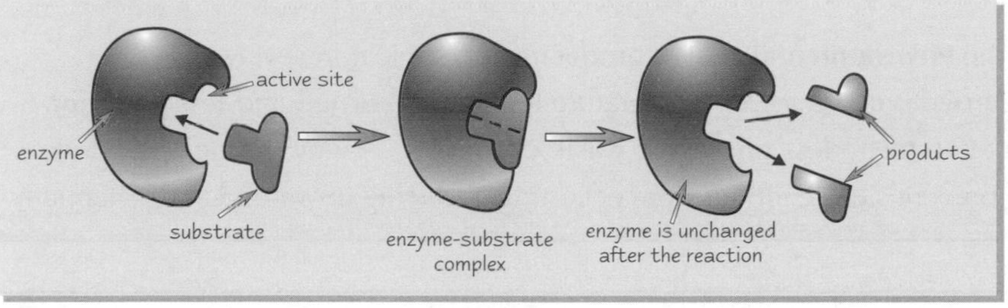

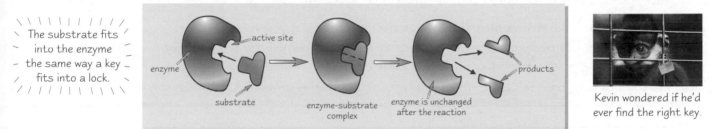

Kevin wondered if he'd ever find the right key.

3) The substrate is held in the active site by **temporary** bonds such as hydrogen bonds and van der Waals forces. These temporary bonds form between the substrate and "R" groups of the enzyme's amino acids.

## *Enzymes Only Work Well in a Narrow Range of Temperatures and pH*

The graphs below show how the rate of an **enzyme-catalysed reaction** changes at different temperatures and pH values.

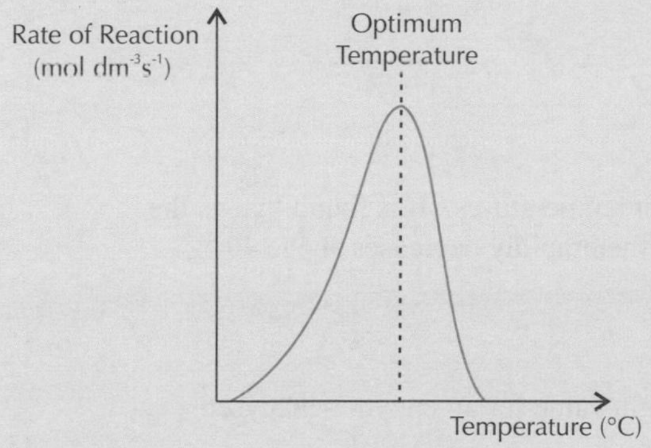


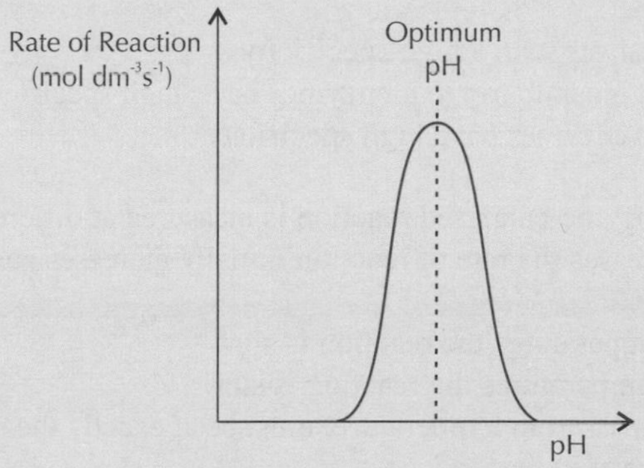


There is an **optimum temperature** and **pH** at which the reaction rate is at a maximum — here the enzyme works best.

1) At **low temperatures**, the reaction is **slow** because the reactant molecules have low kinetic energy.
2) At **higher temperatures**, or at **higher or lower pH values**, the reaction rate drops off dramatically because the enzyme becomes **denatured**. It stops working properly and can no longer effectively catalyse the reaction.

Enzymes **denature** when they become too hot, or are exposed to too high a concentration of acid or alkali. The bonds that define the **active site** break, changing the **tertiary structure** of the enzyme molecule. The active site is no longer the **correct shape** for the substrate to fit into.

# Enzymes

## **Inhibitors Slow Down** the Rate of Reaction

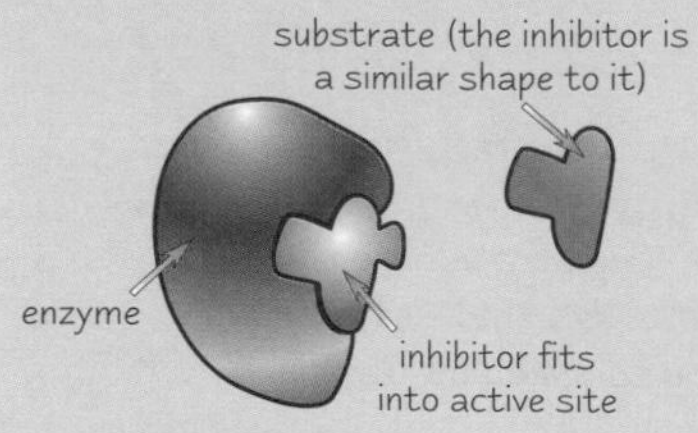


1) **Inhibitors** are molecules with a **similar shape to the substrate**.
2) They compete with the substrate to bond to the active site, but no reaction follows. Instead they **block** the active site, so **no substrate** can **fit** in it.
3) How much inhibition happens depends on the **relative concentrations** of inhibitor and substrate — if there's a lot more of the inhibitor, it'll take up most of the active sites and very little substrate will be able to get to the enzyme. The amount of inhibition is also affected by how **strongly** the inhibitor bonds to the active site.

## Enzymes can Reduce the **Environmental Impact** of **Industrial** Reactions

Enzymes are widely used in industry to :

1) Make commercial reactions proceed **quickly** at relatively **low temperatures.**
2) **Increase** the **yields** of reactions and make them more **selective**.

This can help to reduce the **environmental cost** of producing a chemical in several ways:

1) If the reaction is carried out at a lower temperature **less fuel is burned** and **less pollution** is created.
2) Higher yields can often mean **less unreacted waste chemicals** — again reducing pollution.
3) Enzymes can also prevent side-reactions from occurring, **reducing unwanted** and potentially **harmful by-products**.

## Practice Questions

Q1 What type of molecule is an enzyme?

Q2 Name the model that explains why enzymes are very specific.

Q3 What holds substrate molecules to the active site of an enzyme?

Q4 How does an inhibitor prevent an enzyme from catalysing a reaction?

**Exam Questions**

1 Enzymes are catalysts with a high specificity.
a) What does it mean to say that enzymes have 'high specificity'. [1 mark]
b) Explain why enzymes have high specificity. [2 marks]

2 The rate of an enzyme-catalysed reaction is measured at different temperatures. It is found that as the temperature increases the rate of reaction initially increases and then rapidly decreases above 40 °C.
a) Explain why:
i) At low temperatures the reaction is slow. [2 marks]
ii) At high temperatures the reaction is slow. [2 marks]
b) What else, apart from temperature, must be at exactly the right value for an enzyme-catalysed reaction to be at its fastest? [1 mark]

3 Sometimes adding a chemical to an enzyme-catalysed reaction can cause the enzyme to stop working properly.
a) What are chemicals that prevent enzymes from working called? [1 mark]
b) One way that such a chemical may act to stop an enzyme working is to cause the shape of the active site to change. Explain another way in which a molecule may prevent an enzyme from working. [3 marks]

## Substrate keys — they fit, but my gosh, don't they know it...

*I don't know what it is with enzymes. They're never bloomin' happy. It's too hot, it's too cold, it's really acidic... You wouldn't catch a non-biological catalyst behaving like that. Still they really do have their uses, so make sure you learn 'em. And make sure you know what makes them tick — the examiners'll love you for it. So will the enzyme, the fickle beast...*

# Polymers

*Polymers are long molecules made by joining lots of little molecules together. They're made using addition or condensation polymerisation, as you're about to see.*

***These pages are for AQA (Unit 4), OCR A (Unit 4), OCR B (Unit 4) and Edexcel (Unit 5).***

Addition polymerisation is a free radical addition reaction.

## Addition Polymers are Formed from Alkenes

The double bonds in alkenes can open up and join together to make long chains called **addition polymers**. It's like they're holding hands in a big line. The individual, small alkenes are called **monomers**.

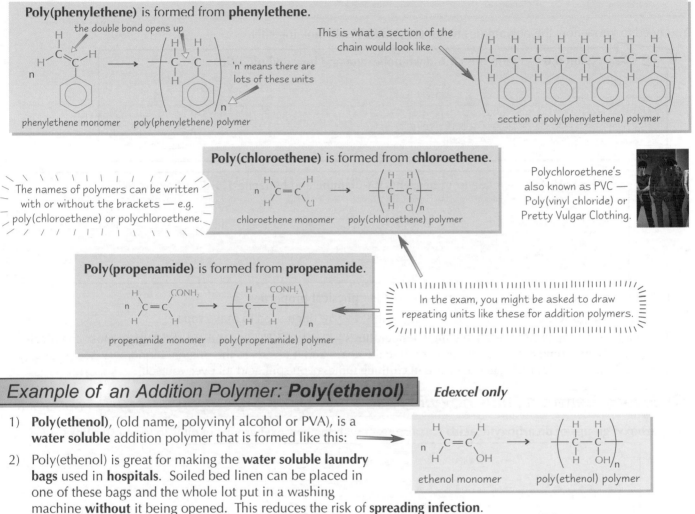

**Poly(phenylethene)** is formed from **phenylethene**.

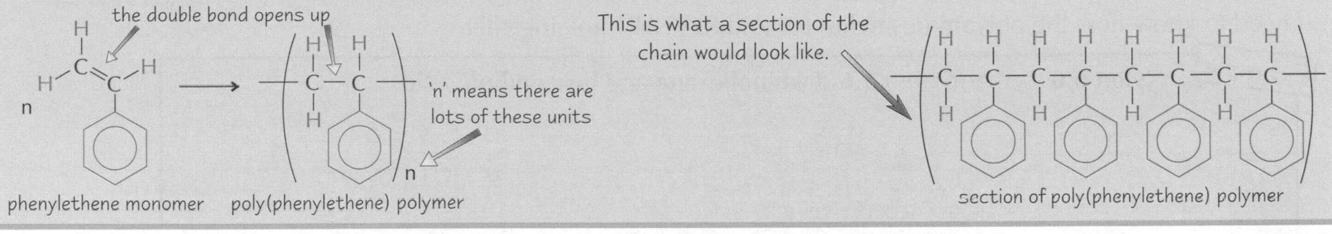


The names of polymers can be written with or without the brackets — e.g. poly(chloroethene) or polychloroethene.

**Poly(chloroethene)** is formed from **chloroethene**.

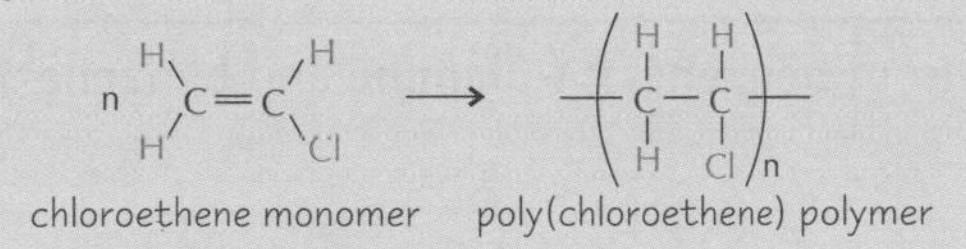

Polychloroethene's also known as PVC — Poly(vinyl chloride) or Pretty Vulgar Clothing.

**Poly(propenamide)** is formed from **propenamide**.

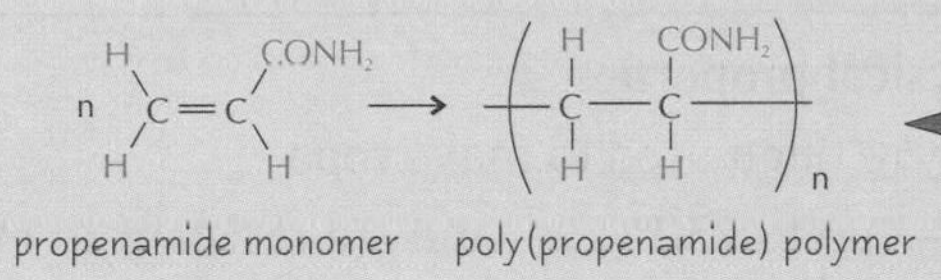


In the exam, you might be asked to draw repeating units like these for addition polymers.

## Example of an Addition Polymer: Poly(ethenol)

***Edexcel only***

1) **Poly(ethenol)**, (old name, polyvinyl alcohol or PVA), is a **water soluble** addition polymer that is formed like this:

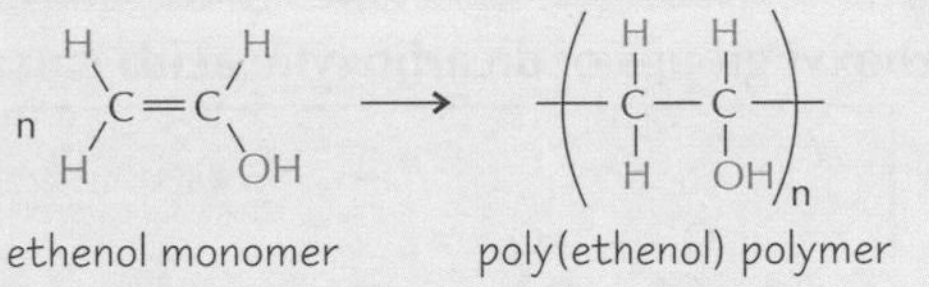


2) Poly(ethenol) is great for making the **water soluble laundry bags** used in **hospitals**. Soiled bed linen can be placed in one of these bags and the whole lot put in a washing machine **without** it being opened. This reduces the risk of **spreading infection**. The poly(ethenol) bag **breaks down** at 40°C in the machine and releases its contents.

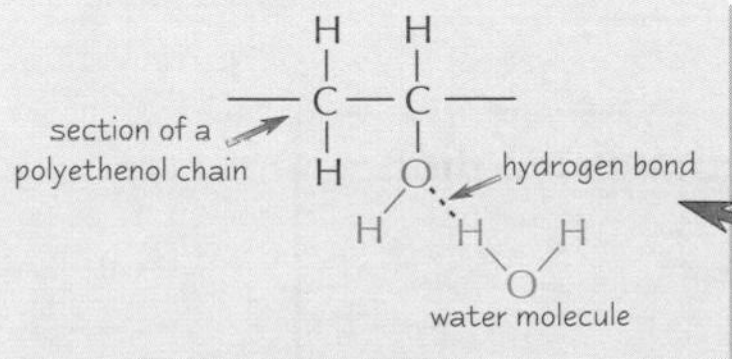


3) The polymer is also used to **wrap liquid detergent**, as a clean and convenient way of handling it. The whole package — called a **liquitab** — can be put in the washing machine, where the wrapping **dissolves**.
4) Poly(ethenol) is soluble because it can **hydrogen bond** with water through the **OH groups** along its chain.

## Condensation Polymers Include Polyamides, Polyesters and Polypeptides

The other type of polymerisation is called **condensation polymerisation**.

1) Condensation polymerisation usually involves **two different** types of monomer.
2) Each monomer has at least **two functional groups**. Each functional group reacts with a group on another monomer to form a link, creating polymer chains.
3) Each time a link is formed, a small molecule is lost (water) — that's why it's called **condensation** polymerisation.
4) Examples of condensation polymers include **polyamides**, **polyesters** and **polypeptides** (examples of these are on the next page) and **proteins** (see page 87).

# Polymers

## Reactions Between Dicarboxylic Acids and Diamines Make Polyamides

*Not OCR B*

The **carboxyl** groups of **dicarboxylic acids** react with the **amino** groups of **diamines** to form **amide links.**

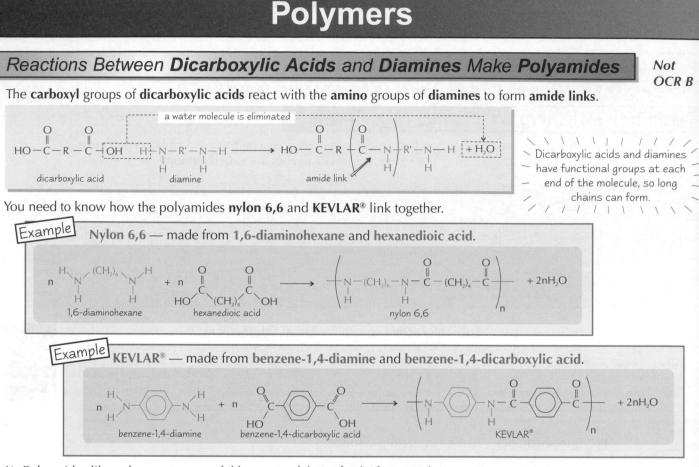

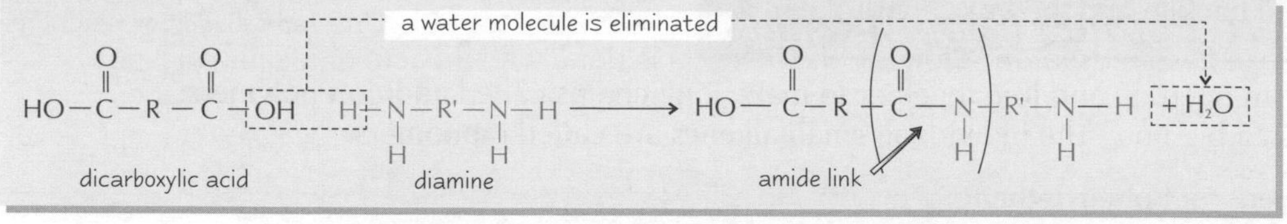


Dicarboxylic acids and diamines have functional groups at each end of the molecule, so long chains can form.

You need to know how the polyamides **nylon 6,6** and **KEVLAR®** link together.

Example

**Nylon 6,6** — made from **1,6-diaminohexane** and **hexanedioic acid**.

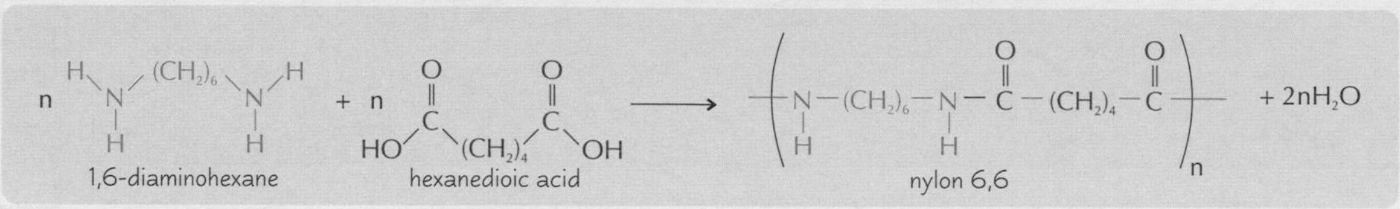


Example

**KEVLAR®** — made from **benzene-1,4-diamine** and **benzene-1,4-dicarboxylic acid**.

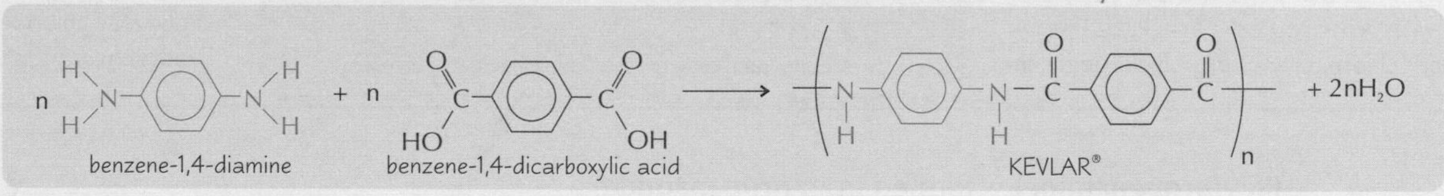


1) Polyamides like nylon are very useful because of their **physical properties**.
2) They have a **high tensile strength** and because of this, they're often used to make **rope**.
3) They can be also be used at **relatively high temperatures** — up to 150°C — and are **resistant to most chemicals** except acids and some alcohols. Acids hydrolyse the chain and it reverts to the original monomers (see page 99). This makes polyamides pretty good for use in **clothing** (unless you spill acid all over yourself).

## Reactions Between Dicarboxylic Acids and Diols Make Polyesters

*Not OCR B*

The **carboxyl** groups of **dicarboxylic acids** can also react with the **hydroxyl** groups of **diols** to form **ester links**.

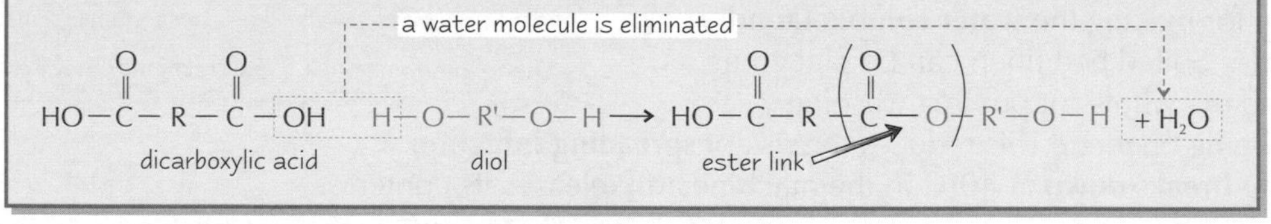

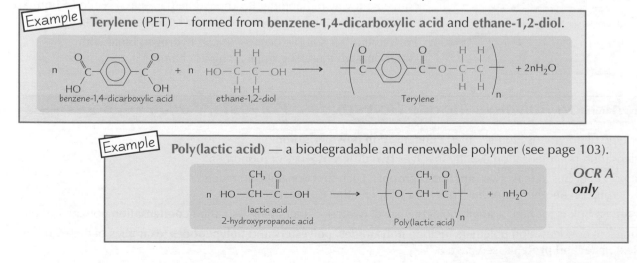

Like polyamides, polyesters are often used to make clothing.

Polymers joined by **ester links** are called **polyesters** — an example is **Terylene**.

Example

**Terylene** (PET) — formed from **benzene-1,4-dicarboxylic acid** and **ethane-1,2-diol**.

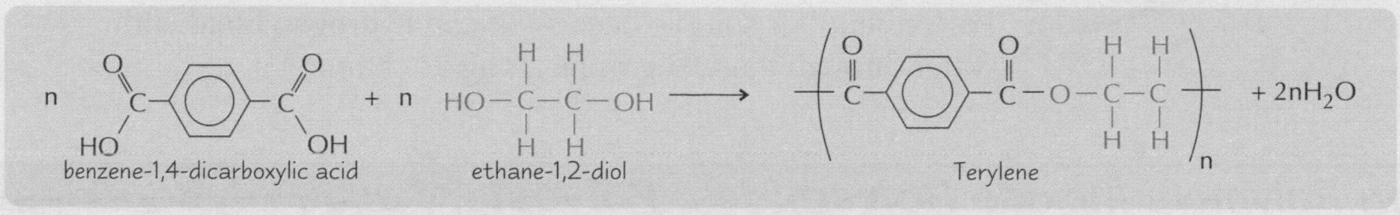


Example

**Poly(lactic acid)** — a biodegradable and renewable polymer (see page 103).

*OCR A only*

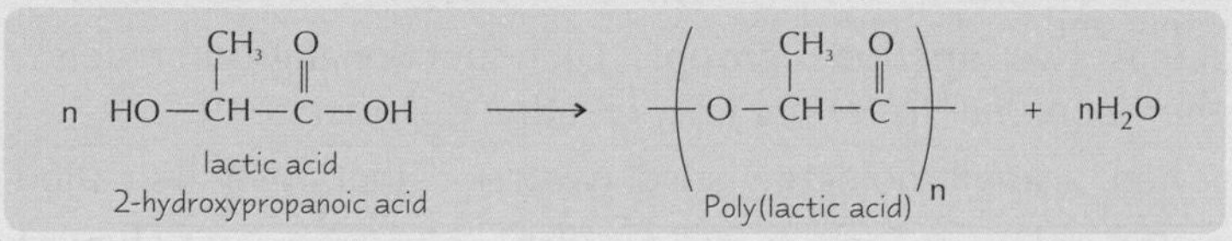

# Polymers

## Hydrolysis Produces the Original Monomers

*OCR A only*

1) Condensation polymerisation can be reversed by **hydrolysis** — water molecules are added back in and the links are broken.
2) In practice, hydrolysis with just water is far too **slow**, so the reaction is done with an **acid** or **alkali**.
3) **Polyamides** will hydrolyse more easily with an **acid** than an alkali:

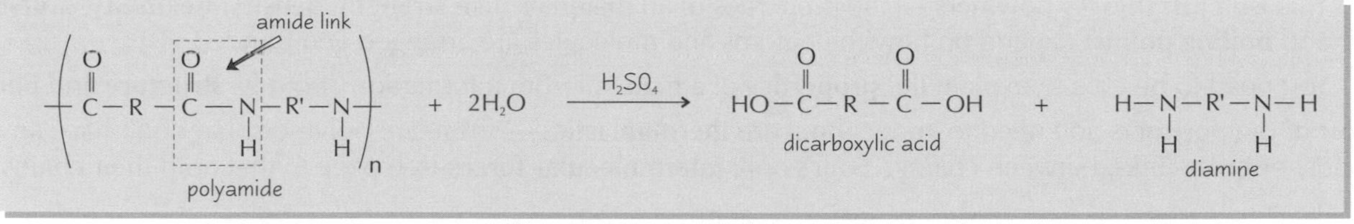


4) **Polyesters** will hydrolyse more easily with an **alkali**. A **salt** of the carboxylic acid is formed.

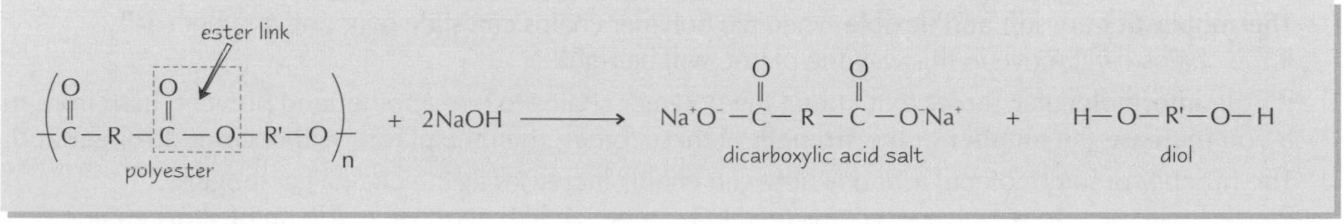


## Practice Questions

Q1 What type of polymer is: a) polyethene, b) polyester?

Q2 What molecule is eliminated when a polyester is made?

Q3 Which type of condensation polymer is made when a dicarboxylic acid reacts with a diamine?

Q4 Name an example of a polyester.

**Exam Questions**

1 The diagram shows three repeating units of a polymer.

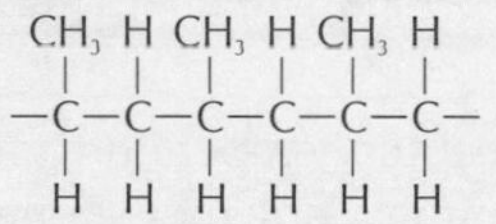

a) Name the polymer. [1 mark]

b) Name the **type** of polymerisation reaction by which this polymer would be formed. [1 mark]

c) Write an equation for the formation of this polymer from its monomers. [1 mark]

2 a) Nylon 6,6 is the most commonly produced nylon. A section of the polymer is shown below:

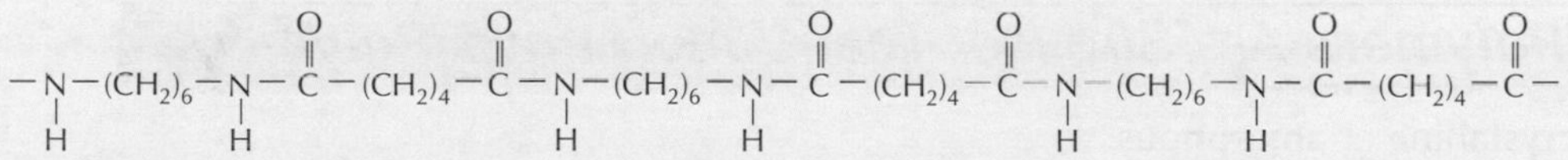

i) Draw the structural formulae of the monomers from which nylon 6,6 is formed. It is not necessary to draw the carbon chains out in full. [2 marks]

ii) Suggest why this nylon polymer is called nylon 6,6. [1 mark]

iii) Give a name for the linkage between the monomers in this polymer. [1 mark]

b) A polyester is formed by the reaction between the monomers hexanedioic acid and 1,6-hexanediol.

i) Draw the repeating unit for the polyester. [1 mark]

ii) Explain why this is an example of condensation polymerisation. [1 mark]

## Never miss your friends again — form a polymer...

*These polymers are really useful — KEVLAR® is used for bulletproof vests and nylon's used for parachutes. And someone had to invent them. Just think, you could be the next mad inventor, working for the biggest secret agency in the world. And you'd have a really fast car, which would obviously turn into a yacht with the press of a button...*

# Polymer Properties

*If you actually want to make something out of a polymer, you need to choose one with the right properties for the job...*
***These pages are for OCR B (Unit 4) only.***

## Structure and Bonding Control the Properties of All Materials

1) The **physical properties** of polymers depend on the **intermolecular bonds** between chains — and these depend on the **structure** of the polymer.
2) This isn't just true for polymers — the properties of all materials (like **strength**, **density**, **flexibility**, and **melting** and **boiling points**) depend on how their atoms and molecules are arranged and bonded.
3) You need to be able to explain the **properties** of a material from information about its **structure** and **bonding**.

Most of the polymers you need to know about are **thermoplastics** — these are polymers that don't have any covalent bonds, or **cross-links**, between chains. So it's only **intermolecular forces** (see page 6) that hold their chains together.

## Plastics With Longer Chains are Stronger and Less Flexible

1) **Thermoplastics** are **soft** and **flexible** when the polymer chains can **slide** over one another easily. If the chains can't move in this way the plastic will be **rigid**.
2) It's the **intermolecular forces** that attract the polymer chains to one another and prevent them from moving. If you **increase** the **number** or the **strength** of these forces, then the plastic will become **stronger** and more **rigid**.
3) The number of intermolecular bonds between chains **increases** as the chains get **longer**. Plastics with very **long** polymer chains tend to be **more rigid** than those made up of **short** chains.

## Polymers Soften and Melt When You Heat Them Above $T_m$

Thermoplastics all have a **melting point**, $T_m$.
If you heat a thermoplastic polymer to a temperature above its $T_m$ it will soften, and then **melt**.
The heat energy that you're adding disrupts the **intermolecular bonds** that hold the polymer chains together.
The chains start to be able to **slide** over one another — so the plastic can **change shape** more easily.

## Polymers Become Brittle and Shatter When You Cool Them Below $T_g$

If you cool a thermoplastic to below a certain temperature called its **glass transition temperature**, $T_g$, its physical properties will change. Cooling a polymer strengthens the **intermolecular bonds** that hold the chains together, so the plastic will become very **rigid**.
If you try to **bend** a plastic that is **colder** than its $T_g$, the polymer chains will not slide past each other to allow the plastic to change shape, and it will eventually **snap** or **shatter**.

## Crystalline Polymers Are Stronger Than Amorphous Polymers

Polymers can be **crystalline** or **amorphous**.

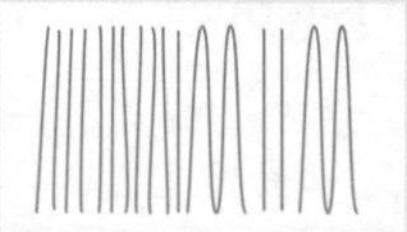

In a **crystalline** polymer, the arrangement of the chains is **ordered** — they all run in the **same direction**, or fold up neatly and stack next to each other

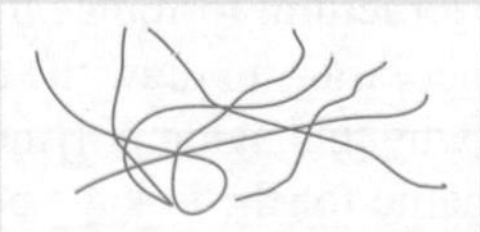

In an **amorphous** polymer, the arrangement of the chains is **random** — they all run in **different directions**.

1) In a **crystalline** polymer, where the chains are neatly packed, they can get very close together.
2) This means that the **intermolecular forces** between the polymer chains are much **greater** in crystalline polymers than in amorphous polymers. So crystalline polymers are **stronger** than **amorphous** polymers.
3) Most polymers are a mixture — they'll have some **crystalline regions** and some **amorphous regions**.

# Polymer Properties

## Polymer Properties can be *Modified* to Meet a *Particular Need*

You can alter the **properties** of a polymer **physically** or **chemically** in several different ways.

1) You can make a polymer using a mixture of **monomer** molecules. You will end up with a **polymer chain** that has different properties from a polymer made from any of the monomers alone — this is called **copolymerisation**.

> ***Example:*** Making a **styrene-butadiene copolymer**
> - **Polystyrene** has a **high** glass transition temperature, so it is very **hard**, but **brittle**, at room temperature.
> - **Polybutadiene** has a **low** glass transition temperature, and is **rubbery** and **flexible** at low temperatures.
> - If you make a polymer from a **mixture** of styrene and butadiene monomers, you produce a plastic that is very **tough** and **hard-wearing**, but also **flexible**. It's used to make **tyres** and **shoe soles**.

2) Adding a **plasticiser** makes a polymer **bendier**. The plasticiser molecules get **between** the polymer chains and push them apart. This **reduces** the strength of the **intermolecular forces** between the chains — so they can slide around more. Plasticers are added to polymers with **high** glass transition temperatures to make them more **flexible**.

> ***Example:*** Using plasticisers to make **flexible PVC**
> - **Poly(chloroethene)** (or **PVC**) has a **high** $T_g$. It has long, closely packed polymer chains, making it **hard** but **brittle** at room temperature. **Rigid PVC** is used to make drainpipes and window frames.
> - If you add a **plasticiser** to the PVC it **spaces out** the polymer chains. This **lowers** the $T_g$, and the plastic becomes **flexible**. **Plasticised PVC** is used to make electrical cable insulation, flooring tiles and clothing.

3) **Cold-drawing** increases the **crystallinity** of a polymer.

> The chains of an **amorphous polymer** are **randomly tangled**. They don't lie close together, and the intermolecular forces between them are **weak**. By pulling, or **drawing**, the polymer chains out in straight lines, they are forced to **straighten out** and lie close together. The intermolecular forces between chains **increase**, so the polymer is **more crystalline** and **stronger**.

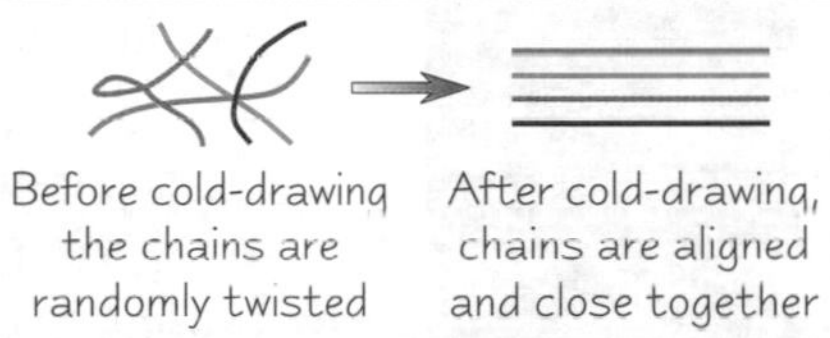
Before cold-drawing the chains are randomly twisted
After cold-drawing, chains are aligned and close together

Cold-drawing is used to make strong polymer fibres — nylon fibre is usually cold-drawn to increase its strength.

## *Practice Questions*

Q1 Describe what happens to a polymer if you cool it below its glass transition temperature.

Q2 Explain why amorphous polymers are less strong than crystalline ones.

Q3 What is a plasticiser and why would you add it to a polymer?

**Exam Questions**

1 Poly(ethene) can be made in two different forms. Low density poly(ethene) (LDPE) is not very strong, but it is light and has a low melting point. High density poly(ethene) (HDPE) is very strong and has a high melting point.
A scientist examines samples of the two forms of poly(ethene), which have been labelled A and B.
She finds that Polymer A is 85% crystalline, and Polymer B is 50% crystalline.

a) Which of the polymer samples is HDPE? Explain your answer. [3 marks]

b) Suggest why increasing the crystallinity of a polymer increases its melting point. [3 marks]

c) Name a technique that can be used to make a polymer more crystalline. [1 mark]

2 Poly(chloroethene), or PVC, is a hard, brittle plastic. Adding a plasticiser lowers its glass transition temperature.

a) Why is unplasticised PVC so hard and strong at room temperature? [2 marks]

b) Explain why adding a plasticiser lowers the $T_g$ of PVC, and how it changes the properties of the plastic. [3 marks]

## *I had a plasticised PVC drainpipe business — it folded...*

*...and I thought bendy guttering was going to be this season's big thing. Don't make the same mistake that I did. Make sure that you understand how the strength of its intermolecular bonds affects the properties of a polymer, and how you can alter them to get a polymer that's fit for a particular task. That way lies the path to lots of exam marks...*

# Polymers and the Environment

*Polymers are amazingly useful. But they have one big drawback...*
***These pages are for AQA (Unit 4), OCR A (Unit 4) and OCR B (Unit 4).***

## *Polymers — **Useful** but Difficult to **Get Rid Of***

1) Synthetic polymers have loads of **advantages**, so they're incredibly widespread these days — we take them pretty much for granted. Just imagine what you'd have to live without if there were no polymers...
2) It's estimated that in the UK we throw away over **3 million tons** of plastic (i.e. synthetic polymers) every year. The big problem is that plastics either take a **very long time** to biodegrade or are **non-biodegradable**.

> **Addition polymers** such as poly(ethene) and polystyrene are very unreactive which is an advantage when they are being used, but it makes them **non-biodegradable**.

> **Condensation polymers** such as PET and nylon are biodegradable — **fungi** and **bacteria** break down the polymer links by **hydrolysis**. But the process is very slow e.g. nylon can take 40 years.

3) So the question of what to do with all those plastic objects when we've finished using them is a big one. The options are basically **burying**, **burning** or sorting for **reusing** or **recycling**. None of these methods is an ideal solution — they all have **advantages** and **disadvantages** associated with them.

## *Waste Plastics can be **Buried***

1) **Landfill** is one option for dealing with waste plastics. It is generally used when the plastic is:
   - difficult to separate from other waste,
   - not in sufficient quantities to make separation financially worthwhile,
   - too difficult technically to recycle.
2) Landfill is a relatively **cheap** and **easy** method of waste disposal, but it requires **areas of land**.
3) As the waste decomposes it can release **methane** — a **greenhouse gas**. **Leaks** from landfill sites can also **contaminate water supplies**.
4) The **amount of waste** we generate is becoming more and more of a problem, so there's a need to **reduce** landfill as much as possible.

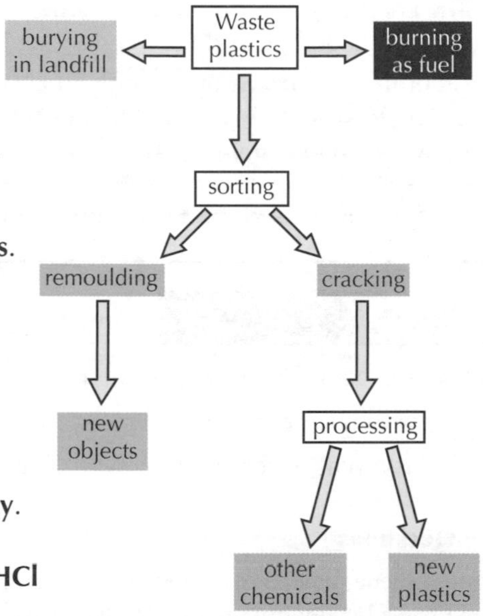


## *Waste Plastics can be **Burned***

1) Waste plastics can be **burned** and the heat used to generate **electricity**.
2) This process needs to be carefully **controlled** to reduce **toxic** gases. For example, polymers that contain **chlorine** (such as **PVC**) produce **HCl** when they're burned — this has to be removed.
3) So, waste gases from the combustion are passed through **scrubbers** which can **neutralise** gases such as HCl by allowing them to react with a **base**.
4) But, the waste gases, e.g. carbon dioxide, will still contribute to the **greenhouse effect**.

## *Waste Plastics can be **Recycled***

There are various ways that plastics can be recycled. For example:
- some plastics, e.g. poly(propene) can be **melted** and **remoulded**,
- others can be **cracked** into **monomers**, and used to make more plastics or other chemicals.

Rex and Dirk enjoy some waist plastic.

A big problem is that before plastics can be recycled, they must be **sorted** first. It's hard to make households do this effectively and it isn't easy to do it as an **automated** process.

# Polymers and the Environment

## *Green Chemistry is an Important Part of Polymer Production and Disposal*

The production of a polymer should have minimal impact on human health and the environment.

When chemists design a 'green' polymer-making process they try to...
- use **safe** reactant molecules that are as environmentally friendly as possible.
- use as **few reagents** as possible e.g. solvents.
- use **renewable raw materials**, e.g. poly(lactic acid) – see below.
- use **catalysts** so less energy is needed.
- create as **few waste products** as possible that are hazardous to human health and the environment.

How a polymer is disposed of is also an important consideration...

Condensation polymers will break down by hydrolysis, but the amount of time this takes to happen naturally means they still create **waste problems**. **Addition polymers** are even more of a problem — they are very **stable** molecules and won't be broken down by hydrolysis.

So chemists are trying to design new polymers that will biodegrade more easily.

*Example:* The biodegradable polymer **poly(lactic acid)**

1) **Poly(lactic acid)**, or **PLA**, is a **polyester** made from **lactic acid**, which is produced by fermenting maize or sugar cane, which are both renewable crops.
2) PLA will **biodegrade** easily — it is hydrolysed by water if kept at a **high temperature** for **several days** in an industrial composter or more slowly at lower temperatures in **landfill** or home **compost heaps**.
3) PLA has many uses, including **rubbish bags**, food and electronic **packaging**, disposable **eating utensils** and internal **sutures** (stitches) that break down without having to open wounds to remove them.

## *Light can Degrade Some Condensation Polymers*

*OCR A only*

Condensation polymers that contain **C=O (carbonyl) groups**, such as polyamides are **photodegradable** — they can be broken down by light as the C=O bond absorbs **ultraviolet radiation**. This energy can cause bonds to break either side of the carbonyl group and the polymer breaks down into smaller units.

## *Practice Questions*

Q1 What is the difference between addition and condensation polymerisation?

Q2 What type of bond do the monomers used to make addition polymers all have in their structure?

Q3 Give two environmental advantages of poly(lactic acid) over polythene.

Q4 What does photodegradable mean?

**Exam Question**

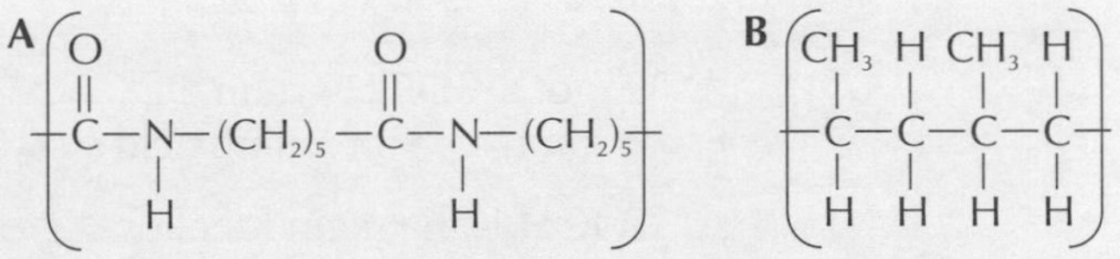


1 The diagram on the right shows sections of two polymers.

a) Name:

i) the general family of polymers that polymer A and polymer B belong to. [2 marks]

ii) the monomers that polymer A and polymer B are formed from. [2 marks]

b) Which of the two polymers, A or B, is biodegradable? [1 mark]

c) Give one advantage and one disadvantage of landfill as a disposal method for waste plastic. [2 marks]

## *Phil's my recycled plastic plane — but I don't know where to land Phil...*

*You might have noticed that all this recycling business is a hot topic these days. And not just in the usual places, such as Chemistry books. No, no, no... recycling even makes it onto the news regularly as well. This suits examiners just fine — they like you to know how useful and important chemistry is. So learn this stuff, pass your exam, and do some recycling.*

# Organic Functional Groups

*I spy with my little eye a functional group starting with A...*
***These pages are for AQA (Unit 4), OCR A (Unit 4), OCR B (Unit 4 and 5) and Edexcel (Unit 5).***

## Functional Groups are the Most Important Parts of a Molecule

Functional groups are the parts of a molecule that are responsible for the way the molecule reacts. These are the main ones you need to know (which are all covered earlier in the book)...

| Group | Found in | Prefix / Suffix | Example |
|---|---|---|---|
| $-C(=O)OH$ | carboxylic acids | carboxy– –oic acid | ethanoic acid |
| $-C(=O)Cl$ | acyl chlorides | –oyl chloride | ethanoyl chloride |
| $-C(=O)-O-C(=O)-$ | acid anhydrides | –oic anhydride | ethanoic anhydride |
| $-C(=O)-O-$ | esters, polyesters | –oate | ethyl methanoate |
| $-C(=O)H$ | aldehydes | –al | propanal |
| $>C=O$ | ketones | –one | propanone |

| Group | Found in | Prefix / Suffix | Example |
|---|---|---|---|
| $-OH$ | alcohols, phenols | hydroxy– –ol | propanol |
| $-NH_2$ | primary amines | amino– –amine | methylamine |
| $>NH$ | secondary amines | –amine | dimethylamine |
| $>N-$ | tertiary amines | –amine | trimethylamine |
| $-NO_2$ | nitro benzenes | nitro- | nitrobenzene |
| $-C_6H_5$ (benzene ring) | aromatic compounds | phenyl– –benzene | phenylamine |
| $>C=C<$ | alkenes | -ene | butene |

The functional groups in a molecule give you clues about its **properties** and the **reactions** it might take part in. For example, a **–COOH group** will (usually) make a molecule **acidic** and mean it will react with alcohols to make esters.

## Use the Functional Groups for Classifying and Naming Compounds

Organic molecules can get pretty complicated, often with many functional groups. You need to be able to **pick out** the functional groups on an unknown molecule, **name them** and **name the molecule** in a systematic way.

1) The **main functional group** is used as the **suffix** and the other functional groups are added as **prefixes**.
2) The table above shows the order of importance of the functional groups, with COOH being the most important, down to phenyl which is the least. (Note — alkenes are treated differently, with 'ene' always appearing in the suffix.)
3) If you need to include more than one functional group prefix, then list them in **alphabetical order**.

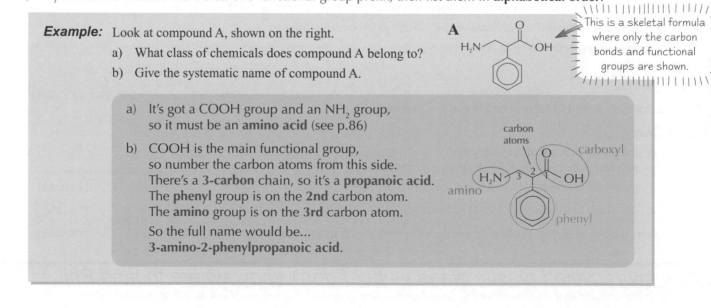

***Example:*** Look at compound A, shown on the right.

a) What class of chemicals does compound A belong to?

b) Give the systematic name of compound A.

**A**

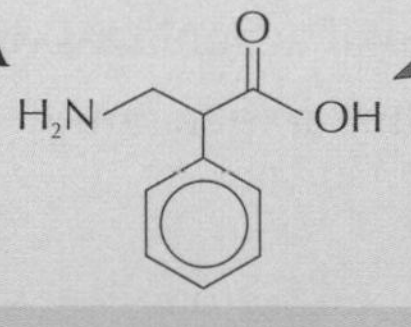


This is a skeletal formula where only the carbon bonds and functional groups are shown.

a) It's got a COOH group and an $NH_2$ group, so it must be an **amino acid** (see p.86)

b) COOH is the main functional group, so number the carbon atoms from this side. There's a **3-carbon** chain, so it's a **propanoic acid**. The **phenyl** group is on the **2nd** carbon atom. The **amino** group is on the **3rd** carbon atom.
So the full name would be...
**3-amino-2-phenylpropanoic acid**.

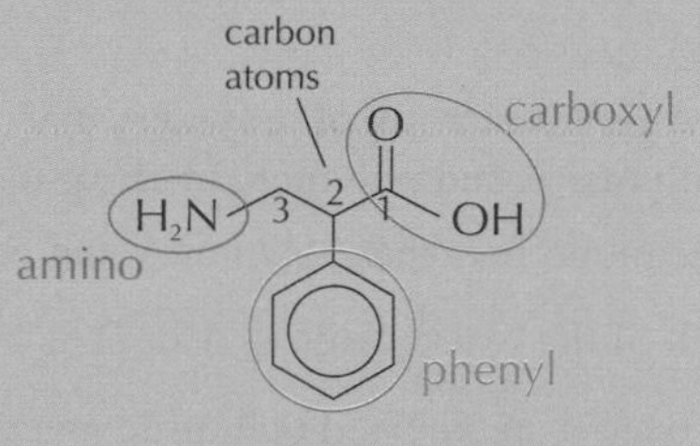

# Organic Functional Groups

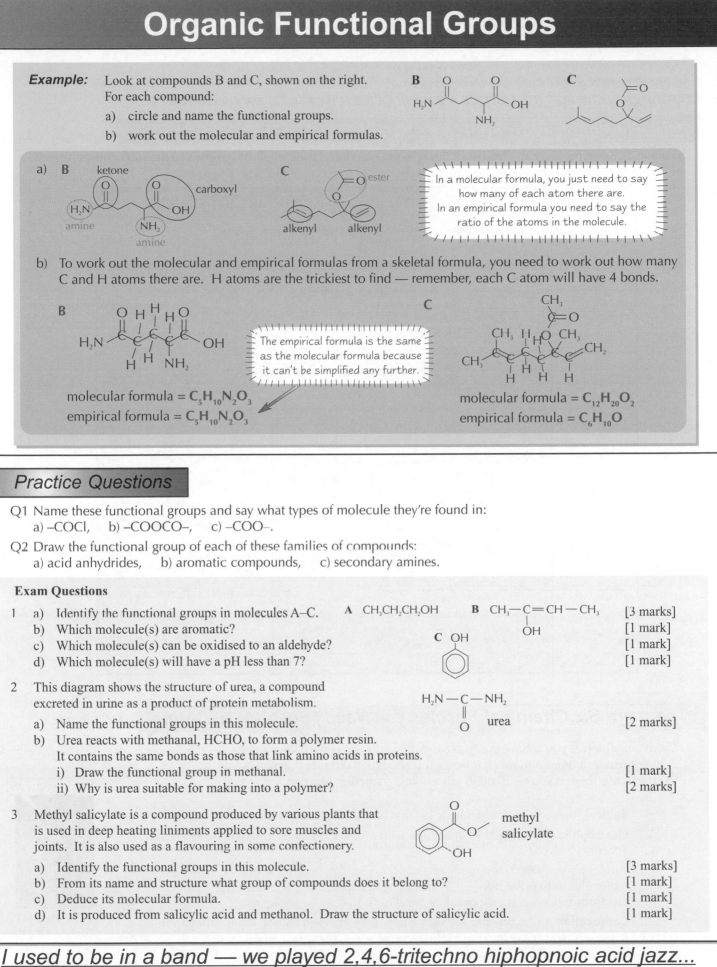

***Example:*** Look at compounds B and C, shown on the right.
For each compound:

a) circle and name the functional groups.

b) work out the molecular and empirical formulas.

B 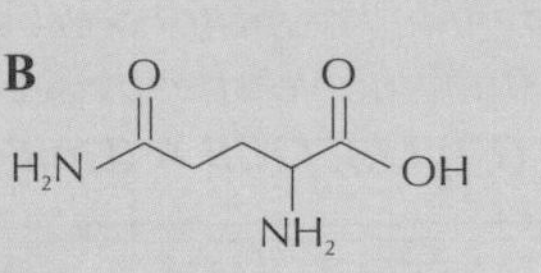


C 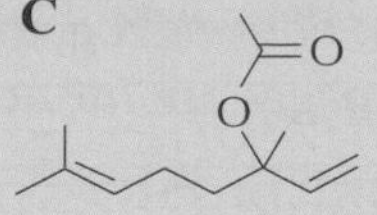


a) B 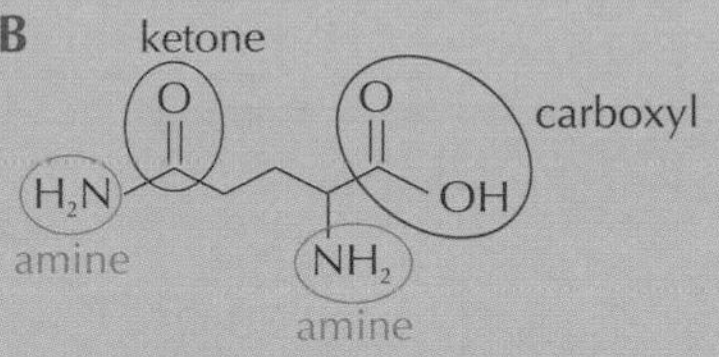


C 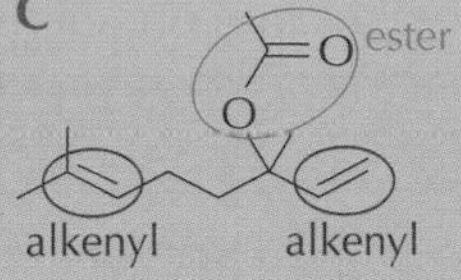


In a molecular formula, you just need to say how many of each atom there are. In an empirical formula you need to say the ratio of the atoms in the molecule.

b) To work out the molecular and empirical formulas from a skeletal formula, you need to work out how many C and H atoms there are. H atoms are the trickiest to find — remember, each C atom will have 4 bonds.

B 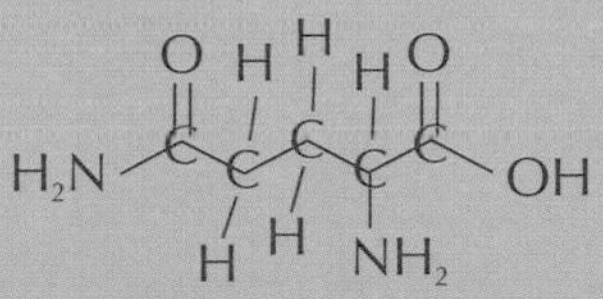


molecular formula = $C_5H_{10}N_2O_3$

empirical formula = $C_5H_{10}N_2O_3$

The empirical formula is the same as the molecular formula because it can't be simplified any further.

C 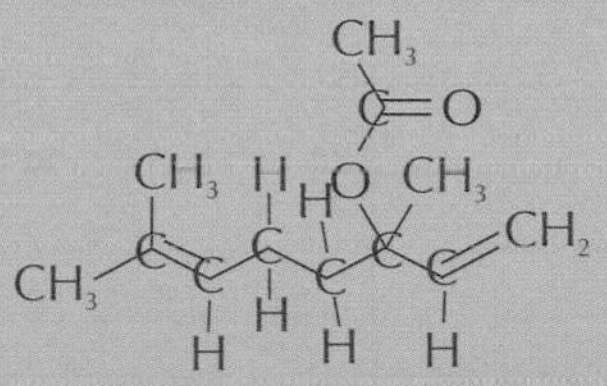


molecular formula = $C_{12}H_{20}O_2$

empirical formula = $C_6H_{10}O$

## Practice Questions

Q1 Name these functional groups and say what types of molecule they're found in:
a) –COCl, b) –COOCO–, c) –COO–.

Q2 Draw the functional group of each of these families of compounds:
a) acid anhydrides, b) aromatic compounds, c) secondary amines.

**Exam Questions**

1 a) Identify the functional groups in molecules A–C. **A** $CH_3CH_2CH_2OH$ **B** $CH_3-C(OH)=CH-CH_3$ [3 marks]

**C** 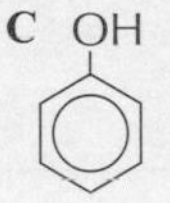


b) Which molecule(s) are aromatic? [1 mark]

c) Which molecule(s) can be oxidised to an aldehyde? [1 mark]

d) Which molecule(s) will have a pH less than 7? [1 mark]

2 This diagram shows the structure of urea, a compound excreted in urine as a product of protein metabolism.

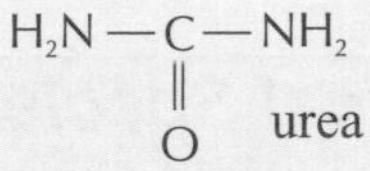


urea

a) Name the functional groups in this molecule. [2 marks]

b) Urea reacts with methanal, HCHO, to form a polymer resin. It contains the same bonds as those that link amino acids in proteins.

i) Draw the functional group in methanal. [1 mark]

ii) Why is urea suitable for making into a polymer? [2 marks]

3 Methyl salicylate is a compound produced by various plants that is used in deep heating liniments applied to sore muscles and joints. It is also used as a flavouring in some confectionery.

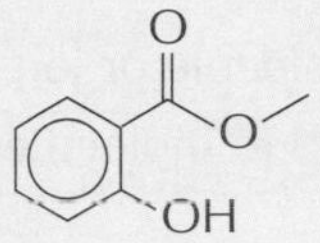


methyl salicylate

a) Identify the functional groups in this molecule. [3 marks]

b) From its name and structure what group of compounds does it belong to? [1 mark]

c) Deduce its molecular formula. [1 mark]

d) It is produced from salicylic acid and methanol. Draw the structure of salicylic acid. [1 mark]

## *I used to be in a band — we played 2,4,6-tritechno hiphopnoic acid jazz...*

*As well as recognising functional groups, this page gives you practice of a few other useful skills you'll need for your exam, e.g. interpreting different types of formula. If you're rusty on the difference between structural, molecular and displayed formulas, have a look back at your AS book – it's fundamental stuff that could trip you up in the exam if you don't know it.*

# Types of Reaction

*There's a whole load of organic chemistry coming on these pages. But don't panic.*
*It's just drawing together stuff you've already seen.*
***These pages are for AQA (Unit 4), OCR A (Unit 4), OCR B (Unit 4 and 5) and Edexcel (Unit 5).***

## Organic Chemistry **Reactions** can be Classified into **Seven Types**

In organic chemistry you can **classify** all the different reactions based on what happens to the molecules involved. All of the reactions you've met at AS and A2 levels will fit into one of these seven types.

| Reaction Type | Description | Functional groups that undergo this type of reaction |
|---|---|---|
| Addition | Two molecules join together to form a single product. Involves breaking a double bond. | 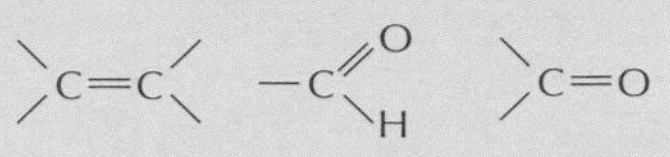 |
| Elimination | Involves removing a functional group which is released as part of a small molecule. Often a double bond is formed. | —X (H–X eliminated)<br>—OH ($H_2O$ eliminated)<br>X = halogen |
| Substitution | A functional group on a molecule is swapped for a new one. | —X<br>—OH<br> (H replaced) |
| Condensation | Two molecules get joined together with the loss of a small molecule, e.g. water. Opposite of hydrolysis. | 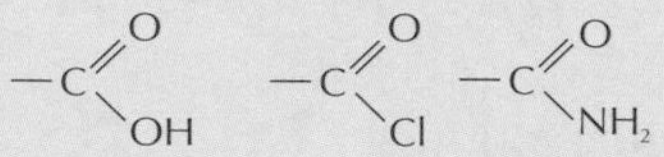 |
| Hydrolysis | Water is used to split apart a molecule creating two smaller ones. Opposite of condensation. | 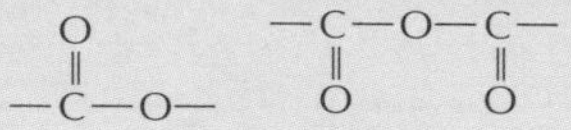<br>polyamides (e.g. nylon, proteins)<br>polyesters (e.g. Terylene®, PET) |
| Oxidation | Oxidation is loss of electrons. In organic chemistry it usually means gaining an oxygen atom or losing a hydrogen atom. | 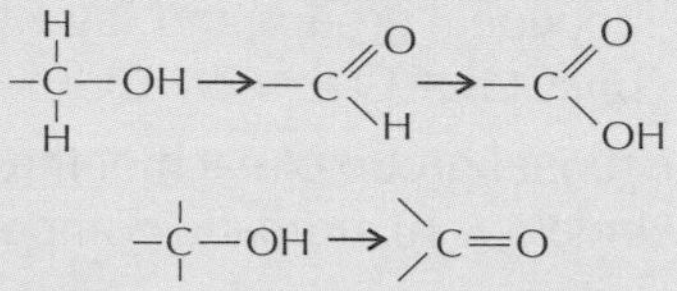 |
| Reduction | Reduction is gain of electrons. In organic chemistry it usually means gaining a hydrogen atom or losing an oxygen atom. | 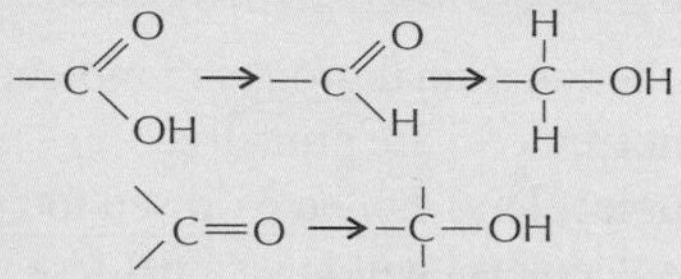 |

## There are Six **Chemical Species** you Need to be Able to **Define**

***OCR B only***

These are all terms you'll have come across when you've been looking at the different reaction types and mechanisms. You need to make sure you can define them and use them if you're asked to talk about a particular reaction.

1) **Radical** — An atom, molecule or ion that has an unpaired electron.
2) **Electrophile** — Attracted to molecules with areas of high electron density where it accepts electrons.
3) **Nucleophile** — Attracted to regions of positive charge density e.g. δ+ C atoms in molecules with polar bonds (C–Halogen, C–O and C=O). It can donate a pair of electrons to form a dative covalent bond (so it must have a lone pair).
4) **Carbocation** — An organic ion with a positively charged carbon atom. They form when a bond breaks and the electrons move away from the carbon atom.
5) **Saturated molecule** — All the C–C bonds are single.
6) **Unsaturated molecule** — There is at least one C=C double bond.

Meet Professor P. Orbital — he puts the 'func' into 'functional groups'.

# Types of Reaction

## Organic Reactions Come Under Five Different Types of Mechanism

If you're asked to draw a mechanism remember to include all the curly arrows, dipoles and charges for full marks.

| | |
|---|---|
| 1) **Radical substitution** — covered at AS<br>A molecule splits into two free radicals (initiation). The radicals react and are regenerated in a chain reaction (propagation). Radicals are removed by reacting with themselves (termination). | Initiation<br>$Cl{-}Cl \xrightarrow{UV} 2Cl^\bullet$<br>UV radiation is used to start the reaction<br>Propagation<br>$H_3C{-}H + Cl^\bullet \longrightarrow H_3C^\bullet + HCl$<br>$H_3C^\bullet + Cl{-}Cl \longrightarrow CH_3Cl + Cl^\bullet$<br>Termination<br>$2Cl^\bullet \longrightarrow Cl_2$<br>$Cl^\bullet + H_3C^\bullet \longrightarrow CH_3Cl$<br>$2H_3C^\bullet \longrightarrow CH_3CH_3$ |
| 2) **Electrophilic addition** — covered at AS<br>The δ+ of a polar molecule or a positive ion (electrophile) is attracted to the electrons in a double bond. The double bond opens up and the molecule or ion is added. | e.g. addition of bromine to ethene<br>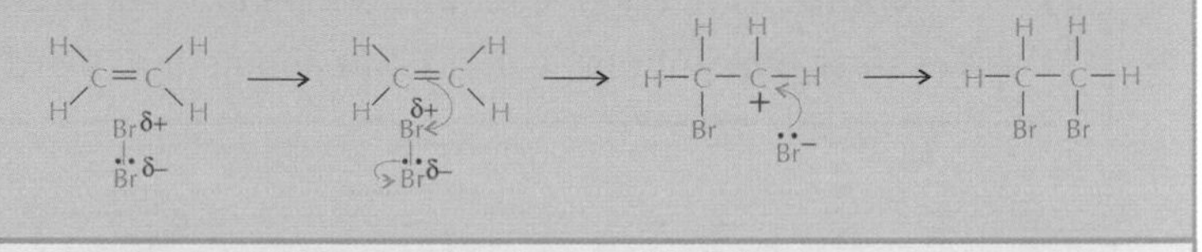 |
| 3) **Nucleophilic substitution** — covered on page 22<br>The δ– of a polar molecule or a negative ion (nucleophile) is attracted to the δ+ of a polar bond in a molecule. The nucleophile replaces an atom or group in the molecule. | e.g. reaction of hydroxide ions with 2-bromopropane<br>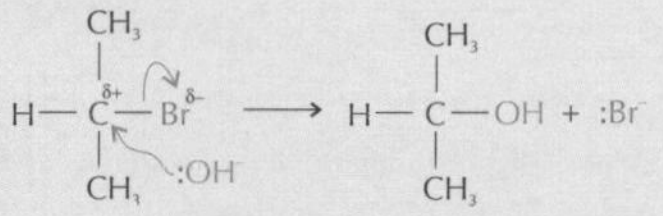 |
| 4) **Electrophilic substitution** — covered on page 72<br>Usually happens to aromatic compounds. The δ+ of a polar molecule or a positive ion (electrophile) is attracted to an electron rich region and is substituted for an existing group. | e.g. formation of nitrobenzene<br>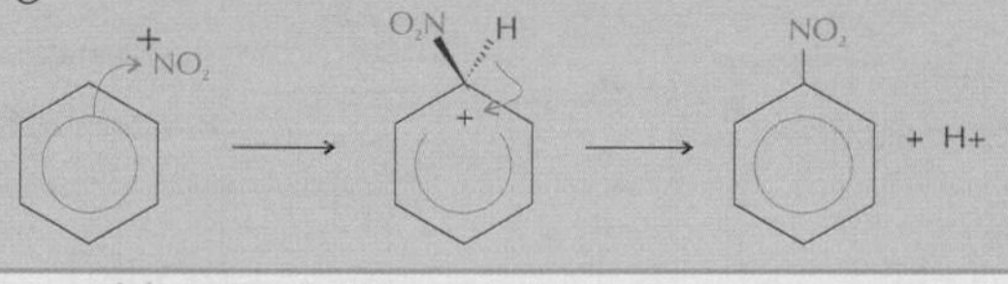 |
| 5) **Nucleophilic addition** — covered on page 57<br>The δ– of a polar molecule or a negative ion (nucleophile) is attracted to the δ+ of a polar double bond. The double bond opens up and the nucleophile is added. | e.g. addition of $CN^-$ to a ketone<br>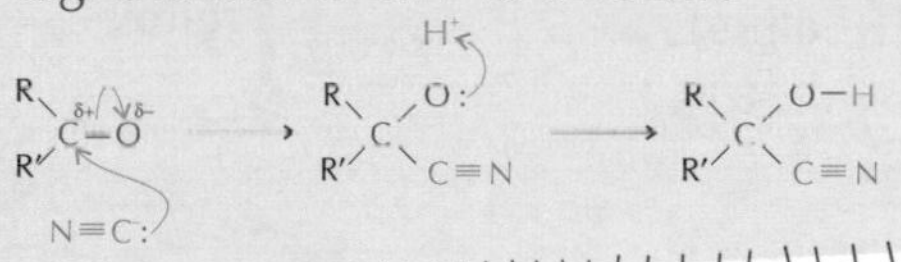 |

A curly arrow with one head shows the movement of one electron.
A curly arrow with two heads shows the movement of two electrons.

## Practice Questions

Q1 Which functional groups undergo: i) elimination reactions, ii) substitution reactions, iii) reduction reactions.

Q2 What is the definition of a: i) radical, ii) nucleophile.

Q3 Describe what happens in a: i) condensation reaction, ii) addition reaction.

Q4 Draw a reaction mechanism for a: i) nucleophilic substitution, ii) nucleophilic addition.

**Exam Questions**

1 Say whether the following are most likely to behave as electrophiles or nucleophiles, giving a reason in each case.
a) $H^+$ b) $NH_3$ c) $OH^-$ d) $H_2$ [4 marks]

2 a) Classify the reaction that occurs between each of the following as addition, elimination or substitution:
i) **HCN** and $CH_3COCH_3$ (propanone)
ii) $CH_2{=}CH_2$ and **HBr**
iii) $CH_3CH_2Cl$ and **NaOH** (cold, dilute aqueous solution) [3 marks]

b) For each reaction, give the name or structural formula of the organic product(s) and say whether the species in bold is acting as an electrophile, nucleophile or neither. [6 marks]

## Holy organic reaction Baitman — that's a lotta chemistry...

Baitman

*Well these pages aren't exactly short on information are they. The good news is that you have seen all of it before, either at AS or earlier in this book. So, if you can't remember all the details on something, flick back and have another read of it. Then close the book and start writing it all out until the pen runs dry.*

# Organic Synthesis

*In your exam you may be asked to suggest a pathway for the synthesis of a particular molecule.*
*These pages contain a summary of the main reactions you should know.*
***These pages are for AQA (Unit 4), OCR A (Unit 4), OCR B (Unit 4 and 5) and Edexcel (Unit 5).***

## Chemists use **Synthesis Routes** to Get from One Compound to Another

Chemists have got to be able to make one compound from another. It's vital for things like **designing medicines**. It's also good for making imitations of **useful natural substances** when the real things are hard to extract.

If you're asked how to make one compound from another in the exam, make sure you include:

1) any **special procedures**, such as refluxing (see page 112).
2) the **conditions** needed, e.g. high temperature or pressure, or the presence of a catalyst.
3) any **safety** precautions, e.g. do it in a fume cupboard.

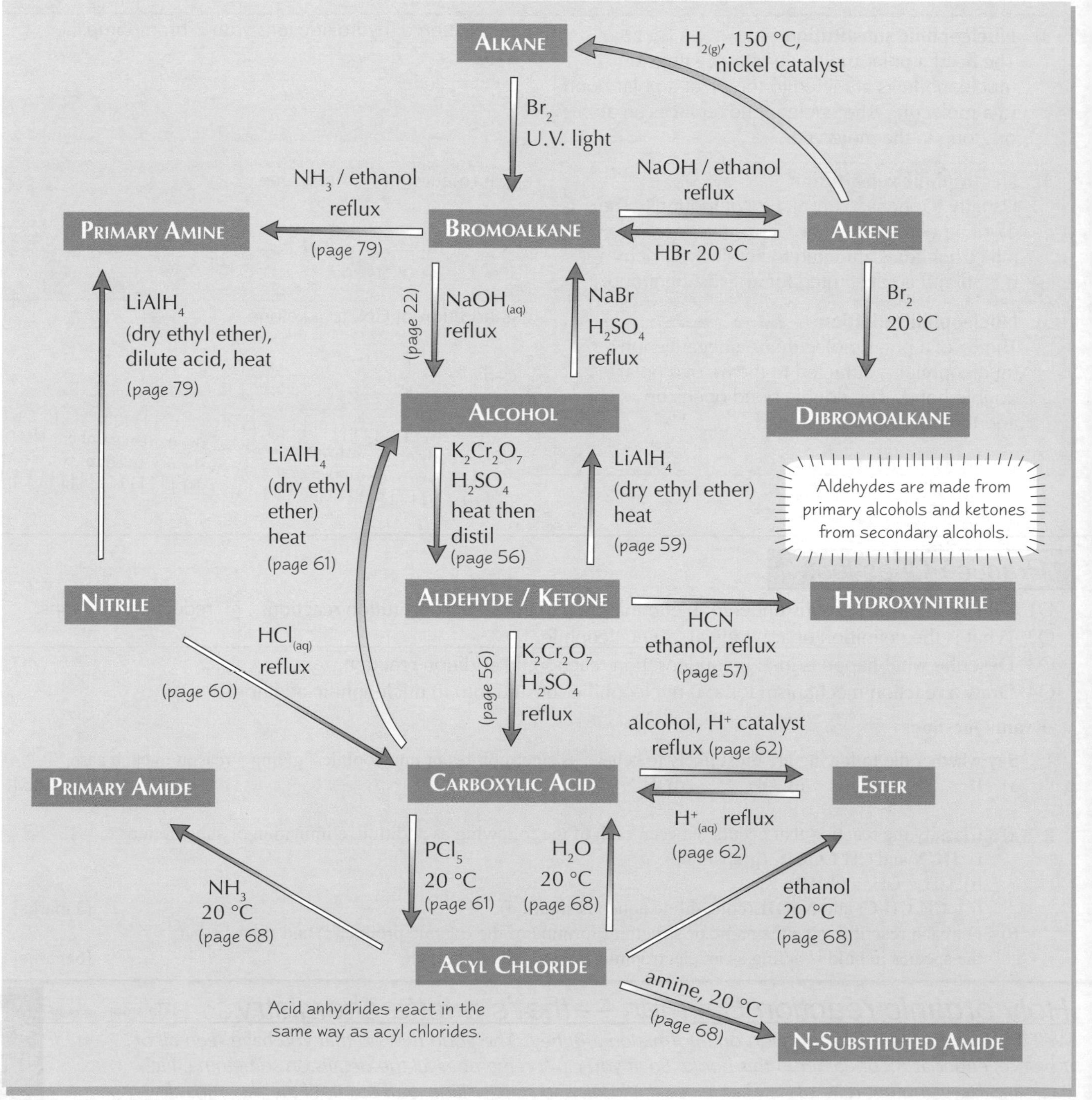

# Organic Synthesis

## There are Synthesis Routes for **Aromatic Compounds** Too

There are quite a lot of these to remember too — if you can't remember any of the reactions, look back to the relevant pages and take a quick peek over them.

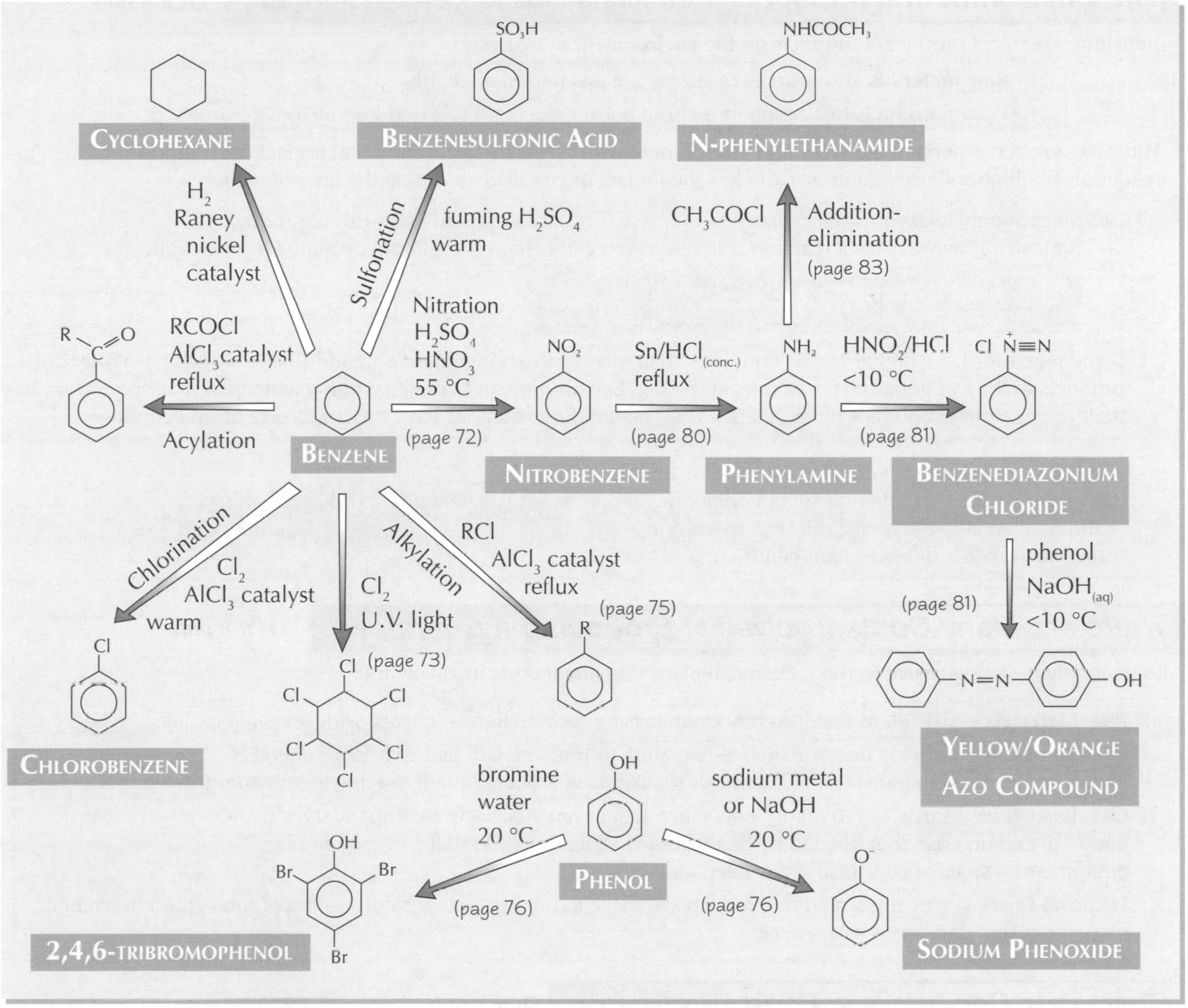


## Practice Questions

Q1 How do you convert an ester to a carboxylic acid?
Q2 How do you make an aldehyde from a primary alcohol?
Q3 What do you produce if you reflux a primary amide with an acid?
Q4 How do you make phenylamine from benzene?

**Exam Questions**

1 Ethyl methanoate is one of the compounds responsible for the smell of raspberries.
Outline, with reaction conditions, how it could be synthesised in the laboratory from methanol. [7 marks]

2 How would you synthesise propanol starting with propane? State the reaction conditions and reagents needed for each step and any particular safety considerations. [8 marks]

## *I saw a farmer turn a tractor into a field once — now that's impressive...*

*There's loads of information here. Tons and tons of it. But you've covered pretty much all of it before, so it shouldn't be too hard to make sure it's firmly embedded in your head. If it's not, you know what to do — go back over it again. Then cover the diagrams up, and try to draw them out from memory. Keep going until you can do it perfectly.*

# More on Organic Synthesis

*This may seem like a series of random, unrelated topics, but let me assure you nothing could be further from the truth. It's all about chemicals and... erm, industry... and food... and stuff.*
***These pages are for OCR B (Unit 5) and Edexcel (Unit 5).***

## The **Environmental Impact** of Reactions Has to be Considered — *OCR B only*

Industrial chemical production **impacts on the environment** in two ways:

1) **Raw materials** and **sources of energy** are taken from the Earth.
2) **Waste products** (including those from burning fuel) are released into the environment.

You can look at the **percentage yield** and **atom economy** to assess the environmental impact of an industrial reaction. The **higher** these figures are, the less the impact there's likely to be on the environment.

1) **Atom economy** tells you what proportion of the starting materials end up in useful products — basically, how wasteful a reaction is in itself. You can't change it without changing the reaction.

$$\%\ \text{atom economy} = \frac{\text{mass of desired product}}{\text{total mass of reactants}} \times 100$$

You can use the masses in grams, or their relative molecular masses.

Some reactions have higher atom economies than others. **Rearrangement** and **addition** reactions have only one product, so they've got atom economies of 100%. **Substitution** and **condensation** reactions form a by-product so they've got atom economies of less than 100%. **Elimination** reactions have an even lower **atom economy**.

2) **Percentage yield** tells you how efficient the entire process is under a particular set of conditions. You may be able to change this, e.g. by carrying out the reaction at a different temperature or pressure.

$$\%\ \text{yield} = \frac{\text{actual product yield}}{\text{theoretical yield}} \times 100$$

## There are Many **Costs** Involved in **Producing a Chemical** — *OCR B only*

It's generally quite **expensive** to run a chemical plant. The main costs involved are:

1) **Raw Materials** — The plant needs to buy chemicals for the reaction — cheap, widely available ones are best.
2) **Fuel/Energy** — Reactions needing high temperature or pressure will use up a lot of energy. Energy is also used in transporting chemicals to, from and around a plant, mixing them and purifying products.
3) **Overheads/Fixed Costs** — No matter how much fuel or raw materials a company uses, there are certain costs that need to be met regularly. These include staff wages, rent of equipment or space, taxes, insurance, telephone bills, etc.
4) **Disposal Costs** — Any unwanted by-products will have to be disposed of safely — this is subject to government regulations and can be very expensive.

## Chemicals Can Improve **Food Production** — *OCR B only*

Feeding the world's population is a **huge challenge**.
There are three main ways the **chemical industry** helps food production:

**1) Fertilising the soil** — providing crops with extra nutrients helps **improve plant growth** and **increase yield**.
But overuse of artificial fertilisers can cause problems:
- Rain can wash the fertilisers into lakes and rivers and cause excessive **growth of algae**, which **block out light** and cause plants to die. **Bacteria** multiply by feeding on the decaying plants and **deoxygenate** the water.
- Nitrate(V) ions from fertilisers can get into **drinking water**. There are concerns about the **health risks** of this.

**2) Acid neutralisation** — Maintaining the correct soil pH for a particular crop helps increase yield.
**Limestone** (calcium carbonate) or **lime** (calcium hydroxide) can be added to soils to neutralise excess acid.

**3) Killing pests** — pesticides are used to kill **insects**, **weeds** or **moulds** that can **reduce crop yield** and **quality**.
But the use of pesticides has **downsides** too:
- Pesticides can kill non-pest organisms.
- Some **don't break down** and can **accumulate** in food chains, harming larger bird and animal species.
- As with fertilisers, they can be washed from the soil and end up in **drinking water**.

# More on Organic Synthesis

## Chemical Production has some Risks... *OCR B only*

**Large-scale production** of chemicals like **medicines**, **fertilisers**, **cleaning products** and **dyes**, as well as new materials like **plastics**, has revolutionised our lives. But chemical production is not without **risks**...

1) Some chemicals, especially gases, are **highly flammable** and carry the risk of **explosion**, e.g. ammonia, propane, pressurised hydrogen. They must be stored and handled correctly to minimise this risk.
2) Some chemicals are **harmful to our health** if we come into contact with them or their vapours. Chlorine, for example, is **toxic** if inhaled and can irritate the eyes and lungs. Workers in the chemical industry are most at risk, but an **accident** or **fire** at a chemical plant, or a **spill** during transportation, could also **expose the public** to hazardous material.
3) Some chemicals can also **damage the environment**. Sulfur dioxide is a **by-product** of sulfuric acid production. It's an **acidic gas** and a contributor to **acid rain**.

## Organic Synthesis is Important for Research and Making Useful Products *Edexcel only*

A lot of drugs were originally produced from **natural substances** in plants. But often it isn't viable to use the plants to make large quantities. So, a lot of research goes into developing them from more available reagents.

**Example**: Paclitaxel is a **cancer drug** that was discovered in the bark of the **Pacific Yew tree**. The Pacific Yew tree is a **rare protected species** and the forests it grows in are inhabited by a number of **protected birds**.

So chemists developed a method of synthesising the molecule from the needles and twigs of other species of yew tree that grow freely in Europe.

Organic synthesis can also be used to **change** a natural product, either to **improve its qualities** or **reduce its side effects**.

**Example**: The first form of the painkiller aspirin was called **salicylic acid** and was derived from the bark of willow trees. The problem was that it caused mouth and stomach **irritation**.

Chemists modified the functional groups until **acetylsalicylic acid** was discovered. It still had the same painkilling properties but without the nasty side effects.

## Analysis Techniques Tell You if Your Synthesis Worked *Edexcel only*

It's important to know if a synthesis has been successful or not. The chemical industry uses a wide **range** of **analytical techniques** to monitor the **progression of a reaction**, **identify products** and **detect impurities**.
These include IR spectroscopy (page 123), mass spectrometry (page 116), gas chromatography (page 114) and UV spectrometry. It is also possible to use different types of chemical test to identify certain functional groups.

## Practice Questions

Q1 State two ways in which the industrial production of chemicals impacts upon the environment.

Q2 Why do reactions with higher atom economies and percentage yields tend to be less harmful to the environment?

Q3 How do artificial fertilisers allow farmers to get a greater yield of crop?

Q4 Give an example of when organic synthesis has been used to improve a drug.

**Exam Questions**

1 Bromomethane is reacted with sodium hydroxide to make methanol:

$$CH_3Br + NaOH \rightarrow CH_3OH + NaBr$$

Calculate the atom economy for this reaction. [4 marks]

2 Agrochemicals are chemical products used by farmers to improve the quantity or quality of the food that they produce.

a) Describe three different ways that agrochemicals are used in farming. [3 marks]

b) Explain two problems associated with the use of agrochemicals. [4 marks]

## I've got a chemical plant — it's a chemis-tree...

*I know it seems like there's a lot of random stuff on these two pages, but it's mostly pretty straightforward. Make sure you're happy with calculating atom economy and percentage yield though — that's pretty important. In the grand scheme of things, probably not as important as war, or widespread famine... but, you know... useful for the exam and all that.*

# Practical Techniques

*You can't call yourself a chemist unless you know these practical techniques. Unless your name's Boots.*
***These pages are for OCR B (Unit 4) and Edexcel (Unit 5).***

## *Refluxing* Makes Sure You *Don't Lose* Any *Volatile Organic Substances*

**Organic reactions** are **slow** and the substances are usually **flammable** and **volatile** (they've got **low boiling points**). If you stick them in a beaker and heat them with a Bunsen they'll **evaporate** or **catch fire** before they have **time to react.**

You can **reflux** a reaction to get round this problem.

The mixture's **heated in a flask** fitted with a **vertical 'Liebig' condenser** — this condenses the vapours and **recycles** them back into the flask, giving them **time to react.**

The **heating** is usually **electrical** — hot plates, heating mantles, or electrically controlled water baths are normally used. This **avoids naked flames** that might ignite the compounds.

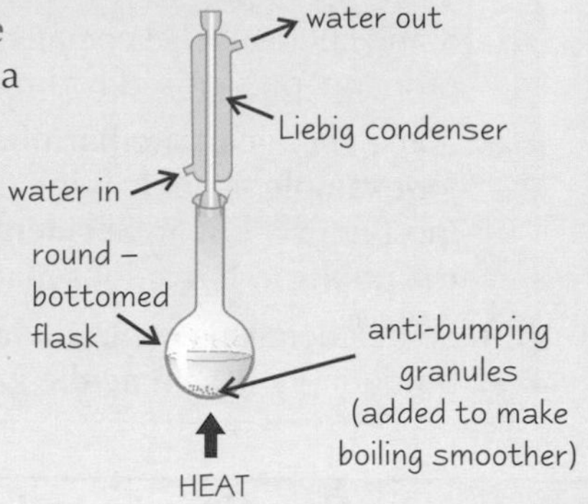


## There are *Lots of Ways* to *Purify* a Sample

***Edexcel only***

### Washing

The product of a reaction can be **contaminated** with unreacted reagents or unwanted sideproducts. You can **remove** some of these by **washing** the product.
E.g. aqueous **sodium hydrogencarbonate** solution can be used to remove **acid** from an organic product. Any excess acid is reacted with the sodium hydrogencarbonate to give $CO_2$ gas, and the organic product (assuming it's insoluble in the aqueous layer) can be easily removed using a separating funnel.

### Solvent Extraction

You can **separate** a product from a mixture by dissolving it in a **solvent**. This only works if **only the product dissolves**. Shake the mixture with fresh solvent several times to make sure you extract as much product as possible from the mixture.

### Drying

A lot of organic reactions either use water or produce water. To dry a liquid product you can add **anhydrous calcium chloride granules**. Calcium chloride removes water from the mixture by forming solid crystals, which can be filtered off.

### Recrystallisation

***OCR B as well***

Recrystallisation will let you remove a small amount of an **impurity** in a **solid.**

1) Add **very hot solvent** to the **impure** solid until it **just** dissolves – it's really important not to add too much.
2) This should give a **saturated solution** of **impure product**.
3) Let the solution **cool** down **slowly**. **Crystals** of the **product** will form as it cools.
4) It's important that the product is very soluble at high temperatures and nearly insoluble at low temperatures.
5) The **impurities** stay in solution. They're present in much smaller amounts than the product, so they'd take much longer to crystallise out.
6) Remove the crystals by **filtration**, **wash** with ice-cold solvent and leave to dry. You're left with crystals of the product that are **much purer** than the original solid.

## *Melting* and *Boiling* Points are Good Indicators of *Purity*

***Edexcel only***

Most **pure substances** have a **specific melting** and **boiling point**. If they're **impure**, the **melting point's lowered** and the **boiling point is raised**. If they're **very impure**, melting and boiling will occur across a wide range of temperatures.

To accurately measure the melting point:
Put a small amount of the solid in a **capillary tube** and place in a beaker of an oil with a very sensitive thermometer. **Slowly heat**, with constant stirring, until the solid **just melts** and read the temperature on the thermometer.

To measure the boiling point:
Measure the temperature that the liquid is collected at during **distillation**.

# Practical Techniques

## Fractional Distillation Separates Two or More Liquids

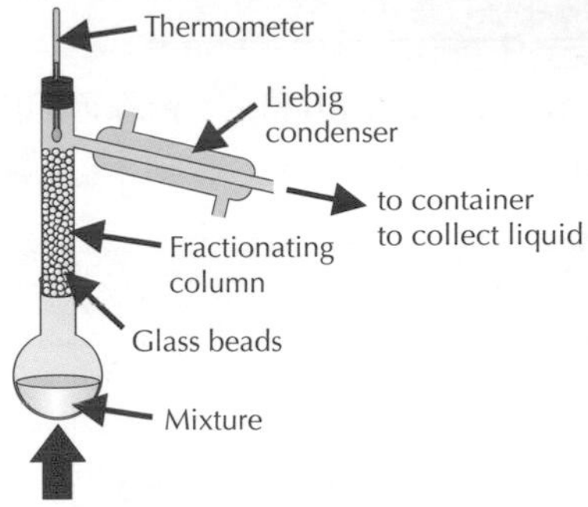


Fractional distillation separates liquids with **different boiling points**.

The mixture's **heated** in the apparatus shown and the liquid in the flask boils. As the vapour goes up the **fractionating column**, it gets **cooler**. If the temperature falls below its boiling point, the molecules **condense** and run back down through the glass beads. As the temperature increases, each liquid will reach the top of the column at a different time, in order of their boiling points. The liquid with the lowest boiling point will be distilled first.

Sometimes the high temperatures used during distillation can cause a product to **decompose**. To help stop this happening **steam** can be passed into the mixture — this **lowers** the **boiling point** of the product so it can evaporate at a temperature that doesn't cause it to decompose.

## Lots of Techniques are Used To Prepare A Compound

*Edexcel only*

Here are a couple of preparations you need to know about.

**Example: Cholesteryl benzoate** is used in liquid crystal displays, hair colours and cosmetics. It's an ester of cholesterol (alcohol) and benzoic acid, but is prepared from benzoyl chloride.

1) Start by dissolving the cholesterol in the solvent pyridine (toxic).
2) Then add the benzoyl chloride (a lachrymator — makes you cry like tear gas).
3) Heat in a steam bath for 10 minutes, then cool and add methanol.
4) Filter off the crystals of the ester that form and wash them with methanol.
5) Recrystallise the ester using ethyl ethanoate as the solvent.

The preparation is done in a fume cupboard because of the harmful reagents.

**Example: Methyl 3-nitrobenzoate** is prepared by nitrating methyl benzoate.

1) Dissolve methyl benzoate in concentrated sulfuric acid that has been cooled in an ice bath.
2) Then add a 50:50 mixture of concentrated sulfuric and nitric acids dropwise, with constant stirring. You need to keep the temperature below 10 °C with ice.
3) Stir the mixture for 15 minutes, then pour it over crushed ice in a beaker. When the ice has melted, filter off the crystals of product that have formed.
4) Wash the crystals with water and then recrystallise them using ethanol.

The experiment needs to be carried out below 10 °C to keep the yield high.

## Practice Questions

Q1 Why is refluxing needed in many organic reactions?

Q2 Why is the melting point helpful in deciding the purity of a substance?

Q3 Draw the apparatus needed for fractional distillation.

Q4 Why is electrical heating often used in organic chemistry?

**Exam Question**

1 Two samples of stearic acid melt at 69 °C and 64 °C respectively. Stearic acid dissolves in propanone but not in water.

a) Explain which sample is purer. [2 marks]

b) How could the impure sample be purified? [5 marks]

c) How could the sample from b) be tested for purity? [1 mark]

## There's just a **fraction** too much information on these pages for me... boom boom

*And that, my friends, is what chemistry is all about — playing with funny looking pieces of glass and making crystals in pretty colours whilst wearing a white coat, goggles and stood in a fume cupboard. Ok, not actually stood in the fume cupboard, that would just be silly. You'd keep hitting you head and you can't do chemistry with a bumped head.*

# Chromatography

*You've probably tried chromatography with a spot of ink on a piece of filter paper — it's a classic experiment.*
***These pages are for AQA (Unit 4), OCR A (Unit 4), OCR B (Unit 5) and Edexcel (Unit 4).***

## Chromatography is Good for **Separating** and **Identifying** Things

Chromatography is used to **separate** stuff in a mixture — once it's separated out, you can often **identify** the components. There are quite a few different types of chromatography — but they all have the same basic set up:

1) A **mobile phase** — where the molecules can move. This is always a liquid or a gas.
2) A **stationary phase** — where the molecules can't move. This must be a solid, or a liquid on a solid support.

And they all use the same basic principle:

1) The mobile phase **moves through** or **over** the stationary phase.
2) The components in the mixture spend **different amounts of time** in the mobile phase and the stationary phase.
3) The components that spend longer in the **mobile phase** travel **faster** or **further**.
4) The time spent in the different phases is what **separates out** the components of the mixture.

## **TLC** and **Column Chromatography** Separate Components by **Adsorption**

In thin layer and column chromatography, the mixture **separates** based on **how strongly** the components are **attracted** to the stationary phase. The **attraction** between a substance and the surface of the stationary phase is called **adsorption**. A substance that is **strongly adsorbed** will move **slowly**, so it **won't travel as far** or **as quickly** as one that's only **weakly adsorbed**.

### Thin-Layer Chromatography

***Just OCR A and OCR B***

Stationary phase — **thin layer of solid**, e.g. silica gel or alumina powder, on a **glass or plastic plate**.
Mobile phase — **solvent**, e.g. ethanol, which passes over the stationary phase.

To make the spots visible, the TLC plate might have a **fluorescent dye** added that glows under **UV light**. The spots of chemical show up against the fluorescent dye. Or they can be exposed to **iodine vapour**, which sticks to the chemicals and shows up as **brown spots**.

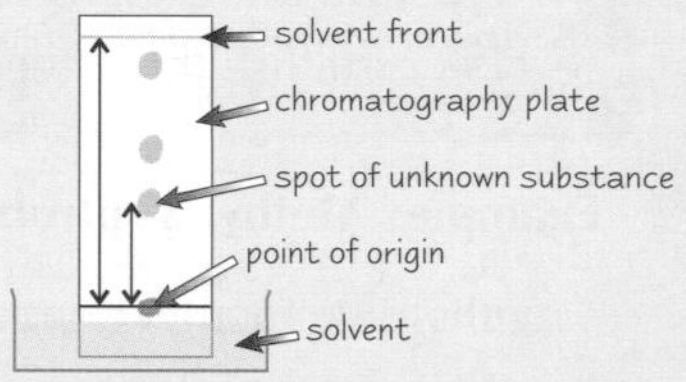


You can work out what was in the mixture by calculating an $R_f$ **value** for each spot and looking them up in a **table of known values**.

$$R_f \text{ value} = \frac{\text{distance travelled by spot}}{\text{distance travelled by solvent}}$$

The stationary phase and solvent used will affect the $R_f$ value.

### Column Chromatography

***Just AQA***

Stationary phase — slurry of an **absorbent material** e.g. aluminium oxide, coated with water packed into a **glass column**.

Mobile phase — **solvent** that is run slowly and continually through the column.

The mixture is separated by **how long** it takes for a component to move through the column. The time it takes to get to the end is called the **retention time**.

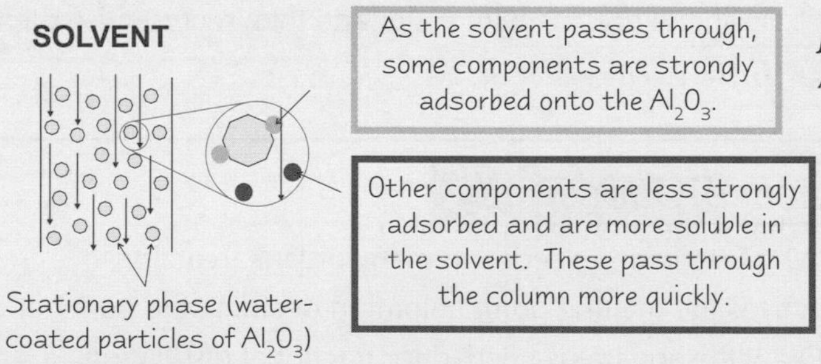

SOLVENT
Stationary phase (water-coated particles of $Al_2O_3$)
As the solvent passes through, some components are strongly adsorbed onto the $Al_2O_3$.
Other components are less strongly adsorbed and are more soluble in the solvent. These pass through the column more quickly.


## **Gas Chromatography** is a Bit More **High-Tech**

It's sometimes called gas-liquid chromatography if the stationary phase is a liquid.

Gas chromatography (GC) can be used to separate a mixture of volatile liquids and is often used to check the **purity** of products in the chemical industry.

1) The mobile phase is an **unreactive carrier gas** such as nitrogen or helium.
2) The stationary phase can be a **viscous liquid**, e.g. an oil, or a **solid**, which coats the inside of a long tube built into an oven (so you can control the **temperature**).
3) The different components **dissolve** into the stationary and **evaporate** into the mobile phase. How long they spend in the two phases determines how long it takes for them to travel through the tube.

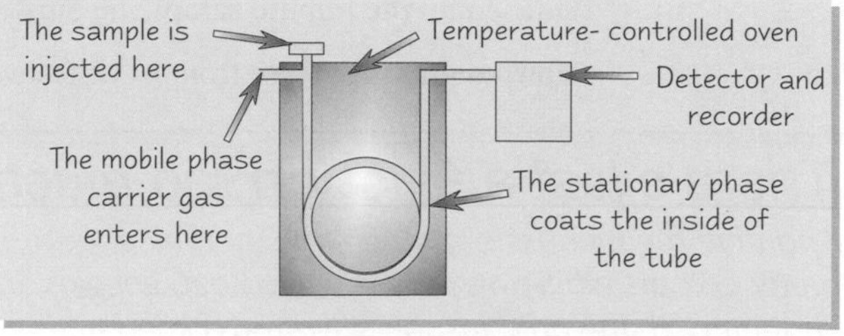

# Chromatography

## GC Chromatograms Show the Proportions of Components in a Mixture

***OCR B and OCR A only***

The detector produces a **gas chromatogram**, which shows a **series of peaks** when something other than the carrier gas is **leaving the tube**. They can be used to **identify substances** within a sample and their **relative proportions**.

1) Each **peak** on a chromatogram corresponds to a substance with a particular **retention time**.
2) **Retention times** can be looked up in a **reference table** to **identify** the **substances** present.
3) The **area** under each peak is proportional to the relative **amount of each substance** in the original mixture. Remember, it's **area**, not height, that's important — the **tallest** peak on the chromatogram **won't always** represent the **most abundant substance**.

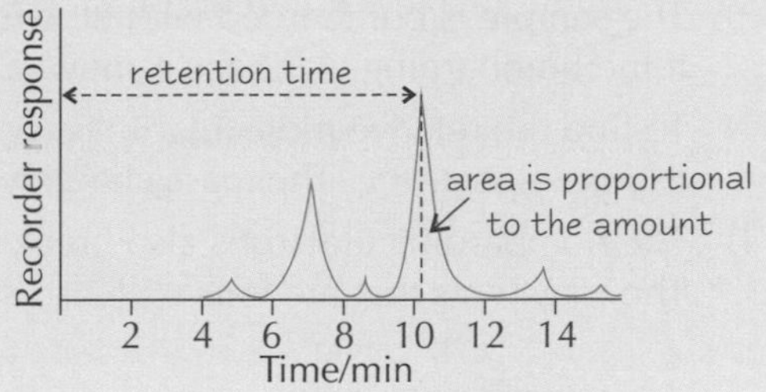


## Gas Chromatography has Limitations

***Just OCR A***

Although a very useful and widely used technique, GC does have **limitations** when it comes to identifying chemicals.

1) **Compounds** which are **similar** often have **very similar retention times**. A mixture of **two similar substances** may only produce **one peak** so you **can't tell how much** of each one there is.
2) You can only use GC to identify substances that you already have **reliable reference retention times** for. (That means someone must have run a sample of the same pure substance under exactly the same conditions already.)

You can combine GC with mass spectrometry to make a much more powerful identification tool — there's more on this on page 118.

## High-Pressure Liquid Chromatography is a Useful Alternative to GC

***OCR A and Edexcel***

High-pressure (or high-performance) liquid chromatography (HPLC) is another method that is used to check for impurities during drug manufacture.

The mobile phase is often a **polar liquid mixture** e.g. methanol and water.

The stationary phase can be various **hydrocarbons bonded to silica particles** that are packed into a tube.

The retention time is measured using a detector and can be used to produce chromatograms and check the purity of a sample.

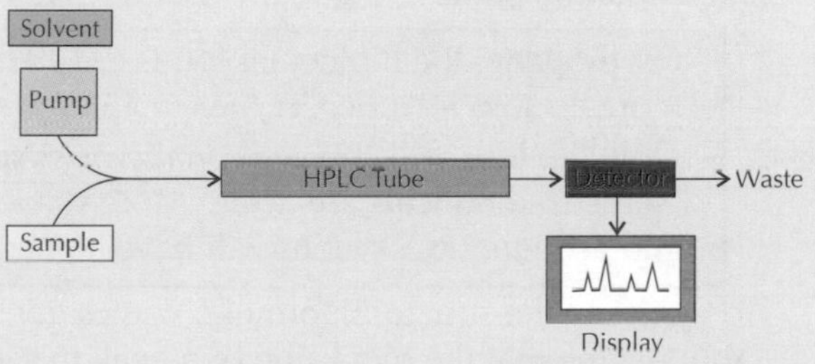

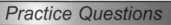

## Practice Questions

Q1 Explain the terms 'stationary phase' and 'mobile phase' in the context of chromatography.

Q2 What is the stationary phase in TLC?

Q3 What is the mobile phase in GC?

Q4 Describe how you would calculate the $R_f$ value of a substance on a TLC plate.

**Exam Questions**

1 Look at this diagram of a chromatogram produced using TLC on a mixture of substances A and B.

a) Calculate the $R_f$ value of spot A. [2 marks]

b) Explain why substance A has moved further up the plate than substance B. [3 marks]

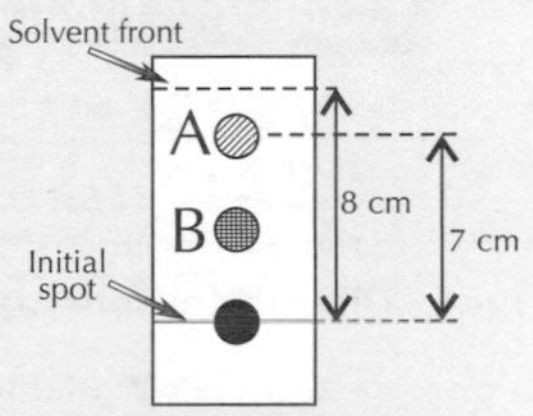


2 A mixture of 25% ethanol and 75% benzene is run through a GC apparatus.

a) Describe what happens to the mixture in the apparatus. [4 marks]

b) Explain why the substances separate. [2 marks]

c) How will the resulting chromatogram show the proportions of ethanol and benzene present in the mixture? [1 mark]

## A little bit of TLC is what you need...

*If you only remember one thing about chromatography, remember that it's really good at separating mixtures, but not so reliable at identifying the substances that make up the mixture. Or does that count as two things? Hmm... well it's probably not the best idea to only learn one thing from each page anyway. Learn lots of stuff, that's my advice.*

# Mass Spectrometry

*Mass spectrometry is an analysis technique that can be used with chromatography to positively identify compounds.*
***These pages are for AQA (Unit 4), OCR A (Unit 4), OCR B (Unit 4) and Edexcel (Unit 4 and 5).***

## ***Mass Spectrometry** Can Help to Identify Compounds*

1) A mass spectrum is produced when a sample of a **gaseous compound** is analysed in a mass spectrometer.
2) The sample is bombarded with electrons, causing other electrons to break off from the molecules. If the bombarding electrons remove a single electron from a molecule, the **molecular ion**, $M^+_{(g)}$, is formed.
3) To find the relative molecular mass of a compound you can look at the **molecular ion peak** (the **M peak**) on its mass spectrum. The mass/charge value of the molecular ion peak is the **molecular mass** of the compound.
4) The bombarding electrons also break some of the molecules up into **fragments**. The fragments that are **ions** will also show up on the mass spectrum, giving a **fragmentation pattern**.

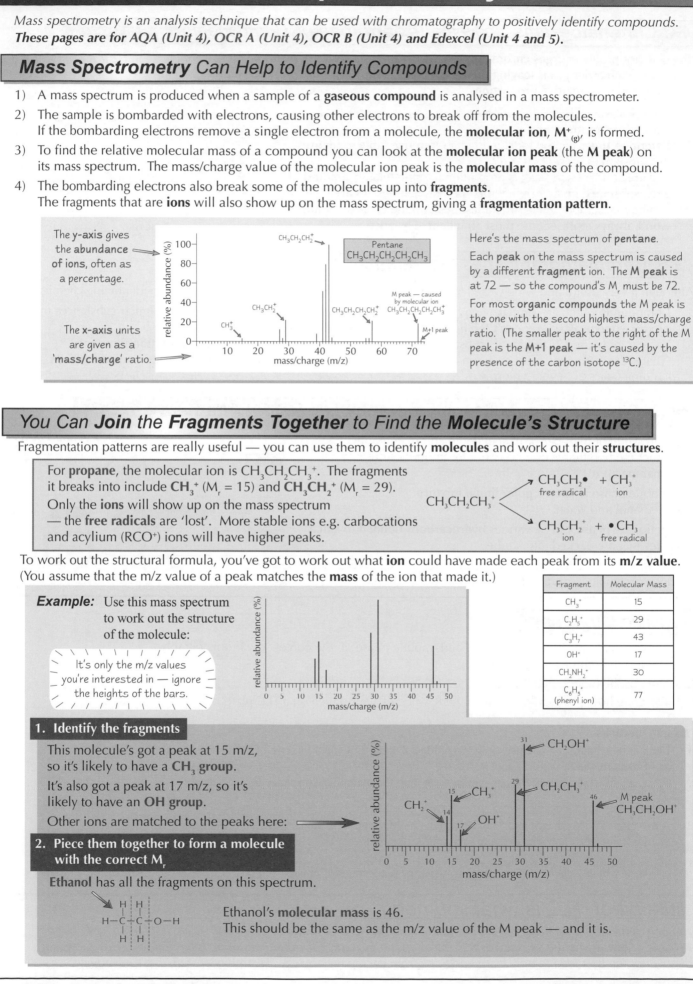

The **y-axis** gives the **abundance of ions**, often as a percentage.

The **x-axis** units are given as a '**mass/charge**' ratio.

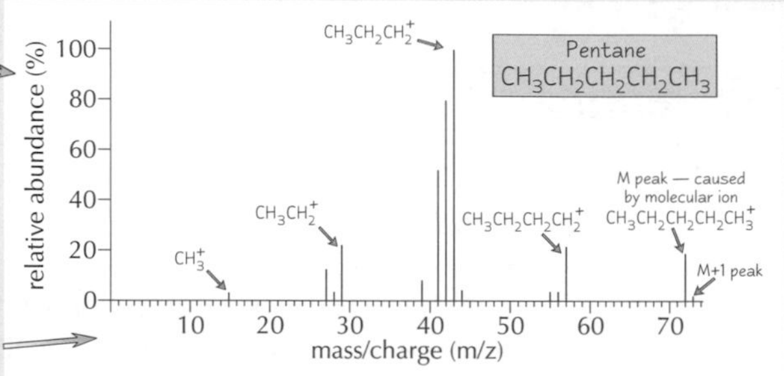


Here's the mass spectrum of **pentane**.

Each **peak** on the mass spectrum is caused by a different **fragment** ion. The **M peak** is at 72 — so the compound's $M_r$ must be 72.

For most **organic compounds** the M peak is the one with the second highest mass/charge ratio. (The smaller peak to the right of the M peak is the **M+1 peak** — it's caused by the presence of the carbon isotope $^{13}C$.)

## *You Can **Join the Fragments Together** to Find the **Molecule's Structure***

Fragmentation patterns are really useful — you can use them to identify **molecules** and work out their **structures**.

For **propane**, the molecular ion is $CH_3CH_2CH_3^+$. The fragments it breaks into include $\mathbf{CH_3^+}$ ($M_r$ = 15) and $\mathbf{CH_3CH_2^+}$ ($M_r$ = 29). Only the **ions** will show up on the mass spectrum — the **free radicals** are 'lost'. More stable ions e.g. carbocations and acylium ($RCO^+$) ions will have higher peaks.

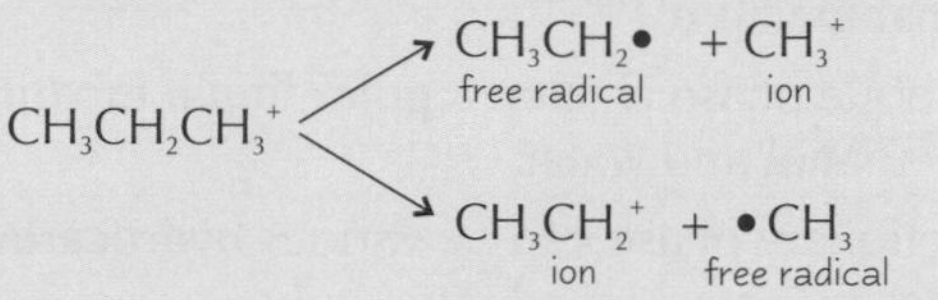


To work out the structural formula, you've got to work out what **ion** could have made each peak from its **m/z value**. (You assume that the m/z value of a peak matches the **mass** of the ion that made it.)

| Fragment | Molecular Mass |
|---|---|
| $CH_3^+$ | 15 |
| $C_2H_5^+$ | 29 |
| $C_3H_7^+$ | 43 |
| $OH^+$ | 17 |
| $CH_2NH_2^+$ | 30 |
| $C_6H_5^+$ (phenyl ion) | 77 |

***Example:*** Use this mass spectrum to work out the structure of the molecule:

It's only the m/z values you're interested in — ignore the heights of the bars.

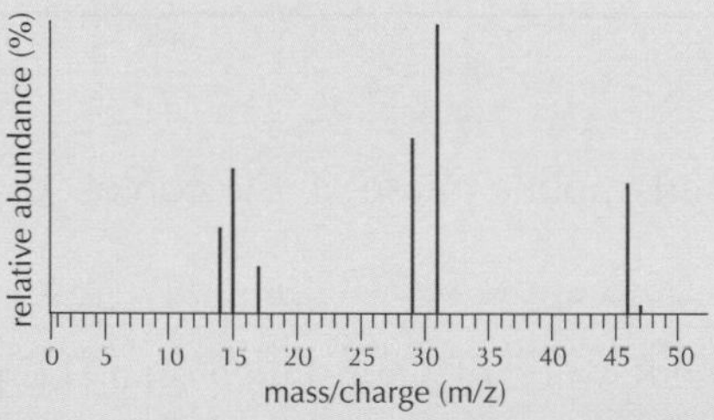


**1. Identify the fragments**

This molecule's got a peak at 15 m/z, so it's likely to have a $\mathbf{CH_3}$ **group**.

It's also got a peak at 17 m/z, so it's likely to have an **OH group**.

Other ions are matched to the peaks here:

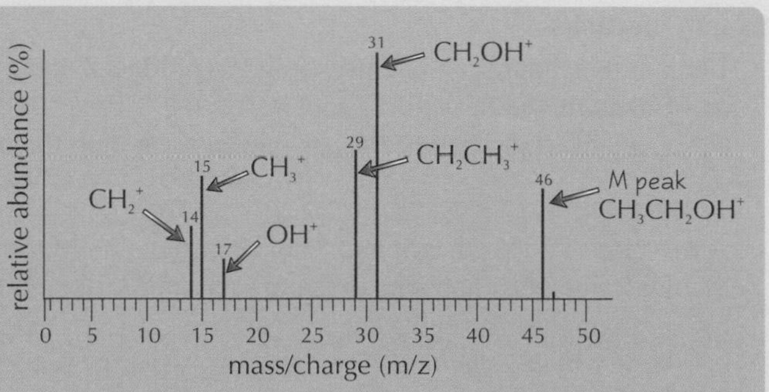


**2. Piece them together to form a molecule with the correct $M_r$**

**Ethanol** has all the fragments on this spectrum.

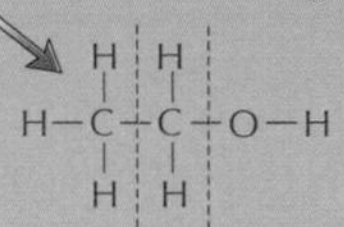

Ethanol's **molecular mass** is 46.
This should be the same as the m/z value of the M peak — and it is.

# Mass Spectrometry

## *The **Difference** Between Peaks Tells You About **'Lost' Fragments*** *OCR B only*

1) If you look at the **difference** between the m/z values of two peaks on a mass spectrum you can work out the mass of the fragment that was 'lost'. This'll be clearer from the example below.

The peak at m/z = 44 is due to the molecular ion $CH_3CH_2CH_3^+$.
The next peak (at m/z = 29) is 15 units of mass less.
So the free radical (or 'lost') fragment that fell off to produce this had a mass of 15 — which corresponds to $CH_3\bullet$.

$$CH_3CH_2CH_3^+ \rightarrow CH_3CH_2^+ + CH_3\bullet$$

**Simplified mass spectrum of propane**

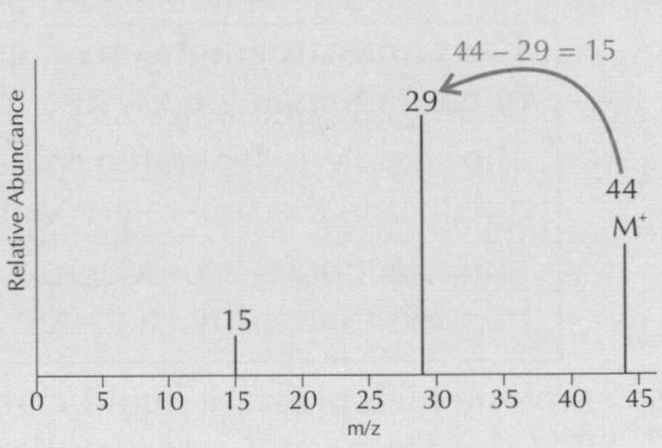


2) If a fragment is unstable or doesn't form with a positive charge easily, there might not be a peak for it at all. In such a case, the difference between the m/z values of other peaks will be the **only** evidence for that fragment.
3) Look at the mass spectrum of **bromobenzene** below. There are no really clear peaks at 79 or 81 representing a **Br⁺ ion** (remember Br has two isotopes – $^{79}$Br and $^{81}$Br). **BUT**, the difference between the M⁺ ion at 156 and the peak at 77 is **79** — showing that a $^{79}$Br atom has been lost.
4) If a molecule's got either **chlorine** or **bromine** in it you'll get an **M+2 peak** as well as an M⁺ peak — this is because both elements have **natural isotopes** with different masses and they all show up on the spectrum.
Bromine's got two isotopes, **Br-79** and **Br-81**, that occur in almost **equal amounts**. So if a molecule contains bromine, the M⁺ peak and the M+2 peak will both have roughly the **same height**.

**Mass spectrum of Bromobenzene ($C_6H_5Br$):**

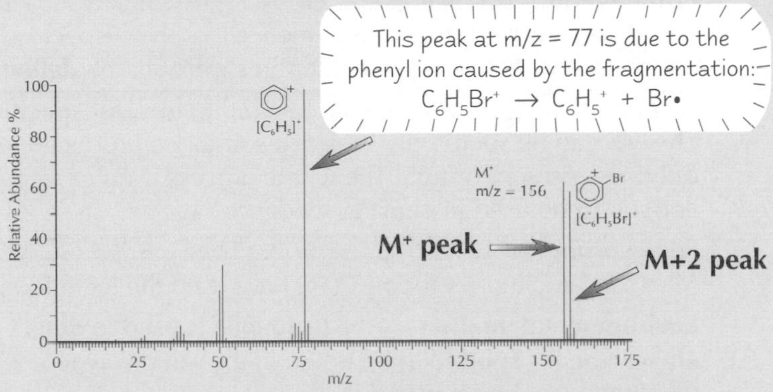


## ***High Resolution Mass Spectrometry** Measures Very Accurate Masses* *OCR B only*

1) **High-resolution** mass spectrometers can measure m/z values to at least **4 decimal places**.
2) Very **accurate measurements** of m/z values allow you to compare elements and compounds using **relative isotopic masses**.
3) The relative isotopic mass of **$^{12}$C** is defined as **exactly 12** — everything else is measured **relative** to this.
4) The relative masses of protons and neutrons are not exactly equal to 1, so **nothing else** apart from $^{12}$C has a relative isotopic mass that's a whole number.

$^{1}$H = 1.0078
$^{12}$C = 12.0000
$^{14}$N = 14.0031
$^{16}$O = 15.9949

This isn't the same as relative atomic mass (which is an average of the masses of all the different isotopes of an element) — these masses are the **relative masses of a single isotope**.

## ***Accurate Molecular Masses** Can Help in Working out a Formula* *OCR B only*

1) In low-resolution mass spectrometry, an M⁺ peak at **m/z = 28** could be produced by several different molecules — **$N_2$**, **CO** and **$C_2H_4$** all have molecular masses of 28 when rounded to the nearest whole number.
2) If you use the accurate masses given above, however, you find the three molecules have slightly different molecular masses:
So a high-resolution mass spectrum could tell you which one of the three it was.

$N_2$ = 28.0062
CO = 27.9949
$C_2H_4$ = 28.0312

# Mass Spectrometry

## *Mass Spectroscopy* can be *Combined* with *Gas Chromatography*

*OCR A only*

**Gas chromatography** is very good at **separating** a mixture into its individual components (page 114), but not so good at identifying those components. **Mass spectroscopy**, on the other hand, is great at **identifying** unknown compounds, but would give confusing results from a mixture of substances.
If you put these **two techniques together**, you get an **extremely useful** analytical tool.

> **Gas chromatography-mass spectroscopy** (GC-MS) **combines the benefits** of gas chromatography and mass spectrometry to make a super analysis tool.
> The sample is **separated** using **gas chromatography**, but instead of going to a detector, the separated components are fed into a **mass spectrometer**.
> The spectrometer produces a **mass spectrum** for each **component**, which can be used to **identify** each one and show what the original **sample** consisted of.

You can also combine **high pressure liquid chromatography**, **(HPLC)**, with **mass spectrometry** to get **HPLC-MS**.
Just like GC, HPLC is more useful for **separating** mixtures of substances than **identifying** them — **combining it** with **mass spectrometry** gives a better **identification** tool than either method alone.

## *GC-MS* is used in *Forensics* and *Security*

*OCR A only*

**GC-MS** is a really **important analytical tool**, and not just in chemistry labs — check out the four uses below.

1) **Forensics** — GC-MS can be used to **identify unknown substances** found on **victims** or **suspects** or at **crime scenes**. For example, if GC-MS shows that a substance found at a crime scene is **identical** to one found on a suspect, then it is evidence that the suspect was at the crime scene. Or **fire investigators** can use the method to detect whether fires were started **deliberately** using substances such as petrol or paraffin.
2) **Airport security** — GC-MS can be used to look for **specific substances** — e.g. **explosives** or **illegal drugs**. The MS can be set to only look at a substance produced at a particular retention time on the GC to find out if it is present or not. The whole process is quick — it takes just a few minutes — and is accurate enough to be used in **court** as evidence.
3) **Space probes** — several space probes have carried GC-MS machines. Missions to the planets Venus and Mars, and to Saturn's moon Titan, have used the technique to examine the **atmosphere** and **rocks**.
4) **Environmental analysis** — the technique is used to **detect and track pollutants** such as **pesticides** in the environment. **Foods** can be tested in the same way to check that they do not contain harmful levels of substances such as pesticides.

## *Practice Questions*

Q1 What is a molecular ion?
Q2 What process causes peaks in a mass spectrum to have m/z values less than the molecular mass?
Q3 What feature on a mass spectrum tells you that chlorine or bromine is present?
Q4 What would be the mass of the fragment $CH_3CH_2CH_2^+$ ?

**Exam Questions**

1 Below is the mass spectrum of a carboxylic acid. Use the spectrum to answer this question.

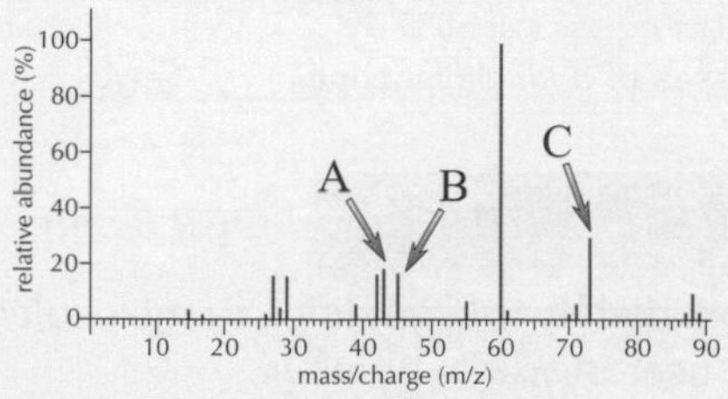


a) What is the molecular mass of this acid? [1 mark]
b) Suggest the formulas of the fragment ions that are responsible for the peaks labelled A, B and C. [3 marks]
c) Use your answers from parts (a) and (b) to draw the structure of the acid, and give its name. [2 marks]

## *Mass spectrometry — weight watching for molecules...*

*So mass spectrometry's a bit like weighing yourself, then taking bits off your body, weighing them separately, then trying to work out how they all fit together. Luckily you won't get anything as complicated as a body, and you won't need to cut yourself up either. Good news all round then. Just learn these pages and watch out for the M peak in the exam.*

# NMR Spectroscopy

*NMR isn't the easiest of things, so ingest this information one piece at a time — a bit like eating a bar of chocolate.*
***These pages are for AQA (Unit 4), OCR A (Unit 4), OCR B (Unit 5) and Edexcel (Unit 4 and 5).***

## **NMR** Gives You Information About a Molecule's **Structure**

Any atomic nucleus with an **odd** number of nucleons (protons and neutrons) has a **nuclear spin**. This causes it to have a weak **magnetic field** — a bit like a bar magnet. NMR spectroscopy looks at how this tiny magnetic field reacts when you put it in a much larger external magnetic field.

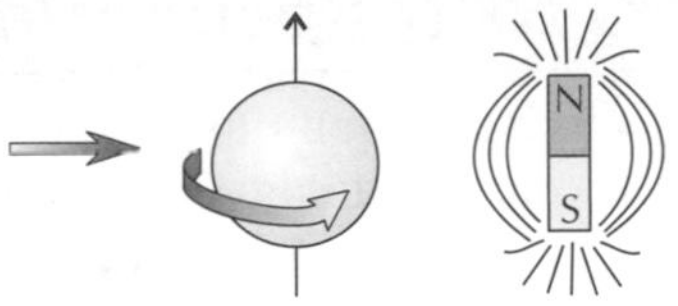


There are two types of **nuclear magnetic resonance** (**NMR**) spectroscopy that you might need to know about — **$^{1}$H** (or **proton**) **NMR**, and **$^{13}$C NMR**. **Hydrogen** nuclei are **single protons**, so they have spin. **Carbon** usually has six protons and six neutrons, so it **doesn't** have spin. But about 1% of carbon atoms are the isotope **$^{13}$C** (six protons and seven neutrons), which does have spin.

## Nuclei **Align** in Two Directions in an **External Magnetic Field**

1) Normally, the nuclei are spinning in **random directions** — so their magnetic fields **cancel out**.
2) But when a strong **external** magnetic field is applied, the nuclei align themselves either in the direction of the field (**aligned with it**), or in the opposite direction (**opposed to it**).
3) The aligned nuclei are at a slightly **lower** energy level than the opposed nuclei. But if they **absorb radio waves** of the right frequency, they can **flip** to the **higher** energy level. The opposed nuclei can **emit** radio waves at the same frequency when they **flip** back to the **lower energy** level.

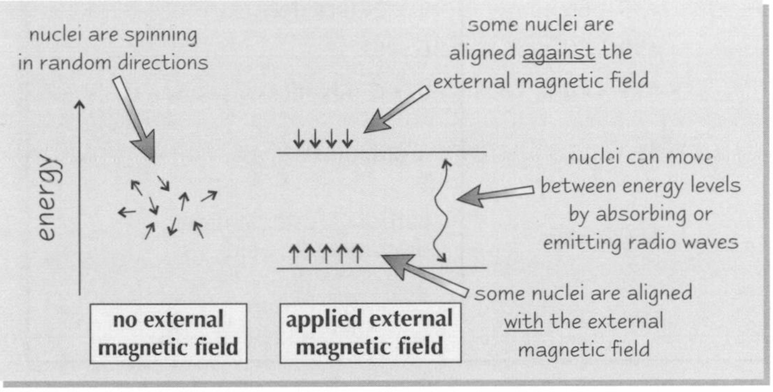


4) There tends to be more aligned nuclei, so there's an **overall absorption** of energy. NMR spectroscopy **measures** this **absorption** of energy.

## Nuclei in **Different Environments** Absorb **Different Amounts of Energy**

1) A nucleus is partly **shielded** from the effects of external magnetic fields by its **surrounding electrons**.
2) Any **other atoms** and **groups of atoms** that are around a nucleus will also affect its amount of electron shielding.
   E.g. If a carbon atom bonds to a more electronegative atom (like oxygen) the amount of electron shielding around its nucleus will decrease.
3) This means that the nuclei in a molecule feel different magnetic fields depending on their **environments**. This means that they will absorb **different amounts** of energy at **different frequencies**.
4) It's these **differences in absorption** of energy between environments that you're looking for in **NMR spectroscopy**.
5) An atom's **environment** depends on **all** the groups that it's connected to, going **right along the molecule** — not just the atoms it's actually bonded to. To be in the **same environment**, two atoms must be joined to **exactly the same things**.

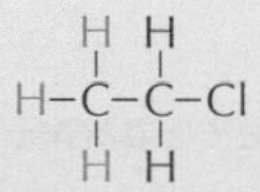

**Chloroethane** has **2** hydrogen environments — the Hs are bonded to $CH_2CH_2Cl$ and the Hs are bonded to $CHCl(CH_3)$.

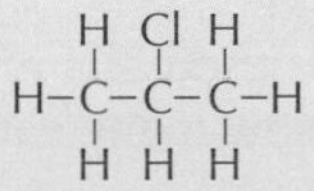

**2-chloropropane** has **2** carbon environments:
- **1 C** in a CHCl group, bonded to $(CH_3)_2$
- **2 Cs** in $CH_3$ groups, bonded to $CHCl(CH_3)$

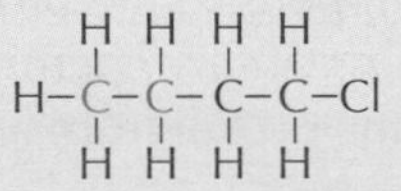

**1-chlorobutane** has **4** carbon environments. (The two carbons in $CH_2$ groups are **different distances** from the **electronegative** Cl atom — so their **environments** are **different**.)

## **Tetramethylsilane** is Used as a **Standard**

The **peaks** on an NMR spectrum show the **frequencies** at which **energy was absorbed** by the nuclei.

1) The **differences in absorption** are measured relative to a **standard substance** — **tetramethylsilane** (**TMS**).
2) TMS produces a **single absorption peak** in both types of NMR because all its carbon and hydrogen nuclei are in the **same environment**.
3) It's chosen as a standard because the **absorption peak** is at a **lower frequency** than just about everything else.
4) This peak is given a value of **0** and all the peaks in other substances are measured as **chemical shifts** relative to this.

# NMR Spectroscopy

***This page is for AQA (Unit 4) and OCR A (Unit 4). If you're doing OCR B or Edexcel you won't get asked about $^{13}C$, but have a gander anyway — it'll make the next page on $^1H$ NMR a lot easier to get your head around.***

## $^{13}C$ NMR Spectra Tell You About Carbon Environments

If you have a sample of a chemical that contains **carbon** atoms, you can use a $^{13}C$ NMR spectrum of the molecule to help work out what it is. $^{13}C$ NMR spectra are usually much **simpler** than $^1H$ NMR spectra — they have fewer, sharper peaks.

1) First, count the **number of peaks** in the spectrum — this is the **number of carbon environments** in the molecule. (If there's a peak at $\delta$ **= 0**, **don't count it** — it's the reference peak from **TMS**.) This number isn't necessarily the number of carbons, as it could have **more than one carbon** in the **same environment**.

| $^{13}C$ NMR Chemical Shifts Relative to TMS | |
|---|---|
| **Chemical shift, δ (ppm)** | **Type of Carbon** |
| 5 – 55 | C – C |
| 30 – 70 | C – Cl or C – Br |
| 35 – 60 | C – N (amines) |
| 50 – 70 | C – O |
| 115 – 140 | C = C (alkenes) |
| 110 – 165 | aromatic  |
| 160 – 185 | carbonyl (ester, amide, or carboxylic acid) 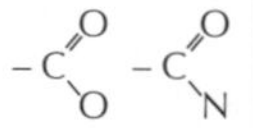 |
| 190 – 220 | carbonyl (ketone or aldehyde) 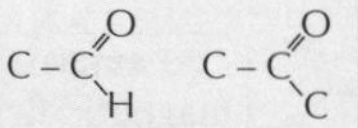 |

2) Next you need to **match up** the **peaks** in the spectrum with the **chemical shifts** in the table to work out which **carbon environments** they could represent.

   In your exam you'll get a **data sheet** that will include a **table** like this. The table shows the **chemical shifts** experienced by **carbon nuclei** in **different environments**.

   Matching peaks to the groups that cause them isn't always straightforward, because the chemical shifts can **overlap**. For example, a peak at $\delta \approx$ **30** might be caused by **C–C**, **C–Cl** or **C–Br**.

   A peak at $\delta \approx$ **210** will be due to a **C=O** group in an **aldehyde** or a **ketone** — but you **don't** know which.

3) To work out **how many** carbon nuclei are in **each environment**, you look at the **area under each peak**. Sometimes the relative area is given as numbers above a peak or in the form of an integration trace (see next page).

Example: $^{13}C$ NMR spectra of pentan-3-one.

1) **Pentan-3-one** has **three** carbon environments — two $CH_3$ carbons, each bonded to $CH_2COCH_2CH_3$, two $CH_2$ carbons, each bonded to $CH_3$ and $COCH_2CH_3$, and one CO carbon bonded to $(CH_2CH_3)_2$.
2) The chemical shifts show what kinds of environment there are in the molecule.
3) The areas under the peaks (shown by the numbers above the peaks) show how many C atoms there are in each environment.

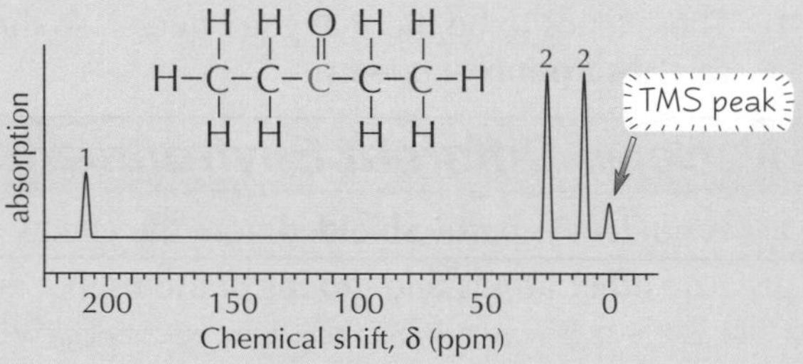

Carbon-13 NMR Spectrum

## Practice Questions

Q1 What part of the electromagnetic spectrum does NMR spectroscopy use?
Q2 What happens to the protons when they absorb energy?
Q3 What is meant by chemical shift? What compound is used as a reference for chemical shifts?
Q4 How can you tell from a carbon-13 NMR spectrum how many carbon environments a molecule contains?

**Exam Question**

1 The carbon-13 NMR spectrum shown on the right was produced by a compound with the molecular formula $C_3H_9N$.

a) Explain why there is a peak at δ = 0. [1 mark]

b) The compound cannot have the formula $CH_3CH_2CH_2NH_2$. Explain how the spectrum shows this. [2 marks]

c) Suggest and explain a possible structure for the compound. [2 marks]

Carbon-13 NMR Spectrum

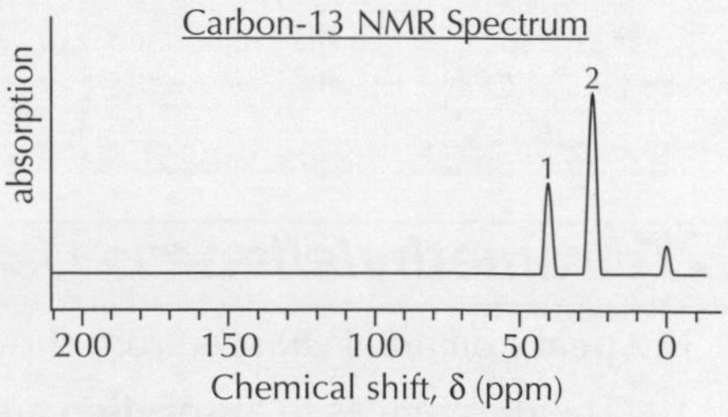


## Why did the carbon flip? Because it saw the radio wave...

The ideas behind NMR are difficult, but don't worry too much if you don't really understand them. The important thing is to make sure you know how to interpret a spectrum — that's what will get you marks in the exam. If you're having trouble, go over the examples and practice questions a few more times. You should have the "ahh... I get it" moment sooner or later.

# Proton NMR

*Now it's time to get your teeth into some proton NMR spectra — watch your fillings though...*
***These pages are for AQA (Unit 4), OCR A (Unit 4), OCR B (Unit 5) and Edexcel (Unit 4 and 5).***

## $^1$H NMR Spectra Tell You About Hydrogen Environments

'Protons' and 'hydrogen nuclei' are used interchangeably here so don't get confused.

**Proton** or **$^1$H NMR spectra** look quite complicated. Here's how to interpret them:

1) Count the number of peaks to find out the **number of hydrogen environments**.
2) Look up the **chemical shifts** in the **$^1$H NMR data table** to identify possible environments.
3) Compare the **area under each peak** to find the number of hydrogens in each environment — this is sometimes given with ratio numbers or sometimes with an **integration trace**.

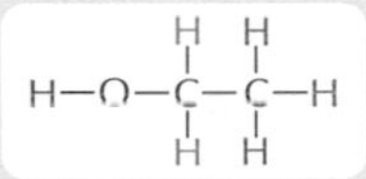

For example, **ethanol** has 3 **hydrogen environments**. They're in the ratio 1 : 2 : 3.

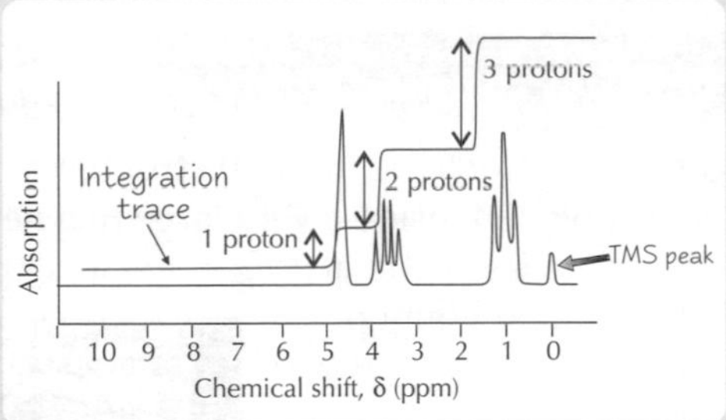

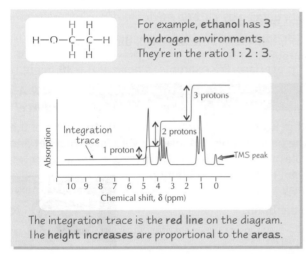

The integration trace is the **red line** on the diagram. The **height increases** are proportional to the **areas**.

**$^1$H NMR Chemical Shifts Relative to TMS**

| Chemical shift, δ (ppm) | Type of Proton | | |
|---|---|---|---|
| 0.7 – 1.6 | $R-CH_3$ | | |
| 1.0 – 5.5 | $N-H$ | $R-OH$ | |
| 1.2 – 1.4 | $R-CH_2-R$ | | |
| 1.6 – 2.0 | $R_3CH$ | | |
| 2.0 – 2.9 | $H_3C-C(=O)$ | $RCH_2-C(=O)$ | $R_2CH-C(=O)$ |
| 2.3 – 2.7 | ⌬$-CH_3$ | ⌬$-CH_2R$ | ⌬$-CHR_2$ |
| 2.3 – 2.9 | $N-CH_3$ | $N-CH_2R$ | $N-CHR_2$ |
| 3.3 – 4.3 | $O-CH_3$ | $O-CH_2R$ | $O-CHR_2$ |
| 3.0 – 4.2 | $Br/Cl-CH_3$ | $Br/Cl-CH_2R$ | $Br/Cl-CHR_2$ |
| 4.5 – 10.0 | ⌬$-OH$ | | |
| 4.5 – 6.0 | $-CH=CH-$ | | |
| 5.0 – 12.0 | $-C(=O)NH_2$ | $-C(=O)NH-$ | |
| 6.5 – 8.0 | ⌬$-H$ | | |
| 9.0 – 10.0 | $-C(=O)H$ | | |
| 11.0 – 12.0 | $-C(=O)O-H$ | | |

## Spin-Spin Coupling Splits the Peaks in a Proton NMR Spectrum

Proton NMR spectra are made more complicated because the peaks representing a particular hydrogen environment can also be **split**. The effect is called **spin-spin coupling** and is caused by interactions with hydrogen atoms on **adjacent** carbon atoms.

These **split peaks** are called **multiplets**. They always split into one more than the number of hydrogens on the neighbouring carbon atoms — it's called the **n + 1 rule**. For example, if there are **2 hydrogens** on the adjacent carbon atoms, the peak will be split into 2 + 1 = 3.

You can work out the **number** of **neighbouring hydrogens** by looking at how the peak splits:
If a peak's split into **two** (a **doublet**) then there's **one hydrogen** on the neighbouring carbon atoms.
If a peak's split into **three** (a **triplet**) then there are **two hydrogens** on the neighbouring carbon atoms.
If a peak's split into **four** (a **quartet**) then there are **three hydrogens** on the neighbouring carbon atoms.

For example, here's the $^1$H NMR spectrum of **1,1,2-trichloroethane**:

The peak due to the green hydrogens is split into **two** because there's **one hydrogen** on the adjacent carbon atom.

The peak due to the red hydrogen is split into **three** because there are **two hydrogens** on the adjacent carbon atom.

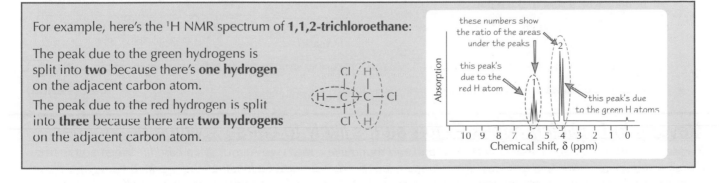

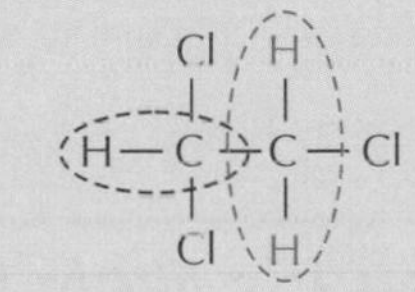

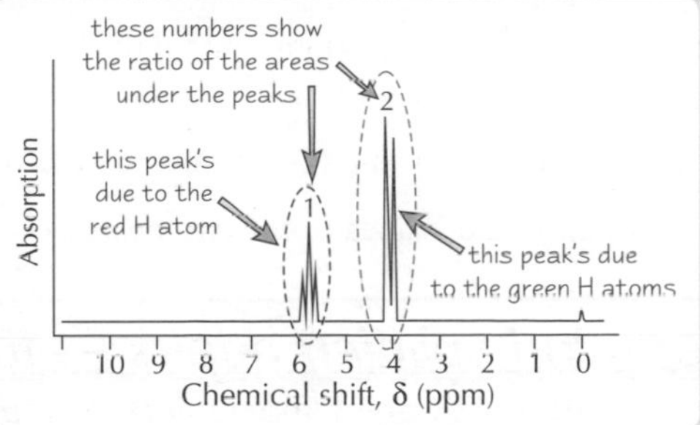

# Proton NMR

## Samples are Dissolved in Hydrogen-Free Solvents

*AQA and OCR A only*

1) If a sample has to be dissolved, then a solvent is needed that doesn't contain any **$^1$H atoms** — because these would show up on the spectrum and confuse things.
2) **Deuterated solvents** are often used — their hydrogen atoms have been replaced by **deuterium** (D or $^2$H). Deuterium's an isotope of hydrogen that's got two nucleons (a proton and a neutron).
3) Because deuterium has an **even number** of nucleons, it doesn't have a spin (so it doesn't create a magnetic field).
4) **$CCl_4$** can also be used — it doesn't contain any $^1$H atoms either.

## OH and NH Protons can be Identified by Proton Exchange Using $D_2O$

*OCR A only*

The **chemical shift** due to protons attached to oxygen (OH) or nitrogen (NH) is very **variable** — check out the huge **ranges** given in the **table** on the previous page. They make quite a **broad** peak that isn't usually split.

But there's a clever little trick chemists use to identify OH and NH protons:

1) Run **two** spectra of the molecule — one with a little **deuterium oxide**, $D_2O$, added.
2) If an OH or NH proton is present it'll swap with deuterium and, hey presto, the peak will **disappear**. (This is because deuterium doesn't absorb the radio wave energy).

## NMR Technology is Used in Hospitals and the Chemical Industry

*OCR A and Edexcel*

**Magnetic resonance imaging** (**MRI**) is a **scanning** technique used in **hospitals** to study the **internal structures** of the body. MRI uses the **same technology** as NMR spectroscopy — the patient is placed inside a very **large magnet** and **radio waves** are used to look at **hydrogen nuclei** in **water molecules**. The **response** of the hydrogen nuclei depends on the kind of **tissue** that the water is in, so an **image** of the different tissues can be built up.

The **benefit** of MRI is that it **doesn't** use **damaging radiation** like **X-rays** or gamma rays, but does give **high quality images** of soft tissue like the **brain**.

NMR is also used in the pharmaceutical industry to **monitor** the **purity** of a product. The **NMR spectrum** is like a **fingerprint** so if there were impurities in the product they would be easily spotted on the spectrum.

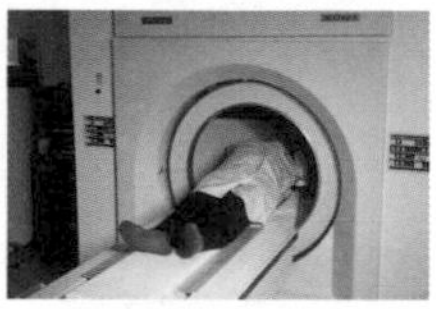

Never stick your head into a giant washing machine.

## Practice Questions

Q1 What causes the peaks on a high resolution proton NMR spectrum to split?

Q2 What causes a triplet of peaks on a high resolution proton NMR spectrum?

Q3 What are deuterated solvents? Why are they needed?

Q4 How can you get rid of a peak caused by an OH group?

**Exam Question**

1 The proton NMR spectrum below is for a halogenoalkane.
Use the table of chemical shifts on page 121 to answer this question.

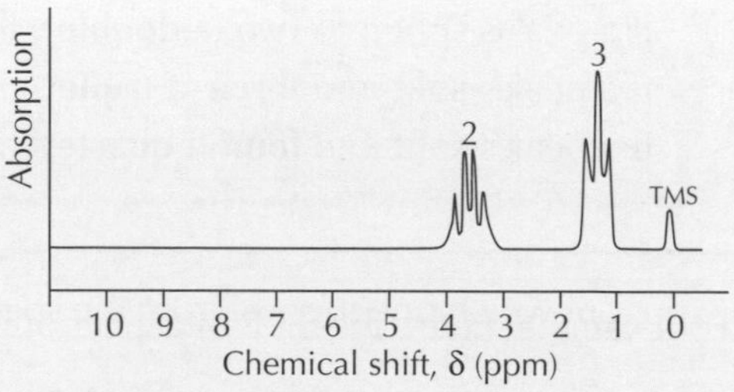


a) What is the likely environment of the two protons with a shift of 3.6 p.p.m.? [1 mark]

b) What is the likely environment of the three protons with a shift of 1.3 p.p.m.? [1 mark]

c) The molecular mass of the molecule is 64.5. Suggest a possible structure and explain your suggestion. [2 marks]

d) Explain the shapes of the two peaks. [4 marks]

## Never mind splitting peaks — this stuff's likely to cause splitting headaches...

*Is your head spinning yet? I know mine is. Round and round like a merry-go-round. It's a hard life when you're tied to a desk trying to get NMR spectroscopy firmly fixed in your head. You must be looking quite peaky by now... so go on, learn this stuff, take the dog around the block, then come back and see if you can still remember it all.*

# Infrared Spectroscopy

*Eeek... more spectroscopy. Infrared (IR to its friends) radiation has less energy than visible light, and a longer wavelength.* ***These pages are for AQA (Unit 4), OCR A (Unit 4), OCR B (Unit 4) and Edexcel (Unit 4).***

## *Infrared Radiation* is Absorbed by *Covalent Bonds*

1) In infrared (IR) spectroscopy, a beam of **IR radiation** is passed through a sample of a chemical.
2) The IR radiation is absorbed by the **covalent bonds** in the molecules, increasing their **vibrational** energy.
3) **Bonds between different atoms** absorb **different frequencies** of IR radiation. Bonds in different **places** in a molecule absorb different frequencies too — so the O–H group in an **alcohol** and the O–H in a **carboxylic acid** absorb different frequencies.

This table shows what **frequencies** different bonds absorb:

| Bond | Where it's found | Frequency/ Wavenumber ($cm^{-1}$) |
|---|---|---|
| C–O | alcohols, carboxylic acids and esters | 1000 – 1300 |
| C=O | aldehydes, ketones, carboxylic acids, esters and amides | 1640 – 1750 |
| O–H | carboxylic acids | 2500 – 3300 (strong absorbance, very broad) |
| C–H | organic compounds | 2850 – 3100 (medium absorbance) |
| N–H | amines and amides | 3200 – 3500 (medium absorbance) |
| O–H | alcohols, phenols | 3200 – 3550 (strong absorbance, broad) |

This data will be on the data sheet in the exam, so you don't need to learn it. BUT you do need to understand how to use it.

Clark began to regret having an infrared mechanism installed in his glasses.

## *Infrared Spectroscopy* Helps You Identify *Organic Molecules*

An infrared spectrometer produces a **graph** that shows you what frequencies of radiation the molecules are absorbing. You can use it to identify the **functional groups** in a molecule:

***Example:*** The diagram on the right shows the infrared absorption spectrum of an organic molecule with a molecular mass of 46. What is the molecule?

The troughs show you the wavelengths of radiation that have been absorbed.

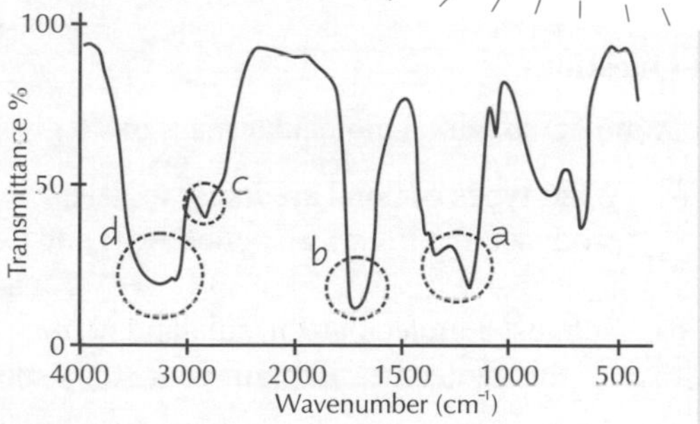


Start off by looking at the troughs to try to identify which **functional groups** the molecule has:

a) A trough at around **1200 $cm^{-1}$**. This could be due to the **C–O bond** in an **alcohol**, **carboxylic acid** or **ester**.
b) A trough at around **1700 $cm^{-1}$**, which is the characteristic place for a **C=O bond** in an aldehyde, ketone, carboxylic acid, ester or amide.
c) A **small trough** with a medium absorbance just below **3000 $cm^{-1}$**, which is characteristic of **C–H bonds** in an organic molecule.
d) A **very broad** trough with **strong** absorbance at around **3200 $cm^{-1}$**. This is due to the **O–H bond** in a **carboxylic acid**.

So the only type of molecule that could create this pattern of absorptions is a **carboxylic acid**.

Now you know that the molecule is a **carboxylic acid**. But you'd need a **database** of **all possible carboxylic acids** to work out which one it is just from the spectrum. Instead, you can use the **molecular mass** to work out its **molecular formula**.

First look at the **general formula** of a **carboxylic acid**:

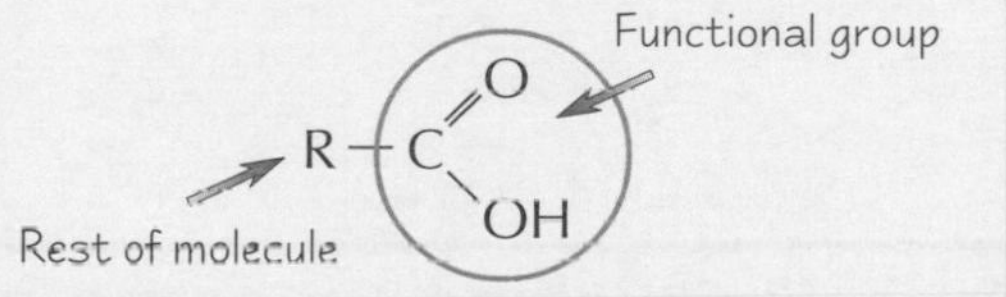


The mass of the whole molecule is **46**.
So by **subtracting** the mass of the **functional group**, you can find the mass of the **rest of the molecule**.

$46 - [12 + (2 \times 16) + 1] = 46 - 45 = 1$.

To have a **mass of 1**, the rest of the molecule must just be **H**, so the molecule is **HCOOH**— or **methanoic acid**.

# Infrared Spectroscopy

## Infrared Spectroscopy Has Several Commercial Uses

*Edexcel only*

1) IR spectroscopy can be used to follow reactions in the chemical industry so that the point where one functional group **changes to another** can be seen.
E.g. in the oxidation of a **secondary alcohol** to a **ketone**, the point at which all the **OH groups** in the alcohol have gone can be seen as can the point when the first **C=O groups** in the ketone appear.

2) Another good example is in polymer manufacture where IR spectroscopy is used to measure the degree of **polymerisation**. The instruments monitor the **absorption** at the frequency of the **double bond** in the monomer. So you can watch the number of double bonds change as the polymerisation takes place.

## Microwaves Are Used for Heating

*Edexcel only*

Microwaves are another form of **electromagnetic** radiation with a slightly longer wavelength than infrared. They're widely used in communications, but also for **heating** stuff up.

A microwave oven works by forming an **electric field** of microwave radiation. Any polar molecules (e.g. water) in the food try to **line themselves up** with the field by **rotating** into line.
This makes them **collide** with other molecules and generates **heat energy**.

Liam didn't care how 'safe' his microwave was — he wasn't taking any chances.

## Practice Questions

Q1 What happens when bonds absorb infrared radiation?

Q2 What do the troughs on a spectrum show?

Q3 Which bond absorbs strongly at 1700 $cm^{-1}$?

Q4 How can microwave radiation be used to generate heat energy?

**Exam Questions**

1 A molecule with a molecular mass of 74 gives the following IR spectrum.

a) What types of bond are likely to have produced the troughs labelled A, B and C? [3 marks]

b) Suggest a molecular formula and name for this molecule. Explain your suggestion. [3 marks]

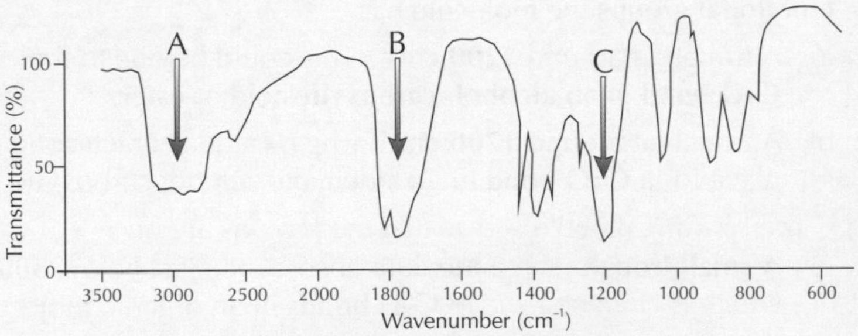


2 An unknown substance gives this IR spectrum.
It has a molecular mass of 46.

a) What types of bond could have caused the troughs labelled X, Y and Z? [3 marks]

b) Suggest a molecular formula and explain your reasoning. [3 marks]

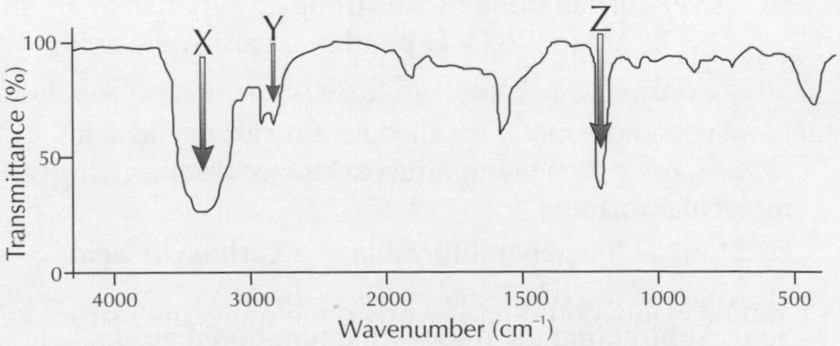


## Ooooh — I'm picking up some good vibrations...

Now, I've warned you — infrared glasses are not for fun. They're highly advanced pieces of technology which if placed in the wrong hands could cause havoc and destruction across the universe. There's not much to learn on these pages — so make sure you can apply it. You'll be given a data table, so you don't have to bother learning all the wavenumber ranges.

# Combining Spectra

*Yes, I know, it's yet another page on spectra — but it's the last one (alright, three) I promise.*
***These pages are for AQA (Unit 4), OCR A (Unit 4), OCR B (Unit 4) and Edexcel (Unit 4).***

## You Can Use **Data From Several Spectra** to **Work Out a Structure**

All the **spectroscopy techniques** in this section will **give clues** to the **identity of a mystery molecule**, but you can be more **certain** about a structure (and avoid jumping to wrong conclusions) if you look at **data from several different types of spectrum**.

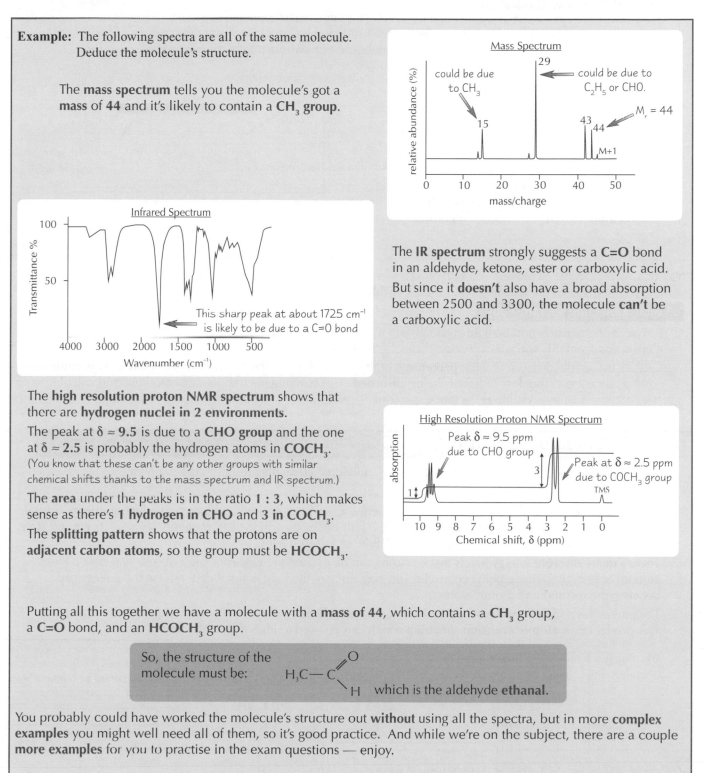

**Example:** The following spectra are all of the same molecule. Deduce the molecule's structure.

The **mass spectrum** tells you the molecule's got a **mass of 44** and it's likely to contain a **$CH_3$ group**.

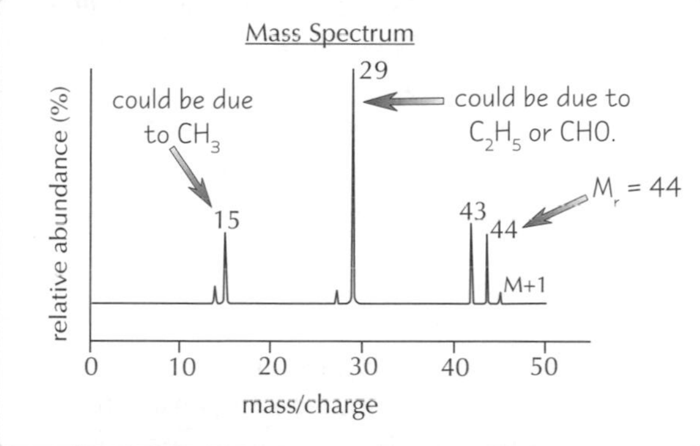


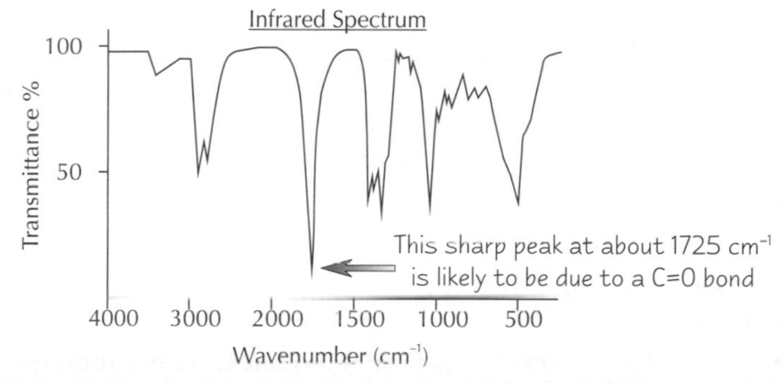


The **IR spectrum** strongly suggests a **C=O** bond in an aldehyde, ketone, ester or carboxylic acid. But since it **doesn't** also have a broad absorption between 2500 and 3300, the molecule **can't** be a carboxylic acid.

The **high resolution proton NMR spectrum** shows that there are **hydrogen nuclei in 2 environments**.

The peak at **$\delta \approx 9.5$** is due to a **CHO group** and the one at **$\delta \approx 2.5$** is probably the hydrogen atoms in **$COCH_3$**.
(You know that these can't be any other groups with similar chemical shifts thanks to the mass spectrum and IR spectrum.)

The **area** under the peaks is in the ratio **1 : 3**, which makes sense as there's **1 hydrogen in CHO** and **3 in $COCH_3$**.

The **splitting pattern** shows that the protons are on **adjacent carbon atoms**, so the group must be **$HCOCH_3$**.

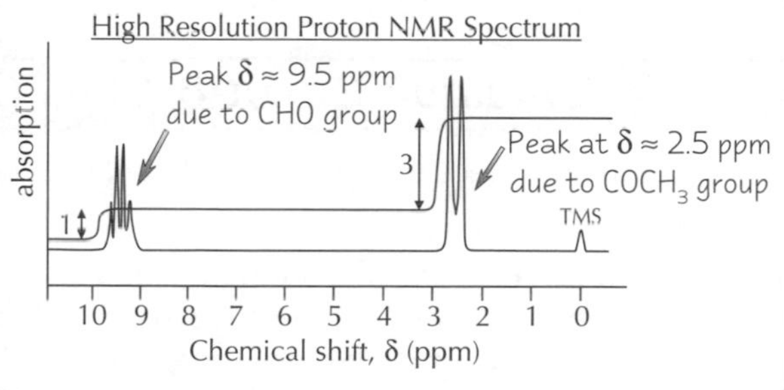


Putting all this together we have a molecule with a **mass of 44**, which contains a **$CH_3$** group, a **C=O** bond, and an **$HCOCH_3$** group.

So, the structure of the molecule must be:

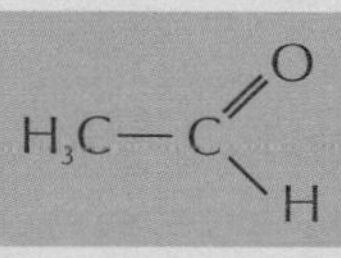


which is the aldehyde **ethanal**.

You probably could have worked the molecule's structure out **without** using all the spectra, but in more **complex examples** you might well need all of them, so it's good practice. And while we're on the subject, there are a couple **more examples** for you to practise in the exam questions — enjoy.

# Combining Spectra

***This page is for OCR B only — the lucky devils.***
*Knowing what kinds of colours or pigments are used in a painting is important for dating the picture and also restoring it. There are a few techniques that can help do this — GC (page 114) and Visible and Atomic Emission Spectroscopy.*

## Visible Spectroscopy Can Help Identify Pigments in a Painting

There are two variations of this technique — **visible absorption** and **visible reflection** spectroscopy.
Both techniques use beams of **monochromatic light** — light of a **single wavelength** or **colour**.

There's more on light absorbance and colour on pages 84 and page 162.

### Visible Absorption Spectroscopy

1) A beam of monochromatic light is passed through a **dilute solution** of the pigment. A detector measures the **intensity of light** before and after it's passed through the solution. From this you can calculate **absorbance** — a measure of how much light the pigment has absorbed.
2) Different frequencies of monochromatic light are used to produce a **visible absorption spectrum** (a graph of frequency or **wavelength** against absorbance). The **peaks** in the graph tell you which colours of light the pigment absorbs most **strongly**.
3) Every pigment has a unique colour, so produces a **unique** visible **absorption spectrum**. This allows it to be **identified**.

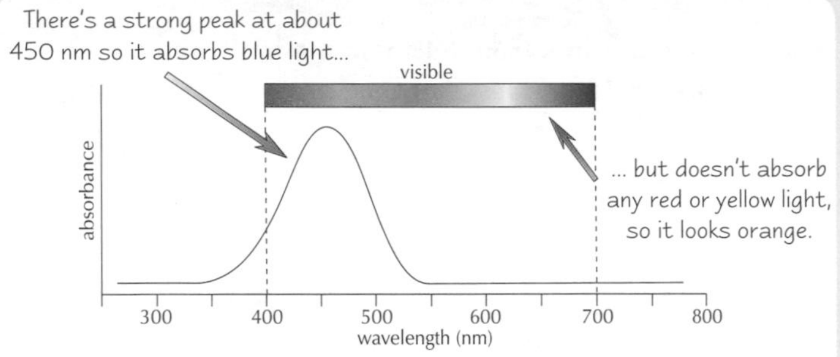
There's a strong peak at about 450 nm so it absorbs blue light...
visible
absorbance
... but doesn't absorb any red or yellow light, so it looks orange.
300
400
500
600
700
800
wavelength (nm)

Example: the visible **absorption** spectrum of **carotene** – the pigment in carrots:

It's not always possible to make a solution of a pigment — it might not dissolve easily, or you may not want to remove it from the painting. In this case **visible reflection spectroscopy** can help.

### Visible Reflection Spectroscopy

1) A beam of monochromatic light is shone onto the **surface of a solid**. The intensity of the beam before and after reflection from this surface is measured and the **reflectance** is calculated.
2) Reflectance is a measure of what **percentage** of the light falling on the solid is **reflected back**. **Low values** of reflectance mean that **lots** of light is being **absorbed**. By changing the frequency of the light and calculating reflectance values a **visible reflectance spectrum** is produced.

## Atomic Emission Spectroscopy Can Identify the **Elements** in a Pigment...

Atomic emission spectroscopy is used to analyse the **individual elements** present in the pigment.
This is how it works:

1) When an electron absorbs the right amount of energy, it becomes **excited** and jumps to a **higher energy orbital**. But it doesn't remain in this **excited state**. When it falls back down to the lower energy level — its **ground state** — the electron **emits** its excess energy as **UV**, **visible**, or **infrared light**.
2) There's **many discrete** energy levels that electrons can be excited to. Electrons must absorb and emit a fixed amount of energy to move between levels. The frequency of the light emitted depends on the **energy gap** between the excited and ground states.
3) The energy levels in every element are different, so **each element** will emit its own **unique** set of frequencies. This produces an **atomic emission spectrum** which can be used to identify the element.

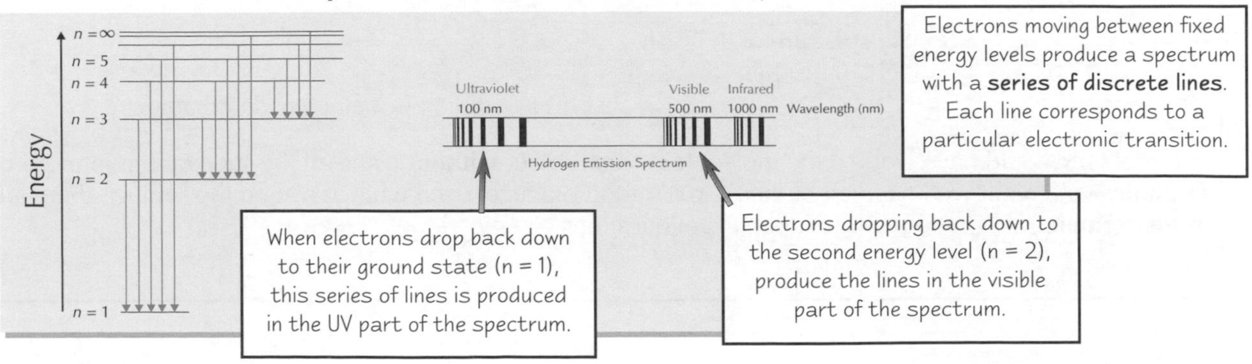
Energy
$n = \infty$
$n = 5$
$n = 4$
$n = 3$
$n = 2$
$n = 1$
Ultraviolet
100 nm
Visible
500 nm
Infrared
1000 nm
Wavelength (nm)
Hydrogen Emission Spectrum
Electrons moving between fixed energy levels produce a spectrum with a **series of discrete lines**. Each line corresponds to a particular electronic transition.
When electrons drop back down to their ground state (n = 1), this series of lines is produced in the UV part of the spectrum.
Electrons dropping back down to the second energy level (n = 2), produce the lines in the visible part of the spectrum.

# Combining Spectra

## Practice Questions

Q1 Which type of spectrum gives you the mass of a molecule?

Q2 Which spectrum can tell you how many different hydrogen environments there are in a molecule?

Q3 Which spectrum involves radio wave radiation?

Q4 Describe how visible absorption spectroscopy is used to identify a pigment.

**Exam Questions**

1 The four spectra below were produced by running different tests on samples of the same pure organic compound.

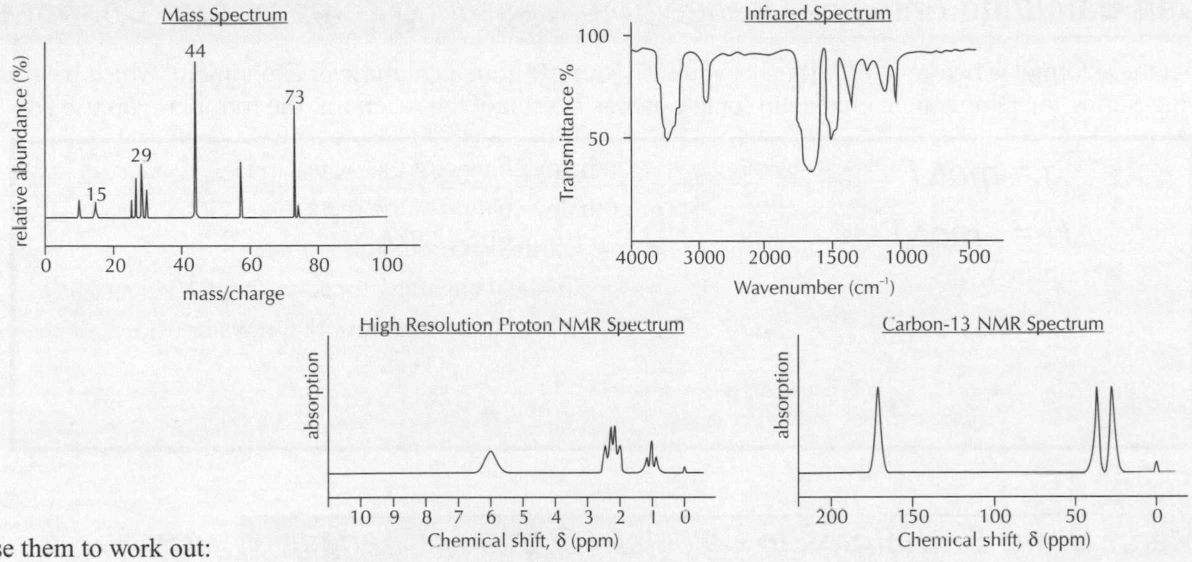


Use them to work out:

a) The molecular mass of the compound. [1 mark]

b) The probable structure of the molecule. Explain your reasoning. [6 marks]

2 The four spectra below were produced by running different tests on samples of the same pure organic compound.

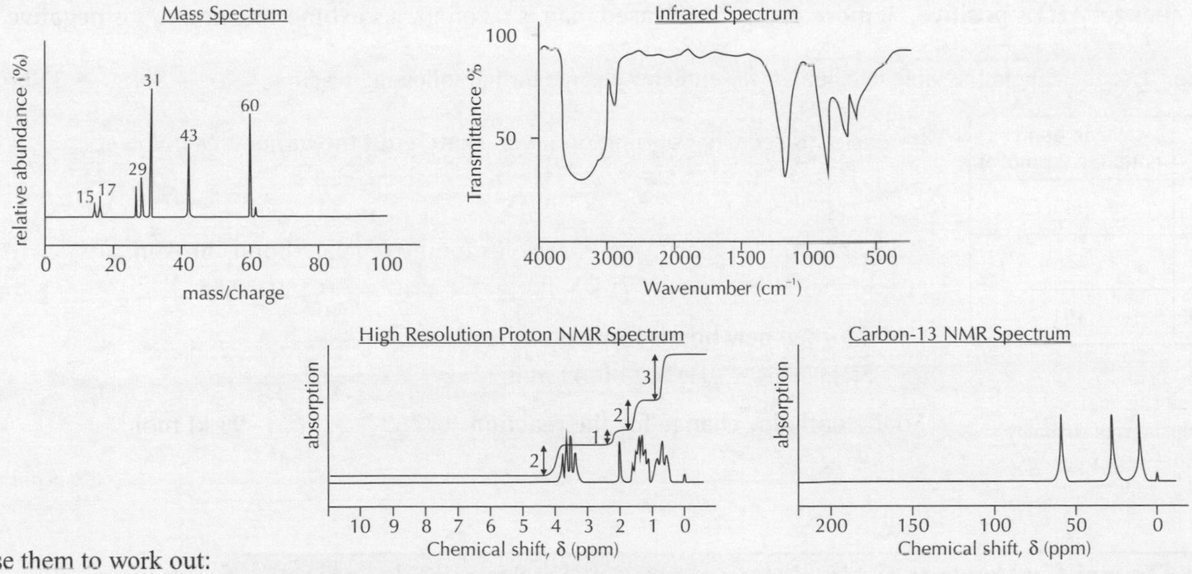


Use them to work out:

a) The molecular mass of the compound. [1 mark]

b) The probable structure of the molecule. Explain your reasoning. [6 marks]

## Spectral analysis — psychology for ghosts...

*So that's analysis done and dusted, you'll be pleased to hear. But before you rush off to learn about thermodynamics, take a moment to check that you really know how to interpret all the different spectra. You need to know what each technique will tell you about a molecule, e.g. its mass, functional groups, number of H environments, star sign, favourite food etc...*

# Enthalpy Changes

*I'm sure you all remember enthalpies — but here's a quick reminder just in case...*
***These pages are for AQA (Unit 5), OCR A (Unit 5), OCR B (Unit 5) and Edexcel (Unit 4).***

## First — A Few Definitions You Should Remember

***ΔH*** is the symbol for **enthalpy change**. Enthalpy change is the **heat** energy transferred in a reaction at **constant pressure**.
***ΔH***$^{\ominus}$ means that the enthalpy change was measured under **standard conditions** (**100 kPa and 298 K**).
**Exothermic** reactions have a **negative *ΔH*** value, because heat energy is given out.
**Endothermic** reactions have a **positive *ΔH*** value, because heat energy is absorbed.

## You Can Calculate Enthalpy Change from Measuring Temperature Changes

*OCR A only*

You've met these formulas before at AS. They let you work out ***ΔH*** from a calorimeter experiment, which basically involves measuring the temperature change in some water as a result of the reaction. The formulas you use are:

$$q = mc\Delta T$$

$$\Delta H = -mc\Delta T$$

where, $q$ = enthalpy change of the water (in kJ)
$\Delta H$ = enthalpy change of the reactants (in kJ)
$m$ = mass of the water (in kg)
$c$ = specific heat capacity (for water it's 4.18 kJ $kg^{-1}$ $K^{-1}$)
$\Delta T$ = the change in temperature of the water (K)

The change of sign is because $\Delta H$ is looking at the reactants, not the surroundings.

## Use Mean Bond Enthalpies to Calculate Enthalpy Changes

*AQA only*

Energy is **taken in** when bonds are **broken**, and **released** when bonds are **formed**, so:

enthalpy change for a reaction = sum of enthalpies of bonds broken – sum of enthalpies of bonds formed

If you need **more** energy to **break** bonds than is released when bonds are made, it's an **endothermic reaction** and the enthalpy change, $\Delta H$, is **positive**. If **more** energy is **released** than is taken in, it's **exothermic** and $\Delta H$ is **negative**.

***Example:*** Use the data in the table to calculate the enthalpy change for the following reaction: $N_{2(g)} + 3H_{2(g)} \rightarrow 2NH_{3(g)}$

| Bond | Mean bond enthalpy (kJ $mol^{-1}$) |
|---|---|
| N≡N | 945 |
| H—H | 436 |
| N—H | 391 |

You can use this method to calculate the lattice enthalpy of formation — see page 130.

It's easier to see what's going on if you **sketch out** the molecules involved:

N≡N + 3H—H ⟶ 2H—N(—H)—H

Now add up the mean bond enthalpies for the reactant **bonds broken**...

(1 × N≡N) + (3 × H–H) = (1 × 945) + (3 × 436) = 2253 kJ $mol^{-1}$

...and for the **new bonds formed** in the products

(6 × N–H) = (6 × 391) = 2346 kJ $mol^{-1}$

So the **enthalpy change for the reaction** = 2253 – 2346 = **–93 kJ $mol^{-1}$**.

It's negative, so it's exothermic.

## Mean Bond Enthalpy Calculations are Only Approximations

*AQA only*

The bond enthalpy given above for N–H bonds is **not** exactly right for **every** N–H bond.
A given type of bond will **vary in strength** from compound to compound and can even vary **within** a compound.
Mean bond enthalpies are the **averages** of these bond enthalpies. Only the bond enthalpies of **diatomic molecules**, such as $H_2$ and HCl, will always be the same.
So calculations done using **mean bond enthalpies** will never be perfectly accurate.
You get much **more exact** results from **experimental data** obtained from the **specific compounds**.

# Enthalpy Changes

## *Learn These Definitions for the Different Types of Enthalpy Change*

There are lots of different enthalpy terms you need to **know** on the next few pages.
So spend some time looking at them now and it'll make everything coming up a bit easier.

**Enthalpy change of formation**, $\Delta H_f^\ominus$, is the enthalpy change when **1 mole** of a **compound** is formed from its **elements** in their standard states under standard conditions, e.g. $2C_{(s)} + 3H_{2(g)} + \frac{1}{2}O_{2(g)} \rightarrow C_2H_5OH_{(l)}$

The **bond dissociation enthalpy**, $\Delta H_{diss}^\circ$, is the enthalpy change when all the **bonds of the same type** in **1 mole** of **gaseous molecules** are broken, e.g. $Cl_{2(g)} \rightarrow 2Cl_{(g)}$

**Enthalpy change of atomisation of an element**, $\Delta H_{at}^\ominus$, is the enthalpy change when **1 mole** of **gaseous atoms** is formed from an element in its **standard state**, e.g. $\frac{1}{2}Cl_{2(g)} \rightarrow Cl_{(g)}$

**Enthalpy change of atomisation of a compound**, $\Delta H_{at}^\ominus$, is the enthalpy change when **1 mole** of **gaseous atoms** is formed from a compound in its **standard state**, e.g. $NaCl_{(s)} \rightarrow Na_{(g)} + Cl_{(g)}$

The **first ionisation enthalpy**, $\Delta H_{ie1}^\ominus$, is the enthalpy change when **1 mole** of **gaseous 1+ ions** is formed from **1 mole** of **gaseous atoms**, e.g. $Mg_{(g)} \rightarrow Mg^+_{(g)} + e^-$

The **second ionisation enthalpy**, $\Delta H_{ie2}^\ominus$, is the enthalpy change when **1 mole** of **gaseous 2+ ions** is formed from **1 mole** of **gaseous 1+ ions**, e.g. $Mg^+_{(g)} \rightarrow Mg^{2+}_{(g)} + e^-$

**First electron affinity**, $\Delta H_{ea1}^\ominus$, is the enthalpy change when **1 mole** of gaseous **1– ions** is made from **1 mole** of gaseous **atoms**, e.g. $O_{(g)} + e^- \rightarrow O^-_{(g)}$

**Second electron affinity**, $\Delta H_{ea2}^\ominus$, is the enthalpy change when **1 mole** of **gaseous 2– ions** is made from **1 mole** of gaseous **1– ions**, e.g. $O^-_{(g)} + e^- \rightarrow O^{2-}_{(g)}$

The **enthalpy change of hydration**, $\Delta H_{hyd}^\ominus$, is the enthalpy change when **1 mole** of **aqueous ions** is formed from **1 mole** of gaseous ions, e.g. $Na^+_{(g)} \rightarrow Na^+_{(aq)}$

The **enthalpy change of solution**, $\Delta H_{solution}^\ominus$, is the enthalpy change when **1 mole** of **solute** is dissolved in **sufficient solvent** that no further enthalpy change occurs on further dilution, e.g. $NaCl_{(s)} \rightarrow NaCl_{(aq)}$

## *First Ionisation Enthalpies Show Trends in the Periodic Table*

***OCR B only***

1) **First ionisation enthalpies decrease down a group.**
   This is because there's **less attraction** between the nucleus and outer electrons.
   The outer electrons are in shells **further** from the nucleus and there's more **shielding** from inner shells.
2) **First ionisation enthalpies generally increase across a period.**
   This is because the number of protons is increasing, which means a stronger **nuclear attraction**. And since all the outer-shell electrons are at **roughly the same** energy level, there's generally little **extra shielding** effect or **extra distance** to lessen the attraction from the nucleus.

I say 'generally' because there are **small drops** between Groups 2 and 3, and Groups 5 and 6.

## *Practice Questions*

Q1 Define *first ionisation enthalpy* and *first electron affinity*.

Q2 What is defined as "the enthalpy change when 1 mole of gaseous atoms is formed from a compound in its standard state"?

**Exam Question**

1 a) Using the bond enthalpies in the table calculate the enthalpy change for:
$CH_{4(g)} + 2O_{2(g)} \rightarrow CO_{2(g)} + 2H_2O_{(g)}$ [3 marks]

| Bond | C–H | O=O | C=O | O–H |
|---|---|---|---|---|
| Mean bond enthalpy (kJ mol⁻¹) | 412 | 496 | 743 | 463 |

b) Give a reason why the enthalpy change calculated by this method is not likely to be as accurate as one calculated using experimental data. [2 marks]

## *My eyes, MY EYES — the definitions make them hurt...*

*The worst thing about this page is all the definitions. And is it's not enough to just have a vague idea what each one means. You have to know the ins and outs — like whether it applies to gases, or to elements in their standard states. If you've forgotten, standard conditions are 298 K (otherwise known as 25 °C) and 100 kPa pressure.*

# Lattice Enthalpy

*Now you know all your enthalpy change definitions, here's how to use them... Enjoy.*
***These pages are for AQA (Unit 5), OCR A (Unit 5), OCR B (Unit 5) and Edexcel (Unit 4).***

## *Lattice Enthalpy is a Measure of Ionic Bond Strength*

**Lattice enthalpy** can be defined as:

> **Lattice formation enthalpy**, $\Delta H^{\ominus}_{latt}$, is the enthalpy change when **1 mole** of a **solid ionic compound** is **formed** from its **gaseous ions** under standard conditions.
>
> E.g. $Na^+_{(g)} + Cl^-_{(g)} \rightarrow NaCl_{(s)}$ $\quad \Delta H^{\ominus} = -787\ kJ\ mol^{-1}$
> $Mg^{2+}_{(g)} + 2Cl^-_{(g)} \rightarrow MgCl_{2(s)}$ $\quad \Delta H^{\ominus} = -2526\ kJ\ mol^{-1}$

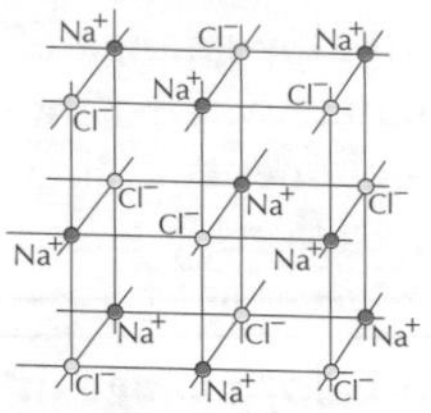


Ions held together by electrostatic interactions form a lattice.

Lattice enthalpy is sometimes defined as **lattice dissociation enthalpy**.
This has the **same** value as the lattice formation enthalpy but the **sign is reversed**.

## *Born-Haber Cycles can be Used to Calculate Lattice Enthalpies*

You can't measure lattice enthalpy **directly**, so you have to use a **Born-Haber cycle** to figure out what the enthalpy change would be if you took **another, less direct, route**. **Hess's law** says that the **total enthalpy change** of a reaction is always the **same**, no matter which route is taken.

Here's how to draw a Born-Haber cycle for calculating the lattice enthalpy of **NaCl**:

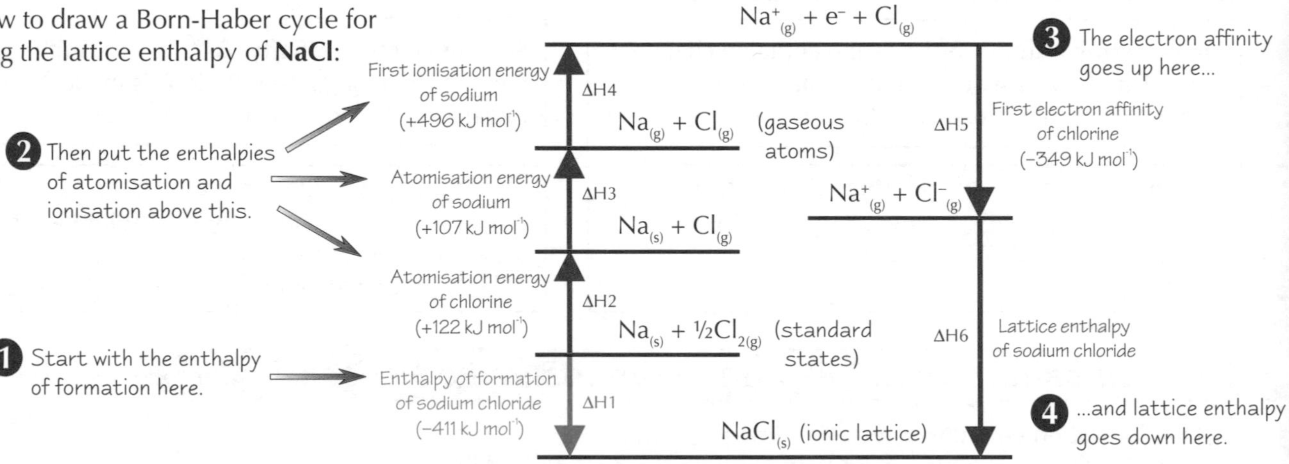


There are **two routes** you can follow to get from the elements in their **standard states** to the **ionic lattice**. The green arrow shows the **direct route** and the purple arrows show the **indirect route**. The enthalpy change for each is the **same**.

From Hess's law: $\Delta H6 = -\Delta H5 - \Delta H4 - \Delta H3 - \Delta H2 + \Delta H1$
$= -(-349) - (+496) - (+107) - (+122) + (-411) = \mathbf{-787\ kJ\ mol^{-1}}$

So the **lattice enthalpy of formation** of sodium chloride is **$-787$ kJ mol$^{-1}$**.

You need a minus sign if you go the wrong way along an arrow.

## *Calculations Involving Group 2 Elements are a Bit Different*

Born-Haber cycles for compounds containing **Group 2 elements** have a few **changes** from the one above. Make sure you understand what's going on so you can handle whatever compound they throw at you.

Here's the Born-Haber cycle for calculating the lattice enthalpy of **magnesium chloride** ($MgCl_2$).

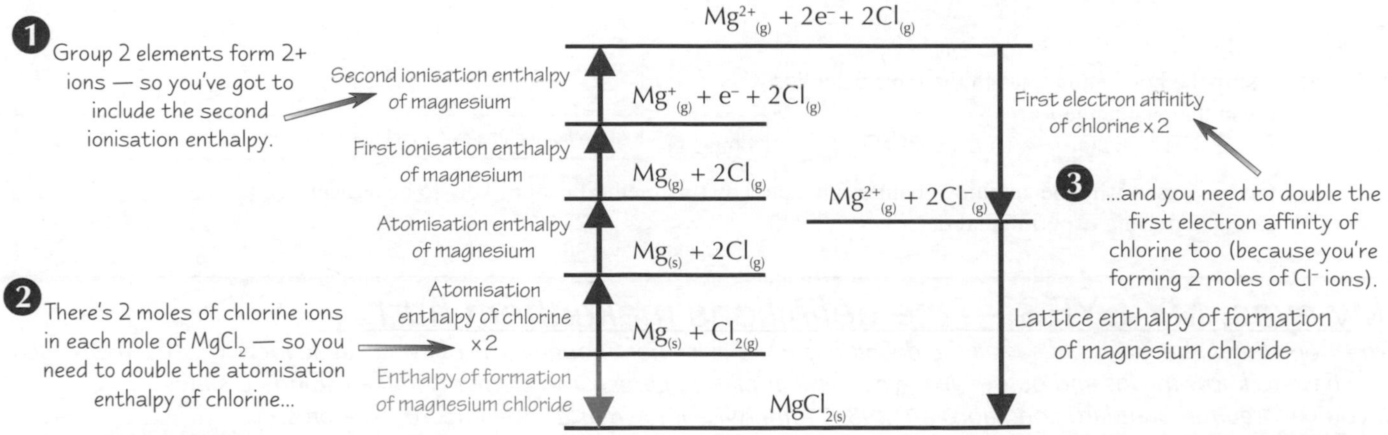

# Lattice Enthalpy

## Ionic Charge and Size Affect Lattice Enthalpy

*OCR A and Edexcel only*

Lattice enthalpy can be affected by a couple of things...

1) The **higher the charge** on the ions, the **more energy** is released when an ionic lattice forms. More energy released means that the lattice enthalpy will be **more negative.** So the lattice enthalpies for compounds with **2+** or **2– ions** (e.g. $Mg^{2+}$ or $S^{2-}$) are **more negative** than those with **1+** or **1– ions** (e.g. $Na^{+}$ or $Cl^{-}$).
2) The **smaller** the **ionic radii** of the ions involved, the **more exothermic** (more negative) the **lattice enthalpy**. Smaller ions attract **more strongly** because their **charge density** is higher.

## Theoretical Lattice Enthalpies Often Differ from Experimental Values

*AQA only*

You can work out a **theoretical lattice enthalpy** by doing some calculations based on the **purely ionic model** of a lattice. This model assumes that all the ions are **spherical**, and have their charge **evenly distributed** around them.

In reality the **experimental lattice enthalpy** from the Born-Haber cycle is usually different because the positive and negative ions in a lattice **aren't** usually exactly spherical.

Positive ions can **polarise** neighbouring negative ions, and the **more polarisation** there is, the **more covalent** the bonding will be. The difference between theoretical and experimental lattice enthalpies is used as **evidence** that ionic compounds usually have some **covalent character**.

***Example:***

1) For the magnesium halides, the sizes of the **experimental** lattice energies are **greater** than the theoretical values, which means the **bonding** is **stronger** than the calculations from the ionic model predict.
2) The difference shows that the ionic bonds in the magnesium halides are quite strongly **polarised**, so they have **quite a lot of covalent character**.
3) The sodium halide experimental and theoretical values are **pretty close** — so these compounds fit the 'purely ionic' model very well.
4) This implies the lattice for these compounds is quite close to being **purely ionic**. There's almost no polarisation so they don't have much covalent character.

| Compound | Lattice Enthalpy of Formation (kJ $mol^{-1}$) | |
|---|---|---|
| | From experimental values in Born-Haber cycle | From theory |
| Magnesium chloride | –2526 | –2326 |
| Magnesium bromide | –2440 | –2097 |
| Magnesium iodide | –2327 | –1944 |
| Sodium chloride | –787 | –766 |
| Sodium bromide | –742 | –731 |
| Sodium iodide | –698 | –686 |

## Practice Questions

Q1 What is the definition of lattice enthalpy?

Q2 Sketch out Born-Haber cycles for calculating the lattice enthalpy of: a) LiF, b) $CaCl_2$.

Q3 Explain why theoretical lattice enthalpies are often different from experimentally determined lattice enthalpies.

**Exam Questions**

1 Using the data below:

a) Construct a Born-Haber cycle for potassium bromide (KBr). [4 marks]

b) Use your Born-Haber cycle to calculate the lattice enthalpy of formation of potassium bromide. [3 marks]

$\Delta H_f^{\ominus}$ [potassium bromide] = –394 kJ $mol^{-1}$ $\Delta H_{at}^{\ominus}$ [bromine] = +112 kJ $mol^{-1}$ $\Delta H_{at}^{\ominus}$ [potassium] = +89 kJ $mol^{-1}$

$\Delta H_{ie1}^{\ominus}$ [potassium] = +419 kJ $mol^{-1}$ $\Delta H_{ea1}^{\ominus}$ [bromine] = –325 kJ $mol^{-1}$

2 The diagram shows part of a Born-Haber cycle for copper(II) chloride.

a) Identify the enthalpy changes X, Y and Z. [3 marks]

b) What other enthalpy changes need to be added in order to complete the cycle? [3 marks]

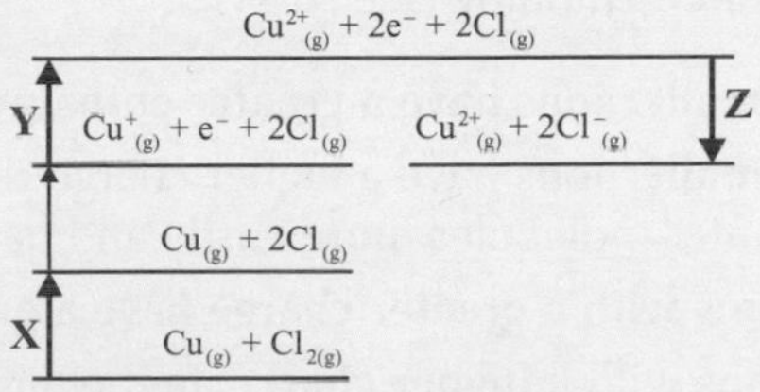


## Using Born-Haber cycles — it's just like riding a bike...

*All this energy going in and out can get a bit confusing. Remember these simple rules: 1) It takes energy to break bonds, but energy is given out when bonds are made. 2) A negative ΔH means energy is given out (it's exothermic). 3) A positive ΔH means energy is taken in (it's endothermic). 4) Never return to a firework once lit.*

# Enthalpies of Solution and Neutralisation

*Once you know what's happening when you stir sugar into your tea, your cuppa'll be twice as enjoyable.*
***These pages are for AQA (Unit 5), OCR A (Unit 5), OCR B (Unit 5) and Edexcel (Unit 4).***

## Dissolving Involves Enthalpy Changes

ionic lattice

When a solid **ionic lattice** dissolves in water these **two** things happen:

1) The bonds between the ions **break** — this is **endothermic**. This enthalpy change is the **lattice enthalpy of dissociation**.
2) Bonds between the ions and the water are **made** — this is **exothermic**. The enthalpy change here is called the **enthalpy change of hydration**.

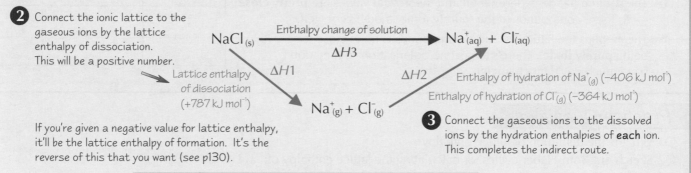

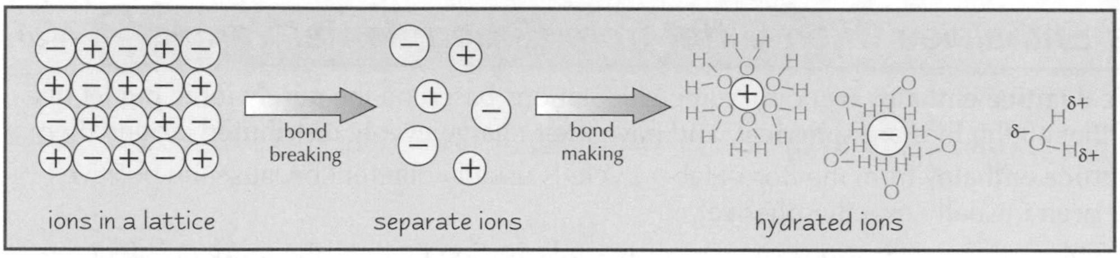


Oxygen is more electronegative than hydrogen, so it draws the bonding electrons towards itself, creating a dipole.

3) The **enthalpy change of solution** is the overall effect on the enthalpy of these two things.

## Enthalpy Change of Solution can be Calculated

You can work out the enthalpy change of solution using an **enthalpy cycle**.
You just need to know the **lattice dissociation enthalpy** of the compound and the enthalpies of **hydration of the ions**.

Here's how to draw the enthalpy cycle for working out the **enthalpy change of solution** for **sodium chloride**.

**1** Put the ionic lattice and the dissolved ions on the top — connect them by the enthalpy change of solution. This is the direct route.

**2** Connect the ionic lattice to the gaseous ions by the lattice enthalpy of dissociation. This will be a positive number.

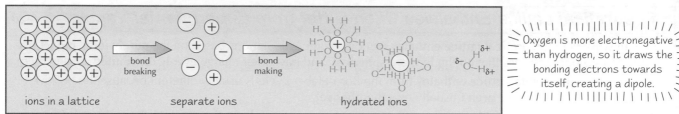

$NaCl_{(s)}$ —— Enthalpy change of solution, $\Delta H3$ ——→ $Na^+_{(aq)} + Cl^-_{(aq)}$

$NaCl_{(s)}$ —— $\Delta H1$: Lattice enthalpy of dissociation ($+787\ kJ\ mol^{-1}$) ——→ $Na^+_{(g)} + Cl^-_{(g)}$

$Na^+_{(g)} + Cl^-_{(g)}$ —— $\Delta H2$: Enthalpy of hydration of $Na^+_{(g)}$ ($-406\ kJ\ mol^{-1}$), Enthalpy of hydration of $Cl^-_{(g)}$ ($-364\ kJ\ mol^{-1}$) ——→ $Na^+_{(aq)} + Cl^-_{(aq)}$

If you're given a negative value for lattice enthalpy, it'll be the lattice enthalpy of formation. It's the reverse of this that you want (see p130).

**3** Connect the gaseous ions to the dissolved ions by the hydration enthalpies of **each** ion. This completes the indirect route.

From Hess's law: $\Delta H3 = \Delta H1 + \Delta H2 = +787 + (-406 + -364) = \mathbf{+17\ kJ\ mol^{-1}}$

The enthalpy change of solution is **slightly endothermic**, but this is compensated for by a small increase in **entropy** (see p137), so sodium chloride still dissolves in water.

## Ionic Charge and Ionic Radius Affect the Enthalpy of Hydration

***OCR A and Edexcel only***

The **enthalpy of hydration** is affected by the **size** and the **charge** of the ions in a similar way to the lattice enthalpy (see p131).

1) **Smaller ions have a greater enthalpy of hydration.**
   **Smaller ions** have a **higher** charge density than bigger ions. They **attract** the water molecules **more easily** and have a **more exothermic** enthalpy of hydration.
2) **Ions with a greater charge have a greater enthalpy of hydration.**
   Ions with a **higher charge** are better at **attracting** water molecules than those with lower charges. **More energy** is released when the bonds are **made** giving them a **more exothermic** enthalpy of hydration.

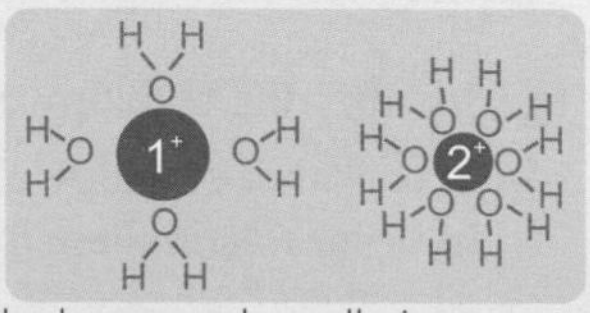
The high charge and small size create a high charge density. This creates a stronger attraction for the water molecules and gives a more exothermic enthalpy of hydration.

E.g. A magnesium ion is smaller and more charged than a sodium ion, which gives it a much bigger enthalpy of hydration: $Mg^{2+} = -1927\ kJ\ mol^{-1}$, $Na^+ = -406\ kJ\ mol^{-1}$

# Enthalpies of Solution and Neutralisation

## *Enthalpy of Neutralisation can be Calculated from Experimental Data*

*OCR A only*

**Neutralisation** of an acid with an alkali always involves the reaction of **hydrogen ions** ($H^+$) with **hydroxide ions** ($OH^-$) to make **water** ($H_2O$). The **enthalpy change of neutralisation**, $\Delta H_{neutralisation}$, is the enthalpy change when **1 mole of water** is formed in a neutralisation reaction. You can calculate its value using $\Delta H = -mc\Delta T$ (p128).

**Example**: 150 ml of hydrochloric acid (concentration 0.25 mol dm$^{-3}$) was neutralised by 150 ml of potassium hydroxide solution. The temperature increased by 1.71 °C. Calculate $\Delta H_{neutralisation}$.

1. The first thing to do is calculate the enthalpy change, $\Delta H$, by plugging the numbers into $\Delta H = -mc\Delta T$.

   $\Delta H = -mc\Delta T = -0.3 \times 4.18 \times 1.71 = -2.144$ kJ

   But this is only the $\Delta H$ and **not** the $\Delta H_{neutralisation}$.

   The 0.3 comes from the mass of the solution — assume the solution has the same specific heat capacity and density as water (1 g/ml).

2. To find the enthalpy of **neutralisation**, you need to calculate $\Delta H$ for **1 mole** of $H_2O$ produced. To find out how many moles of water the reaction makes you can look at the **equation** for it.

   $$HCl + KOH \rightarrow KCl + H_2O$$

3. The number of moles of $H_2O$ **made** is **equal** to the number of moles of acid used. And to work that out you can look back at the question.

   150 ml of 0.25 mol dm$^{-3}$ hydrochloric acid has $0.25 \times 0.15 = 0.0375$ moles

   Don't forget to convert ml to dm$^3$

   So, to make **1 mole** of $H_2O$:

   $\Delta H_{neutralisation} = -2.144 \div 0.0375 = -57.2$ kJ mol$^{-1}$

   The minus sign shows the reaction is exothermic

Weirdly, the value for **any strong acid** is about **–57 kJ mol$^{-1}$**. This is because all strong acids and bases completely ionise in water so essentially the reaction for each of them is the same ($H^+ + OH^- \rightarrow H_2O$).

For **weaker acids** and **alkalis** the value is **less negative** because energy is used to fully dissociate the acid or alkali meaning there's less energy released.

## *Practice Questions*

Q1 Describe, in terms of bonding, what happens when a solid substance dissolves in water.

Q2 Without peeking, draw the enthalpy cycle that you'd use to work out the enthalpy change of solution of NaCl.

Q3 Why is the enthalpy change of neutralisation the same for all strong acids and alkalis?

**Exam Questions**

1 a) Draw an enthalpy cycle for the enthalpy change of solution of $SrF_{2(s)}$. Label each enthalpy change. [5 marks]

b) Calculate the enthalpy change of solution for $SrF_2$ from the following data:

$\Delta H^{\ominus}_{latt}$ [$SrF_{2(s)}$] = –2492 kJ mol$^{-1}$, $\Delta H^{\ominus}_{hyd}$ [$Sr^{2+}_{(g)}$] = –1480 kJ mol$^{-1}$, $\Delta H^{\ominus}_{hyd}$ [$F^-_{(g)}$] = –506 kJ mol$^{-1}$ [2 marks]

2 Show that the enthalpy change of solution for $MgCl_{2(s)}$ is –122 kJ mol$^{-1}$, given that:

$\Delta H^{\ominus}_{latt}$ [$MgCl_{2(s)}$] = –2526 kJ mol$^{-1}$, $\Delta H^{\ominus}_{hyd}$ [$Mg^{2+}_{(g)}$] = –1920 kJ mol$^{-1}$, $\Delta H^{\ominus}_{hyd}$ [$Cl^-_{(g)}$] = –364 kJ mol$^{-1}$ [3 marks]

3 In an experiment, 200 ml of 2.75 mol dm$^{-3}$ $H_2SO_4$ was neutralised by 200 ml of NaOH solution. The temperature rose by 38 °C. Assume the density of the resulting solution is 1 g ml$^{-1}$.

a) Write an equation for the reaction. [1 mark]

b) The specific heat capacity of water is 4.18 kJ kg$^{-1}$ K$^{-1}$. Use this to calculate the enthalpy change of neutralisation for this reaction. [3 marks]

## *Enthalpy change of solution of the Wicked Witch of the West = 8745 kJ mol$^{-1}$...*

*Compared to the ones on page 130, these enthalpy cycles are an absolute breeze. You've got to make sure the definitions are firmly fixed in your mind though. And don't forget there are two opposite definitions of lattice enthalpy.*

# Entropy

*Entropy. You're gonna love this. I really don't want to spoil the surprise, but seriously... just you wait...*
***These pages are for AQA (Unit 5), OCR A (Unit 5), OCR B (Unit 5) and Edexcel (Unit 4).***

## Entropy Tells you How Much Disorder There Is

Entropy is a measure of the **number of ways** that **particles** can be **arranged** and the **number of ways** that the **energy** can be shared out between the particles.

Substances really **like** disorder, they're actually more **energetically stable** when there's more disorder. So the particles naturally move to try to **increase the entropy**.

> *Example:* A gas spontaneously diffusing across a room.
> If you open a bottle of something smelly it will **diffuse** throughout the room **spontaneously** — you don't have to shake it or heat it to make it happen. This is because it has a **higher entropy** when filling the room (there are more ways to arrange the particles) than it has in the bottle.

Baby Jay's experiment into entropy and diffusion was about to begin.

There are a few things that affect entropy:

### Physical State affects Entropy

You have to go back to the good old **solid-liquid-gas** particle explanation thingy to understand this.

**Solid** particles just wobble about a fixed point — there's **hardly any** randomness, so they have the **lowest entropy**.

**Gas** particles whizz around wherever they like. They've got the most **random arrangements** of particles, so they have the **highest entropy**.

**Dissolving** a solid also increases its entropy — dissolved particles can **move freely** as they're no longer held in one place.

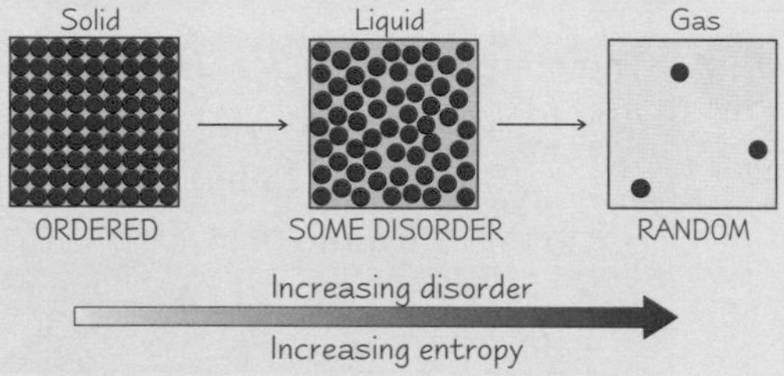

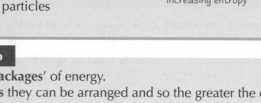

### The Amount of Energy a Substance has affects Entropy too

Energy can be measured in **quanta** — these are fixed '**packages**' of energy.
The more energy quanta a substance has, the **more ways** they can be arranged and so the greater the **entropy**.

### More Particles means More Entropy

It makes sense — the more particles you've got, the **more ways** they and their energy can be **arranged** — so in a reaction like $N_2O_{4(g)} \rightarrow 2NO_{2(g)}$, entropy increases because the **number of moles** increases.

## The Entropy of A Substance Increases with Temperature

***Edexcel only***

If you **raise the temperature** of a substance, you **increase the energy** of its particles.
So the **higher** the temperature, the **more energy quanta** a substance has, and the **more ways** these quanta can be distributed — which means **higher entropy**.

The graph below shows how the entropy of a substance typically changes with temperature:

1) Within the solid, liquid and gas phases, entropy **increases slowly** with temperature.
2) When there's a change in **physical state**, there's also a **rapid change** in entropy. You can see this at points $T_m$ and $T_b$ on the graph.
3) There's a **larger** increase in entropy when a substance changes from **liquid to gas** than when it changes from **solid to liquid**.
4) The curve starts at the origin, (0,0). In other words, at a temperature of **zero kelvin**, a substance will theoretically have **zero entropy**. This could only happen if you had a **perfectly ordered crystal**.

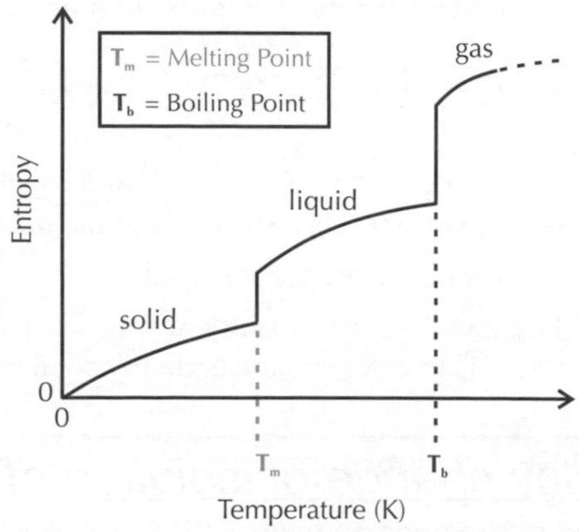

# Entropy

## Physical State and Complexity of a Substance Affect Standard Entropy

1) The **standard entropy** of a substance, $S^\ominus$, is the entropy of **1 mole** of that substance under **standard conditions** (**100 kPa** pressure and **298 K**). Its units are **J K$^{-1}$ mol$^{-1}$**.
2) The standard entropy of a substance depends mainly on its **physical state**. As a **general** rule solid substances tend to have **lower** standard entropies than liquids, which tend to have lower standard entropies than gases.

> ***Example:*** The standard entropy of liquid water is lower than the standard entropy for water vapour.
> $S^\ominus$ of $H_2O_{(l)}$ = 70 J K$^{-1}$ mol$^{-1}$ $S^\ominus$ of $H_2O_{(g)}$ = 189 J K$^{-1}$ mol$^{-1}$

3) The standard entropy of a substance also depends on its **complexity**.
**Simple** atoms or molecules tend to have **lower** standard entropies than more complicated molecules.

> ***Example:*** Carbon dioxide has more atoms than carbon monoxide and has a higher standard entropy.
> $S^\ominus$ of $CO_{2(g)}$ = 214 J K$^{-1}$ mol$^{-1}$ $S^\ominus$ of $CO_{(g)}$ = 198 J K$^{-1}$ mol$^{-1}$

## Entropy Increase May Explain Spontaneous Endothermic Reactions

Some **endothermic** reactions are **spontaneous** — which is a bit weird. You'd normally have to supply **energy** to make an endothermic reaction happen, but if the **entropy** increases enough, the reaction will happen by itself.

The reaction of sodium hydrogencarbonate with hydrochloric acid is a **spontaneous endothermic reaction.**

$$NaHCO_{3(s)} + H^+_{(aq)} \rightarrow Na^+_{(aq)} + CO_{2(g)} + H_2O_{(l)}$$

| $NaHCO_{3(s)}$ | $H^+_{(aq)}$ | $Na^+_{(aq)}$ | $CO_{2(g)}$ | $H_2O_{(l)}$ |
|---|---|---|---|---|
| 1 mole solid | 1 mole aqueous ions | 1 mole aqueous ions | 1 mole gas | 1 mole liquid |

It happens because of the large **increase in entropy** — the product has more particles and also the particles are in higher entropy states overall (gas and liquid, rather than solid).

Both the enthalpy and the entropy have a say in whether a reaction is spontaneous — see p138

## Practice Questions

Q1 How does the energy of a substance affect its entropy?

Q2 Why does entropy increase with increasing temperature?

Q3 Is the change in entropy greater at the melting point of a substance, or at its boiling point? Why?

Q4 In each of the following pairs choose the one with the greater entropy value:

a) 1 mole of $NaCl_{(aq)}$ and 1 mole of $NaCl_{(s)}$ b) 1 mole of $Br_{2(l)}$ and 1 mole of $Br_{2(g)}$

**Exam Questions**

1 a) Define the term *entropy*. [2 marks]

b) Explain whether each of the following reactions is likely to result in an increase or a decrease in entropy.

i) $2NaNO_{3(s)} \rightarrow 2NaNO_{2(s)} + O_{2(g)}$ [2 marks]

ii) $CO_{2(g)} + C_{(s)} \rightarrow 2CO_{(g)}$ [2 marks]

iii) $N_{2(g)} + 3H_{2(g)} \rightarrow 2NH_{3(g)}$ [2 marks]

iv) $H_{2(g)} + \frac{1}{2}O_{2(g)} \rightarrow H_2O_{(l)}$ [2 marks]

2 Based on just the equation, predict whether the reaction below is likely to be spontaneous. Give a reason for your answer.

$$Mg_{(s)} + \tfrac{1}{2}O_{2(g)} \rightarrow MgO_{(s)}$$ [2 marks]

## Being neat and tidy is against the laws of nature...

*Well there you go. Entropy in all its glory. We're not done yet though, oh no. There's plenty more where this came from. Which is why — if random disorder has left you in a spin — I'd suggest making sure you've really got your head around this lot before you turn over. You'll thank me for it, you will... Chocolates are always welcome... Flowers are nice too...*

# Entropy Change

*Here we go, as promised, more entropy. Never say I don't spoil you rotten...*
***These pages are for AQA (Unit 5), OCR A (Unit 5), OCR B (Unit 5) and Edexcel (Unit 4).***

## The **Total Entropy Change** Includes the **System** and the **Surroundings**

During a reaction, there's an entropy change between the **reactants and products** — the entropy change of the **system**.
The entropy of the **surroundings** changes too (because **energy** is transferred to or from the system).
The **total entropy change** is the sum of the entropy changes of the **system** and the **surroundings**.

The units of entropy are $J\ K^{-1}\ mol^{-1}$

$$\Delta S_{total} = \Delta S_{system} + \Delta S_{surroundings}$$

This equation isn't much use unless you know $\Delta S_{system}$ and $\Delta S_{surroundings}$. Luckily, there are formulas for them too:

This is just the difference between the entropies of the reactants and products. →

$$\Delta S_{system} = S_{products} - S_{reactants} \quad \text{and} \quad \Delta S_{surroundings} = -\frac{\Delta H}{T}$$

← $\Delta H$ = enthalpy change (in $J\ mol^{-1}$)
$T$ = temperature (in K)

***Example:*** Calculate the total entropy change for the reaction of ammonia and hydrogen chloride under standard conditions.

$$NH_{3(g)} + HCl_{(g)} \rightarrow NH_4Cl_{(s)} \qquad \Delta H^{\ominus} = -315\ kJ\ mol^{-1}$$

$$S^{\ominus}[NH_{3(g)}] = 192.3\ J\ K^{-1}\ mol^{-1},\ S^{\ominus}[HCl_{(g)}] = 186.8\ J\ K^{-1}\ mol^{-1},\ S^{\ominus}[NH_4Cl_{(s)}] = 94.6\ J\ K^{-1}\ mol^{-1}$$

First find the entropy change of the **system**:

$\Delta S_{system} = S_{products} - S_{reactants} = 94.6 - (192.3 + 186.8) = \mathbf{-284.5\ J\ K^{-1}\ mol^{-1}}$

This shows a negative change in entropy. It's not surprising as 2 moles of gas have combined to form 1 mole of solid.

Now find the entropy change of the **surroundings**:

$\Delta H = -315\ kJ\ mol^{-1} = -315 \times 10^3\ J\ mol^{-1}$ ← Put ΔH in the right units.

$$\Delta S_{surroundings} = -\frac{\Delta H}{T} = \frac{-(-315\times10^3)}{298} = \mathbf{+1057\ J\ K^{-1}\ mol^{-1}}$$

Finally you can find the **total** entropy change:

$\Delta S_{total} = \Delta S_{system} + \Delta S_{surroundings} = -284.5 + (+1057) = \mathbf{+772.5\ J\ K^{-1}\ mol^{-1}}$

Beware — units of entropy contain J, but units of enthalpy changes generally contain kJ.

## For A **Spontaneous** Reaction $\Delta S_{total}$ Must Be **Positive**

***OCR B and Edexcel only***

1) The **total entropy** of a system and its surroundings **has to increase** for a spontaneous reaction to happen.
2) If $\Delta S_{total}$ is **positive** the reaction is **kinetically favourable** — it can happen spontaneously.
   If $\Delta S_{total}$ is **negative** the reactants are said to be **kinetically stable** — this means they won't react on their own.
3) As long as $\Delta S_{total}$ is **positive**, it doesn't matter if one of $\Delta S_{system}$ and $\Delta S_{surroundings}$ is negative.
   Whether or not the **total** entropy change is positive depends on the **balance** between the entropy changes of the system and the surroundings.
4) Remember, $\Delta S_{surroundings} = -\frac{\Delta H}{T}$.
   This means:
   - In an **exothermic** reaction $\Delta H$ is negative, so $\Delta S_{surroundings}$ is always **positive** — heat given out by the system **increases** the entropy of the surroundings.
   - In an **endothermic** reaction $\Delta H$ is positive, so $\Delta S_{surroundings}$ is always **negative** — heat taken in by the system **lowers** the entropy of the surroundings .
   - At **higher temperatures**, $\Delta S_{surroundings}$ gets **smaller**. As a result, it makes a **smaller contribution** to the total entropy change than it does at lower temperatures.
5) The **exothermic** reaction in the example above can happen because the **entropy increase** in the **surroundings** is big enough to make up for the **entropy decrease** in the **system** — the **total entropy** has still **increased**.
6) The same thing applies to endothermic reactions — there's a **drop** in $\Delta S_{surroundings}$, but if the **increase** in $\Delta S_{system}$ is big enough, the reaction **will happen**.

# Entropy Change

## A Reaction that **Can Happen** might not Happen **Quickly**

***Edexcel only***

Just because a reaction **can happen** spontaneously, **doesn't** mean that it happens **quickly**.
The **thermodynamics** of a reaction don't tell you anything about how **fast** it will go — that's to do with **reaction kinetics**.

***Example:*** The conversion of diamond to graphite

$C_{diamond} \rightarrow C_{graphite}$ At 298 K: $\Delta H = -1.9$ kJ mol$^{-1}$, $\Delta S_{system} = +3.3$ J K$^{-1}$ mol$^{-1}$

So at 298 K $\Delta S_{total} = \Delta S_{system} + \Delta S_{surroundings} = 3.3 + (1900 \div 298) = 3.3 + 6.4 = +9.7$ J K$^{-1}$ mol$^{-1}$

The **total entropy change** is **positive**, so this reaction **can** happen spontaneously.
But at room temperature and pressure, the rate of reaction is **extremely slow** — in fact it takes millions of years.
This is because the **activation energy** needed to start this reaction is so high. Diamond is said to be **kinetically inert**.

## **Dissolving** Also Involves **Entropy Changes**

***AQA and Edexcel only***

You can use entropy changes to predict whether an **ionic compound** will dissolve in water.

***Example:*** The dissolution of **sodium bromide** in water.

$NaBr_{(s)} \rightarrow Na^+_{(aq)} + Br^-_{(aq)}$ At 298 K: $\Delta H^{\ominus} = -0.6$ kJ mol$^{-1}$, $\Delta S^{\ominus}_{system} = +55.0$ J K$^{-1}$ mol$^{-1}$

So at 298 K, $\Delta S^{\ominus}_{surroundings} = -\frac{\Delta H}{T} = -(-600 \div 298) = +2.0$ J K$^{-1}$ mol$^{-1}$

$\Delta S^{\ominus}_{total} = \Delta S^{\ominus}_{system} + \Delta S^{\ominus}_{surroundings} = +55.0 + 2.0 = \mathbf{+57.0}$ **J K$^{-1}$ mol$^{-1}$**.

Sodium bromide **will** dissolve in water at 298 K.

## Practice Questions

Q1 How do you work out the total entropy change of a system?

Q2 For a particular reaction, $\Delta H = -420$ kJ mol$^{-1}$. Show that $\Delta S_{surroundings}$ at 298 K is 1409 J K$^{-1}$ mol$^{-1}$

Q3 If a chemical reaction is exothermic, will $\Delta S_{surroundings}$ be positive or negative?

Q4 What does the term 'kinetically inert' mean?

**Exam Questions**

1 When a small amount of ammonium carbonate solid is added to 10 cm$^3$ of 1.0 mol dm$^{-3}$ ethanoic acid, carbon dioxide gas is evolved. This is an endothermic reaction, so the temperature of the solution drops.

$$(NH_4)_2CO_{3(s)} + 2CH_3CO_2H_{(aq)} \rightarrow 2CH_3CO_2NH_{4(aq)} + H_2O_{(l)} + CO_{2(g)} \quad \Delta H^{\ominus} > 0$$

a) Looking at the equation, what would you expect to happen to the entropy of the system during this reaction? Explain your answer. [2 marks]

b) Explain how this reaction can be both endothermic and spontaneous. [3 marks]

2 Thin ribbons of magnesium burn brightly in oxygen to leave a solid, white residue of magnesium oxide. The equation for this reaction is:

$$2Mg_{(s)} + O_{2(g)} \rightarrow 2MgO_{(s)} \quad \Delta H = -1204 \text{ kJ mol}^{-1} \text{ (at 298 K)}$$

$$S^{\ominus}[Mg_{(s)}] = +32.7 \text{ J K}^{-1}\text{mol}^{-1},\ S^{\ominus}[O_{2(g)}] = +205 \text{ J K}^{-1}\text{mol}^{-1},\ S^{\ominus}[MgO_{(s)}] = +26.9 \text{ J K}^{-1}\text{mol}^{-1}$$

a) From the equation, **predict** whether $\Delta S_{system}$ for the reaction will be positive or negative at 298 K. Give a reason for your answer. [2 marks]

b) Using the data given, calculate $\Delta S_{system}$ at 298 K. [3 marks]

c) Calculate $\Delta S_{total}$ for the reaction. [4 marks]

## The entropy of my surroundings is always increasing, take a look at my kitchen...

*Still awake? Great stuff. Let me be the first to congratulate you on making it to the end of this page — I nearly didn't. Bet you thought the diamond-to-graphite stuff was pretty cool though, right? I know, I'm clutching at straws. Never mind. As a reward I suggest ten minutes of looking at clips of reality TV auditionees online. It'll cheer you up no end...*

# Free–Energy Change

*Free energy — I could do with a bit of that. My gas bill is astronomical.*
***These pages are for AQA (Unit 5) and OCR A (Unit 5).***

## For Spontaneous Reactions $\Delta G$ must be Negative or Zero

**Free-energy change**, $\Delta G$, is a measure used to predict whether a reaction is **feasible**.
If $\Delta G$ is **negative or equal to zero**, then the reaction can happen by itself.
Free-energy change takes into account the changes in **enthalpy** and **entropy** in the system. And of course, there's a formula for it:

Even if $\Delta G$ shows that a reaction is theoretically feasible, it might have a really high activation energy and be so slow that you wouldn't notice it happening at all.

$\Delta G$ = free-energy change (in J mol$^{-1}$)

$$\Delta G = \Delta H - T\Delta S_{system}$$

$\Delta H$ = enthalpy change (in J mol$^{-1}$)
$T$ = temperature (in K)
$\Delta S_{system}$ = entropy of the system (in J K$^{-1}$ mol$^{-1}$) (see p136)

***Example:*** Calculate the free-energy change for the following reaction at 298 K.

$$MgCO_{3(s)} \rightarrow MgO_{(s)} + CO_{2(g)} \qquad \Delta H^{\ominus} = +117 \text{ kJ mol}^{-1},\ \Delta S_{system} = +175 \text{ J K}^{-1}\text{mol}^{-1}$$

$$\Delta G = \Delta H - T\Delta S_{system} = +117 \times 10^3 - (298 \times 175) = \mathbf{+64\ 850\ J\ mol^{-1}}$$

$\Delta H$ must be in J not kJ. So, if you're given a value in kJ, multiply it by $10^3$.

$\Delta G$ is positive — so the reaction isn't feasible at this temperature.

## The Feasiblity of Some Reactions Depends on Temperature

1) If a reaction is exothermic (**negative $\Delta H$**) and has a **positive entropy** change, then $\Delta G$ is **always negative** since $\Delta G = \Delta H - T\Delta S_{system}$. These reactions are feasible at **any** temperature.
If a reaction is endothermic (**positive $\Delta H$**) and has a **negative entropy** change, then $\Delta G$ is **always positive**. These reactions are **not** feasible at any temperature.
But for other combinations, temperature has an effect.

2) If $\Delta H$ is **positive** (endothermic) and $\Delta S_{system}$ is **positive** then the reaction won't be feasible at some temperatures but **will be** at a **higher** temperature.
For example, the decomposition of **calcium carbonate** is **endothermic** but results in an **increase in entropy** (the number of molecules increases and $CO_2$ is a gas).

$$CaCO_{3(s)} \rightarrow CaO_{(s)} + CO_{3(g)}$$

The reaction will **only** occur when $CaCO_3$ is **heated** — it isn't feasible at 298 K.

After her surgery, Anne found that a reaction wasn't feasible.

***Here's a random example with numbers:*** $\Delta H$ = +10 kJ mol$^{-1}$, $\Delta S_{system}$ = +10 J K$^{-1}$ mol$^{-1}$

At **300 K**: $\Delta G = \Delta H - T\Delta S_{system}$ $\quad \Delta G = +10 \times 10^3 - (300 \times +10) = \mathbf{+7000\ J\ mol^{-1}}$
At **1500 K**: $\Delta G = \Delta H - T\Delta S_{system}$ $\quad \Delta G = +10 \times 10^3 - (1500 \times +10) = \mathbf{-5000\ J\ mol^{-1}}$

So a reaction with these enthalpy and entropy changes is feasible at 1500 K, but not at 300 K...

3) If $\Delta H$ is **negative** (exothermic) and $\Delta S_{system}$ is **negative** then the reaction will be feasible at some temperatures but **won't** be **feasible** at a **higher** temperature.
For example, the process of turning **water** from a **liquid** to a **solid** is **exothermic** but results in a **decrease in entropy** (a solid is more ordered than a liquid), which means it will only occur at **certain temperatures** (i.e. at 0 °C or below).

***And another example with random numbers:*** $\Delta H$ = –10 kJ mol$^{-1}$, $\Delta S_{system}$ = –10 J K$^{-1}$ mol$^{-1}$

At **300 K**: $\Delta G = \Delta H - T\Delta S_{system}$ $\quad \Delta G = -10 \times 10^3 - (300 \times -10) = \mathbf{-7000\ J\ mol^{-1}}$
At **1500 K**: $\Delta G = \Delta H - T\Delta S_{system}$ $\quad \Delta G = -10 \times 10^3 - (1500 \times -10) = \mathbf{+5000\ J\ mol^{-1}}$

...and this one is feasible at 300 K, but not at 1500 K.

# Free–Energy Change

## You can Calculate the Temperature at which a Reaction Becomes Feasible

***AQA only***

When $\Delta G$ is **zero**, a reaction is **just feasible**.

You can find the **temperature** where $\Delta G$ is zero by rearranging the free-energy equation from the previous page:

$\Delta G = \Delta H - T\Delta S_{system}$, so when $\Delta G = 0$, $T\Delta S_{system} = \Delta H$.

So: $$T = \frac{\Delta H}{\Delta S_{system}}$$

$T$ = temperature at which a reaction becomes feasible (in K)
$\Delta H$ = enthalpy change (in J mol$^{-1}$)
$\Delta S_{system}$ = entropy change of the system (in J K$^{-1}$ mol$^{-1}$)

***Example:*** Tungsten, W, can be extracted from its ore, $WO_3$, by reduction using hydrogen.

$$WO_{3(s)} + 3H_{2(g)} \rightarrow W_{(s)} + 3H_2O_{(g)} \qquad \Delta H^{\ominus} = +117 \text{ kJ mol}^{-1}$$

Use the data in the table to find the minimum temperature at which the reaction becomes feasible.

| Substance | $S^{\ominus}$ J K$^{-1}$ mol$^{-1}$ |
|---|---|
| $WO_{3(s)}$ | 76 |
| $H_{2(g)}$ | 130 |
| $W_{(s)}$ | 33 |
| $H_2O_{(g)}$ | 189 |

First, convert the **enthalpy change**, $\Delta H$, to joules per mole:

$\Delta H = 117 \times 10^3 = \mathbf{117\,000 \text{ J mol}^{-1}}$

Then find the **entropy change**, $\Delta S_{system}$:

$\Delta S_{system} = S_{products} - S_{reactants} = [33 + (3 \times 189)] - [76 + (3 \times 130)] = \mathbf{+134 \text{ J K}^{-1} \text{mol}^{-1}}$

See p136 for more on this formula.

Then divide $\Delta H$ by $\Delta S_{system}$ to find the temperature at which the reaction just becomes feasible:

$$T = \frac{\Delta H}{\Delta S_{system}} = \frac{117\,000}{134} = \mathbf{873 \text{ K}}$$

## Practice Questions

Q1 What does $\Delta G$ stand for? What is it used for?

Q2 State whether each of the following reactions is feasible, feasible at certain temperatures or not feasible:
Reaction A: negative $\Delta H$ and negative $\Delta S$
Reaction B: negative $\Delta H$ and positive $\Delta S$
Reaction C: positive $\Delta H$ and positive $\Delta S$
Reaction D: positive $\Delta H$ and negative $\Delta S$

Q3 Write down the formula for calculating the temperature at which a reaction becomes feasible.

**Exam Questions**

1 The enthalpy change that occurs when water turns from a liquid to a solid is –6 kJ mol$^{-1}$.

$H_2O_{(l)} \rightarrow H_2O_{(s)}$ $\quad S^{\ominus}[H_2O_{(l)}] = 70$ J K$^{-1}$ mol$^{-1}$, $\quad S^{\ominus}[H_2O_{(s)}] = 48$ J K$^{-1}$ mol$^{-1}$,

a) Using this data, calculate the entropy change when one mole of $H_2O_{(l)}$ changes to $H_2O_{(g)}$. [1 mark]

b) Will this reaction be spontaneous at 250 K or 300 K? Explain your answer. [4 marks]

2 Magnesium carbonate decomposes to form magnesium oxide and carbon dioxide:

$MgCO_{3(s)} \rightarrow MgO_{(s)} + CO_{2(g)}$ $\qquad \Delta H^{\ominus} = +117$ kJ mol$^{-1}$ and $\Delta S^{\ominus}_{system} = +175$ J K$^{-1}$ mol$^{-1}$.

a) Will this reaction occur spontaneously at a temperature of 550 K?
Explain your answer. [2 marks]

b) Calculate the minimum temperature at which the reaction becomes feasible. [2 marks]

## The feasibility of revision depends on what's on the telly...

*These pages are a bit confusing if you ask me — so make sure you've properly understood them before you move on. The most important bit to learn is the formula for $\Delta G$. If you know that, then you can always work out whether a reaction is feasible even if you can't remember the rules about positive and negative enthalpy and entropy.*

# Period 3 Elements and Oxides

*Period 3's the third row down on the Periodic Table — the one that starts with sodium and ends with argon.*
***These pages are for AQA (Unit 5).***

## Sodium is More Reactive Than Magnesium

1) **Sodium** and **magnesium** are the first two elements in **Period 3**. Sodium is in **Group 1**, and magnesium is in **Group 2**. When they react, **sodium** loses **one electron** to form an **$Na^+$ ion**, while **magnesium** loses **two electrons** to form **$Mg^{2+}$**.
2) Sodium is **more reactive** than **magnesium** because it takes **less energy** to lose **one electron** than it does to lose two. So **more energy** (usually **heat**) is needed for magnesium to react. This is shown in their reactions with **water**.

### Sodium Reacts Vigorously With Water

1) Sodium reacts **vigorously** with **cold water**, forming a molten ball on the surface, fizzing and producing $H_2$ gas.

$$2Na_{(s)} + 2H_2O_{(l)} \rightarrow 2NaOH_{(aq)} + H_{2(g)}$$

2) The reaction produces **sodium hydroxide**, so forms a strongly **alkaline** solution (pH 12–14).
3) Magnesium reacts **very slowly** with **cold water**. You can't see any reaction, but it forms a **weakly alkaline** solution (pH 9–10), which shows that a reaction has occurred. The solution is only weakly alkaline because magnesium oxide is **not very soluble** in water, so relatively **few hydroxide ions** are produced.

$$Mg_{(s)} + 2H_2O_{(l)} \rightarrow Mg(OH)_{2(aq)} + H_{2(g)}$$

4) Magnesium reacts much faster with **steam** (i.e. when there is **more energy**), to form **magnesium oxide**.

## Most Period 3 Elements React Readily With Oxygen

Period 3 elements form **oxides** when they react with **oxygen**. They're usually oxidised to their **highest** oxidation states — the same as their **group numbers**. Sulfur is the exception to this — it forms **$SO_2$**, in which it's only got a **+4** oxidation state (a **high temperature** and a **catalyst** are needed to make **$SO_3$**).

The equations are all **really similar** — **element + oxygen → oxide**:

$P_4$ is a common allotrope (form) of phosphorus.

| | | | |
|---|---|---|---|
| $2Na_{(s)} + \frac{1}{2}O_{2(g)} \rightarrow Na_2O_{(s)}$ | sodium oxide | $Si_{(s)} + O_{2(g)} \rightarrow SiO_{2(s)}$ | silicon dioxide |
| $Mg_{(s)} + \frac{1}{2}O_{2(g)} \rightarrow MgO_{(s)}$ | magnesium oxide | $P_{4(s)} + 5O_{2(g)} \rightarrow P_4O_{10(s)}$ | phosphorus(V) oxide |
| $2Al_{(s)} + 1\frac{1}{2}O_{2(g)} \rightarrow Al_2O_{3(s)}$ | aluminium oxide | $S_{(s)} + O_{2(g)} \rightarrow SO_{2(g)}$ | sulfur dioxide |

The **more reactive metals** (Na, Mg) and the **non-metals** (P, S) react **readily** in air, while **Al** and **Si** react **slowly**.

| Element | Na | Mg | Al | Si | P | S |
|---|---|---|---|---|---|---|
| Formula of oxide | $Na_2O$ | MgO | $Al_2O_3$ | $SiO_2$ | $P_4O_{10}$ | $SO_2$ |
| Reaction in air | Vigorous | Vigorous | Slow | Slow | Spontaneously combusts | Burns steadily |
| Flame | Yellow | Brilliant white | Brilliant white | | Brilliant white | Blue |

You can identify some of the oxides using flame tests.

## Bonding and Structure Affect Melting Points

1) **$Na_2O$**, **MgO** and **$Al_2O_3$** — the metal oxides — all have **high melting points** because they form **giant ionic lattices**. The **strong forces of attraction** between each ion mean it takes a lot of heat energy to **break the bonds** and melt them.
2) MgO has a **higher melting point** than $Na_2O$ because Mg forms **2+ ions**, so bonds more strongly than the 1+ Na ions in $Na_2O$.
3) $Al_2O_3$ has a **lower melting point** than you might expect because the 3+ ions distort the oxygen's electron cloud making the bonds **partially covalent**.
4) **$SiO_2$** has a **higher melting point** than the other non-metal oxides because it has a **giant macromolecular** structure.

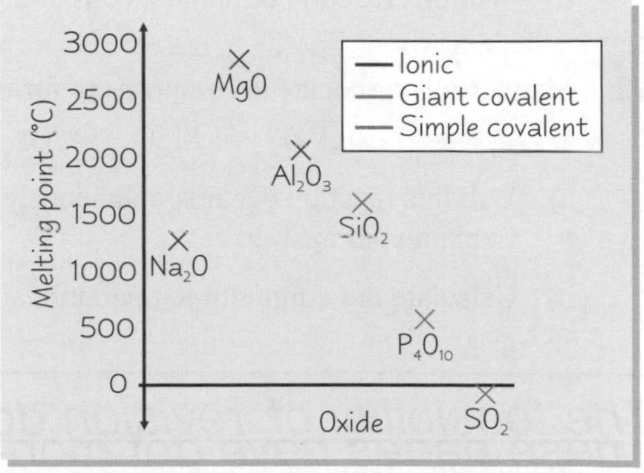


5) **$P_4O_{10}$ and $SO_2$** have relatively **low melting points** because they form **simple molecular** structures. The molecules are bound by **weak intermolecular forces** (see page 7), which take little energy to overcome.

# Period 3 Elements and Oxides

## **Ionic** Oxides are **Alkaline, Covalent** Oxides are **Acidic**

1) The **ionic oxides** of the **metals** Na and Mg dissolve in water to form **hydroxides**. The solutions are both **alkaline**, but **sodium hydroxide** is more soluble in water, so it forms a **more alkaline** solution than magnesium hydroxide.

$Na_2O_{(s)} + H_2O_{(l)} \rightarrow 2NaOH_{(aq)}$ **pH 12-14** $MgO_{(s)} + H_2O_{(l)} \rightarrow Mg(OH)_{2(aq)}$ **pH 9-10**

2) The **simple covalent oxides** of the **non-metals** phosphorus and sulfur form **acidic** solutions. All of the acids are **strong** and so the pH of their solutions is about **0-2**.

$P_4O_{10(s)} + 6H_2O_{(l)} \rightarrow 4H_3PO_{4(aq)}$ **phosphoric(V) acid**
$SO_{2(g)} + H_2O_{(l)} \rightarrow H_2SO_{3(aq)}$ **sulfurous acid (or sulfuric(IV) acid)**
$SO_{3(l)} + H_2O_{(l)} \rightarrow H_2SO_{4(aq)}$ **sulfuric(VI) acid**

An ironic ox-side?

3) The **giant covalent structure** of **silicon dioxide** means that it is **insoluble** in water. However, it will **react with bases** to form salts so it is classed as **acidic**.

4) **Aluminium oxide**, which is partially **ionic** and partially **covalently** bonded, is also **insoluble** in water. But it will react with **acids and bases** to form salts — i.e. it can act as an acid or a base, so it's classed as **amphoteric**.

## Acid + Base → Salt + Water

The equation for **neutralising** an **acid** with a **base** is a classic — **acid + base → salt + water** — and it's no different for reactions of the Period 3 oxides. You may be asked to **write equations** for these reactions, so here are some examples:

1 **Basic oxides neutralise acids:**
$Na_2O_{(s)} + 2HCl_{(aq)} \rightarrow 2NaCl_{(aq)} + H_2O_{(l)}$
$MgO_{(s)} + H_2SO_{4(aq)} \rightarrow MgSO_{4(aq)} + H_2O_{(l)}$

2 **Acidic oxides neutralise bases:**
$SiO_{2(s)} + 2NaOH_{(aq)} \rightarrow Na_2SiO_{3(aq)} + H_2O_{(l)}$
$P_4O_{10(s)} + 12NaOH_{(aq)} \rightarrow 4Na_3PO_{4(aq)} + 6H_2O_{(l)}$
$SO_{2(g)} + 2NaOH_{(aq)} \rightarrow Na_2SO_{3(aq)} + H_2O_{(l)}$
$SO_{3(g)} + 2NaOH_{(aq)} \rightarrow Na_2SO_{4(aq)} + H_2O_{(l)}$

3 **Amphoteric oxides neutralise acids and bases:**
$Al_2O_{3(s)} + 3H_2SO_{4(aq)} \rightarrow Al_2(SO_4)_{3(aq)} + 3H_2O_{(l)}$
$Al_2O_{3(s)} + 2NaOH_{(aq)} + 3H_2O_{(l)} \rightarrow 2NaAl(OH)_{4(aq)}$

## Practice Questions

Q1 Why is Na more reactive than Mg with water?

Q2 What type of oxide is: a) $Na_2O$, b) $P_4O_{10}$?

Q3 Write an equation for the reaction of $Na_2O$ with water.

Q4 Explain why MgO forms a less alkaline solution than $Na_2O$.

**Exam Questions**

1 X and Y are oxides of Period 3 elements.
The Period 3 element in X has an oxidation state of +6 and the oxide forms an acidic solution in water.
The Period 3 element in Y has an oxidation state of +1 and a high melting point.
a) Identify oxide X and write an equation for its reaction with water. [2 marks]
b) i) Identify oxide Y and write an equation for its reaction with water. [2 marks]
ii) Explain the reason for its high melting point. [3 marks]

2 a) Write an equation for the formation of phosphorus(V) oxide, $P_4O_{10}$, from phosphorus and oxygen. [1 mark]
b) i) Write an equation for the reaction between $P_4O_{10}$ and water. [1 mark]
ii) Suggest a value for the pH of the solution obtained from the reaction in part (i). [1 mark]
c) Write an equation for the reaction between $P_4O_{10}$ and potassium hydroxide. [1 mark]

## These pages have got more trends than a school disco...

*Hang on a minute, I hear you cry — what about chlorine and argon? Aren't they in Period 3 too? Well, yes, they are, but you don't need to know about them. Argon's a noble gas, anyway, so it doesn't really react with anything... yawn.*

# Redox Equations

*And now for something a bit different. Read on to learn more about redox...*
***These pages are for AQA (Unit 5), OCR A (Unit 5), OCR B (Units 4 and 5) and Edexcel (Unit 5).***

## If Electrons are Transferred, it's a **Redox Reaction**

1) A **loss** of electrons is called **oxidation**. A **gain** of electrons is called **reduction**.
2) Reduction and oxidation happen **simultaneously** — hence the term "**redox**" reaction.
3) An **oxidising agent accepts** electrons and gets reduced.
4) A **reducing agent donates** electrons and gets oxidised.

$$Na + \frac{1}{2}Cl_2 \longrightarrow Na^+\,Cl^- \quad (-e^-,\ +e^-)$$

Na is oxidised
Cl is reduced

I couldn't find a red ox, so you'll have to make do with a multicoloured donkey instead.

## Sometimes it's Easier to Talk About **Oxidation Numbers**

(It's also called oxidation state.)

There are lots of rules. Take a deep breath...

1) All atoms are treated as **ions** for this, even if they're covalently bonded.
2) Uncombined **elements** have an oxidation number of **0**.
3) Elements just bonded to **identical atoms**, like $O_2$ and $H_2$, also have an oxidation number of **0**.
4) The oxidation number of a simple **monatomic ion**, e.g. $Na^+$, is the same as its **charge**.
5) In **compounds** or **compound ions**, the **overall oxidation number** is just the ion charge.

   E.g. $SO_4^{2-}$ — **overall oxidation number = –2**,
   oxidation number of **O = –2** (total = –8),
   so oxidation number of **S = +6**

   Within an ion, the most electronegative element has a negative oxidation number (equal to its ionic charge). Other elements have more positive oxidation numbers.

6) The sum of the oxidation numbers for a **neutral compound** is 0.

   E.g. $Fe_2O_3$ — **overall oxidation number = 0**, oxidation number of **O = –2** (total = –6), so oxidation number of **Fe = +3**

7) Combined **oxygen** is –2 (except in $O_2$ where it's 0).
8) Combined **hydrogen** is +1 (except in $H_2$ where it's 0).

There are a few exceptions to these but you don't need to know about them.

If you see **Roman numerals** in a chemical name, it's an **oxidation number** — it applies to the atom or group immediately before it.
E.g. copper has oxidation number **2** in **copper(II) sulfate**,
and manganese has oxidation number **7** in a **manganate(VII) ion** ($MnO_4^-$).

## Oxidation States go **Up** or **Down** as Electrons are **Lost** or **Gained**

$$Na + \frac{1}{2}Cl_2 \longrightarrow Na^+\,Cl^- \quad (-e^-,\ +e^-)$$

| | Na | ½Cl₂ | Na⁺ | Cl⁻ |
|---|---|---|---|---|
| Oxidation No. | 0 | 0 | +1 | –1 |

1) The oxidation state for an atom will **increase by 1** for each **electron lost**.
2) The oxidation state will **decrease by 1** for each **electron gained**.

# Redox Equations

## You can Separate Redox Reactions into *Half-Reactions*

1) A redox reaction is made up of an **oxidation half-reaction** and a **reduction half-reaction**.
2) You can write an **ionic half-equation** for each of these **half-reactions**.

***Example:*** **Zinc metal** displaces **silver ions** from silver nitrate solution to form **zinc nitrate** and a deposit of **silver metal**.

The zinc atoms each lose 2 electrons (oxidation) $Zn_{(s)} \rightarrow Zn^{2+}_{(aq)} + 2e^-$

The silver ions each gain 1 electron (reduction) $Ag^+_{(aq)} + e^- \rightarrow Ag_{(s)}$

**Two silver ions** are needed to accept the **two electrons** released by each zinc atom.
So you need to double the silver half-equation before the two half-equations can be combined: $2Ag^+_{(aq)} + 2e^- \rightarrow 2Ag_{(s)}$

Now the number of electrons lost and gained **balance**, so the half-equations can be combined: $Zn_{(s)} + 2Ag^+_{(aq)} \rightarrow Zn^{2+}_{(aq)} + 2Ag_{(s)}$

Electrons aren't included in the full equation.

## *H⁺ Ions* May be Needed to *Reduce* Some *Oxidising Agents*

1) **Manganate(VII) ions**, $MnO_4^-$, contain manganese with an oxidation number of **+7**.
When these ions are **reduced** they gain five electrons to become $Mn^{2+}$ ions, with an oxidation number of **+2**.
2) In a **+2 state**, manganese can exist as simple $\mathbf{Mn^{2+}_{(aq)}}$ ions.
But in a **+7 state**, it has to combine with **oxygen** to form $MnO_4^-$ ions, as $Mn^{7+}_{(aq)}$ ions wouldn't be stable.
3) $MnO_4^-$ ions are good **oxidising agents**. The trouble is, when they get reduced to $Mn^{2+}$ the four $O^{2-}$ ions have to go somewhere. To solve this problem, **$H^+$ ions** are added. The $4O^{2-}$ ions can now react with $8H^+$ ions to form $4H_2O$.
This is why manganate(VII) ions are usually **acidified** before they're used as an oxidising agent.

***Example:*** Acidified manganate(VII) ions can be reduced by $Fe^{2+}$ ions.

The half-equations are:

$MnO_4^-{}_{(aq)} + 8H^+_{(aq)} + 5e^- \rightarrow Mn^{2+}_{(aq)} + 4H_2O_{(l)}$

$Fe^{2+}_{(aq)} \rightarrow Fe^{3+}_{(aq)} + e^-$

To balance the electrons you have to multiply the second half-equation by 5: $5Fe^{2+}_{(aq)} \rightarrow 5Fe^{3+}_{(aq)} + 5e^-$

Now you can combine both half-equations: $MnO_4^-{}_{(aq)} + 8H^+_{(aq)} + 5Fe^{2+}_{(aq)} \rightarrow Mn^{2+}_{(aq)} + 4H_2O_{(l)} + 5Fe^{3+}_{(aq)}$

## *Practice Questions*

Q1 What is an oxidising agent?

Q2 Why do manganate(VII) ions have to be acidified to oxidise metals?

**Exam Questions**

1 What is the oxidation number of the following elements?

a) Ti in $TiCl_4$ b) V in $V_2O_5$ c) Cr in $CrO_4^{2-}$ d) Cr in $Cr_2O_7^{2-}$ [4 marks]

2 Acidified manganate(VII) ions will react with aqueous iodide ions to form iodine.
The two half-equations for the changes that occur are:

$MnO_4^-{}_{(aq)} + 8H^+_{(aq)} + 5e^- \rightarrow Mn^{2+}_{(aq)} + 4H_2O_{(l)}$ and $2I^-_{(aq)} \rightarrow I_{2(aq)} + 2e^-$

a) Write a balanced equation to show the reaction taking place. [2 marks]

b) Use oxidation numbers to explain the redox processes which have occurred. [4 marks]

c) Suggest why a fairly reactive metal such as zinc will not react with aqueous iodide ions in a similar manner to manganate(VII) ions. [2 marks]

## *Redox — relax in a lovely warm bubble bath...*

*The words oxidation and reduction are tossed about a lot in chemistry — so they're important.*
*Don't forget, oxidation is really about electrons being lost,* ***not*** *oxygen being gained.*
*I suppose you ought to learn the most famous memory aid thingy in the world — here it is...*

**OIL RIG**
- **Oxidation Is Loss**
- **Reduction Is Gain**
(of electrons)

# Electrode Potentials

*There are electrons toing and froing in redox reactions. And when electrons move, you get electricity.*
***These pages are for AQA (Unit 5), OCR A (Unit 5), OCR B (Unit 4) and Edexcel (Unit 5).***

## Electrochemical Cells Make Electricity

Electrochemical cells can be made from **two different metals** dipped in salt solutions of their **own ions** and connected by a wire (the **external circuit**).

There are always **two** reactions within an electrochemical cell — one's an oxidation and one's a reduction — so it's a **redox process** (see page 142).

Here's what happens in the **zinc/copper** electrochemical cell on the right:

1) Zinc **loses electrons** more easily than copper. So in the half-cell on the left, zinc (from the zinc electrode) is **OXIDISED** to form $\mathbf{Zn^{2+}_{(aq)}}$ ions. This releases electrons into the external circuit.
2) In the other half-cell, the **same number of electrons** are taken from the external circuit, **REDUCING** the $Cu^{2+}$ ions to copper atoms.

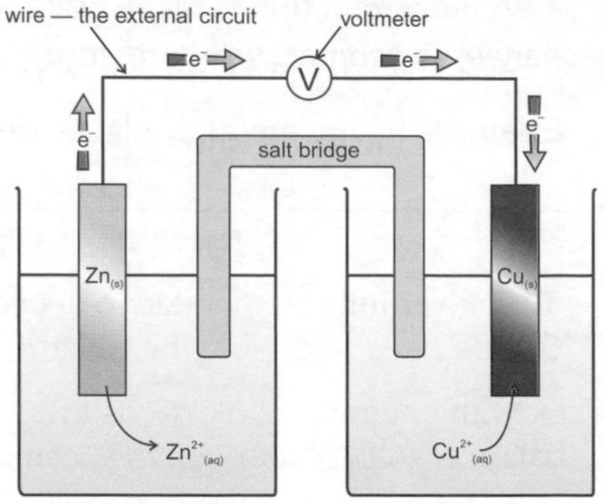


The solutions are connected by a **salt bridge** made from filter paper soaked in $KNO_{3(aq)}$. The $K^+$ and $NO_3^-$ ions flow through the salt bridge and balance out the charges in the beakers.

So **electrons** flow through the wire from the most reactive metal to the least.

A voltmeter in the external circuit shows the **voltage** between the two half-cells. This is the **cell potential** or **e.m.f.**, $E_{cell}$.

The boys tested the strength of the bridge, whilst the girls just stood and watched.

You can also have half-cells involving **solutions of two aqueous ions of the same element**, such as $\mathbf{Fe^{2+}_{(aq)}/Fe^{3+}_{(aq)}}$.

The conversion from $Fe^{2+}$ to $Fe^{3+}$, or vice versa, happens on the surface of the **electrode**.

The electrode is made of **platinum** because it is an **inert metal**.

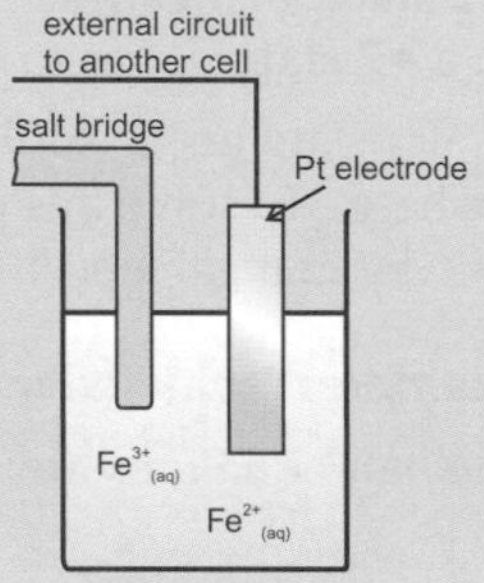


## The Reactions at Each Electrode are Reversible

1) The **reactions** that occur at each electrode in the **zinc/copper cell** above are:

$$Zn^{2+}_{(aq)} + 2e^- \rightleftharpoons Zn_{(s)}$$
$$Cu^{2+}_{(aq)} + 2e^- \rightleftharpoons Cu_{(s)}$$

2) The **reversible arrows** show that both reactions can go in **either direction**. **Which direction** each reaction goes in depends on **how easily** each metal **loses electrons** (i.e. how easily it's **oxidised**).
3) How easily a metal is oxidised is measured using **electrode potentials**. A metal that's **easily oxidised** has a very **negative electrode potential**, while one that's harder to oxidise has a less negative or **positive electrode potential**.

| Half-cell | Electrode potential (V) |
|---|---|
| $Zn^{2+}_{(aq)}/Zn_{(s)}$ | –0.76 |
| $Cu^{2+}_{(aq)}/Cu_{(s)}$ | +0.34 |

4) The table on the left shows the electrode potentials for the copper and zinc half-cells. The **zinc half-cell** has a **more negative** electrode potential, so **zinc is oxidised** (the reaction goes **backwards**), while **copper is reduced** (the reaction goes **forwards**).

## There's a Convention for Drawing Electrochemical Cells

***AQA only***

It's a bit of a faff drawing pictures of electrochemical cells. There's a **shorthand** way of representing them though — this is the **Zn/Cu cell**:

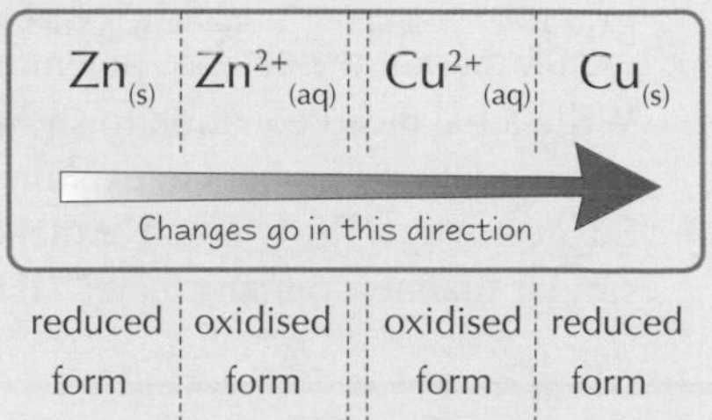


There are a couple of important **conventions** when drawing cells:

1) The **half-cell** with the **more negative** potential goes on the **left**.
2) The **oxidised forms** go in the **centre** of the cell diagram.

If you follow the conventions, you can **calculate** the **cell potential** by doing the calculation:

$$E^\ominus_{cell} = (E^\ominus_{\text{right hand side}} - E^\ominus_{\text{left hand side}})$$

The symbol for electrode potential is $E^\ominus$.

The cell potential will always be a **positive voltage**, because the more negative $E^\ominus$ value is being subtracted from the more positive $E^\ominus$ value. For example, the cell potential for the Zn/Cu cell = +0.34 – (–0.76) = **+1.10 V**

# Electrode Potentials

## **Conditions** Affect the Value of the **Electrode Potential**

Half-cell reactions are **reversible**. So just like any other reversible reaction, the **equilibrium position** is affected by changes in **temperature, pressure** and **concentration**. Changing the equilibrium position changes the **cell potential**. To get around this, **standard conditions** are used to measure electrode potentials — using these conditions means you always get the **same value** for the electrode potential and you can **compare values** for different cells.

## **Electrode Potentials** are Measured Against **Standard Hydrogen Electrodes**

You measure the electrode potential of a half-cell against a **standard hydrogen electrode**.

The **standard electrode potential** of a half-cell is the **voltage measured** under **standard conditions** when the **half-cell** is connected to a **standard hydrogen electrode**.

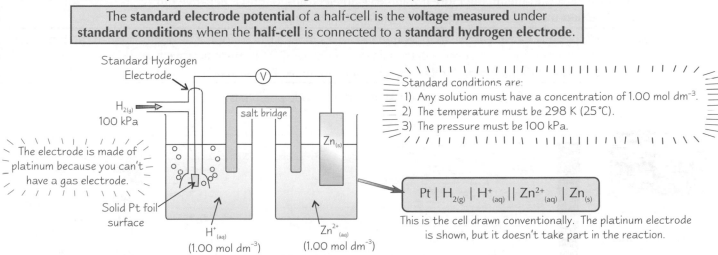

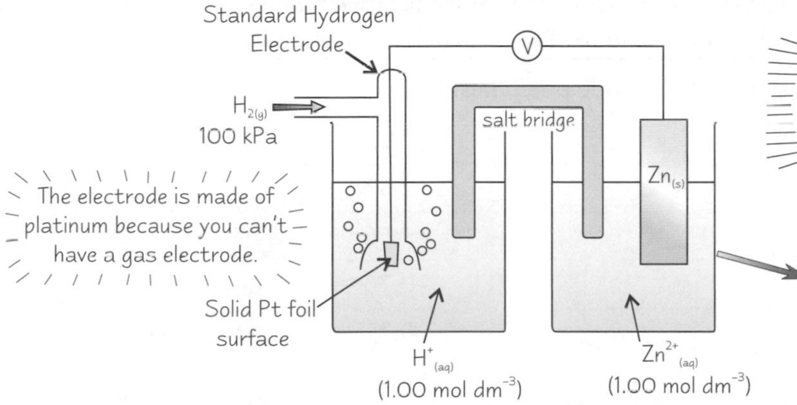


Standard conditions are:
1) Any solution must have a concentration of 1.00 mol dm$^{-3}$.
2) The temperature must be 298 K (25 °C).
3) The pressure must be 100 kPa.

$Pt \mid H_{2(g)} \mid H^+_{(aq)} \parallel Zn^{2+}_{(aq)} \mid Zn_{(s)}$

This is the cell drawn conventionally. The platinum electrode is shown, but it doesn't take part in the reaction.

1) The **standard hydrogen electrode** is always shown on the **left** — it doesn't matter whether or not the other half-cell has a more positive value. The standard hydrogen electrode half-cell has an electrode potential of **0.00 V**.

2) The whole cell potential = $E^\circ_{\text{right-hand side}} - E^\circ_{\text{left-hand side}}$.
$E^\circ_{\text{left-hand side}}$ = 0.00 V, so the **voltage reading** will be equal to $E^\circ_{\text{right-hand side}}$.
This reading could be **positive** or **negative**, depending which way the **electrons flow**.

## Practice Questions

Q1 Draw the cell used for determining the value of $E^\circ$ for the $Fe^{3+}/Fe^{2+}$ system using the conventional representation.

Q2 $Fe^{3+} + e^- \rightleftharpoons Fe^{2+}$, $E^\circ = +0.77$ V $\qquad$ $Mn^{3+} + e^- \rightleftharpoons Mn^{2+}$, $E^\circ = +1.48$ V
Show that the e.m.f. of an iron/manganese cell under standard conditions is +0.71 V.

Q3 List the three standard conditions used when measuring standard electrode potentials.

**Exam Question**

1 An electrochemical cell containing a zinc half-cell and a silver half-cell was set up using a potassium nitrate salt bridge. The cell potential at 298K was measured to be 1.40 V.

$Zn^{2+}_{(aq)} + 2e^- \rightleftharpoons Zn_{(s)}$ $\qquad E^\circ = -0.76$ V

$Ag^+_{(aq)} + e^- \rightleftharpoons Ag_{(s)}$ $\qquad E^\circ = +0.80$ V

a) Draw this cell using the conventional representation. [2 marks]

b) Use the standard electrode potentials given to calculate the standard cell potential for a zinc-silver cell. [1 mark]

c) Suggest two possible reasons why the actual cell potential was different from the value calculated in part (b). [2 marks]

d) Write an equation for the overall cell reaction. [1 mark]

e) Which half-cell released the electrons into the circuit? Explain how you know this. [1 mark]

## Exam potential = hours revising – hours on the PlayStation®...

*You've just got to think long and hard about this stuff. The metal on the left-hand electrode disappears off into the solution, leaving its electrons behind. This makes the left-hand electrode the negative one. So the right-hand electrode's got to be the positive one. It makes sense if you think about it. This electrode gives up electrons to turn the positive ions into atoms.*

# The Electrochemical Series

*The electrochemical series is like a pop chart of the most reactive metals – except without the pop so it's really just a chart.*
***These pages are for AQA (Unit 5), OCR A (Unit 5), OCR B (Unit 4) and Edexcel (Unit 5).***

## *The **Electrochemical Series** Shows You What's **Reactive** and What's Not*

1) The **more reactive** a **metal** is, the **more** it wants to **lose electrons** to form a **positive ion**. **More reactive metals** have **more negative standard electrode potentials**.

> ***Example:*** Magnesium is **more reactive** than zinc — so it's more eager to form 2+ ions than zinc is. The list of standard electrode potentials shows that $Mg^{2+}/Mg$ has a **more negative** value than $Zn^{2+}/Zn$. In terms of oxidation and reduction, magnesium would **reduce** $Zn^{2+}$ (and $Zn^{2+}$ would **oxidise** magnesium).

2) The more reactive a **non-metal**, the **more** it wants to **gain electrons** to form a **negative ion**. **More reactive non-metals** have **more positive standard electrode potentials**.

> ***Example:*** Chlorine is **more reactive** than bromine — so it's more eager to form a negative ion than bromine is. The list of standard electrode potentials shows that $Cl_2/2Cl^-$ is **more positive** than $Br_2/2Br^-$. In terms of oxidation and reduction, chlorine would **oxidise** $Br^-$ (and $Br^-$ would **reduce** chlorine).

3) Here's an **electrochemical series** showing some standard electrode potentials:

Chestnut wondered if his load was hindering his pulling potential.

| Half-reaction | $E^\circ$/V |
|---|---|
| $Mg^{2+}_{(aq)} + 2e^- \rightleftharpoons Mg_{(s)}$ | –2.37 |
| $Al^{3+}_{(aq)} + 3e^- \rightleftharpoons Al_{(s)}$ | –1.66 |
| $Zn^{2+}_{(aq)} + 2e^- \rightleftharpoons Zn_{(s)}$ | –0.76 |
| $Ni^{2+}_{(aq)} + 2e^- \rightleftharpoons Ni_{(s)}$ | –0.25 |
| $2H^+_{(aq)} + 2e^- \rightleftharpoons H_{2(g)}$ | 0.00 |
| $Sn^{4+}_{(aq)} + 2e^- \rightleftharpoons Sn^{2+}_{(aq)}$ | +0.15 |
| $Cu^{2+}_{(aq)} + 2e^- \rightleftharpoons Cu_{(s)}$ | +0.34 |
| $Fe^{3+}_{(aq)} + e^- \rightleftharpoons Fe^{2+}_{(aq)}$ | +0.77 |
| $Ag^+_{(aq)} + e^- \rightleftharpoons Ag_{(s)}$ | +0.80 |
| $Br_{2(aq)} + 2e^- \rightleftharpoons 2Br^-_{(aq)}$ | +1.08 |
| $Cr_2O_7^{2-}{}_{(aq)} + 14H^+_{(aq)} + 6e^- \rightleftharpoons 2Cr^{3+}_{(aq)} + 7H_2O_{(l)}$ | +1.33 |
| $Cl_{2(aq)} + 2e^- \rightleftharpoons 2Cl^-_{(aq)}$ | +1.36 |
| $MnO_4^-{}_{(aq)} + 8H^+_{(aq)} + 5e^- \rightleftharpoons Mn^{2+}_{(aq)} + 4H_2O_{(l)}$ | +1.51 |

More positive electrode potentials mean that:
1. The left-hand substances are more easily reduced.
2. The right-hand substances are more stable.

More negative electrode potentials mean that:
1. The right-hand substances are more easily oxidised.
2. The left-hand substances are more stable.

## *The **Anticlockwise Rule** Predicts Whether a Reaction Will Happen*

To figure out if a metal will react with the aqueous ions of another metal, you can use the $E^\circ$ and the **anticlockwise rule**.

***For example, will zinc react with aqueous copper ions?***
First you write the two half-equations down, putting the one with the **more negative** standard electrode potential on **top**. Then you draw on some **anticlockwise arrows** — these give you the **direction** of each half-reaction.

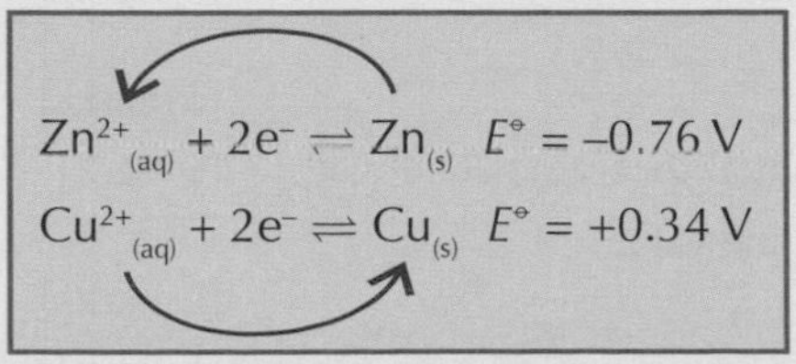


The **half-equations** are: $Zn_{(s)} \rightleftharpoons Zn^{2+}_{(aq)} + 2e^-$
$Cu^{2+}_{(aq)} + 2e^- \rightleftharpoons Cu_{(s)}$

Which combine to give: $Zn_{(s)} + Cu^{2+}_{(aq)} \rightleftharpoons Zn^{2+}_{(aq)} + Cu_{(s)}$

So zinc **does** react with aqueous copper ions.

To find the **cell potential** you always do $E^\circ_{bottom} - E^\circ_{top}$, so the cell potential for this reaction is +0.34 – (–0.76) = +1.10 V.

You can also draw an **electrode potential chart**. It's the same sort of idea.
You draw an '**upside-down y-axis**' with the more negative number at the top.
Then you put both half-reactions on the chart and draw on your **anticlockwise** arrows which give you the **direction** of each half-reaction.
The **difference** between the values is the **cell potential** — in this case it's **+1.10 V**.

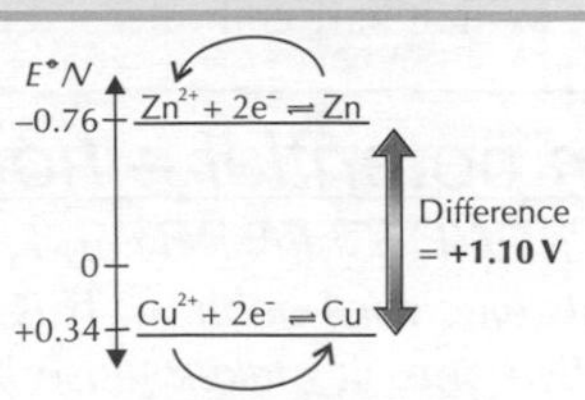

# The Electrochemical Series

## *Sometimes* the Prediction is *Wrong*

*Not AQA*

A **prediction** using $E^\circ$ and the anticlockwise rule only states if a reaction is **possible** under **standard conditions**. The prediction might be **wrong if...**

**...the conditions are not standard**

1) Changing the **concentration** (or temperature) of the solution can cause the electrode potential to **change**.
2) For example the zinc/copper cell has these half-equations in equilibrium...

$$Zn_{(s)} \rightleftharpoons Zn^{2+}_{(aq)} + 2e^-$$
$$Cu^{2+}_{(aq)} + 2e^- \rightleftharpoons Cu_{(s)}$$

3) ...if you **increase** the concentration of $Zn^{2+}$, the **equilibrium** will shift to the **left**, **reducing** the ease of **electron loss**. The whole cell potential will be lower.
4) ...if you **increase** the concentration of $Cu^{2+}$, the **equilibrium** will shift to the **right**, **increasing** the ease of **electron gain**. The whole cell potential will be higher.

**...the reaction kinetics are not favourable**

1) The **rate of a reaction** may be so **slow** that the reaction might **not appear** to happen.
2) If a reaction has a **high activation energy**, this may stop it happening.

Gary was hopeful, but Sue's high activation energy meant it was never going to happen

## *Cell Potential* is Related to the *Entropy* and the *Equilibrium Constant*

*Edexcel only*

The bigger the **total entropy change** from the reaction happening in the cell, the bigger the overall **cell potential**. And (sounds a bit random but) the total entropy change is proportional to the **natural log** of the **equilibrium constant** (*K*). You don't need to know where these relationships come from, but you **do** have to remember them, so here they are:

$E^\circ \propto \Delta S_{Total}$ and $E^\circ \propto \ln K$

where $\Delta S_{Total}$ is the total entropy change (see p.134) and ln *K* is the natural log of the equilibrium constant for the reaction (see p.26).

## Practice Questions

Q1 Cu is less reactive than Pb. Which half-reaction has a more negative $E^\circ$ value, $Pb^{2+} + 2e^- \rightleftharpoons Pb$ or $Cu^{2+} + 2e^- \rightleftharpoons Cu$?
Q2 Use electrode potentials to show that magnesium will reduce $Zn^{2+}$.
Q3 What is the anticlockwise rule used for? Outline how you use it.
Q4 Use the table on the opposite page to predict whether or not $Zn^{2+}$ ions can oxidise $Fe^{2+}$ ions to $Fe^{3+}$ ions.

**Exam Questions**

1 Use $E^\circ$ values quoted on the opposite page to determine the outcome of mixing the following solutions. If there is a reaction, determine the $E^\circ$ value and write the equation. If there isn't a reaction, state this and explain why.
a) Zinc metal and $Ni^{2+}$ ions [2 marks]
b) Acidified $MnO_4^-$ ions and $Sn^{2+}$ ions [2 marks]
c) $Br_2$ and acidified $Cr_2O_7^{2-}$ ions [2 marks]
d) $Ag^+$ ions and $Fe^{2+}$ ions [2 marks]

2 Manganate(VII), $MnO_4^-$, and dichromate(VI) $Cr_2O_7^{2-}$, are both used as oxidising agents.
a) From their electrode potentials, which would you predict is the stronger oxidising agent? Explain why. [2 marks]
b) Write equations to show each oxidising agent reacting with a solution of $Fe^{2+}$ ions. [2 marks]
c) Calculate the cell potential for each reaction. [2 marks]

3 A cell is set up with copper and nickel electrodes in 1 mol dm$^{-3}$ solutions of their ions, $Cu^{2+}$ and $Ni^{2+}$, connected by a salt bridge.
a) Write equations for the reactions that occur in each half-cell. [2 marks]
b) Find the voltage of the cell. [1 mark]
c) What is the overall equation for this reaction? [1 mark]
d) How would the voltage of the cell change if:
i) A more dilute copper solution was used? ii) A more concentrated nickel solution was used? [2 marks]

## The forward reaction that happens is the one with the most positive $E^\circ$ value...

*So to see if a reaction will happen, you find the two half-equations in the electrochemical series and see if you can draw anticlockwise arrows from your reactants to your products. If you can — great. If you can't — well, it ain't gonna work.*

# Storage and Fuel Cells

*It turns out that electrochemical cells aren't just found in the lab — they're all over the place... read on.*
***These pages are for AQA (Unit 5), OCR A (Unit 5) and Edexcel (Unit 5).***

## *Energy Storage Cells (Batteries) are Electrochemical Cells* — *AQA and OCR A*

### Non-Rechargeable Cells use Irreversible Reactions

For example, **zinc-carbon dry cell batteries** have a **zinc anode** and a **mixture of manganese dioxide and carbon** for a **cathode**. In between the electrodes is a paste of **ammonium chloride**, which acts as an **electrolyte**.

The **half-equations** are:

$Zn_{(s)} \rightarrow Zn^{2+}_{(aq)} + 2e^-$ $\qquad E^\ominus = -0.76$ V

$2MnO_{2(s)} + 2NH_4^+{}_{(aq)} + 2e^- \rightarrow Mn_2O_{3(s)} + 2NH_{3(aq)} + H_2O_{(l)}$ $\qquad E^\ominus = +0.75$ V

So the **e.m.f.** of this type of cell is: $E^\ominus_{cell} = E^\ominus_{bottom} - E^\ominus_{top} = +0.75 - (-0.76) = \mathbf{+1.51\ V}$

The reaction is **non-reversible** because the ammonium ions produce **hydrogen gas**, which **escapes** from the battery. Without the hydrogen, the ammonium ions **cannot be reformed** by reversing the reactions.

### Rechargeable Cells use Reversible Reactions

For example, **lead-acid cells** are used in car batteries. Each cell is made up of a **lead(IV) dioxide anode** and a **lead cathode** immersed in a **sulfuric acid** electrolyte. Both electrodes end up coated in **lead(II) sulfate.**

The half-equations are:

$Pb_{(s)} + SO_4^{2-}{}_{(aq)} \rightleftharpoons PbSO_{4(s)} + 2e^-$ $\qquad E^\ominus = -0.36$ V

$PbO_{2(s)} + SO_4^{2-}{}_{(aq)} + 4H^+_{(aq)} + 2e^- \rightleftharpoons PbSO_{4(s)} + 2H_2O_{(l)}$ $\qquad E^\ominus = +1.69$ V

The **e.m.f.** of this type of cell is: $E^\ominus_{cell} = E^\ominus_{bottom} - E^\ominus_{top} = +1.69 - (-0.36) = \mathbf{+2.05\ V}$

To recharge these batteries, a **current** is supplied to force **electrons** in the **opposite direction** around the circuit and **reverse the reactions**. This is possible because **none of the substances escape** or are **used up**.

### Non-Rechargeable Batteries Have Advantages and Disadvantages

1) **Cost**: non-rechargeables are **cheaper** to buy but need **replacing** when they run out, so **cost more in the long run**.
2) **Lifetime**: a non-rechargeable battery will **work for longer** than a rechargeable battery. But once a rechargeable battery has run out, you can **recharge it** and use it again whereas non-rechargeables have to be **disposed** of.
3) **Power**: non-rechargeable batteries **can't supply as much power** as rechargeables, so are **no use** in devices that use a **lot of power** — like a mobile phone or a laptop.
4) **Use of resources and waste**: because they're throw-away, non-rechargeables **use more resources** and create **more waste** than rechargeables. All batteries can be **recycled**, but they often just end up in **landfill**.
5) **Toxicity**: non-rechargeable batteries are **less likely** to contain the **toxic metals lead** and **cadmium** (although they may contain **mercury**), so they are less hazardous in landfill if the contents **leak** out into **water sources**.

## *Fuel Cells Generate Electricity from Reacting a Fuel with an Oxidant*

A **fuel cell** produces electricity by reacting a **fuel**, usually hydrogen, with an **oxidant**, which is most likely to be oxygen.

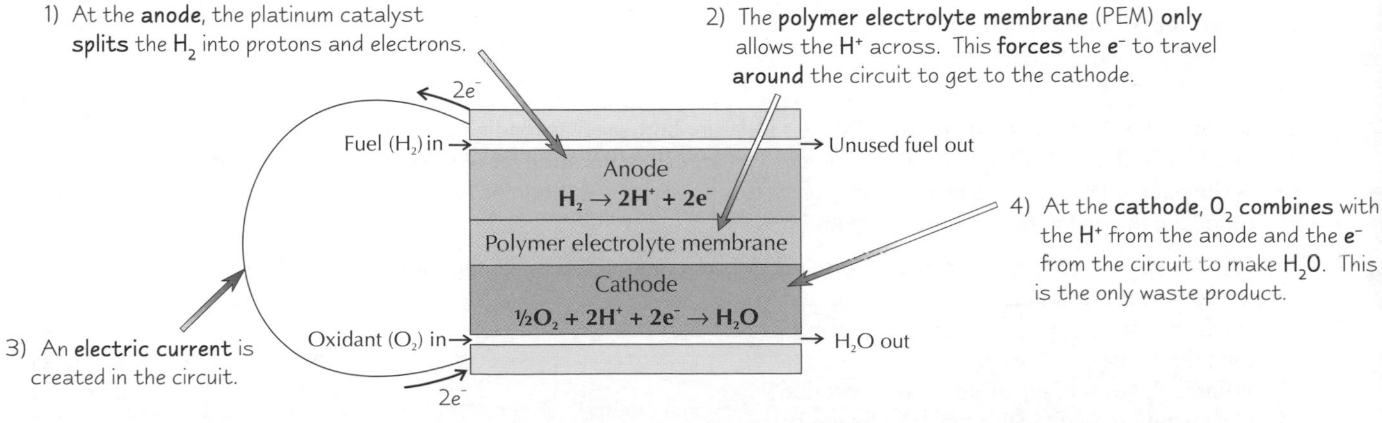
1) At the **anode**, the platinum catalyst **splits** the $H_2$ into protons and electrons.
2) The **polymer electrolyte membrane** (PEM) **only** allows the $H^+$ across. This **forces** the $e^-$ to travel **around** the circuit to get to the cathode.
$2e^-$
Fuel ($H_2$) in
Unused fuel out
Anode
$H_2 \rightarrow 2H^+ + 2e^-$
Polymer electrolyte membrane
Cathode
$\frac{1}{2}O_2 + 2H^+ + 2e^- \rightarrow H_2O$
4) At the **cathode**, $O_2$ **combines** with the $H^+$ from the anode and the $e^-$ from the circuit to make $H_2O$. This is the only waste product.
3) An **electric current** is created in the circuit.
Oxidant ($O_2$) in
$H_2O$ out
$2e^-$

**Fuel cell vehicles** (FCVs) are powered by fuel cells, and they have some **important advantages** over petrol or diesel cars:

1) They are far **less polluting** than a regular car when in use. The only waste product of a hydrogen fuel cell is water. (But most hydrogen is made by reacting natural gas with steam, or by electrolysing water — both of which use lots of energy, which is often made by burning fossil fuels. So hydrogen is really only as clean as the method used to produce it.)
2) A fuel cell is at least **twice as efficient** at converting fuel to power as a petrol engine.

# Storage and Fuel Cells

## *Fuel Cells* Don't Just Use **Hydrogen**

Scientists are developing fuel cells for cars that use **hydrogen-rich fuels**, e.g. **methanol** and **ethanol**, rather than hydrogen. These fuels have a high percentage of hydrogen in their molecules and can be converted into $H_2$ in the car by a **reformer**.

There are a few **advantages** of using **alcohols** instead of hydrogen in fuel cells.

1) They have a higher **hydrogen density** than liquefied hydrogen — that means more hydrogen atoms per $dm^3$.
2) Methanol and ethanol are **already** made on a **large scale** and they can both be produced from **renewable biomass**.
3) **Storing** and **transporting hydrogen** is difficult. If you store it as a **gas** it's very **explosive**. If you store it as a **liquid** you need really **expensive fridges** because it has such a low boiling point. You can also store it **adsorbed** to the surface of a solid like charcoal or **absorbed** into a material like palladium, but these can be very **expensive** and often have a **limited life span**. Alcohols are **much easier** — they're **liquids** at room temperature.
4) **Methanol** can be made from carbon dioxide so it offers a possible way to **reduce $CO_2$ levels** in the **atmosphere**.

***Edexcel only:*** A **new generation** of fuel cells are also being developed that can use alcohols **directly**. In these new fuel cells, the alcohol is **oxidised** at the **anode** in the presence of **water**:

$$\text{E.g. } CH_3OH + H_2O \rightarrow CO_2 + 6e^- + 6H^+$$

The **$H^+$ ions** pass through the electrolyte and are **oxidised** themselves to water.

$$6H^+ + 6e^- + 1\tfrac{1}{2}O_2 \rightarrow 3H_2O$$

## Some **Breathalysers** use Fuel Cells Too

***Edexcel only***

The amount of **alcohol** (ethanol) in someone's **breath** is directly related to the amount in their **blood stream**. **Alcohol vapour** is breathed out as the blood passes through the lungs.
A **breathalyser** is used to find the level of alcohol in the breath.

1) The old way of detecting alcohol in the breath uses the **reaction** between ethanol and **potassium dichromate(VI)**. **Orange** dichromate(VI) is **reduced** to **green** chromium(III) as ethanol is oxidised to ethanoic acid. How much the colour changes is measured using a **photocell system**. This is still often used as a roadside test.
2) Breathalysers used in police stations use **infrared spectrometry** to detect the presence and quantity of ethanol. These machines are very **accurate** but **not** usually easily **portable**.
3) The most recent development is to use an **ethanol fuel cell**. The amount of alcohol is proportional to the **current produced** when the suspect's breath is fed to the **anode** of the cell. These cells are **less susceptible** to giving **false readings** due to other substances in the breath. They're also **easily portable** and **accurate**.

## Practice Questions

Q1 Explain the difference between non-rechargeable and rechargeable batteries in terms of the chemical reactions.
Q2 What are the half-equations for the reactions at each electrode in a hydrogen-oxygen fuel cell?
Q3 Give two advantages of FCVs over conventional cars.
Q4 Give two ways that hydrogen fuel could be stored. What is meant by a hydrogen-rich fuel?

**Exam Questions**

1 a) Sketch a diagram showing the structure and operation of a hydrogen-oxygen fuel cell. Include the relevant half-equations. [5 marks]
b) Label the site of oxidation and the site of reduction on the diagram. [1 mark]
c) Give one advantage and one disadvantage of hydrogen fuel cells over conventional petrol engines. [1 mark]

2 The half-equations for a lead-acid battery are as follows:

$Pb_{(s)} + SO_4^{2-}{}_{(aq)} \rightleftharpoons PbSO_{4(s)} + 2e^-$ $E^\circ = -0.36$ V

$PbO_{2(s)} + SO_4^{2-}{}_{(aq)} + 4H^+{}_{(aq)} + 2e^- \rightleftharpoons PbSO_{4(s)} + 2H_2O_{(l)}$ $E^\circ = +1.69$ V

a) Write out the overall equation for the reaction and calculate the voltage produced by the cell. [2 marks]
b) The lead acid battery is rechargeable. Give tow advantages of a rechargeable battery. [2 marks]

## In the olden days they used donkey-powered mills. They were called...wait for it...

*...mule cells. Moving on... I reckon the cleverest use of fuel cells is in the Space Shuttle. Not only do they produce electricity without heavy batteries, they mean the Shuttle doesn't have to carry water. The cells make all the water the astronauts need.*

# Redox Titrations

*These are redox titrations. They're like acid-base titrations (see p.42), but different. You don't need an indicator for a start.*
***These pages are for AQA (Unit 5), OCR A (Unit 5), OCR B (Unit 4) and Edexcel (Unit 5).***

## Titrations Using **Transition Element Ions** are **Redox** Titrations

Titrations using transition element ions let you find out how much **oxidising agent** is needed to **exactly** react with a quantity of **reducing agent**. If you know the **concentration** of either the oxidising agent or the reducing agent, you can use the titration results to work out the concentration of the other.

1) First measure out a quantity of **reducing agent**, e.g. aqueous $Fe^{2+}$ ions, using a pipette, and put it in a conical flask.
2) Using a **measuring cylinder**, add about **20 cm³ of dilute sulfuric acid** to the flask — this is an excess, so you don't have to be too exact.
3) Now add the **oxidising agent**, e.g. aqueous potassium manganate(VII), to the reducing agent using a **burette**, **swirling** the conical flask as you do so.
4) The **oxidising agent** that you add reacts with the reducing agent. This reaction will continue until **all** of the reducing agent is used up. The **very next drop** you add to the flask will give the mixture the **colour of the oxidising agent**. (You could use a coloured reducing agent and a colourless oxidising agent instead — then you'd be watching for the moment that the colour in the flask disappears.)
5) Stop when the mixture in the flask **just** becomes tainted with the colour of the oxidising agent (the **end point**) and record the volume of the oxidising agent added. This is the **rough titration**.
6) Now you do some **accurate titrations**. You need to do a few until you get **two or more** readings that are **within 0.10 cm³** of each other.

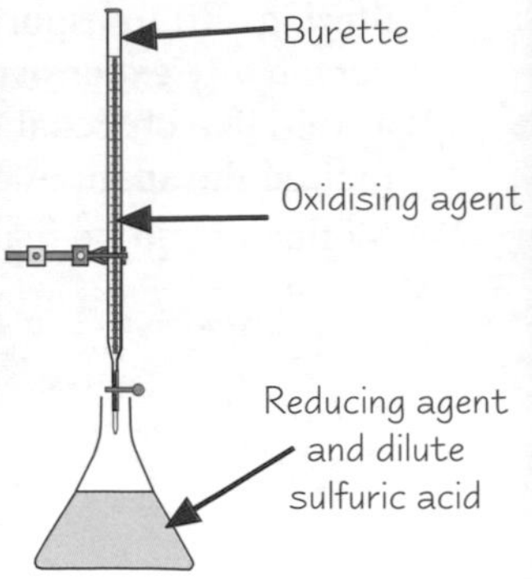


You can also do titrations the other way round — adding the reducing agent to the oxidising agent.

The two main **oxidising agents** used are:

1) **Manganate(VII) ions** ($MnO_4^-$) in **aqueous potassium manganate(VII)** ($KMnO_4$) — these are **purple**.
2) **Dichromate(VI) ions** ($Cr_2O_7^{2-}$) in **aqueous potassium dichromate(VI)** ($K_2Cr_2O_7$) — these are **orange**.

***Example:*** The oxidation of Zn to $Zn^{2+}$ by dichromate(VI) ions in solution.

Half-equations:

$Cr_2O_7^{2-} + 14H^+ + 6e^- \rightarrow 2Cr^{3+} + 7H_2O$ — Chromium is **reduced**

$3Zn \rightarrow 3Zn^{2+} + 6e^-$ — Zinc is **oxidised**

$Cr_2O_7^{2-} + 14H^+ + 3Zn \rightarrow 2Cr^{3+} + 7H_2O + 3Zn^{2+}$

The **acid** is added to make sure there are plenty of **$H^+$ ions** to allow the oxidising agent to be reduced (see p.143).

## Use the **Titration Results** to **Calculate** the **Concentration** of a Reagent

***Example:*** 27.5 cm³ of 0.020 mol dm⁻³ aqueous potassium manganate(VII) reacted with 25.0 cm³ of acidified iron(II) sulfate solution. Calculate the concentration of $Fe^{2+}$ ions in the acidified $FeSO_4$ solution.

$$MnO_{4\ (aq)}^- + 8H^+_{(aq)} + 5Fe^{2+}_{(aq)} \rightarrow Mn^{2+}_{(aq)} + 4H_2O_{(l)} + 5Fe^{3+}_{(aq)}$$

1) Work out the number of **moles of $MnO_4^-$ ions** added to the flask.

$$\text{Number of moles } MnO_4^- \text{ added} = \frac{\text{concentration} \times \text{volume}}{1000} = \frac{0.020 \times 27.5}{1000} = 5.50 \times 10^{-4} \text{ moles}$$

2) Look at the balanced equation to find how many moles of **$Fe^{2+}$** react with **every mole** of $MnO_4^-$. Then you can work out the **number of moles of $Fe^{2+}$** in the flask.

5 moles of $Fe^{2+}$ react with 1 mole of $MnO_4^-$. So moles of $Fe^{2+} = 5.50 \times 10^{-4} \times 5 = 2.75 \times 10^{-3}$ moles.

3) Work out the **number of moles of $Fe^{2+}$** in 1000 cm³ (1 dm³) of solution — this is the **concentration**.

25.0 cm³ of solution contained $2.75 \times 10^{-3}$ moles of $Fe^{2+}$.

1000 cm³ of solution would contain $\frac{(2.75 \times 10^{-3}) \times 1000}{25.0} = 0.11$ moles of $Fe^{2+}$.

So the concentration of $Fe^{2+}$ is **0.11 mol dm⁻³**.

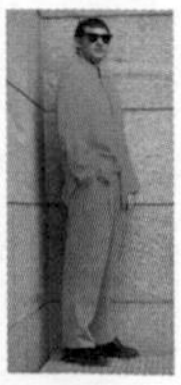

Manganate 007, licensed to oxidise.

# Redox Titrations

## Iodine-Sodium Thiosulfate Titrations are Dead Handy

*OCR A and Edexcel*

Iodine-sodium thiosulfate titrations are a way of finding the concentration of an **oxidising agent**.
The **more concentrated** an oxidising agent is, the **more ions will be oxidised** by a certain volume of it.
So here's how you can find out the concentration of a solution of the oxidising agent **potassium iodate(V)**:

### *STAGE 1: Use a sample of oxidising agent to oxidise as much iodide as possible.*

1) Measure out a certain volume of **potassium iodate(V)** solution (**$KIO_3$**) (the oxidising agent) — say **25 cm³**.
2) Add this to an excess of acidified **potassium iodide** solution (**KI**).
   The iodate(V) ions in the potassium iodate(V) solution **oxidise** some of the **iodide ions** to **iodine**.

$$IO_3^-{}_{(aq)} + 5I^-{}_{(aq)} + 6H^+{}_{(aq)} \rightarrow 3I_{2\,(aq)} + 3H_2O$$

### *STAGE 2: Find out how many moles of iodine have been produced.*

You do this by **titrating** the resulting solution with **sodium thiosulfate** (**$Na_2S_2O_3$**).
(You need to know the concentration of the sodium thiosulfate solution.)

The iodine in the solution reacts with **thiosulfate ions** like this:

$$I_2 + 2S_2O_3^{2-} \rightarrow 2I^- + S_4O_6^{2-}$$

**Titration of Iodine with Sodium Thiosulfate**

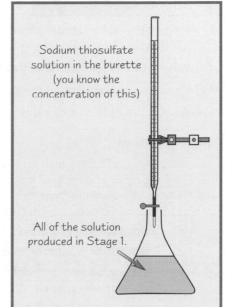

1) Take the flask containing the solution that was produced in Stage 1.
2) From a burette, add sodium thiosulfate solution to the flask drop by drop.
3) It's hard to see the end point, so when the iodine colour fades to a pale yellow, add 2 cm³ of starch solution (to detect the presence of iodine). The solution in the conical flask will go dark blue, showing there's still some iodine there.
4) Add sodium thiosulfate one drop at a time until the blue colour disappears.
5) When this happens, it means all the iodine has just been reacted.
6) Now you can calculate the number of moles of iodine in the solution.

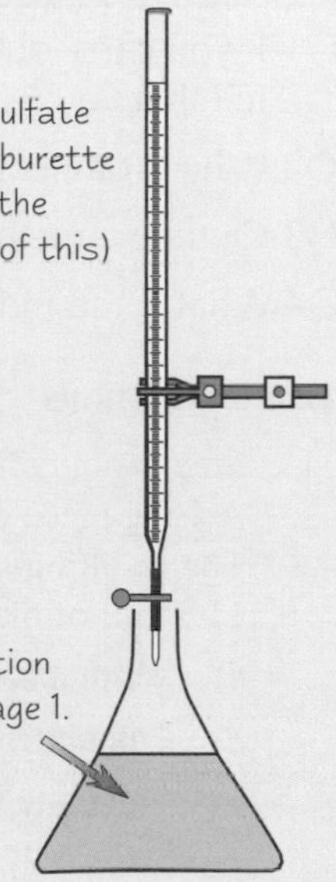

Sodium thiosulfate solution in the burette (you know the concentration of this)
All of the solution produced in Stage 1.

*Example* The iodine produced in Stage 1 reacted fully with 11.1 cm³ of 0.12 mol dm⁻³ thiosulfate solution.

$$I_2 + 2S_2O_3^{2-} \rightarrow 2I^- + S_4O_6^{2-}$$

**11.1 cm³**
**0.12 mol dm⁻³**

**Number of moles of thiosulfate** $= \frac{\text{concentration} \times \text{volume (cm}^3)}{1000} = \frac{0.12 \times 11.1}{1000} = \mathbf{1.332 \times 10^{-3}}$ **moles**

**1 mole** of iodine reacts with **2 moles** of thiosulfate.
So number of **moles of iodine** in the solution = $1.332 \times 10^{-3} \div 2 = \mathbf{6.66 \times 10^{-4}}$ **moles**

### *STAGE 3: Calculate the concentration of the oxidising agent.*

1) Now look back at your original equation: $IO_3^-{}_{(aq)} + 5I^-{}_{(aq)} + 6H^+{}_{(aq)} \rightarrow 3I_{2\,(aq)} + 3H_2O$
2) 25 cm³ of potassium iodate(V) solution produced **$6.66 \times 10^{-4}$ moles of iodine**.
   The equation shows that **one mole** of iodate(V) ions will produce **three moles** of iodine ($I_2$).
3) That means there must have been **$6.66 \times 10^{-4} \div 3 = 2.22 \times 10^{-4}$ moles of iodate(V) ions** in the original solution.
   So now it's straightforward to find the **concentration** of the potassium iodate(V) solution, which is what you're after:

$$\text{number of moles} = \frac{\text{concentration} \times \text{volume (cm}^3)}{1000} \Rightarrow 2.22 \times 10^{-4} = \frac{\text{concentration} \times 25}{1000}$$

⇒ **concentration of potassium iodate(V) solution = $8.88 \times 10^{-3}$ mol dm⁻³**

# Redox Titrations

## There are a Few **Sources of Error** in Iodine-Sodium Thiosulfate Titrations

***Edexcel only***

Iodine-sodium thiosulfate titrations are difficult for several reasons.

1) The **starch indicator** for the sodium thiosulfate titration needs to be added at the right point, when most of the iodine has **reacted**, or else the blue colour will be very **slow to disappear**.
2) The starch solution needs to be **freshly made** or else it won't behave as expected.
3) The **iodine** produced in the reaction can **evaporate** from the solution, giving a **false titration reading**. The final figure for the concentration of the oxidising agent will be **too low** as a result. It helps if the solution is kept **cool**.

You can use this titration to find the **percentage of copper** in an alloy like brass.
The **copper(II)** ions are **reduced** to **copper(I)** in the reaction, creating a **white precipitate** of copper(I) iodide.
The precipitate can make seeing the **colour** of the solution quite hard.

## Practice Questions

Q1 If you carry out a redox titration by slowly adding aqueous $MnO_4^-$ ions to aqueous $Fe^{2+}$ ions, how can you tell that you've reached the end point?

Q2 Why is dilute acid added to the reaction mixture in redox titrations involving $MnO_4^-$ ions?

Q3 Outline a method to find the concentration of an oxidising agent using an iodine-sodium thiosulfate titration.

Q4 What is the indicator in iodine-sodium thiosulfate titrations?

**Exam Questions**

1 Steel wool contains a high percentage of iron, and a small amount of carbon.
A 1.3 g piece of steel wool was dissolved in 50 $cm^3$ of aqueous sulfuric acid.
The resulting solution was titrated with 0.4 mol $dm^{-3}$ of potassium manganate(VII) solution.
11.5 $cm^3$ of the potassium manganate(VII) solution was needed to oxidise all of the iron(II) ions to iron(III).

a) Write a balanced equation for the reaction between the manganate(VII) ions and the iron(II) ions. [3 marks]

b) Calculate the number of moles of iron(II) ions present in the original solution. [3 marks]

c) Calculate the percentage of iron present in the steel wool.
Give your answer to one decimal place. [3 marks]

2 A 10 $cm^3$ sample of 0.5 mol $dm^{-3}$ $SnCl_2$ solution was titrated with acidified potassium manganate(VII) solution.
Exactly 20 $cm^3$ of 0.1 mol $dm^{-3}$ potassium manganate(VII) solution was needed to fully oxidise the tin(II) chloride.

a) What type of reaction is this? [1 mark]

b) How many moles of tin(II) chloride were present in the 10 $cm^3$ sample? [2 marks]

c) How many moles of potassium manganate(VII) were needed to fully oxidise the tin(II) chloride? [2 marks]

The half equation for acidified $MnO_4^-$ acting as an oxidising agent is: $MnO_4^- + 8H^+ + 5e^- \rightarrow Mn^{2+} + 4H_2O$

d) Find the oxidation state of the oxidised tin ions present in the solution at the end of the titration. [4 marks]

3 A 4.20 g coin, made of a copper alloy, was dissolved in acid and the solution made up to 250 ml with deionised water.
25 $cm^3$ of this solution was added to excess potassium iodide solution. The following reaction occurred:

$$2Cu^{2+}_{(aq)} + 4I^-_{(aq)} \rightarrow 2CuI_{(s)} + I_{2(aq)}$$

The resulting solution was neutralised and then titrated with 0.15 mol $dm^{-3}$ sodium thiosulfate.
The iodine and thiosulfate reacted according to this equation:

$$I_{2(aq)} + 2S_2O_3^{2-}{}_{(aq)} \rightarrow 2I^-_{(aq)} + S_4O_6^{2-}{}_{(aq)}$$

The average titration result was 19.33 $cm^3$.

a) How many moles of iodine were present in the solution used in the titration? [2 marks]

b) How many moles of copper ions must have been in the 25 $cm^3$ of solution used for the titration? [2 marks]

c) What percentage of the coin, by mass, was copper? [3 marks]

## And how many moles does it take to change a light bulb...

*...two, one to change the bulb, and another to ask "Why do we need light bulbs? We're moles — most of the time that we're underground, we keep our eyes shut. We've mostly been using our senses of touch and smell to find our way around anyway. And we're not on mains, so the electricity must be costing a packet. We haven't thought this through properly..."*

# Transition Metals — The Basics

*The transition elements are the metallic ones that sit bang in the middle of the periodic table — it's where the party's at.*
***These pages are for AQA (Unit 5), OCR A (Unit 5), OCR B (Unit 4) and Edexcel (Unit 5).***

## ***Transition Metals*** *are Found in the* ***d-Block***

The **d-block** is the block of elements in the middle of the periodic table.
Most of the elements in the d-block are **transition metals** (also known as **transition elements**).
You only need to know about the transition metals in the first row of the d-block — the ones from **titanium to copper**.

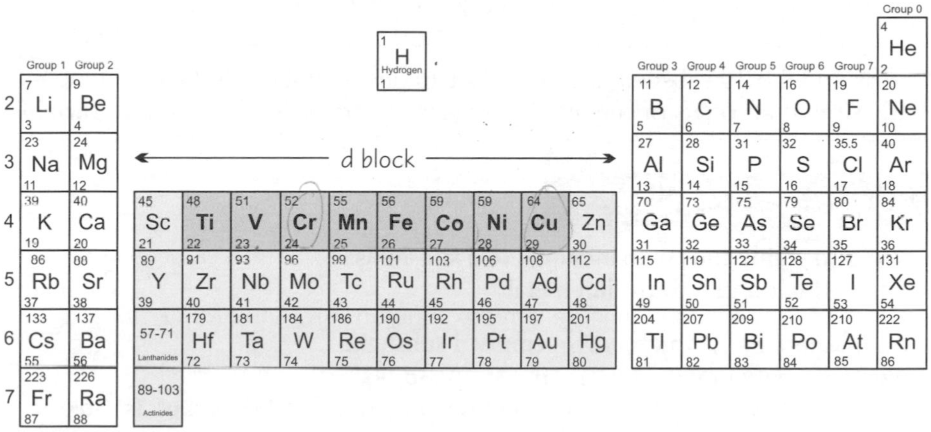


## *You Need to Know the* ***Electron Configurations*** *of the* ***Transition Metals***

1) Make sure you can write down the **electron configurations** of **all** the **Period 4 d-block elements** in subshell notation. Have a look at your AS notes if you've forgotten the details of how to do this. Here are a couple of examples:

**V = $1s^2\ 2s^2\ 2p^6\ 3s^2\ 3p^6\ 3d^3\ 4s^2$** **Co = $1s^2\ 2s^2\ 2p^6\ 3s^2\ 3p^6\ 3d^7\ 4s^2$**

The 4s electrons fill up before the 3d electrons.
But chromium and copper are a trifle odd — see below.

2) Here's the definition of a transition metal:

A **transition metal** is an element that can form **at least one stable ion** with an **incomplete d subshell.**

3) A d subshell can hold **10** electrons. So transition metals must form **at least one ion** that has **between 1 and 9 electrons** in the d subshell. All the Period 4 d-block elements are transition metals apart from **scandium** and **zinc**.
This diagram shows the 3d and 4s subshells of these elements:

The 3d orbitals are occupied singly at first. They only double up when they have to.

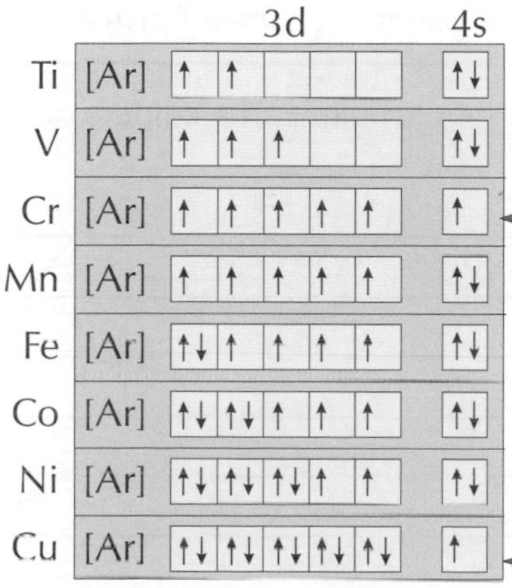


Chromium prefers to have one electron in each orbital of the 3d subshell and just one in the 4s subshell — this gives it more stability.
Cr = $1s^2\ 2s^2\ 2p^6\ 3s^2\ 3p^6\ 3d^5\ 4s^1$

Copper prefers to have a full 3d subshell and just one electron in the 4s subshell — it's more stable that way. Cu = $1s^2\ 2s^2\ 2p^6\ 3s^2\ 3p^6\ 3d^{10}\ 4s^1$
Copper forms a stable $Cu^{2+}$ ion by losing 2 electrons.
The $Cu^{2+}$ ion has an incomplete d sub-shell.

4) It's because of their **incomplete d subshells** that the transition elements have some **special chemical properties**. There's more about this on the next page.

# Transition Metals — The Basics

## When **Ions** are Formed, the **s Electrons** are **Removed First**

When transition metals form **positive** ions, the **s electrons** are removed **first**, **then** the d electrons.

1) Iron can form $Fe^{2+}$ ions and $Fe^{3+}$ ions.
2) When it forms 2+ ions, it loses **both its 4s electrons.**
   **$Fe = 1s^2\ 2s^2\ 2p^6\ 3s^2\ 3p^6\ 3d^6\ 4s^2 \rightarrow Fe^{2+} = 1s^2\ 2s^2\ 2p^6\ 3s^2\ 3p^6\ 3d^6$**
3) Only once the 4s electrons are removed can a **3d electron** be removed.
   E.g. **$Fe^{2+} = 1s^2\ 2s^2\ 2p^6\ 3s^2\ 3p^6\ 3d^6 \rightarrow Fe^{3+} = 1s^2\ 2s^2\ 2p^6\ 3s^2\ 3p^6\ 3d^5$**

The **energy levels** of the 4s and the 3d subshells are **very close** to one another, so different numbers of electrons can be gained or lost using fairly **similar** amounts of energy. This means that transition metals have **variable oxidation** states.

## Sc and Zn **Aren't** Transition Metals

Scandium and zinc can't form **stable ions** with **incomplete d subshells**.
So neither of them fits the definition of a **transition metal.**

**Scandium** only forms one ion, $Sc^{3+}$, which has an **empty d subshell.**
Scandium has the electron configuration **$1s^2\ 2s^2\ 2p^6\ 3s^2\ 3p^6\ 3d^1\ 4s^2$**.
It loses three electrons to form $Sc^{3+}$, which has the electron configuration **$1s^2\ 2s^2\ 2p^6\ 3s^2\ 3p^6$**.

**Zinc** only forms one ion, **$Zn^{2+}$**, which has a **full d subshell.**
Zinc has the electron configuration **$1s^2\ 2s^2\ 2p^6\ 3s^2\ 3p^6\ 3d^{10}\ 4s^2$**.
When it forms $Zn^{2+}$ it loses 2 electrons, both from the 4s subshell — so it keeps its full 3d subshell.

## Transition Metals have **Special Chemical Properties**

1) Transition metals can form **complex ions** — see page 156.
   For example, iron forms a **complex ion with water** — $[Fe(H_2O)_6]^{2+}$.
2) They can exist in **variable oxidation states.**
   E.g. iron can exist in the **+2** oxidation state as **$Fe^{2+}$** ions and in the **+3** oxidation state as **$Fe^{3+}$** ions.
3) They form **coloured ions**. E.g. $Fe^{2+}$ ions are **pale green** and $Fe^{3+}$ ions are **yellow**.
4) Transition metals and their compounds make **good catalysts** because they can **change oxidation states** by gaining or losing electrons within their **d orbitals**. This means they can **transfer electrons** to **speed up** reactions.

- **Iron** is the catalyst used in the **Haber process** to produce ammonia.
- **Vanadium(V) oxide, $V_2O_5$**, is the catalyst used in the **contact process** to make sulfuric acid.

Some common **coloured** ions and **oxidation states** are shown below. The colours refer to the **aqueous ions**.

| oxidation state +7 | +6 | +5 | +4 | +3 | +2 |
|---|---|---|---|---|---|
| | | $VO_2^+$ (yellow) | $VO^{2+}$ (blue) | $V^{3+}$ (green) | $V^{2+}$ (violet) |
| | $Cr_2O_7^{2-}$ (orange) | | | $Cr^{3+}$ (green/violet) | |
| $MnO_4^-$ (purple) | | | See p158 | | $Mn^{2+}$ (pale pink) |
| | | | | $Fe^{3+}$ (yellow) | $Fe^{2+}$ (pale green) |
| | | | | | $Co^{2+}$ (pink) |
| | | | | | $Ni^{2+}$ (green) |
| | | | | | $Cu^{2+}$ (pale blue) |
| | | | | $Ti^{3+}$ (purple) | $Ti^{2+}$ (violet) |

# Transition Metals — The Basics

## Ionisation Energies — Evidence for Electron Configurations

*Edexcel only*

The **ionisation energies** (see p. 129) of transition metals can tell you a lot about their **electron configurations**.

| Transition Element | Sc | Ti | V | Cr | Mn | Fe | Co | Ni | Cu | Zn |
|---|---|---|---|---|---|---|---|---|---|---|
| 1st ionisation energy (kJ/mol) | 630 | 660 | 650 | 650 | 720 | 760 | 760 | 740 | 750 | 910 |
| 2nd ionisation energy (kJ/mol) | 1240 | 1310 | 1410 | **1590** | 1510 | 1560 | 1640 | 1750 | **1960** | 1700 |
| 3rd ionisation energy (kJ/mol) | 2390 | 2650 | 2870 | 2990 | 3260 | **2960** | 3230 | 3390 | 3560 | 3800 |

The **first ionisation energy** is roughly the **same** from **Sc** to **Cu**. This is evidence that they all have a **similar electronic structure**, and lose the first electron from the **same shell** (**4s**).

The **second** ionisation energy **increases steadily** across the elements. **Cr** and **Cu** are slightly **higher** than you'd expect. This shows that the second electron is taken from much **nearer the nucleus** (the **3d** shell) — so you need **more energy** to remove it.

The **third** ionisation energy also **increases** steadily but with a step down in ionisation energy at **iron**. That's because from iron onwards, the third electron removed is one from a **paired 3d orbital**.

## Practice Questions

Q1 What's the definition of a transition metal?

Q2 Give the electron configuration of: (a) a vanadium atom, (b) a $V^{2+}$ ion.

Q3 State four chemical properties which are characteristic of transition elements.

Q4 Describe how the first ionisation energies of the transition elements imply that the transition metals have similar electronic structures.

**Exam Questions**

1 When solid copper(I) sulfate is added to water, a pale blue solution forms with a red-brown precipitate of copper metal.

a) Give the electron configuration of copper(I) ions. [1 mark]

b) Does the formation of copper(I) ions show copper acting as a transition metal? Explain your answer. [3 marks]

c) Identify the pale blue solution. [1 mark]

2 The transition metals are all d-block elements, found in the middle of the periodic table. Chromium is a transition metal, but, although it is also in the d-block of the periodic table, zinc is not.

a) Give the electron configuration of :

i) Zn
ii) $Zn^{2+}$
iii) Cr
iv) $Cr^{3+}$ [4 marks]

b) What is the definition of a transition metal? Use this definition to explain why zinc is not a transition metal. [4 marks]

3 Aluminium and iron are the two most common metals in the Earth's crust. Both can form an ion with a 3+ charge.

a) i) Give the electron configuration of the $Fe^{3+}$ ion. [1 mark]
ii) Give the electron configuration of the $Al^{3+}$ ion. [1 mark]

b) With reference to oxidation states and colours of compounds, explain why iron is a typical transition metal and aluminium is not. [4 marks]

## 4s electrons — like rats leaving a sinking ship...

*Have a quick read of the electronic configuration stuff in your AS notes if it's been pushed to a little corner of your mind labelled, "Well, I won't be needing that again in a hurry". It should come flooding back pretty quickly. These pages are just an overview of transition metal properties. Don't worry — they're all looked at in lots more detail in the coming pages...*

# Complex Ions

*Transition metals are always forming complex ions. These aren't as complicated as they sound, though. Honest.*
***These pages are for AQA (Unit 5), OCR A (Unit 5), OCR B (Unit 4) and Edexcel (Unit 5).***

## *Complex Ions are Metal Ions Surrounded by Ligands*

A **complex ion** is a **metal ion** surrounded by **coordinately bonded ligands.**

1) A **coordinate bond** (or dative covalent bond) is a covalent bond in which **both electrons** in the shared pair come from the **same atom**.
2) So a **ligand** is an atom, ion or molecule that **donates a pair of electrons** to a central metal atom or ion.
3) One ligand can be **swapped** for another ligand — this is **ligand substitution**. It almost always causes a **colour change** (see p177 for more on ligand substitution reactions).
4) The **coordination number** is the **number** of **coordinate bonds** that are formed with the central metal ion.
5) In most of the complex ions that you need to know about, the coordination number will be **4** or **6**. If the ligands are **small**, like $H_2O$, $CN^-$ or $NH_3$, **6** can fit around the central metal ion. But if the ligands are **larger**, like $Cl^-$, **only 4** can fit around the central metal ion.

### 6 COORDINATE BONDS MEAN AN <u>OCTAHEDRAL</u> SHAPE

Here are a few examples:

Don't forget — wedge-shaped arrows represent bonds coming towards you, and dashed arrows represent bonds sticking out behind the molecule.

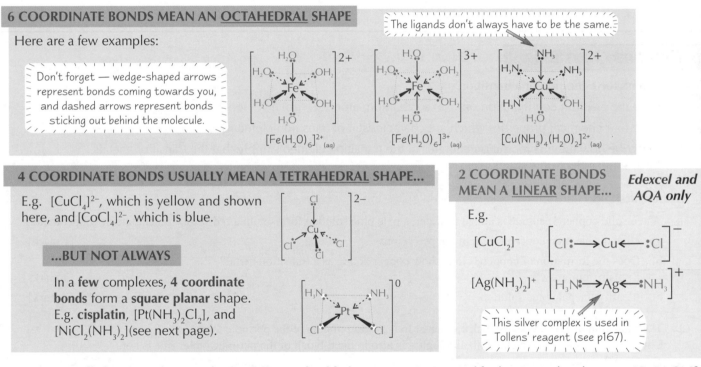

The ligands don't always have to be the same.

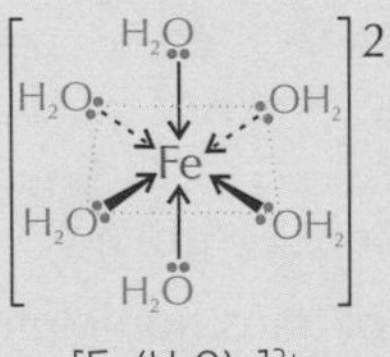


$[Fe(H_2O)_6]^{2+}_{(aq)}$

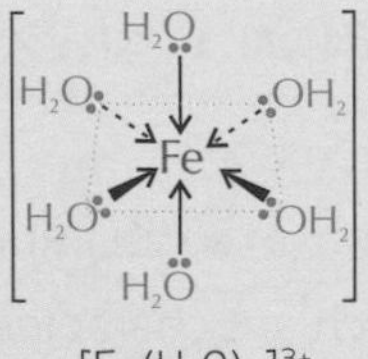


$[Fe(H_2O)_6]^{3+}_{(aq)}$

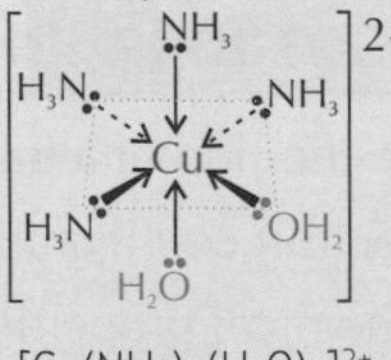


$[Cu(NH_3)_4(H_2O)_2]^{2+}_{(aq)}$

### 4 COORDINATE BONDS USUALLY MEAN A <u>TETRAHEDRAL</u> SHAPE...

E.g. $[CuCl_4]^{2-}$, which is yellow and shown here, and $[CoCl_4]^{2-}$, which is blue.

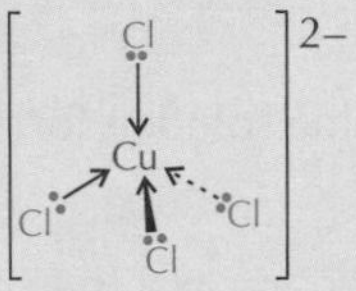


### ...BUT NOT ALWAYS

In a **few** complexes, **4 coordinate bonds** form a **square planar** shape. E.g. **cisplatin**, $[Pt(NH_3)_2Cl_2]$, and $[NiCl_2(NH_3)_2]$(see next page).

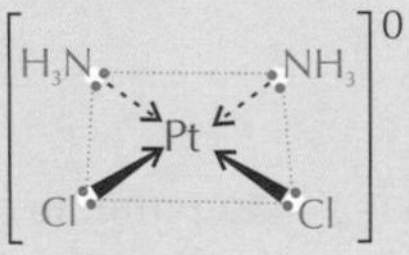


### 2 COORDINATE BONDS MEAN A <u>LINEAR</u> SHAPE...

***Edexcel and AQA only***

E.g.

$[CuCl_2]^-$ $\quad [Cl{:}\rightarrow Cu \leftarrow {:}Cl]^-$

$[Ag(NH_3)_2]^+$ $\quad [H_3N{:}\rightarrow Ag \leftarrow {:}NH_3]^+$

This silver complex is used in Tollens' reagent (see p167).

6) The **overall charge** on the complex ion is its **total oxidation state**. It's put **outside** the **square** brackets e.g. $[Cu(H_2O)_6]^{2+}$
You can work out the **oxidation state of the metal ion** in the complex using this formula:

**The oxidation state of the metal ion = the total oxidation state – the sum of the oxidation states of the ligands**

## *A Ligand Must Have at Least One Lone Pair of Electrons*

A ligand must have **at least one lone pair of electrons**, or it won't have anything to form a **coordinate bond** with.

- Ligands with **one lone pair** available for bonding are called **unidentate** or **monodentate** — e.g. $H_2\ddot{O}$, $\ddot{N}H_3$, $\ddot{C}l^-$, $\ddot{C}N^-$.
- Ligands with **two lone pairs** are called **bidentate** — e.g. ethanedioate $CO\ddot{O}CO\ddot{O}$, and ethane-1,2-diamine: $\ddot{N}H_2CH_2CH_2\ddot{N}H_2$. Bidentate ligands can each form **two coordinate bonds** with a metal ion.

  You might see ethane-1,2-diamine abbreviated to "en".
- Ligands with **more than two lone pairs** are called **multidentate** or **polydentate** — e.g. $EDTA^{4-}$ and haem. Haem is a multidentate ligand that forms part of haemoglobin — a blood protein (see p167).

# Complex Ions

## Complex Ions Can Show **Optical** and **Cis-Trans Isomerism**

*OCR A only*

**Optical and cis-trans isomerism** are types of **stereoisomerism** (see pages 49-50).

1) Complex ions show **optical isomerism** when an ion can exist in **two non-superimposable mirror image** forms. This happens when **three bidentate ligands**, such as ethane-1,2-diamine, $H_2NCH_2CH_2NH_2$, use the lone pairs on **both** nitrogen atoms to coordinately bond with a central metal ion, like **nickel**.

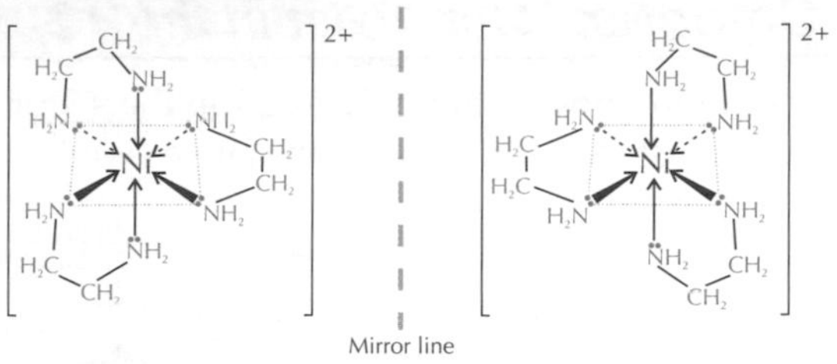


2) **Square planar** complex ions that have **two pairs** of ligands show **cis-trans isomerism**.

*Cis* isomers have the same groups on the <u>same</u> sides.

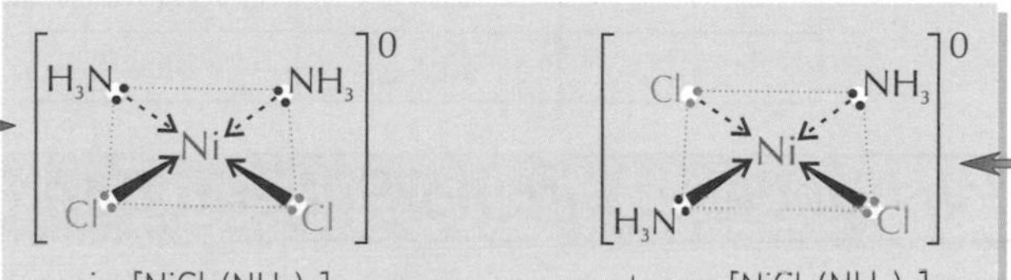

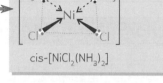

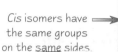

cis-$[NiCl_2(NH_3)_2]$

trans-$[NiCl_2(NH_3)_2]$

*Trans* isomers have the <u>same</u> groups <u>diagonally</u> across from each other.

## **Cisplatin** Can **Bind to DNA** in **Cancer Cells**

*AQA, OCR A and Edexcel only*

**Cisplatin** is a complex of platinum(II) with two chloride ions and two ammonia molecules in a **square planar shape**. It is used as an anti-cancer drug.

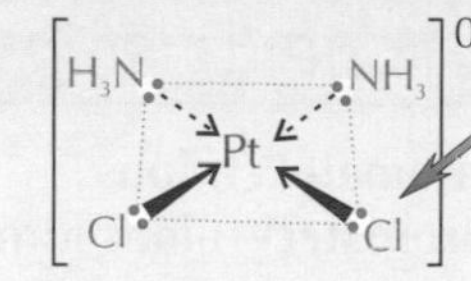

The two chloride ions are next to each other, so this complex is cisplatin.
If they were opposite each other you would have transplatin, which has different biological effects.

This is how it works:

1) The two **chlorine ligands** are very easy to displace. So the cisplatin loses them, and bonds to two **nitrogen atoms** on the **DNA molecule** inside the **cancerous cell** instead.
2) This **block** on its DNA prevents the cancerous cell from **reproducing** by division. The cell will **die**, since it is unable to repair the damage.

## Practice Questions

Q1 Explain what the term 'coordination number' means in relation to a complex ion.

Q2 Draw the shape of the complex ion $[Co(NH_3)_6]^{3+}$. Name the shape.

Q3 Draw the cis and trans isomers of the complex $[NiBr_2(NH_3)_2]$.

Q4 State a medical use of the Pt(II) complex cisplatin.

**Exam Questions**

1 When potassium cyanide is added to iron(II) chloride solution, the complex ion $[Fe(CN)_6]^{4-}$ is produced.

a) What is meant by the term 'complex ion'? [1 mark]

b) Explain how the cyanide ions bond with the central iron ion. [1 mark]

c) Draw a diagram to show the structure of the complex ion. [1 mark]

2 Iron(III) can form the complex ion $[Fe(C_2O_4)_3]^{3-}$ with three ethanedioate ions. The ethanedioate ion is a bidentate ligand. Its structure is shown on the right.

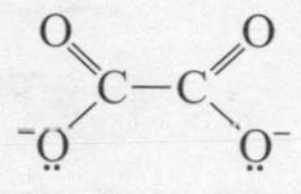

a) Explain the term 'bidentate ligand'. [2 marks]

b) What is the coordination number of the $[Fe(C_2O_4)_3]^{3-}$ complex? [1 mark]

c) Use your answer from part (b) to suggest what shape the $[Fe(C_2O_4)_3]^{3-}$ complex is. [1 mark]

## Put your hands up — we've got you surrounded...

*You'll never get transition metal ions floating around by themselves in a solution — they'll always be surrounded by other molecules. It's kind of like what'd happen if you put a dish of sweets in a room of eight (or eighteen) year-olds. When you're drawing a complex ion, you should always include some wedge-shaped bonds to show that it's 3D.*

# Variable Oxidation States — Chromium

*One of the reasons why transition metal complexes have such a big range of colours is their variable oxidation states.*
***These pages are just for AQA (Unit 5), OCR A (Unit 5) and Edexcel (Unit 5).***

## Chromium Can Exist in the +2, +3 and +6 Oxidation States

Chromium most commonly exists in the **+3** or **+6** oxidation state.
It can exist in the +2 oxidation state as well, but it's much **less stable**.

In the +6 oxidation state, chromium can form chromate(VI) ions, $CrO_4^{2-}$ **and** dichromate(VI) ions, $Cr_2O_7^{2-}$.

| Oxidation state | Formula of ion | Colour of ion |
|---|---|---|
| +6 | $Cr_2O_7^{2-}{}_{(aq)}$ | Orange |
| +6 | $CrO_4^{2-}{}_{(aq)}$ | Yellow |
| +3 | $Cr^{3+}_{(aq)}$ | Green (Violet) |
| +2 | $Cr^{2+}_{(aq)}$ | Blue |

When $Cr^{3+}$ ions are actually surrounded by 6 water ligands they look **violet**. But the water ligands are often replaced by other ligands, so **solutions** of $Cr^{3+}$ ions usually look **green** instead.

## Chromium Complex Ions Undergo **Ligand Substitution** Reactions

***Edexcel only***

Chromium complex ions can exchange ligands.
For example, the six water ligands from the $[Cr(H_2O)_6]^{3+}$ complex can swap places with six $NH_3$ ligands.
(See p177 for more on ligand substitution reactions.)

$$[Cr(H_2O)_6]^{3+}_{(aq)} + 6NH_{3(aq)} \rightarrow [Cr(NH_3)_6]^{3+}_{(aq)} + 6H_2O_{(l)}$$

octahedral violet → octahedral purple

## Chromate(VI) Ions and Dichromate(VI) Ions Exist in **Equilibrium**

***AQA only***

1) When an **alkali** ($OH^-$ ions) is added to aqueous **dichromate(VI) ions**, the orange colour turns **yellow**, because aqueous **chromate(VI) ions** form.

$$Cr_2O_7^{2-}{}_{(aq)} + OH^-_{(aq)} \rightarrow 2CrO_4^{2-}{}_{(aq)} + H^+_{(aq)}$$

orange → yellow

2) When an **acid** ($H^+$ ions) is added to aqueous **chromate(VI) ions**, the yellow colour turns **orange**, because aqueous **dichromate(VI) ions** form.

$$2CrO_4^{2-}{}_{(aq)} + H^+_{(aq)} \rightarrow Cr_2O_7^{2-}{}_{(aq)} + OH^-_{(aq)}$$

yellow → orange

3) These are **opposite processes** and the two ions exist in **equilibrium**.

$$Cr_2O_7^{2-}{}_{(aq)} + H_2O_{(l)} \rightleftharpoons 2CrO_4^{2-}{}_{(aq)} + 2H^+_{(aq)}$$

This isn't a redox reaction because chromium stays in the +6 oxidation state.

The **position** of equilibrium depends on the **pH** — yep, it's good ol' Le Chatelier's principle again.
If $H^+$ **ions** are added, the equilibrium shifts to the **left** so **orange** $Cr_2O_7^{2-}$ **ions** are formed.
If $OH^-$ **ions** are added, H+ ions are **removed** and the equilibrium shifts to the **right**, forming **yellow** $CrO_4^{2-}$ **ions**.

## **Chromium** Ions can be **Oxidised** and **Reduced**

***AQA and Edexcel only***

1) Dichromate(VI) ions can be **reduced** using a good reducing agent, such as **zinc and dilute acid**.

Oxidation states: +6, 0, +2, +3

$$Cr_2O_7^{2-}{}_{(aq)} + 14H^+_{(aq)} + 3Zn_{(s)} \rightarrow 3Zn^{2+}_{(aq)} + 2Cr^{3+}_{(aq)} + 7H_2O_{(l)}$$

orange → green

2) Zinc will **reduce** $Cr^{3+}$ further to $Cr^{2+}$ —

$$2Cr^{3+}_{(aq)} + Zn_{(s)} \rightarrow Zn^{2+}_{(aq)} + 2Cr^{2+}_{(aq)}$$

green → blue

But unless you use an inert atmosphere, you're wasting your time — $Cr^{2+}$ is so **unstable** that it oxidises straight back to $Cr^{3+}$ in air.

3) You can oxidise $Cr^{3+}$ to chromate(VI) ions with **hydrogen peroxide**, $H_2O_2$, in an **alkaline** solution.

Oxidation states: +3, +6

$$2Cr^{3+}_{(aq)} + 10OH^-_{(aq)} + 3H_2O_{2(aq)} \rightarrow 2CrO_4^{2-}{}_{(aq)} + 8H_2O_{(l)}$$

green → yellow

Here's a summary of all the chromium reactions you need to know:

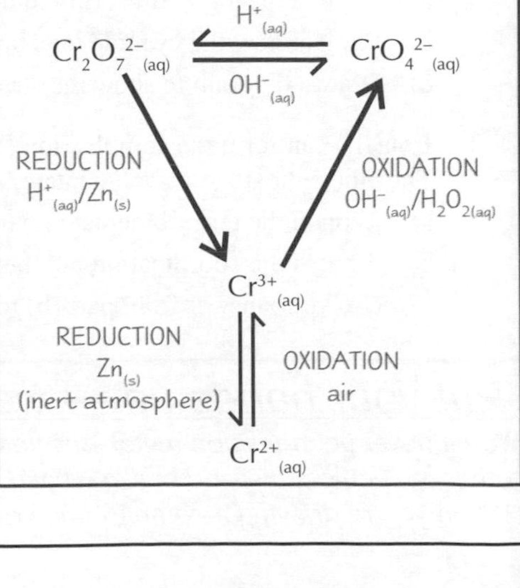

# Variable Oxidation States — Chromium

## Chromium(II) Ethanoate Oxidises Easily — Making it Tricky to Produce

**Edexcel only**

Chromium(II) ethanoate, $Cr_2(CH_3COO)_4(H_2O)_2$, is a chromium(II) complex.
To make it, you start off with chromium(III) chloride solution. The reaction happens in **two parts**.

1) **Green** chromium(III) chloride is **reduced** with zinc in acid solution to give a **blue** solution of $Cr^{2+}$ ions (like you saw on the last page).

$$2Cr^{3+} + Zn \rightarrow 2Cr^{2+} + Zn^{2+}$$

2) **Sodium ethanoate** is mixed with this solution and the **red precipitate chromium(II) ethanoate** forms.

$$2Cr^{2+} + 4CH_3COO^- + 2H_2O \rightarrow [Cr_2(CH_3COO)_4(H_2O)_2]$$

3) Unfortunately it's not that simple as the complex is **very easily oxidised**. You have to do the whole experiment in an **inert atmosphere** (such as nitrogen) to keep the air out (which is very fiddly). Not only that, but you have to remove the oxygen from all the liquids in your experiment before using them (e.g. by bubbling nitrogen though them).

### Experiment — Making Chromium(II) Ethanoate

1) Slowly add **hydrochloric acid** to a flask containing chromium(III) chloride solution and zinc mesh. The reduction of the $Cr^{3+}$ ions will produce **hydrogen**, which can escape through a rubber tube into a beaker of water.
2) As soon as you see the solution turn a **clear blue** colour, **pinch the rubber tube shut** so hydrogen can **no longer escape** from the flask.
3) The build up of **pressure** in the flask will force the $Cr^{2+}$ solution through the open glass tube into a flask of **sodium ethanoate**.
4) As soon as the blue solution reacts with the sodium ethanoate, a **red precipitate** forms. Ta-da, you've made **chromium(II) ethanoate**.

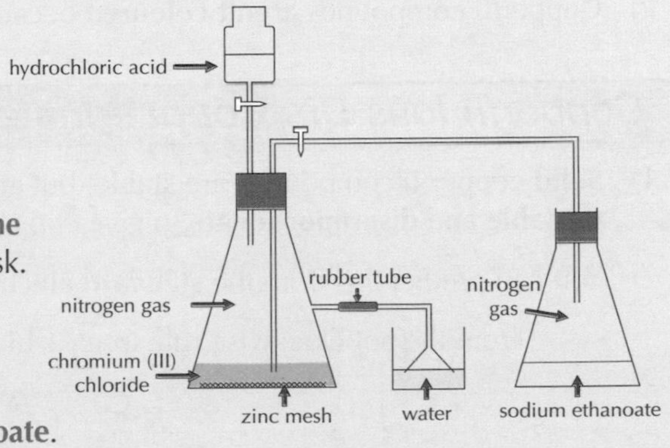


5) **Filter** off the precipitate and **wash** it using **water**, then **ethanol**, then **ether** (while still keeping the chromium(II) ethanoate in an inert atmosphere to stop it getting oxidised).

## Practice Questions

Q1 What colour change is seen when acid is added to aqueous chromate(VI) ions? Name the new chromium ion.

Q2 Name the two reagents needed to oxidise chromium(III) to chromium(VI).

Q3 Write an equation for the reduction of chromium(III) ions to chromium(II) ions using zinc metal.

**Exam Questions**

1 Chromium(II) ethanoate is a complex that can be made from chromium(III) chloride.
  a) The first step in the production process is to lower the oxidation state of the aqueous chromium(III) ions. What type of reaction is this? [1 mark]
  b) Chromium(II) ethanoate is very easily oxidised. Describe the steps you would need to take to prevent oxidation during its production. [2 marks]

2 Acidified dichromate(VI) ions can act as powerful oxidising agents.
  a) Write a half-equation for the reduction of dichromate(VI) ions to chromium(III) ions in acid solution. [1 mark]
  b) Ethanol is oxidised to ethanal by dichromate(VI) ions.
    i) Write a balanced equation for the oxidation of ethanol to ethanal by dichromate(VI) ions in acid solution. [3 marks]
    ii) Give the colour change seen during this reaction. [1 mark]
  c) $SO_2$ gas is oxidised to $SO_4^{2-}$ ions by acidified dichromate(VI) ions in solution.
    i) Write a half-equation for the oxidation of $SO_2$ to $SO_4^{2-}$. [1 mark]
    ii) Write a balanced equation for the oxidation of $SO_2$ by acidified dichromate(VI) ions. [1 mark]

## My girlfriend is usually in the +6 or +8 aggravation states...

*Sorry, I'm too tired to tell you anything meaningful right now, so you're on your own I'm afraid... I'm going to have a nap and probably have another dream where I'm being attacked by a wallaby the size of a house...*

# Variable Oxidation States — Cu and Co

*With all these transition metals that begin with C, it's hard to keep them straight...*
***These pages are for AQA (Unit 5), OCR A (Unit 5), OCR B (Unit 4) and Edexcel (Unit 5).***

## Copper Ions Exist in Two Oxidation States

| Oxidation state | Formula | Electronic configuration | Colour |
|---|---|---|---|
| 0 | Cu | $1s^2\ 2s^2\ 2p^6\ 3s^2\ 3p^6\ 3d^{10}\ 4s^1$ | Shiny brown metal (or pink if in powder form) |
| +1 | $Cu^+$ | $1s^2\ 2s^2\ 2p^6\ 3s^2\ 3p^6\ 3d^{10}$ | White solid |
| +2 | $Cu^{2+}$ | $1s^2\ 2s^2\ 2p^6\ 3s^2\ 3p^6\ 3d^9$ | Blue in aqueous solution |

1) $Cu^{2+}$ ions are **stable** in aqueous solution. They're **reduced** to Cu metal by more **electropositive metals**, like zinc or nickel. E.g. $Cu^{2+} + Zn \rightarrow Cu + Zn^{2+}$. This type of reaction is known as a **displacement** reaction.
2) Copper(I) compounds **aren't coloured** because copper(I) has a full **3d subshell** ($3d^{10}$) — see page 162.

## Copper(I) Ions Disproportionate in Aqueous Solution

***Edexcel only***

1) **Solid** copper(I) compounds are **stable**, but **aqueous** $Cu^+$ ions are **unstable** and **disproportionate** to give copper and copper(II) ions.

$$2Cu^+_{(aq)} \rightarrow Cu^{2+}_{(aq)} + Cu_{(s)}$$

2) You can predict this from the **standard electrode potentials** (see p144).

From the anticlockwise rule (see p146) the half equations (and their cell potentials) are:

$$Cu^+ \rightarrow Cu^{2+} + e^- \qquad E^\ominus = +0.52 \text{ volts}$$
$$Cu^+ + e^- \rightarrow Cu \qquad E^\ominus = +0.15 \text{ volts}$$

Which combine to give the overall reaction: $2Cu^+ \rightarrow Cu^{2+} + Cu$

So the whole cell potential $E^\ominus_{cell} = +0.52 - (+0.15) = +$ **0.37 volts** — the reaction is **likely** to happen.

## Cobalt Can Exist as $Co^{2+}$ and $Co^{3+}$

***AQA and OCR A only***

1) Cobalt can exist in two oxidation states — **+2** as $Co^{2+}$, and **+3** as $Co^{3+}$. It much prefers to be in the **+2** state though.
2) $Co^{3+}$ can be made by oxidising $Co^{2+}_{(aq)}$ with **hydrogen peroxide** in alkaline conditions.

$$2Co^{2+}_{(aq)} + H_2O_{2(aq)} \xrightarrow{OH^-_{(aq)}} 2Co^{3+}_{(aq)} + 2OH^-_{(aq)}$$

## Mixing NaOH and Transition Metal Ions gives Coloured Precipitates

When you add **sodium hydroxide** to a transition metal ion solution, each **OH⁻** ion will steal an **H⁺** from a water ligand. When the **hydroxide ions have removed enough H⁺** ions, the complex ion becomes **neutral**, and forms a **precipitate**.

You need to know the **equations** and the **colours** for these examples.

(And no, you're not going mad — those are iron reactions on page about copper and cobalt, but you need to learn them too. )

See p 175 for more on alkali and metal aqua ion reactions.

| | | |
|---|---|---|
| **Copper(II) ions** | $[Cu(H_2O)_6]^{2+} + 2OH^-$ → **Pale blue solution** | $[Cu(H_2O)_4(OH)_2] + 2H_2O$ **Blue precipitate** |
| **Iron(II) ions** | $[Fe(H_2O)_6]^{2+} + 2OH^-$ → **Green solution** | $[Fe(H_2O)_4(OH)_2] + 2H_2O$ **Green precipitate** |
| **Iron(III) ions** | $[Fe(H_2O)_6]^{3+} + 3OH^-$ → **Orange/brown solution** | $[Fe(H_2O)_3(OH)_3] + 3H_2O$ **Rust-brown precipitate** |

# Variable Oxidation States — Cu and Co

## Ligand Substitution can Change the Shape of a Complex Ion

Here are some more ligand substitution reactions you need to know and love (well... know at any rate). Make sure you know the **colour changes** that happen for each reaction.

See p 177 for more on ligand substitution.

Unlike the ligand substitution of $NH_3$ for $H_2O$, $Cl^-$ ions are a **different size** to the $H_2O$ ligands, which means the complex ions **change shape** and **coordination number**.

$[Cu(H_2O)_6]^{2+}_{(aq)} + 4Cl^-_{(aq)} \rightleftharpoons [CuCl_4]^{2-}_{(aq)} + 6H_2O_{(l)}$

octahedral, pale blue → tetrahedral, yellow

$[Co(H_2O)_6]^{2+}_{(aq)} + 4Cl^-_{(aq)} \rightleftharpoons [CoCl_4]^{2-}_{(aq)} + 6H_2O_{(l)}$

octahedral, pink → tetrahedral, blue

## Ammonia Reacts With Transition Metal Ion Solutions In Two Ways

Adding a **little** ammonia solution to an aqueous solution of $Cu^{2+}$ or $Co^{2+}$ ions, causes the **same reaction** as **hydroxide ions** do — it removes $H^+$ ions and forms a neutral complex **precipitate**.

If you **keep adding** ammonia solution, the precipitate will dissolve and form a **solution of complex ions**. This is because the $NH_3$ molecules can also act as **ligands** — it's good ol' **ligand substitution** again.

### Copper (II) ions

**1st reaction – a little $NH_3$**

$[Cu(H_2O)_6]^{2+} + 2NH_3 \rightarrow [Cu(H_2O)_4(OH)_2] + 2NH_4^+$

**Pale blue solution** → **Blue precipitate**

**2nd reaction – a lot of $NH_3$**

$[Cu(H_2O)_6]^{2+} + 4NH_3 \rightarrow [Cu(NH_3)_4(H_2O)_2]^{2+} + 6H_2O$

**Pale blue solution** → **Intense blue solution**

If you're doing ***OCR B*** you need to know this ion as $[Cu(NH_3)_4]^{2+}$.

### Cobalt (II) ions

*AQA only*

**1st reaction – a little $NH_3$**

$[Co(H_2O)_6]^{2+} + 2NH_3 \rightarrow [Co(H_2O)_4(OH)_2] + 2NH_4^+$

**Pink solution** → **Blue precipitate**

**2nd reaction – a lot of $NH_3$**

$[Co(H_2O)_6]^{2+} + 4NH_3 \rightarrow [Co(NH_3)_6]^{2+} + 6H_2O$

**Pink solution** → **Straw coloured solution**

If the $[Co(NH_3)_6]^{2+}$ complex is left to stand in **air**, **oxygen** oxidises the cobalt ion to $Co^{3+}$ and the complex becomes **brown** $[Co(NH_3)_6]^{3+}$.

## Practice Questions

Q1 Why aren't Cu(I) compounds coloured?

Q2 Why do ligands such as $Cl^-$ ions form complexes with lower coordination numbers than ligands such as $H_2O$?

Q3 What would you usually observe happening during a ligand substitution reaction?

**Exam Questions**

1 Look at the two reactions below:

Reaction A: $[Co(H_2O)_6]^{3+} + Cl^- \rightarrow [Co(H_2O)_5Cl]^{2+} + H_2O$

Reaction B: $[Co(H_2O)_6]^{2+} + 4Cl^- \rightarrow [CoCl_4]^{2-} + 6H_2O$

a) What is the name for these types of reaction? [1 mark]

b) What do $H_2O$ and $Cl^-$ have in common that allows them to act as ligands? [1 mark]

c) Which of the reactions – A, B, or both – involves a change in shape? [1 mark]

d) State all the shape changes involved in your answer to c) and explain why there is a change of shape. [4 marks]

2 Solutions of ammonia and sodium hydroxide both react with solutions of copper(II) compounds.

a) Describe one similarity and one difference in what you would observe as increasing amounts of NaOH or $NH_3$ were added. [2 marks]

b) Write an equation to show what happens when a solution of a copper(II) compound reacts with:

i) a small amount of ammonia solution,

ii) excess ammonia solution. [4 marks]

## That copper's gone mad — he's 1 electron short of a full 4s-orbital...

*I fancy pasta for tea tonight. OK, so it's only gonna be a tin of tomatoes with some mixed herbs that have been on the shelf since I moved in, but we can't all be master chefs. Anyway, whilst I go and cook you make sure you can remember all those examples of ligand complexes. It might not be fun, but knowing your complex colours can pick you up some easy marks.*

# Formation of Coloured Ions

*Transition metal complex ions have distinctive colours. This page explains why they're so colourful. Enjoy...*
***These pages are for AQA (Unit 5), OCR A (Unit 5), OCR B (Unit 4 and Unit 5) and Edexcel (Unit 5).***

## *Ligands **Split** the 3d Subshell into **Two Energy Levels***

***AQA, OCR B and Edexcel only***

Normally the 3d orbitals of transition element ions **all** have the **same energy**. But when **ligands** come along and bond to the ions, some of the orbitals are given more energy than others. This splits the 3d orbitals into **two different energy levels**.

Electrons tend to **occupy the lower orbitals** (the ground state). To jump up to the higher orbitals (excited states) they need **energy** equal to the energy gap, $\Delta E$. They get this energy from **visible light**.

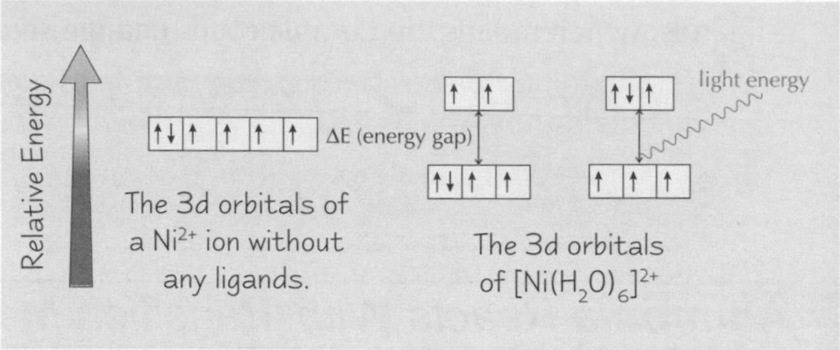


The energy **absorbed** when electrons jump up can be worked out using this formula:

$\Delta E = h\nu$ where $\nu$ = frequency of light absorbed (hertz/Hz) and $h$ = Planck's constant ($6.63 \times 10^{-34}$ Js)

The amount of energy needed to make electrons jump depends upon the **central metal ion** and its **oxidation state**, the **ligands** and the **coordination number**, as these affect the **size of the energy gap**.

## *The **Colours** of Compounds are the **Complement** of Those That are **Absorbed***

***AQA, OCR B and Edexcel only***

When **visible light** hits a transition metal ion, some frequencies are **absorbed** when electrons jump up to the higher orbitals. The frequencies absorbed depend on the size of the **energy gap**.

The rest of the frequencies are **reflected**. These **reflected** frequencies combine to make the **complement** of the colour of the absorbed frequencies — this is the **colour** you see.

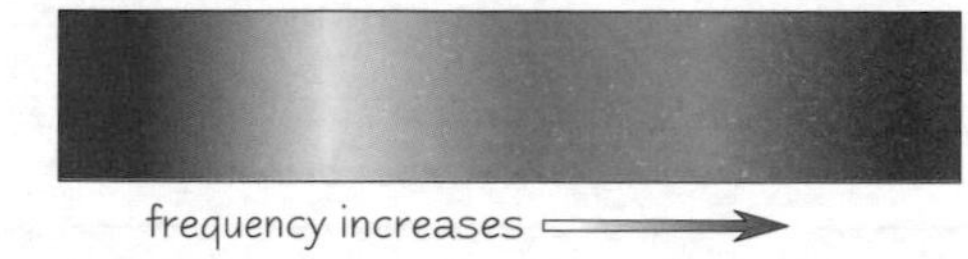


For example, **$[Cu(H_2O)_6]^{2+}$** ions absorb **yellow light**. The remaining frequencies **combine** to produce the **complementary colour** — in this case that's blue. So $[Cu(H_2O)_6]^{2+}$ solution appears **blue**.

If there are **no** 3d electrons or the 3d subshell is **full**, then no electrons will jump, so **no energy** will be absorbed. If there's no energy absorbed, the compound will look **white** or **colourless**.

## ***Transition Metal Ions** can be **Identified** by their **Colour***

It'd be nice if each transition metal formed ions or complexes with just one colour, but sadly it's not that simple. The **colour of a complex** can be altered by any of the factors that can affect the size of the **energy gap**.

1) **Changes in oxidation state.**

| | | | | | | | | |
|---|---|---|---|---|---|---|---|---|
| Complex: | $[Fe(H_2O)_6]^{2+}_{(aq)}$ | → | $[Fe(H_2O)_6]^{3+}_{(aq)}$ | | $[V(H_2O)_6]^{2+}_{(aq)}$ | → | $[V(H_2O)_6]^{3+}_{(aq)}$ |
| Oxidation state: | +2 | → | +3 | and | +2 | → | +3 |
| Colour: | **pale green** | → | **yellow** | | **violet** | → | **green** |

2) **Changes in coordination number** — this always involves a change of ligand too.

| | | | |
|---|---|---|---|
| Complex: | $[Cu(H_2O)_6]^{2+} + 4Cl^-$ | → | $[CuCl_4]^{2-} + 6H_2O$ |
| Coordination number: | 6 | → | 4 |
| Colour: | **blue** | → | **yellow** |

3) **Changes in ligand** — this can cause a colour change even if the oxidation state and coordination number remain the same.

| | | | |
|---|---|---|---|
| Complex: | $[Co(H_2O)_6]^{2+} + 6NH_3$ | → | $[Co(NH_3)_6]^{2+} + 6H_2O$ |
| Oxidation state: | +2 | → | +2 |
| Colour: | **pink** | → | **straw coloured** |

# Formation of Coloured Ions

## *Spectrometry* can be used to Find the *Concentration* of Solutions

*AQA and OCR B only*

**Spectrometry** can be used to determine the **concentration of ions in a solution** by measuring how much **light** it **absorbs**.

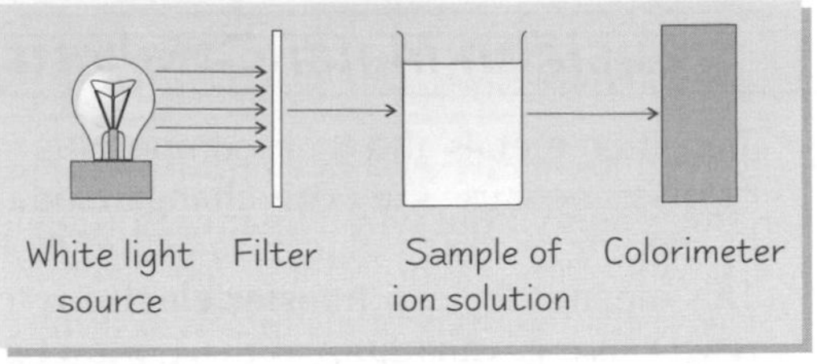


1) **White light** is shone through a **filter**, which **only** lets through the **one frequency** of light that is **absorbed** by the metal ions in the sample.
2) The light then passes through the sample to a **colorimeter**, which calculates **how much light** was **absorbed** by the sample.
3) The more **concentrated** a coloured solution is, the more light it will absorb. So you can use this measurement to work out the **concentration** of a solution of transition metal ions.
4) You need to set your colorimeter **to zero** by measuring the absorbance of a sample of the **solvent** that your metal ions are dissolved in — usually it's just water. This way the colorimeter can go on to measure just the absorbance of the metal ions.
5) To work out the concentration of an unknown transition metal solution you will need a **calibration graph**. This is made by **measuring** the absorbance of **standard samples** with **known concentrations**.

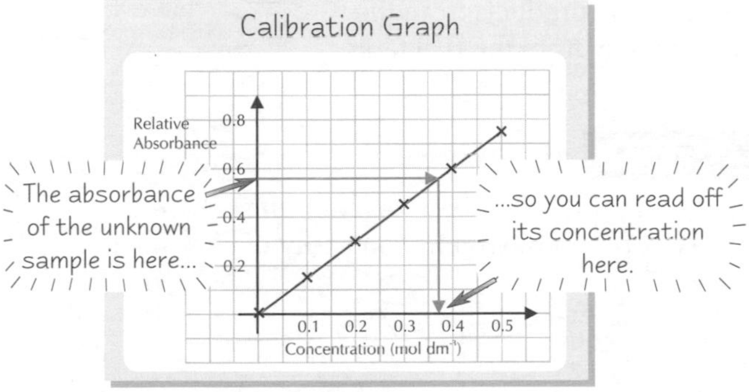


**Standard samples** can be made by **dissolving** different amounts of the metal ion in a **fixed** volume of water or by making **consecutive dilutions** of a single concentrated solution. They must contain the **same metal ion** as the unknown sample and be in the **same solution** or **solvent**.

6) You **plot** the **absorbance** of each of these samples against their **concentration** to get a **calibration graph**.
7) Now when you **measure** the absorbance of the **unknown** sample you can use the standard curve to **read off** its **concentration**. Lovely.

## *Practice Questions*

Q1 Which subshell is split by the presence of ligands?

Q2 Name **two** factors that will cause a colour change in this reaction: $[Co(H_2O)_6]^{2+} + 4Cl^- \rightarrow [CoCl_4]^{2-} + 6H_2O$

Q3 What does a colorimeter measure?

Q4 What is the purpose of the filter in spectrometry?

**Exam Questions**

1 a) Explain why complex transition metal ions such as $[Fe(H_2O)_6]^{2+}$ are coloured. [2 marks]

b) State three changes to a complex ion that would result in a change in colour. [3 marks]

2 Colorimetry can be used to determine the concentration of a coloured solution. Briefly describe how you would construct a calibration graph, given a coloured solution of known concentration. [3 marks]

3 The frequency of light absorbed by a transition metal complex ion can be determined from the equation $\Delta E = h\nu$.

a) State what is meant by $\Delta E$ and what change this represents within the complex ion. [2 marks]

b) The electron configuration of Ar is $1s^2\ 2s^2 2p^6\ 3s^2 3p^6$.
Using this noble gas core, complete the electron arrangements for the following ions:
i) $Cu^+$ ii) $Cu^{2+}$ [2 marks]

c) Which one of the above ions has coloured compounds?
State the feature of its electron arrangement that suggests this. [2 marks]

## *Blue's not my complementary colour — it clashes with my hair...*

*Transition metal ions are pretty colours, don't you think? The Romans did — they used iron, copper, cobalt and manganese compounds to add colour to glass objects. I'm not sure that they knew the colours were affected by variable oxidation states, ligands and coordination number, but it's pretty impressive even so.*

# Transition Metal Catalysts

*Transition metals aren't just good — they're grrrreat.*

***These pages are for AQA (Unit 5), OCR A (Unit 5), OCR B (Unit 4) and Edexcel (Unit 5).***

## Transition Metal Catalysts Work by Changing Oxidation States

Transition metals and their compounds make good catalysts because they can **change oxidation states** by gaining or losing electrons within their **d orbitals**. This means they can **transfer electrons** to **speed up** reactions e.g. vanadium in the **Contact process**.

Vanadium oxidises $SO_2$ to $SO_3$ and is reduced itself.

$$\overset{+5}{V_2O_5} + SO_2 \rightarrow \overset{+4}{V_2O_4} + SO_3$$

vanadium(V) → vanadium(IV)

The reduced catalyst is then oxidised by oxygen gas back to its original state.

$$\overset{+4}{V_2O_4} + \tfrac{1}{2}O_2 \rightarrow \overset{+5}{V_2O_5}$$

vanadium(IV) → vanadium(V)

## Homogeneous Catalysts are in the Same Phase as the Reactants

*AQA only*

The **reactants** combine with a **homogeneous catalyst** to make an **intermediate species**, which then reacts to form the **products** and **reform the catalyst**. This causes the enthalpy profile (see p20) to have **two humps** in it, corresponding to the two reactions.

The activation energy needed to form the **intermediates** (and form the products from the intermediates) is **lower** than that needed to make the products directly from the reactants.

The catalyst is always **reformed** so it can carry on catalysing the reaction.

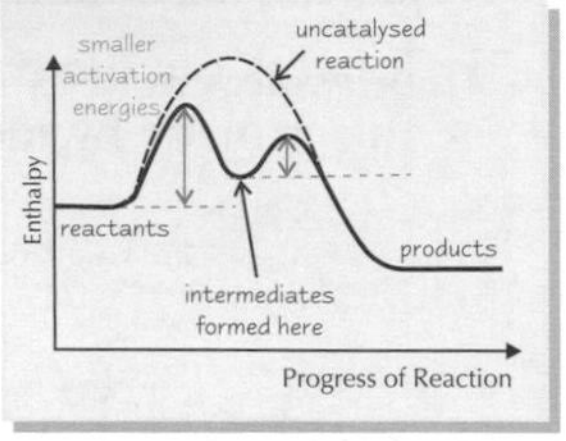

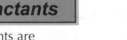

**Example 1 — $Fe^{2+}$ Catalyses the Redox Reaction Between $S_2O_8^{2-}$ and $I^-$**

Iodide ions and peroxodisulfate ($S_2O_8^{2-}$) ions **repel** each other, so it's unlikely they'll **react** on their own. Catalyst **$Fe^{2+}$ ions** are oxidised to **intermediate $Fe^{3+}$** ions by the ($S_2O_8^{2-}$) ions, which then **easily oxidise** the $I^-$ ions.

$$S_2O_8^{2-}{}_{(aq)} + 2I^-{}_{(aq)} \rightarrow I_{2(aq)} + 2SO_4^{2-}{}_{(aq)}$$

$$S_2O_8^{2-}{}_{(aq)} + 2Fe^{2+}{}_{(aq)} \rightarrow 2Fe^{3+}{}_{(aq)} + 2SO_4^{2-}{}_{(aq)}$$

$$2Fe^{3+}{}_{(aq)} + 2I^-{}_{(aq)} \rightarrow I_{2(aq)} + 2Fe^{2+}{}_{(aq)}$$

**Example 2 — Autocatalysis**

**Autocatalysis** is when a **product** catalyses the reaction e.g. $Mn^{2+}$ in the reaction between $C_2O_4^{2-}$ and $MnO_4^-$.
As the reaction progresses and the **amount** of **product increases**, the reaction **speeds up**.

$$2MnO_4^-{}_{(aq)} + 16H^+{}_{(aq)} + 5C_2O_4^{2-}{}_{(aq)} \rightarrow 2Mn^{2+}{}_{(aq)} + 8H_2O_{(l)} + 10CO_{2(g)}$$

## Heterogeneous Catalysts are in a Different Phase From the Reactants

A **heterogeneous catalyst** is in a **different phase** from the reactants (see p20). Usually the reactants are gases or in solution and the catalyst is a solid — the reaction happens on the **surface** of the catalyst.

*OCR B only*

Transition metals make good heterogeneous catalysts because they can use their **s- and d-orbitals** for **bonding** to the reactant molecules. The reaction works in three stages:

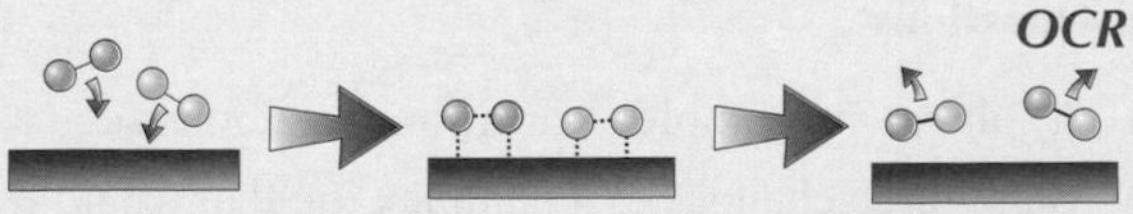

1) The **reactant** molecules are **attracted** to the surface of the catalyst and stick to it — this is called **adsorption**.
2) The surface of the catalyst **activates** the molecules so they react more easily. E.g. interaction with the catalyst **weakens** the bonds in the molecule making them **easier** to **break** and reform as the products.
3) The **product** molecules **leave** the catalyst's surface, making room for fresh reactants. This is called **desorption**.

**Increasing** the catalyst's **surface area** increases the number of molecules that can **react** at the same time, **increasing the rate** of the reaction. **Support mediums** are often used to make the **area** of a catalyst **as large as possible**.

For example, **catalytic converters** in car exhausts contain a **ceramic lattice** coated with a thin layer of the catalyst **rhodium** (see p20). The lattice structure **maximises the surface area** of the catalyst, making it more effective. And it **minimises the cost** of the catalyst because only a **thin coating** is needed.

*AQA only*

Examples of **heterogeneous catalysts** include:

1) **Iron** in the **Haber process** for making **ammonia:** $N_{2(g)} + 3H_{2(g)} \xrightarrow{Fe_{(s)}\text{ catalyst}} 2NH_{3(g)}$
2) **Vanadium(V) oxide** in the **Contact process** for making **sulfuric acid:** $SO_{2(g)} + \frac{1}{2}O_{2(g)} \xrightarrow{V_2O_{5(s)}\text{ catalyst}} SO_{3(g)}$
3) **Chromium(III) oxide** in the manufacture of **methanol from CO:** $CO_{(g)} + 2H_{2(g)} \xrightarrow{Cr_2O_{3(s)}\text{ catalyst}} CH_3OH_{(g)}$

# Transition Metal Catalysts

## Heterogeneous Catalyst Poisoning can be Costly

*AQA only*

1) **Impurities** in a reaction mixture may **bind** to the catalyst's surface and **block reactants** from being adsorbed. This process is called **catalyst poisoning** (see p20).
2) Catalyst poisoning **reduces the surface area** of the catalyst available to the reactants, **slowing down the reaction**.
3) Catalyst poisoning **increases the cost** of a chemical process because **less product** can be made in a certain **time** or with a certain amount of **energy**. The **catalyst** may even need **replacing** or **regenerating**, which also costs money.

> 1) **Lead** can **coat the surface** of the **rhodium** catalyst in a car's catalytic converter.
> 2) Any **sulfur** impurities not removed from the natural gas used in the **Haber process** will poison the **iron** catalyst.

## Catalyst Development can Make Chemistry Greener

*Edexcel only*

1) The **development** of new catalysts is an important area of chemical research. It's all about finding ways to make industrial chemical reactions more **environmentally friendly**.
2) Finding the right catalyst for a reaction can dramatically **reduce** the **temperature** and **pressure** needed to make it happen. This reduces the **energy** you need to use in order get a reaction to occur (which reduces the **cost** too).
3) Sometimes finding a **new catalyst** for a reaction means that the chemical industry can start to use a **greener method** to produce a chemical.

**Example: making ethanoic acid from methanol and carbon monoxide**

1) Originally, ethanoic acid was produced by oxidising **butane**. This process produces a lot of by-products, so it has a **low atom economy**.

$$2C_4H_{10} + 5O_2 \rightarrow 4CH_3COOH + 2H_2O$$

2) There's an alternative reaction you can use to make ethanoic acid from **methanol** and **carbon monoxide**. It produces fewer by-products, and has a much **higher** atom economy. But the uncatalysed reaction is much **too slow** to be useful.

$$CH_3OH + CO \rightarrow CH_3COOH$$

3) In the 1960s a **cobalt/iodide** catalyst was discovered, which enabled the methanol reaction to run reasonably fast and produce a high yield at 200 °C and 700 atmospheres.
4) By 1966 a new **rhodium/iodide catalyst** had been developed. It made the reaction even more efficient, and meant the temperature and pressure required for the reaction could be **reduced** even further — to 180 °C and 30 atmospheres. This saved a huge amount of **energy**, which meant **lower production costs** and **less pollution**.
5) In the 1980s, an **iridium/iodide** catalyst was developed — it made the reaction even faster and more efficient.

## Practice Questions

Q1 What property of transition elements makes them good catalysts?

Q2 Which catalyst is used in the manufacture of methanol from carbon monoxide?

Q3 What term describes the process when a product catalyses a reaction?

**Exam Questions**

1 a) Using equations, explain how vanadium(V) oxide acts as a catalyst in the Contact process. [4 marks]
 b) i) Describe how heterogeneous catalysts can become poisoned and give an example. [3 marks]
  ii) What are the consequences of catalytic poisoning? [2 marks]

2 a) Explain the difference between homogeneous and heterogeneous catalysts. [2 marks]
 b) $H^+$ ions are used to catalyse the reaction between $C_2H_5OH_{(aq)}$ and $CH_3COOH_{(aq)}$.
  i) What type of catalysis is this? [1 mark]
  ii) Sketch an enthalpy profile diagram to show the catalysed and uncatalysed routes for this exothermic reaction. [3 marks]

## Bagpuss, Sylvester, Tom — the top three on my catalyst...

*So, after all that you should know that transition metal catalysts are pretty darn useful. You should also know the difference between heterogeneous and homogeneous catalysts, and why the variable oxidation states of transition metals make them good catalysts. If you do, then go grab yourself a cup of tea— it speeds up the rate of revision, you know.*

# Other Uses of Transition Metals

*Transition metals — so useful that you (literally) couldn't live without them.*
***These pages are for AQA (Unit 5), OCR A (Unit 5), OCR B (Unit 4) and Edexcel (Unit 5).***

## **Rusting** is All Down to **Electrochemical Processes**

***OCR B only***

If iron's exposed to **oxygen** and **water**, it'll turn into crumbly, flaky stuff called **rust**. Here's how:

1) There are two half-equations involved: $Fe_{(s)} \rightleftharpoons Fe^{2+}_{(aq)} + 2e^-$ $E^\circ = +0.44$ V

$2H_2O_{(l)} + O_{2(g)} + 4e^- \rightleftharpoons 4OH^-_{(aq)}$ $E^\circ = +1.23$ V

So the overall reaction is: $2H_2O_{(l)} + O_{2(g)} + 2Fe_{(s)} \rightarrow 2Fe^{2+}_{(aq)} + 4OH^-_{(aq)}$ $E^\circ = +1.67$ V

Double the first half equation to keep the $e^-$ balanced.

2) The $Fe^{2+}_{(aq)}$ and $OH^-_{(aq)}$ ions produced combine to form a precipitate of iron(II) hydroxide, $Fe(OH)_2$. $Fe^{2+}_{(aq)} + 2OH^-_{(aq)} \rightarrow Fe(OH)_{2(s)}$

3) The $Fe(OH)_2$ is further oxidised to $Fe(OH)_3$ by oxygen and water. $2H_2O_{(l)} + O_{2(g)} + 4Fe(OH)_{2(s)} \rightarrow 4Fe(OH)_{3(s)}$

4) Iron(III) hydroxide gradually turns into hydrated iron(III) oxide, $\mathbf{Fe_2O_3.xH_2O}$ — this is **rust**.

## There are Two Main Ways to **Prevent Rusting**

***OCR B only***

1) The obvious way to prevent rusting is to coat the iron with a **barrier** to keep out either the oxygen, the water or both.

Barrier methods include:

**Painting/Coating with a polymer** — ideal for big and small structures alike. It can be decorative too.
**Oiling/Greasing** — this has to be used when moving parts are involved, like on bike chains.

2) The other way is the **sacrificial method**. This involves placing a **more reactive metal** with the iron. The water and oxygen then react with this **sacrificial metal** instead of with the iron.

Zinc is often used as a sacrificial metal.
The $Zn/Zn^{2+}$ system has a **more negative** $E^\circ$ value than the $Fe/Fe^{2+}$ system.
This means the **zinc** will be **oxidised** to $Zn^{2+}$ ions in preference to the iron.

$Zn^{2+}_{(aq)} + 2e^- \rightleftharpoons Zn_{(s)}$ $E^\circ = -0.76$ V
$Fe^{2+}_{(aq)} + 2e^- \rightleftharpoons Fe_{(s)}$ $E^\circ = -0.44$ V

A coating of **zinc** can be sprayed onto the object — this is known as **galvanising**.
Alternatively, **blocks of zinc** can be bolted to the iron. This is used on ships' hulls, or on underground iron pipes.

## **Almost** all Iron and Steel Packaging Can be **Recycled**

***OCR B only***

Recycling iron and its alloys, such as steel, is really important — digging and extracting new ore takes **a lot of energy** and generates a lot of **pollution**. And the disposal of it in landfill also takes up **space**.

Fortunately, **almost** all iron and steel packaging (e.g. food and drinks cans) can be recycled. Aerosol cans are more of a problem — they can be **dangerous** if they aren't completely empty and need **special facilities** to empty them before they can be recycled.

Gary combined his love of steel recycling with his flair for fashion.

The first step is to **separate** the iron and steel from other stuff, e.g. aluminium and plastics. This is easy because iron and steel are **magnetic**. The mixture of materials is passed under a giant magnet and... bish bash bosh all the iron and steel stick to it, and are separated out.

Next, the iron needs to be **cleaned**. To do this the iron is **melted** in a **furnace** and then **oxygen** is blown through it to **burn off** the impurities e.g. carbon. Since the burning is an exothermic reaction (gives energy out), the **temperature** will **rise** as the impurities are removed. To stop it getting too hot **more** solid **iron** and **steel** is added to be recycled.

After the impurities have been removed, **carbon** and **other elements** such as nickel, chromium or manganese may need to be added in carefully **controlled amounts** to obtain steel with exactly the **desired properties**.

# Other Uses of Transition Metals

## *Metals Are Extracted From Their Ores By Reduction*

*OCR B only*

Most metals occur in the Earth's crust **combined** with **oxygen** (as an oxide), **sulfur** (as a sulfide) or with **silicon and oxygen** (as a silicate). To extract the metal it needs to be **reduced** (gain electrons). Here are three ways of doing this...

**Heating with carbon**

The **carbon** is **oxidised** to carbon monoxide and then to carbon dioxide. At each step the carbon **loses electrons** and reduces the metal. This is a **cheap** method because there are lots of cheap sources of carbon — but it **doesn't work** with **reactive metals** because carbon isn't a strong enough reducing agent.

**Reduction by a more reactive metal**

Very reactive metals (e.g. sodium) are **powerful reducing agents**. They're used in the extraction of metals like titanium. In order to get pure titanium, the compound $TiCl_4$ is heated with sodium or magnesium. It's an **expensive** process because of the high cost of sodium metal.

**Electrolysis**

Metals can be extracted from their ores by passing an **electric current** through the **molten ore**. Aluminium is extracted like this. It's an **expensive** process because **high temperatures** are needed to melt the ore and **a lot** of **electricity** is used.

Metals can also be **refined** (purified) by electrolysis. Copper is usually extracted from its ore by other processes, e.g. reduction by carbon, but then electrolysis is used to purify it (see diagram).

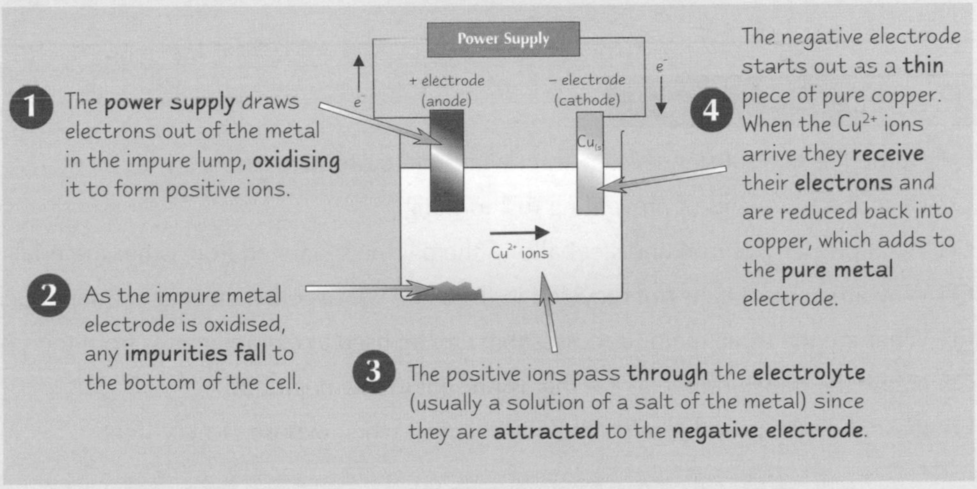
Power Supply
+ electrode (anode)
– electrode (cathode)
e⁻
$Cu_{(s)}$
$Cu^{2+}$ ions
1 The **power supply** draws electrons out of the metal in the impure lump, **oxidising** it to form positive ions.
2 As the impure metal electrode is oxidised, any **impurities fall** to the bottom of the cell.
3 The positive ions pass **through** the **electrolyte** (usually a solution of a salt of the metal) since they are **attracted** to the **negative electrode**.
4 The negative electrode starts out as a **thin** piece of pure copper. When the $Cu^{2+}$ ions arrive they **receive** their **electrons** and are reduced back into copper, which adds to the **pure metal** electrode.

## *$Fe^{2+}$ in Haemoglobin Allows Oxygen to be Carried in the Blood*

*AQA and OCR A only*

The blood product, **haemoglobin**, is a complex formed from **$Fe^{2+}$ ions**. Both **water** and **oxygen** will bind to the $Fe^{2+}$ ion as **ligands**, so the complex can **transport oxygen** to where it's needed, and then swap it for a water molecule. Here's **how it works**:

1) In the lungs, where the oxygen concentration is high, the water ligand is **substituted** for an **oxygen molecule** to form **oxyhaemoglobin**, which is carried **around the body** in the blood.
2) When the **oxyhaemoglobin** gets to a place where oxygen is needed, the **oxygen molecule** is **exchanged** for a **water molecule**. The haemoglobin then **returns to the lungs** and the whole process starts again.

This process can be disrupted if **carbon monoxide** is inhaled. The **haemoglobin** swaps its **water** ligand for a **carbon monoxide** ligand, forming **carboxyhaemoglobin**. This is bad news because carbon monoxide is a **strong** ligand and **doesn't** readily exchange with oxygen or water ligands, meaning the haemoglobin **can't transport oxygen** any more. **Carbon monoxide poisoning** starves the organs of oxygen — it can cause **headaches**, **dizziness**, **unconsciousness** and even **death** if it's not treated.

## *Tollens' Reagent Contains a Silver Complex*

*AQA only*

**Tollens' reagent** is prepared by adding just enough ammonia solution to silver nitrate solution to form a colourless solution containing the complex ion $[Ag(NH_3)_2]^+$.

Tollens' reagent is used to distinguish between **aldehydes** and **ketones** (see p58) — aldehydes react to give a **silver mirror** on the inside of the test tube. **Ketones don't react** with Tollens' reagent.

$$RCHO + 2[Ag(NH_3)_2]^+ + 3OH^- \rightarrow RCOO^- + 2Ag + 4NH_3 + 2H_2O$$

Steve was seeking help for his silver complex.

# Other Uses of Transition Metals

## Polychromic Sunglasses are Light Sensitive

*Edexcel only*

Kyle's fashion tip: Polychromic sunglasses add a touch of cool to any outfit.

**Polychromic sunglasses** will **darken** in direct sunlight, but handily return to being **untinted** when you step indoors. Here's how they work:

1) Polychromic lenses are usually embedded with a **silver halide** (e.g. silver choride), which **decomposes** in UV radiation to form **silver atoms**.
2) These silver atoms cause the lenses to **darken**.
3) If you increase the level of UV radiation, the number of silver atoms produced will **increase**. So the lenses **vary in darkness** depending on the level of UV radiation.
4) The process is **reversed** when the lenses are no longer exposed to UV radiation (e.g. if you go indoors). The silver chloride reforms and the lenses go back to being untinted. Clever...

## Practice Questions

Q1 Name the two substances that react with iron to produce rust.

Q2 Describe four ways of preventing rust forming.

Q3 What property of iron and steel allows them to be separated from other materials?

Q4 Why are aerosol cans not recycled in the same way as other steel containers, such as food and drink cans?

Q5 What are the three main processes that can be used to extract metals from their ores?

Q6 Name the transition metal ion that is present in haemoglobin.

Q7 Describe why polychromic sunglasses darken when exposed to UV light.

**Exam Questions**

1 Use the data in the table to answer the following questions:

a) 'Tin' cans are mainly made of steel with a very thin coating of tin to prevent the steel from rusting. Explain why the tin is acting only as a barrier and is not a sacrificial protector. [2 marks]

b) 'Galvanising' is a method of protecting steel that involves coating the steel object with a layer of zinc. Is this a barrier or sacrificial method of protection? Explain your answer. [3 marks]

| Half-cell | |
|---|---|
| $Zn^{2+}_{(aq)}/Zn_{(s)}$ | –0.76 |
| $Fe^{2+}_{(aq)}/Fe_{(s)}$ | –0.44 |
| $Sn^{2+}_{(aq)}/Sn_{(s)}$ | –0.14 |

2 Explain how electrolysis can be used to remove impurities from a sample of crude copper metal. Your explanation should describe how the electrochemical cell is set up and include details of the reactions at the anode and at the cathode, with relevant half-equations. [6 marks]

3 Tollens' reagent contains a transition metal complex ion.

a) Which two types of organic compound is Tollens' reagent used to distinguish between? [1 mark]

b) What is seen when a positive reaction occurs with Tollens' reagent? [1 mark]

c) Give the:
i) formula ii) shape iii) colour
of the transition metal complex ion in Tollens' reagent. [3 marks]

## The Sacrificial Method — who knew chemistry could sound so bloodthirsty...

*Hopefully you'll have realised from these last five pages that transition metals are really quite useful. I'm surprised there aren't statues built in their honour. Make sure you know all the uses you need to for your exam — then why not celebrate with a cheese triangle of triumph (or any victory foodstuff of your choice) — you've made it to the end of the section.*

# Water and Carbon Dioxide

*A new day, a new chemistry section. But don't worry, this is the last one — whooppeeee!*
***These pages are for OCR B (Unit 5).***

## Water forms Hydrogen Bonds

1) Water molecules form bonds with each other called **hydrogen bonds**. In a hydrogen bond, an H atom is attracted to a lone electron pair on an O atom (see diagram).
2) It happens because water molecules are **polar** — the electronegative O atoms draw bonding electrons **away** from the H atoms, creating δ+ (slightly positive) charges on the Hs.
3) Hydrogen bonds are strong for **intermolecular forces**, but **very weak** compared to the likes of ionic or covalent bonds.

You also get hydrogen bonding when hydrogen is covalently bonded to other electronegative atoms like fluorine or nitrogen (e.g. in ammonia).

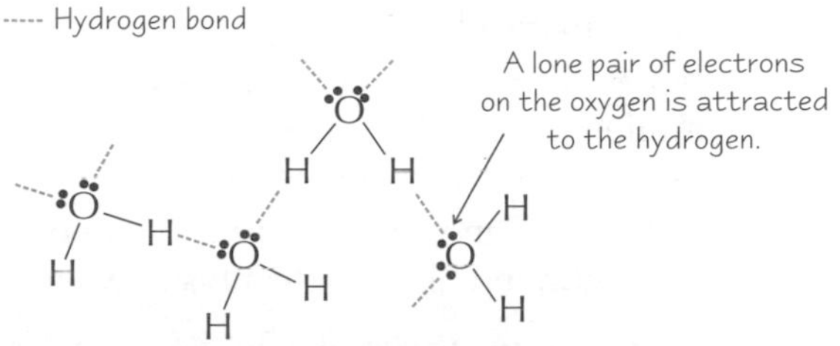


## Hydrogen Bonding Explains Water's Unusual Physical Properties Like...

### 1) High Boiling Point

1) To **boil** a liquid, you need to **overcome** the intermolecular forces, so that the molecules can **escape**. Liquids with stronger intermolecular forces have **higher boiling points**.
2) Hydrogen bonding is a **strong** intermolecular force, compared to instantaneous dipole-induced dipole attractions. This is why water has a much higher boiling point than the other Group 6 hydrides.

The boiling temperatures of Group 6 hydrides

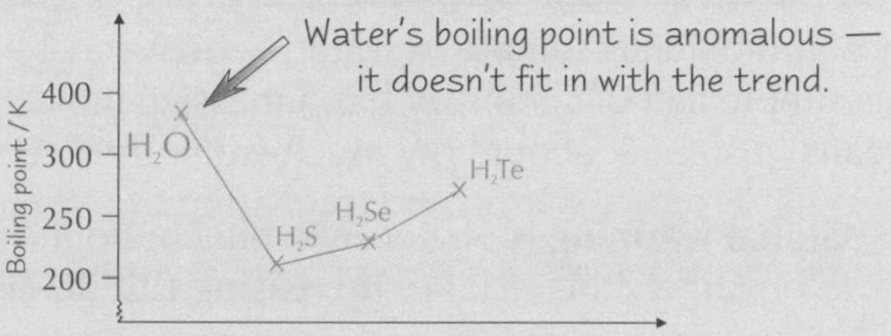


### 2) High Specific Heat Capacity

1) **Specific heat capacity** measures how easy it is to raise the temperature of something — it's the energy needed to raise the temperature of a unit mass of a substance by 1 °C. It depends on a substance's **internal structure**.
2) Water's got a **high** specific heat capacity — that's why the sea heats up (and cools down) a lot slower than land.
3) The Earth's **oceans** can absorb and store huge amounts of heat energy from the Sun. **Ocean currents** transport this heat energy around the world, e.g. by carrying energy absorbed at the equator to colder regions of the world.

### 3) High Enthalpy of Vaporisation

1) **Enthalpy of vaporisation** is the amount of energy needed to change a substance from its standard state to a **vapour**.
2) Water needs a lot more energy to **evaporate** than most other liquids. If it's on your skin, it takes loads of energy (in the form of heat) from your skin as it evaporates — so it cools you down quickly.

### 4) Ice is Less Dense than Water

1) Normally, density **increases** as temperature falls — think gas, liquid, solid.
2) But as water freezes into ice, the density actually **decreases**. Water is actually at its most dense at about 4 °C.
3) It's to do with the way hydrogen bonds affect the structure of ice. As water freezes, all the hydrogen bonds that could form, do form — this forms a lattice structure with lots of wasted space, making it **less dense**.
4) As ice **melts**, some hydrogen bonds **break** and the lattice **breaks down**, allowing water molecules to 'fill in' the gaps, increasing the density.

## Non-Polar Substances Don't Usually Dissolve in Water

See page 6 for a reminder about polar molecules.

1) **Non-polar solutes** tend to only dissolve in **non-polar solvents** (e.g. hexane). And **polar solutes** tend to only dissolve in **polar solvents** (e.g. water).
2) In each case, the solute-solute, solvent-solvent and new solute-solvent bonds are all of a **similar strength** so it's fairly easy to break the existing bonds and form new ones.
3) Non-polar solutes **won't dissolve** in polar solvents because the solvent-solvent bonds in a polar liquid are **much stronger** than the solute-solvent bonds would be. Polar solutes don't tend to dissolve in non-polar solvents either, this time it's the solute-solute bonds that are **too strong** compared to the solute-solvent ones that could form.

# Water and Carbon Dioxide

## *Ionic Solids* Dissolve in *Polar Solvents*

Ionic compounds can be dissolved by **polar solvents** like water. It's the polar H–O bonds in water that make it work...

1) The $\delta+$ H atoms are attracted to the **negative ions** and the $\delta-$ O atoms are attracted to the **positive ions**.
2) The ions **separate** from the ionic lattice and become **surrounded** by water molecules.
3) Although the water-ion bonds are a lot weaker, the **total attraction** from all the water molecules is enough to **overcome** the strong ionic attraction in the lattice.
4) The process of the ions being surrounded by water molecules is called **hydration**. If the solvent isn't water, it's called **solvation**.

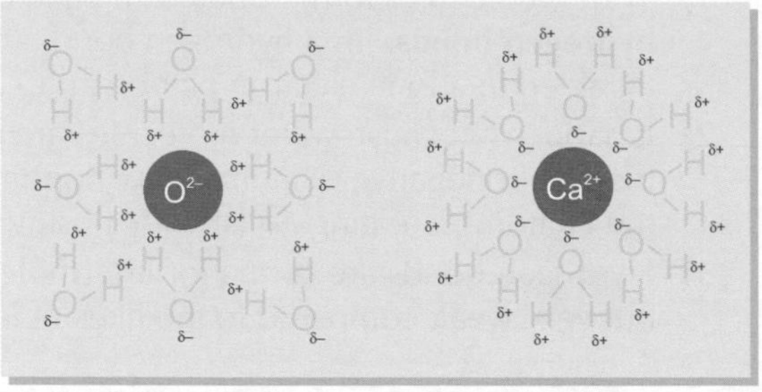


**Ionic** substances **won't** dissolve in **non-polar** solvents.
Non-polar molecules **don't** interact strongly enough with ions to **pull them away** from the ionic lattice. The **electrostatic forces** between the ions are way **stronger** than any bonds that could form between the ions and the solvent molecules.

## Carbon Dioxide *Dissolves* in the *Oceans*

Carbon dioxide is **soluble** in water — between 1 and 3 g of it will dissolve in a litre of water, depending on temperature. This simple fact of chemistry has a massive impact on the environment — **huge amounts** of $CO_2$ can be stored in the **oceans** (just think about how much water they contain...) which affects things in and out of the seas.

**Global warming** is obviously a big environmental issue these days — it's generally accepted to be largely the result of **increasing $CO_2$ levels** in the atmosphere from **human activity**.
As the levels of $CO_2$ have been increasing, the **amount dissolved** in the oceans has also been **increasing**. This is good for us as it's likely to have helped **slow down** global warming.

But it's not all good news, sadly...
The seas are **naturally alkaline**. When $CO_2$ dissolves in water, it's slightly acidic because of this reaction:

$$CO_2 + H_2O \rightleftharpoons H^+ + HCO_3^-$$

So too much $CO_2$ being dissolved can affect the **overall pH** of the oceans which harms many species and **upsets ecosystems**. E.g. crustaceans and molluscs can't form and maintain their shells if conditions are too acidic. Other species that aren't directly harmed are also affected as **food chains** are disturbed.

## There are Ways of *Removing Carbon Dioxide* and *Storing It*

**Photosynthesis**

You'll remember from your GCSE Biology that green plants use **photosynthesis** to convert $CO_2$ from the atmosphere and water into sugar and oxygen. This has maintained the **balance** of $CO_2$ and $O_2$ in our atmosphere for millions of years.
But once again, **humans** have **upset the balance**. Decades of large-scale **deforestation** have significantly reduced tree coverage around the globe, meaning less photosynthesis and less removal of $CO_2$. A good way to tackle this would be **reforestation** schemes — planting large areas of fast-growing trees to increase photosynthesis and $CO_2$ removal.

You are sentenced to 10 years for the theft of the Big Diamond.

'Quick Fingers' Maguire's excuse that it was only carbon capture wasn't fooling the judge.

**Carbon Capture and Storage**

This involves (as it says) **capturing $CO_2$** as we produce it, rather than simply releasing it into the atmosphere, and finding **somewhere to put it**.
One way would be to collect **$CO_2$** produced by **power stations** and pipe it into porous rock under the sea to be **stored**. This is potentially a good way for Britain to **reduce** its $CO_2$ emissions because there's a lot of porous rock under the North Sea and the old infrastructure from the oil fields could be used to transport it.

# Water and Carbon Dioxide

## There are Ways of **Reducing** the **Release** of **Carbon Dioxide**...

Here are a few more of the current ideas for tackling the $CO_2$ problem that you need to know about:

**Use less fuel**

**Increasing the efficiency** of devices such as vehicle engines, heating systems, industrial machines and domestic devices, means **less energy is needed**, so less fuel is burned and **less $CO_2$ released**. Governments can take steps to encourage the development and use of these new technologies, e.g. by lowering taxes on more efficient cars.

Will's new vehicle was certainly green, but the fuel economy wasn't great.

**Use different fuels**

$CO_2$ is released when **fossil fuels**, oil, coal and gas, are burned.
An obvious way to reduce $CO_2$ emissions is to use alternative fuels that don't produce so much $CO_2$ — for example, **nuclear energy** and **hydrogen**.

**Nuclear energy** is already used around the world. Some people believe that using nuclear energy is the best way to reduce $CO_2$ emissions. But many people are opposed to this for various reasons...

- worries about possible **cancer risks** for workers.
- there's a risk of **accidental leaks** or **major disasters**.
- the **waste** stays radioactive for hundreds of years.
- quite a bit of $CO_2$ is produced during the **mining**, **processing**, and **transportation** of the nuclear fuel.

**Hydrogen fuel cells** (see pages 148) could be used to power electric cars, but there are a few issues that need to be ironed out first...

- hydrogen is hard to **store** and **transport**.
- **huge investment** would be needed to set up a new supply infrastructure like we have for petrol.
- although hydrogen itself is a very **clean fuel**, producing it in the first place requires **energy**.

## Practice Questions

Q1 Give three unusual properties of water that are caused by hydrogen bonding.

Q2 Explain briefly how polar solvents are able to dissolve ionic solids.

Q3 How is carbon dioxide dissolving into seawater both a good and a bad thing for the environment?

Q4 Explain the idea behind carbon capture and storage.

Q5 Outline some different ways to reduce the amount of $CO_2$ that we produce and describe any problems with them.

**Exam Questions**

1 The diagram on the right shows some water molecules in liquid water. Explain, in terms of bonding, what happens when water boils and why it is said to have an 'anomalous' boiling point. [3 marks]

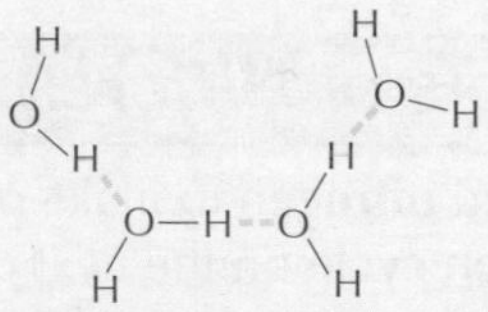


2 Capsaicin is a non-polar molecule that causes chillies to taste 'hot' when ingested. Using your knowledge of dissolving, suggest why water is not a suitable drink to reduce the burning sensation. [3 marks]

3 A carbon sink is something that is able to store carbon-containing molecules for a long time. Both the oceans and plants are considered to be carbon sinks.

a) Why is it important to reduce the levels of atmospheric $CO_2$? [1 mark]

b) Explain why the oceans are considered a carbon sink and discuss the possible effects of this on global warming and ocean ecosystems. [6 marks]

c) Briefly outline how plants are able to act as a carbon sink and comment on how human activity has impacted on this. [4 marks]

## *You need to know this stuff — that's the inconvenient truth...*

*You may be sick of hearing about carbon dioxide emissions, but it's such a hot topic these days that examiners reckon you need to know all about it. So learn these pages, and remember — never leave your hamster's curling tongs on standby...*

# Nitrogen Chemistry

*Ah nitrogen — my favourite element... After cobalt, obviously... Not forgetting boron... Lithium's pretty nifty too...*
***These pages are for OCR B (Unit 5).***

## **Nitrogen** Occurs Naturally as a **Diatomic Molecule**

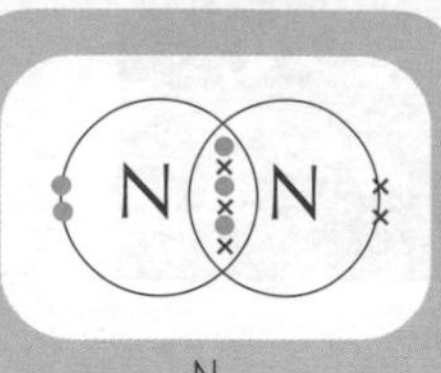

$N_2$

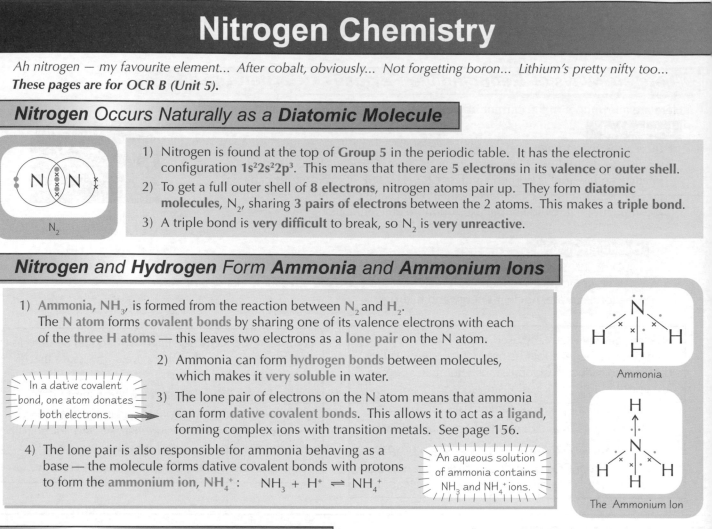

1) Nitrogen is found at the top of **Group 5** in the periodic table. It has the electronic configuration **$1s^22s^22p^3$**. This means that there are **5 electrons** in its **valence** or **outer shell**.
2) To get a full outer shell of **8 electrons**, nitrogen atoms pair up. They form **diatomic molecules**, $N_2$, sharing **3 pairs of electrons** between the 2 atoms. This makes a **triple bond**.
3) A triple bond is **very difficult** to break, so $N_2$ is **very unreactive**.

## **Nitrogen** and **Hydrogen** Form **Ammonia** and **Ammonium Ions**

1) **Ammonia, $NH_3$**, is formed from the reaction between $N_2$ and $H_2$. The **N atom** forms **covalent bonds** by sharing one of its valence electrons with each of the **three H atoms** — this leaves two electrons as a **lone pair** on the N atom.
2) Ammonia can form **hydrogen bonds** between molecules, which makes it **very soluble** in water.
3) The lone pair of electrons on the N atom means that ammonia can form **dative covalent bonds**. This allows it to act as a **ligand**, forming complex ions with transition metals. See page 156.
4) The lone pair is also responsible for ammonia behaving as a base — the molecule forms dative covalent bonds with protons to form the **ammonium ion, $NH_4^+$**: $NH_3 + H^+ \rightleftharpoons NH_4^+$

In a dative covalent bond, one atom donates both electrons.

An aqueous solution of ammonia contains $NH_3$ and $NH_4^+$ ions.

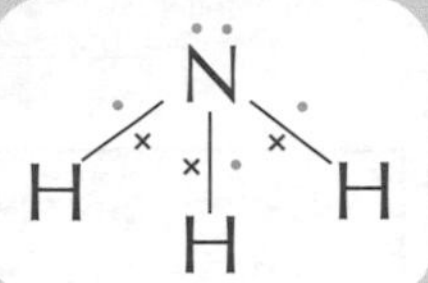

Ammonia

The Ammonium Ion

## Nitrogen Also Forms **Several Oxides**

There are lots of different oxides of nitrogen, but here are the ones you need to know about:

1) **NO** is called **nitrogen monoxide**, **nitric oxide** or **nitrogen(II) oxide**. It is a colourless gas.
2) **$N_2O$** is called **dinitrogen monoxide** or **nitrogen(I) oxide** (you might've heard of it as 'laughing gas'). It has a sweet smell and is also colourless.
3) **$NO_2$** is called **nitrogen dioxide** or **nitrogen(IV) oxide**. Also a gas, it's brown, has a sharp odour and is toxic.

## Nitrogen Has Lots of **Different Oxidation States**

Plants and animals need **nitrogen** to make **proteins**, but they can't absorb it from the air.
This is what the **nitrogen cycle** on the next page is for — to convert nitrogen into more **accessible** forms.
The cycle converts nitrogen through its different **oxidation states**.

| Form of nitrogen | Formula | Oxidation state | What produces this form of nitrogen |
|---|---|---|---|
| Nitrogen in the air | $N_{2(g)}$ | 0 | Denitrifying bacteria |
| Ammonium ions in the soil | $NH_4^+{}_{(aq)}$ | –3 | Bacteria and micro-organisms in the soil |
| Nitrate(V) ions in the soil | $NO_3^-{}_{(aq)}$ | +5 | Nitrifying bacteria in the soil, bacteria in root nodules |
| Nitrate(III) ions in the soil | $NO_2^-{}_{(aq)}$ | +3 | Nitrifying bacteria in the soil, bacteria in root nodules |
| Nitrogen(II) oxide | $NO_{(g)}$ | +2 | Thunderstorms, car engines, denitrifying bacteria in the soil |
| Nitrogen(IV) oxide | $NO_{2(g)}$ | +4 | Oxidation of NO in the atmosphere |
| Nitrogen(I) oxide | $N_2O_{(g)}$ | +1 | Denitrifying bacteria in the soil |

Here are a couple of handy tips for calculating oxidation states:

1) Remember that the **roman numeral** in brackets (e.g. nitrogen(IV) oxide) is telling you the **oxidation state for N** (e.g. **+4**).
2) If you have to **calculate** the oxidation state for nitrogen, remember that — **when combined with N, O** has an oxidation state of **–2** and H has an oxidation state of **+1**. The oxidation states should add up to the **overall charge** of the compound (i.e. 0) or ion.

# Nitrogen Chemistry

## The Nitrogen Cycle Involves Many **Redox Reactions**

Redox reactions involve the **transfer of electrons** — nitrogen, the little devil, gets involved in loads of 'em as part of the nitrogen cycle. It can **donate electrons** and be **oxidised**, or **accept electrons** and be **reduced**. You need to know the major redox reactions involving nitrogen and be able to write equations and half equations for them. Lucky you.

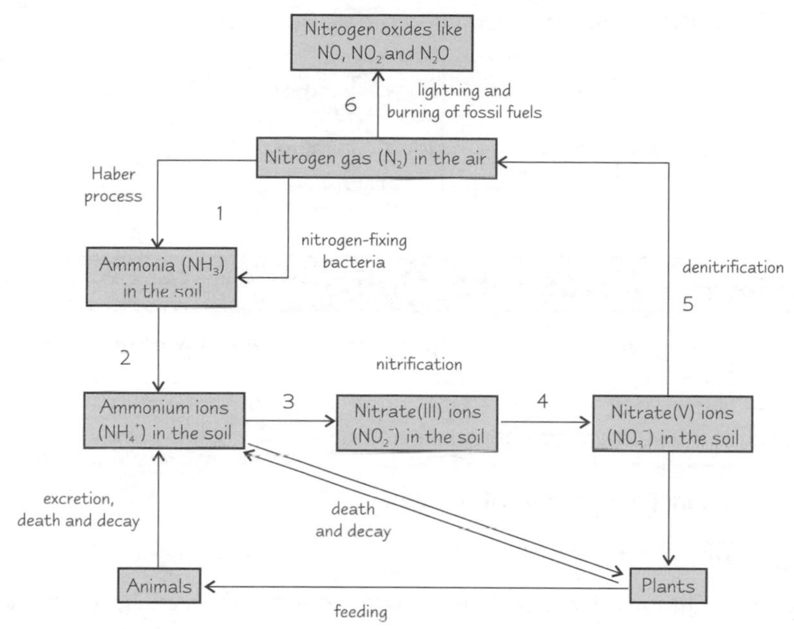

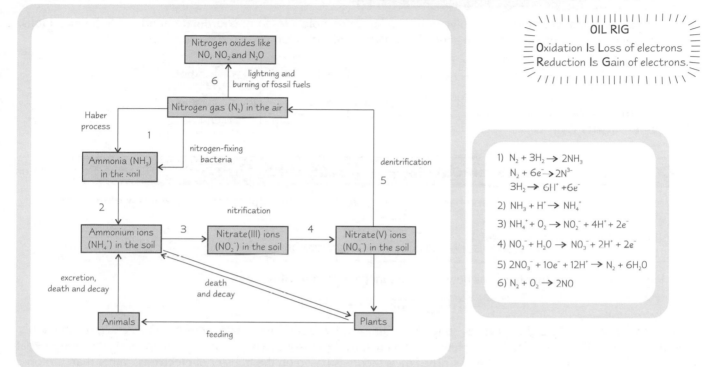

OIL RIG
Oxidation Is Loss of electrons
Reduction Is Gain of electrons.

1) $N_2 + 3H_2 \rightarrow 2NH_3$
$N_2 + 6e^- \rightarrow 2N^{3-}$
$3H_2 \rightarrow 6H^+ + 6e^-$

2) $NH_3 + H^+ \rightarrow NH_4^+$

3) $NH_4^+ + O_2 \rightarrow NO_2^- + 4H^+ + 2e^-$

4) $NO_2^- + H_2O \rightarrow NO_3^- + 2H^+ + 2e^-$

5) $2NO_3^- + 10e^- + 12H^+ \rightarrow N_2 + 6H_2O$

6) $N_2 + O_2 \rightarrow 2NO$

There are lots of **different ways** that compounds in the nitrogen cycle can **inter-convert** and **not** all of them are listed here — ammonium ions can be oxidised directly to nitrate(V) ions for example. You need to feel comfortable with writing equations **from scratch** rather than learning them by rote.

## Practice Questions

Q1 Explain why ammonia can act as a base.

Q2 What is the oxidation state of nitrogen in nitrogen dioxide?

Q3 What are the definitions of oxidation and reduction in terms of electrons?

**Exam Questions**

1 Aqueous solutions of ammonium ions, $NH_4^+$, can be converted to nitrate ions, $NO_3^-$.

a) What is the oxidation state of N in:
i) $NH_4^+$
ii) $NO_3^-$ [2 marks]

b) Is nitrogen being oxidised or reduced when $NH_4^+$ ions turn into $NO_3^-$ ions? Explain your answer. [1 mark]

c) Write a half-equation for the reaction of $NH_4^+$ in the presence of water to form $NO_3^-$. [3 marks]

2 During lightning storms, nitrogen and oxygen in the air can react to form nitrogen monoxide.

a) Write an equation for this reaction. [2 marks]

b) In $N_2$, nitrogen has an oxidation state of 0. What is its oxidation state in nitrogen monoxide? [1 mark]

c) Nitrogen monoxide reacts further with oxygen to form nitrogen dioxide.
If you carried this reaction out in a sealed container, what would you see? [1 mark]

## The nitrogen cycle — enough to make you soil yourself...

*Redox reactions were a major topic at AS and like a good 90's boy band they're back for another crack at the top spot. Well, the exam anyway... Excuse me if my analogies don't always go to plan... If you're unsure about all this oxidation is loss / reduction is gain malarkey, I'd suggest dusting off the AS notes and brushing up on your equation writing technique. Fabulous.*

# Metal-Aqua Ions

*Remember all the stuff on pages 162-163 about complex ions and their pretty coloured solutions?*
*Well this section's all about their reactions. So prepare yourself for more colour changes than a chameleon playing Twister...*
***These pages are for AQA (Unit 5), OCR A (Unit 5) and Edexcel (Unit 5).***

## Metal Ions Become **Hydrated** in Water

When **transition metal compounds** dissolve in water, the water molecules form **coordinate bonds** with the **metal ions**. This forms **metal-aqua complex ions**. In general, **six water molecules** form coordinate bonds with each metal ion.

The water molecules do this by donating a **non-bonding pair of electrons** from their oxygen.

The diagrams show examples of metal-aqua ions formed by **iron** — $[Fe(H_2O)_6]^{2+}$ and by **chromium** — $[Cr(H_2O)_6]^{3+}$.

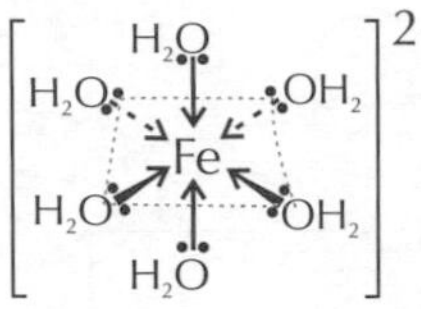


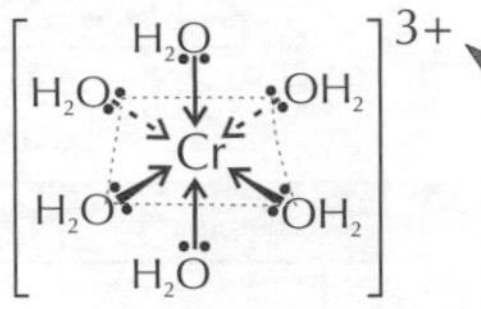


This is the charge on the metal ion (water molecules are neutral).

## A **Lewis Acid** Accepts Electrons — A **Lewis Base** Donates Electrons

*AQA only*

The Brønsted-Lowry theory of acids and bases says that an **acid** is a **proton donor**, and a **base** is a **proton acceptor**.

$$NH_{3(aq)} + HCl_{(aq)} \rightarrow NH_4{}^+{}_{(aq)} + Cl^-{}_{(aq)}$$

**HCl** is **donating** a proton, so it's acting as a **Brønsted-Lowry acid.**
$NH_3$ is **accepting** a proton, so it's acting as a **Brønsted-Lowry base.**

Now look at the reaction that happens between **ammonia** and **boron trifluoride**:

$$NH_{3(aq)} + BF_{3(aq)} \rightarrow NH_3BF_{3(aq)}$$

This **doesn't** involve transferring protons, so it doesn't fit in with the Brønsted-Lowry acid-base theory. You'd think this would mean that it's not an acid-base reaction, but a chemist, Professor Lewis, came up with an alternative theory that broadens the definition of acids and bases. The Lewis theory is based on the transfer of **electrons**, rather than protons:

A **Lewis acid** is an **electron pair acceptor.**
A **Lewis base** is an **electron pair donor.**

In the reaction above, the **ammonia** molecule **donates** a pair of electrons to the boron atom, forming a **coordinate bond.** So $\mathbf{NH_3}$ is acting as a **Lewis base**, and $\mathbf{BF_3}$ is acting as a **Lewis acid.**

$$H_3N\!:\rightarrow BF_3$$

Some substances fit both the Brønsted-Lowry and the Lewis definitions of an acid or base. Others only fit one.
So if you're describing something as an acid or base, you should say whether it's a **Brønsted-Lowry** or a **Lewis** acid or base.

## You Need to be Able to Spot **Lewis Acids and Bases**

*AQA only*

Have a look at these examples:

$H_2O + H^+ \rightarrow H_3O^+$ ⟹

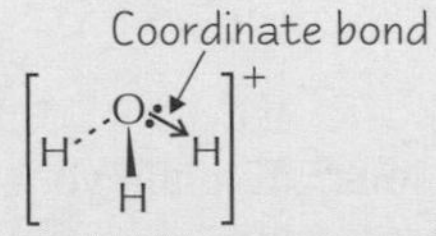


The water molecule's donating an electron pair to the hydrogen ion, and the hydrogen ion is accepting an electron pair from the water. So the water molecule is the Lewis base and the hydrogen ion's the Lewis acid.

$AlCl_3 + Cl^- \rightarrow AlCl_4^-$ ⟹

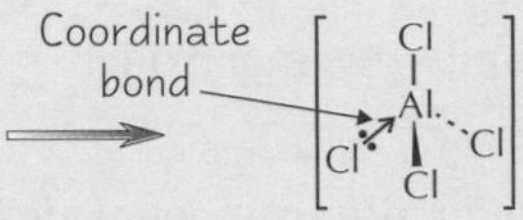


The aluminium chloride is accepting an electron pair — so it's the Lewis acid.
The chloride ion is donating an electron pair — so it's the Lewis base.

**Coordinate bonds** always involve one substance donating an electron pair to another. So if there's a coordinate bond, there are no two ways about it — it **must** have been formed in a **Lewis acid-base reaction.**

They're **not** Brønsted-Lowry acids because they can't donate a proton ($H^+$).

Metal ions act as **Lewis acids** in aqueous solution because they **accept electron pairs** from the water molecules that surround them. And the water molecules, like any **ligands**, are **electron pair donors** so they must be **Lewis bases.**

# Metal-Aqua Ions

## Solutions Containing *Metal-Aqua Ions* are *Acidic*

*AQA only*

In a solution containing metal-aqua **2+** ions, there's a reaction between the metal-aqua ion and the water — this is a **hydrolysis** or **acidity reaction**.

E.g. $[Fe(H_2O)_6]^{2+}{}_{(aq)} + H_2O_{(l)} \rightleftharpoons [Fe(H_2O)_5(OH)]^{+}{}_{(aq)} + H_3O^{+}{}_{(aq)}$

Aqua-ironing — it keeps those flat fish smooth.

In these forward reactions, the **metal-aqua ion** is acting as a **Brønsted-Lowry acid**. It **donates a proton** from one of its water ligands to a free water molecule.

The metal-aqua **2+** ions release $H^+$ ions, so an **acidic** solution is formed. There's only **slight** dissociation though, so the solution is only **weakly acidic**.

Metal-aqua **3+** ions react in the same way. They form **more acidic** solutions though.

E.g. $[Al(H_2O)_6]^{3+}{}_{(aq)} + H_2O_{(l)} \rightleftharpoons [Al(H_2O)_5(OH)]^{2+}{}_{(aq)} + H_3O^{+}{}_{(aq)}$

**Here's why 3+ metal-aqua ions form more acidic solutions than 2+ metal-aqua ions:**
Metal 3+ ions are pretty **small** but have a **big charge** — so they've got a **high charge density** (otherwise known as **charge/size ratio**). The metal 2+ ions have a **much lower** charge density.

This makes the 3+ ions much more **polarising** than the 2+ ions. More polarising power means that they attract **electrons** from the oxygen atoms of the coordinated water molecules more strongly, weakening the O–H bond.

So it's more likely that a **hydrogen ion** will be released. And more hydrogen ions means a **more acidic** solution.

## Adding *Alkali* to Metal-Aqua Ions *Forms Precipitates*

Adding **$OH^-$ ions** to solutions of **metal-aqua ions** produces **insoluble metal hydroxides**.
Here's why:

M might be Fe, Al or Cr.

1) In water, **metal-aqua 3+ ions** form the equilibrium: $[M(H_2O)_6]^{3+}{}_{(aq)} + H_2O_{(l)} \rightleftharpoons [M(H_2O)_5(OH)]^{2+}{}_{(aq)} + H_3O^{+}{}_{(aq)}$.
If you add **$OH^-$ ions** to the equilibrium **$H_3O^+$ ions** are removed — this shifts the equilibrium to the **right**.
2) Now another equilibrium is set up in the solution: $[M(H_2O)_5(OH)]^{2+}{}_{(aq)} + H_2O_{(l)} \rightleftharpoons [M(H_2O)_4(OH)_2]^{+}{}_{(aq)} + H_3O^{+}{}_{(aq)}$.
Again the $OH^-$ ions remove $H_3O^+$ ions from the solution, pulling the equilibrium to the right.
3) This happens one last time — now you're left with an **insoluble uncharged metal hydroxide**:
$[M(H_2O)_4(OH)_2]^{+}{}_{(aq)} + H_2O_{(l)} \rightleftharpoons M(H_2O)_3(OH)_{3(s)} + H_3O^{+}{}_{(aq)}$.

The same thing happens with **metal-aqua 2+ ions** (e.g. Fe, Co or Cu), except this time there are only **two** steps:
$[M(H_2O)_6]^{2+}{}_{(aq)} + H_2O_{(l)} \rightleftharpoons [M(H_2O)_5(OH)]^{+}{}_{(aq)} + H_3O^{+}{}_{(aq)} \longrightarrow [M(H_2O)_5(OH)]^{+}{}_{(aq)} + H_2O_{(l)} \rightleftharpoons M(H_2O)_4(OH)_{2(s)} + H_3O^{+}{}_{(aq)}$

**All** the metal hydroxide precipitates **will dissolve in acid**. They act as Brønsted-Lowry bases and **accept $H^+$ ions**. This **reverses** the **hydrolysis** reactions above.

Some metal hydroxides are **amphoteric** — they can act as both acids and bases. This means they'll **dissolve in an excess of base** as well as in **acids**. **Aluminium hydroxide** and **chromium(III) hydroxide** are **amphoteric**. They act as **Brønsted-Lowry acids** and **donate $H^+$ ions** to the $OH^-$ ions, forming **soluble compounds**.

$Al(H_2O)_3(OH)_{3(s)} + OH^-{}_{(aq)} \rightleftharpoons [Al(H_2O)_2(OH)_4]^-{}_{(aq)} + H_2O_{(l)}$ $\quad$ $Cr(OH)_3(H_2O)_{3(s)} + 3OH^-{}_{(aq)} \rightleftharpoons [Cr(OH)_6]^{3-}{}_{(aq)} + 3H_2O_{(l)}$

## *Precipitates* Form with *Sodium Hydroxide* and *Ammonia Solution*...

The obvious way of adding hydroxide ions is to use a strong alkali, like **sodium hydroxide solution** — but you can use **ammonia solution** too. When ammonia dissolves in water this equilibrium occurs: $NH_3 + H_2O \rightleftharpoons NH_4^+ + OH^-$
Because $OH^-$ ions are formed, adding a **small** amount of $NH_3$ solution gives the same results as NaOH.

In some cases, a further reaction happens if you add an **excess** of ammonia solution — the $H_2O$ and $OH^-$ ligands are displaced by $NH_3$ ligands. Have a look at the table on the next page to see which complexes this applies to.

## ...and *Sodium Carbonate* Too

*AQA only*

**Metal 2+** ions react with **sodium carbonate** to form **insoluble metal carbonates**, like this: $M(H_2O)_6^{2+}{}_{(aq)} + CO_3^{2-}{}_{(aq)} \rightleftharpoons MCO_{3(s)} + 6H_2O_{(l)}$

But, **metal 3+** ions are stronger acids so they always form **hydroxide precipitates** when you add sodium carbonate. The **carbonate ions** react with the **$H_3O^+$** ions, removing them from the solution just like $OH^-$ ions do.
So you only get $M(H_2O)_3(OH)_{3(s)}$ formed and not $M_2(CO_3)_3$.

# Metal-Aqua Ions

## Learn the Colours of All the Complex Ion Solutions and Precipitates

This handy table summarises all the compounds that are formed in the reactions on these pages. You need to know the **formulas** of all the complex ions (so you can write **ionic equations**), and their **colours**.

If you're doing ***OCR A***, you only need the **first two columns** and **first four rows** of the table.

| Metal-aqua ion | With $OH^-_{(aq)}$ or $NH_{3(aq)}$ | With excess $OH^-_{(aq)}$ | With excess $NH_{3(aq)}$ | With $Na_2CO_{3(aq)}$ (*AQA only*) |
|---|---|---|---|---|
| $[Co(H_2O)_6]^{2+}$ pink solution | $Co(H_2O)_4(OH)_2$ blue-green precipitate | no change | $[Co(NH_3)_6]^{2+}$ straw coloured solution | $CoCO_3$ pink precipitate |
| $[Cu(H_2O)_6]^{2+}$ blue solution | $Cu(H_2O)_4(OH)_2$ blue precipitate | no change | $[Cu(NH_3)_4(H_2O)_2]^{2+}$ deep blue solution | $CuCO_3$ green-blue precipitate |
| $[Fe(H_2O)_6]^{2+}$ green solution | $Fe(H_2O)_4(OH)_2$ green precipitate | no change | no change | $FeCO_3$ green precipitate |
| $[Fe(H_2O)_6]^{3+}$ yellow solution | $Fe(H_2O)_3(OH)_3$ brown precipitate | no change | no change | $Fe(H_2O)_3(OH)_3$ brown precipitate |
| $[Al(H_2O)_6]^{3+}$ colourless solution | $Al(H_2O)_3(OH)_3$ white precipitate | $[Al(H_2O)_2(OH)_4]^-$ colourless solution | no change | $Al(H_2O)_3(OH)_3$ white precipitate |
| $[Cr(H_2O)_6]^{3+}$ violet solution | $Cr(H_2O)_3(OH)_3$ green precipitate | $[Cr(OH)_6]^{3-}$ green solution | $[Cr(NH_3)_6]^{3+}$ purple solution | $Cr(H_2O)_3(OH)_3$ green precipitate |
| *Edexcel only:* $[Mn(H_2O)_6]^{2+}$ very pale pink solution | $Mn(H_2O)_4(OH)_2$ brown precipitate | no change | no change | |
| *Edexcel only:* $[Ni(H_2O)_6]^{2+}$ green solution | $Ni(H_2O)_4(OH)_2$ green precipitate | no change | $[Ni(NH_3)_6]^{2+}$ blue solution | |
| *Edexcel only:* $[Zn(H_2O)_6]^{2+}$ colourless solution | $Zn(H_2O)_3(OH)_3$ white precipitate | $[Zn(OH)_4]^{2-}$ colourless solution | $[Zn(NH_3)_4]^{2+}$ colourless solution | |

If you're doing ***Edexcel***, you can ignore the **cobalt** row at the top.

## Practice Questions

Q1 Explain why $AlCl_3$ can act as a Lewis acid.

Q2 Show by equations how $Al(OH)_3$ can act as both a Brønsted-Lowry acid and a Brønsted-Lowry base.

Q3 What colour solution is formed when you add excess ammonia to a solution containing $[Co(H_2O)_6]^{2+}$ ions?

**Exam Questions**

1 Explain why separate solutions of iron(II) sulfate and iron(III) sulfate with equal concentrations have different pH values. [4 marks]

2 Describe what you would see when ammonia solution is added slowly to a solution containing copper(II) sulfate until it is in excess. Write equations for each reaction that occurs. [8 marks]

3 Aqueous ammonia was added to an aqueous solution of chromium(III) sulfate.
a) Identify the chromium complex ion present in:
i) the aqueous chromium(III) sulfate. [1 mark]
ii) the green precipitate initially formed when aqueous ammonia is added. [1 mark]
iii) the purple solution when an excess of aqueous ammonia is added. [1 mark]
b) Write an equation for the reaction in which the purple solution is formed from the green precipitate. [1 mark]

4 a) Describe what you would observe when aqueous sodium carbonate is added to:
i) aqueous iron(III) chloride. [1 mark]
ii) freshly-prepared aqueous iron(II) sulfate. [1 mark]
b) Write an equation for the reaction of the iron(II)-aqua ion with the carbonate ion. [1 mark]
c) If iron(II) sulfate solution is left to stand overnight in an open beaker before the aqueous sodium carbonate is added, then a different reaction is observed.
i) Describe the new observation. [1 mark]
ii) Explain this change. [1 mark]

## Test tube reactions — proper chemistry at last...

*So many pretty colours. The only downside is that you have to remember them. But examiners do love to ask questions about colours of solutions and precipitates. So learn them all, or come exam day you'll end up feeling blue. Or possibly blue-green...*

# Substitution Reactions

*There are more equations on this page than the number of elephants you can fit in a Mini.*
***These pages are for AQA (Unit 5), OCR A (Unit 5) and Edexcel (Unit 5).***

## Ligands can Change Places with One Another

One ligand can be **swapped** for another ligand — this is **ligand exchange**. It pretty much always causes a **colour change**.

1) If the ligands are of **similar size**, e.g. $H_2O$ and $NH_3$, then the **coordination number** of the complex ion doesn't change, and neither does the **shape**.

$[Co(H_2O)_6]^{2+}_{(aq)} + 6NH_{3(aq)} \rightarrow [Co(NH_3)_6]^{2+}_{(aq)} + 6H_2O_{(l)}$
octahedral, pink → octahedral, straw coloured

$[Cr(H_2O)_6]^{3+}_{(aq)} + 6OH^-_{(aq)} \rightarrow [Cr(OH)_6]^{3-}_{(aq)} + 6H_2O_{(l)}$
octahedral, violet → octahedral, green

2) If the ligands are **different sizes**, e.g. $H_2O$ and $Cl^-$, there's a **change of coordination number** and a **change of shape**.

$[Cu(H_2O)_6]^{2+}_{(aq)} + 4Cl^-_{(aq)} \rightleftharpoons [CuCl_4]^{2-}_{(aq)} + 6H_2O_{(l)}$
octahedral, pale blue → tetrahedral, yellow

$[Co(H_2O)_6]^{2+}_{(aq)} + 4Cl^-_{(aq)} \rightleftharpoons [CoCl_4]^{2-}_{(aq)} + 6H_2O_{(l)}$
octahedral, pink → tetrahedral, blue

The forward reaction is endothermic, so the equilibrium can be shifted to the right-hand side by heating. The equilibrium will also shift to the right if you add more concentrated hydrochloric acid. Adding water to this equilibrium shifts it back to the left.

3) Sometimes the substitution is only **partial**.

$[Cu(H_2O)_6]^{2+}_{(aq)} + 4NH_{3(aq)} \rightarrow [Cu(NH_3)_4(H_2O)_2]^{2+}_{(aq)} + 4H_2O_{(l)}$
octahedral, pale blue → elongated octahedral, deep blue

$[Fe(H_2O)_6]^{3+}_{(aq)} + SCN^-_{(aq)} \rightarrow [Fe(H_2O)_5SCN]^{2+}_{(aq)} + H_2O_{(l)}$
octahedral, pale violet when pure (but this usually looks yellow) → distorted octahedral, blood red

Have a quick peek back at the reactions on the last page — these were **ligand exchange reactions** too. In these, **hydroxide precipitates** were formed when a little bit of **sodium hydroxide** or **ammonia solution** was added to metal-aqua ions. The hydroxide precipitates sometimes **dissolved** when excess sodium hydroxide or ammonia solution was added.

## A Positive Entropy Change Makes a More Stable Complex

***AQA and Edexcel only***

When a **ligand exchange reaction** occurs, bonds are **broken** and **formed**.
The **strength** of the bonds being broken is often very similar to the strength of the new bonds being made.
So the **enthalpy change** for a ligand exchange reaction is usually very **small**.

***Example:*** Substituting ammonia with ethane-1,2-diamine in a nickel complex:

$[Ni(NH_3)_6]^{2+}_{(aq)} + 3NH_2CH_2CH_2NH_{2(aq)} \rightarrow [Ni(NH_2CH_2CH_2NH_2)_3]^{2+}_{(aq)} + 6NH_{3(aq)}$ $\Delta H = -13$ kJ mol$^{-1}$

Break 6 coordinate bonds between Ni and N → Form 6 coordinate bonds between Ni and N

This is actually a **reversible** reaction, but the equilibrium lies so **far to the right** that it is thought of as being irreversible. $[Ni(NH_2CH_2CH_2NH_2)_3]^{2+}$ is **much more stable** than $[Ni(NH_3)_6]^{2+}$. This isn't accounted for by an enthalpy change, but an **increase in entropy** explains it:

When unidentate ligands are substituted with bidentate or multidentate ligands, the number of particles increases — the **more particles**, the **greater the entropy**. Reactions that result in an increase in entropy are **more likely** to occur. This is known as the **chelate effect**.

In the reaction above the number of particles increased from 4 to 7.

So that's why multidentate ligands always form much more stable complexes than unidentate ligands.

When the **hexadentate ligand EDTA⁴⁻** replaces unidentate or bidentate ligands, the complex formed is **loads more stable**.

$[Cr(NH_3)_6]^{3+}_{(aq)} + EDTA^{4-}_{(aq)} \rightarrow [Cr(EDTA)]^-_{(aq)} + 6NH_{3(aq)}$ **2 particles → 7 particles**

$[Cr(NH_2CH_2CH_2NH_2)_3]^{3+}_{(aq)} + EDTA^{4-}_{(aq)} \rightarrow [Cr(EDTA)]^-_{(aq)} + 3NH_2CH_2CH_2NH_{2(aq)}$ **2 particles → 4 particles**

It's difficult to reverse these reactions, because reversing them would cause a **decrease in entropy**.

# Substitution Reactions

## Stability Constants are Special Equilibrium Constants

*OCR A only*

The **stability constant of a complex ion** is just what it sounds like — it tells you how stable a complex ion is in solution.

The **stability constant**, $K_{stab}$, of a **complex ion** is the **equilibrium constant** for the **formation** of the complex ion from its **constituent ions** in solution.

For a reminder about equilibrium constants, look back at page 26.

**Example:** Write an expression for the stability constant for the formation of the complex ion $[Fe(CN)_6]^{4-}$

Here is the equation for the formation of this ion in solution:

$$Fe^{2+}_{(aq)} + 6CN^-_{(aq)} \rightleftharpoons [Fe(CN)_6]^{4-}_{(aq)}$$

So the stability constant for this reaction is: $K_{stab} = \dfrac{[(Fe(CN)_6)^{4-}]}{[Fe^{2+}][CN^-]^6}$

The square brackets in the $K_{stab}$ expression mean 'the concentrations of the ions'. Don't mix them up with the square brackets you'd use in the formula of a complex ion — they just keep everything together.

1) The stability constant, $K_{stab}$, is also used for ligand **substitutions** — these are always **reversible** reactions.
2) If the complex that you start with **only** has **water** ligands, **don't** include $[H_2O]$ in the stability constant expression. Since all the ions are in solution, there's so much water around that a few extra molecules doesn't make any difference.
3) The **larger** the stability constant, the **more stable** the new complex ion is, and the more **likely** it is to form.

**Example:** Write an expression for the stability constant, $K_{stab}$, of the following ligand substitution reaction:

$$[Cu(H_2O)_6]^{2+}_{(aq)} + 4Cl^-_{(aq)} \rightleftharpoons [CuCl_4]^{2-}_{(aq)} + 6H_2O_{(l)}$$

$$K_{stab} = \frac{[(CuCl_4)^{2-}]}{[(Cu(H_2O)_6)^{2+}][Cl^-]^4}$$

Remember that you don't need to include $[H_2O]$ in the expression.

## Practice Questions

Q1 Give an example of a ligand substitution reaction that involves a change of coordination number.

Q2 What is the chelate effect?

Q3 What does the size of the stability constant for a particular ligand substitution reaction tell you?

**Exam Questions**

1 An aqueous solution of copper sulfate contains the complex ion $[Cu(H_2O)_6]^{2+}$.

a) Write an equation for a ligand substitution reaction between $[Cu(H_2O)_6]^{2+}$ and chloride ions, in which all of the water ligands are replaced. Give the colour of the new complex formed. [3 marks]

b) The ethanedioate ion, $C_2O_4^{2-}$, is a bidentate ligand. Write an equation for a ligand substitution reaction between $[Cu(H_2O)_6]^{2+}$ and ethanedioate ions in which all of the water ligands are substituted. [2 marks]

c) $[Cu(H_2O)_6]^{2+}$ ions react with sodium hydroxide to form a precipitate. State the formula and colour of the complex ion contained in the precipitate. [2 marks]

2 When a solution of $EDTA^{4-}$ ions is added to an aqueous solution of $[Fe(H_2O)_6]^{3+}$ ions, a ligand substitution reaction occurs.

*You might need to check back to page 175 for some of these questions.*

a) Write an equation for the reaction that takes place. [2 marks]

b) The new complex that is formed is more stable than $[Fe(H_2O)_6]^{3+}$. Explain why. [2 marks]

c) Another sample of $[Fe(H_2O)_6]^{3+}$ solution is mixed with a dilute solution of sodium hydroxide. A brown precipitate forms. Give the formula of the complex ion contained in the precipitate. [1 mark]

3 A sample of copper(II) sulfate powder is dissolved in pure water, giving a pale blue solution.

a) Give the formula of the complex ion that is present in the pale blue solution. [1 mark]

b) When an excess of ammonia is added to the solution, its colour changes to deep blue.

i) Write a balanced equation for the ligand substitution reaction that has taken place. [2 marks]

ii) Write an expression for the stability constant of this ligand substitution reaction. [2 marks]

## My friend suffers from Nativity Play Phobia — he's got a stable complex...

*Four things to do with this page — One: learn what a ligand substitution reaction is. Two: make sure you understand the chelate effect. Three: learn the definition of and write expressions for $K_{stab}$. Four: fold it into a lovely origami crane.*

# Practical and Investigative Skills

*You're going to have to do some practical work too — and once you've done it, you have to make sense of your results...*

## *Make it a **Fair Test** — Control your **Variables***

You probably know this all off by heart but it's easy to get mixed up sometimes. So here's a quick recap:

**Variable** — A variable is a **quantity** that has the **potential to change**, e.g. mass.
There are two types of variable commonly referred to in experiments:

- **Independent variable** — the thing that you **change** in an experiment.
- **Dependent variable** — the thing that you **measure** in an experiment.

When drawing graphs, the dependent variable should go on the y-axis, the independent on the x-axis.

So, if you're investigating the effect of **temperature** on rate of reaction using the apparatus on the right, the variables will be:

| | |
|---|---|
| **Independent variable** | Temperature |
| **Dependent variable** | Amount of gas produced — you can measure this by collecting it in a gas syringe |
| **Other variables** — you MUST keep these the same | Concentration and volume of solutions, mass of solids, pressure, the presence of a catalyst and the surface area of any solid reactants |

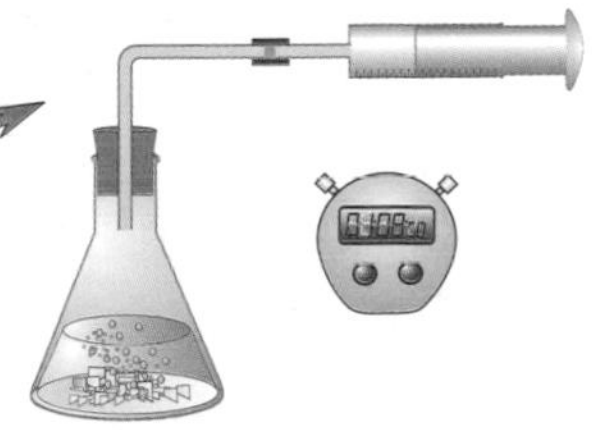

## *Know Your Different Sorts of **Data***

Experiments always involve some sort of measurement to provide **data**.
There are different types of data — and you need to know what they are.

**Discrete** — you get discrete data by **counting**. E.g. the number of bubbles produced in a reaction would be discrete. You can't have 1.25 bubbles. That'd be daft. Shoe size is another good example of a discrete variable.

**Continuous** — a continuous variable can have **any value** on a scale. For example, the volume of gas produced or the mass of products from a reaction. You can never measure the exact value of a continuous variable.

**Categoric** — a categoric variable has values that can be sorted into **categories**. For example, the colours of solutions might be blue, red and green. Or types of material might be wood, steel, glass.

**Ordered (ordinal)** — Ordered data is similar to categoric, but the categories can be **put in order**. For example, if you classify reactions as 'slow', 'fairly fast' and 'very fast' you'd have ordered data.

## *Organise Your Results in a **Table** — And Watch Out For **Anomalous** Ones*

Before you start your experiment, make a **table** to write your results in.
You'll need to repeat each test at least three times to check your results are reliable.

This is the sort of table you might end up with when you investigate the effect of **temperature** on **reaction rate**. (You'd then have to do the same for **different temperatures**.)

| Temperature | Time (s) | Volume of gas evolved ($cm^3$) Run 1 | Volume of gas evolved ($cm^3$) Run 2 | Volume of gas evolved ($cm^3$) Run 3 | Average volume of gas evolved ($cm^3$) |
|---|---|---|---|---|---|
| | **10** | 8 | 7 | 8 | **7.7** |
| **20 °C** | **20** | 17 | 19 | 20 | **18.7** |
| | **30** | 28 | 20 | 30 | **29** |

Find the average of each set of repeated values.

You need to add them all up and divide by how many there are.

E.g.: (8 + 7 + 8) ÷ 3 = 7.7 $cm^3$

Watch out for **anomalous results**. These are ones that don't fit in with the other values and are likely to be wrong. They're likely to be due to random errors — here the syringe plunger may have got stuck.

Ignore anomalous results when you calculate the average.

# Practical and Investigative Skills

## Graphs: *Line, Bar or Scatter — Use the Best Type*

You'll usually be expected to make a **graph** of your results. Not only are graphs **pretty**, they make your data **easier to understand** — so long as you choose the right type.

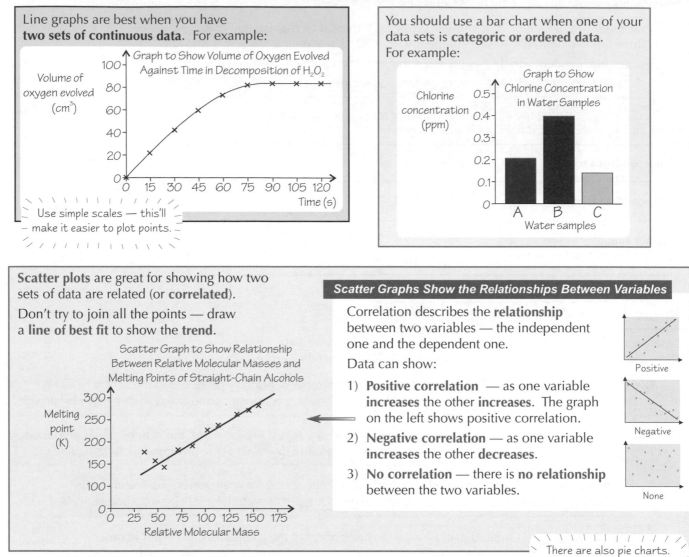

Line graphs are best when you have **two sets of continuous data**. For example:

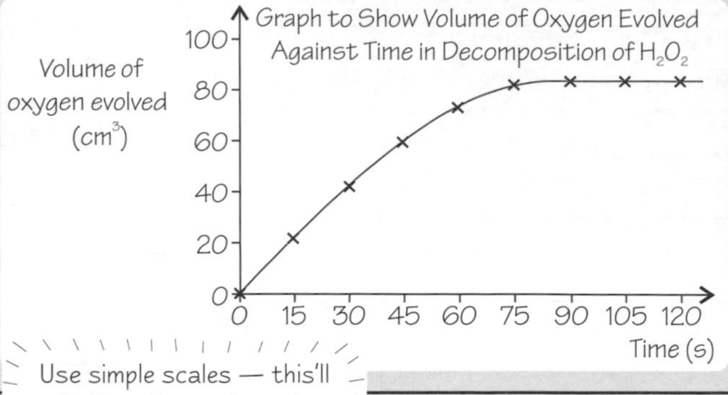


Use simple scales — this'll make it easier to plot points.

You should use a bar chart when one of your data sets is **categoric or ordered data**. For example:

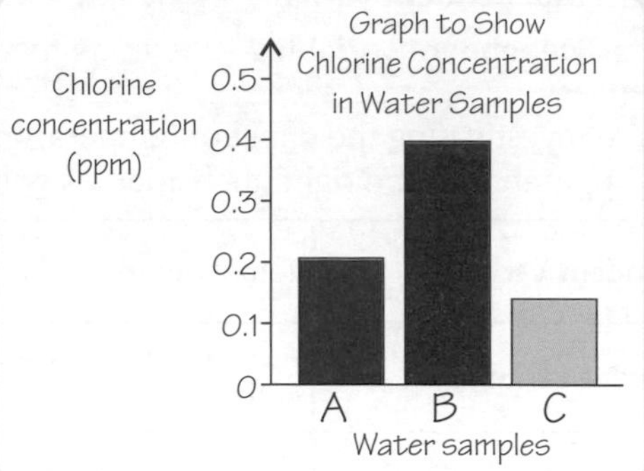


**Scatter plots** are great for showing how two sets of data are related (or **correlated**).

Don't try to join all the points — draw a **line of best fit** to show the **trend**.

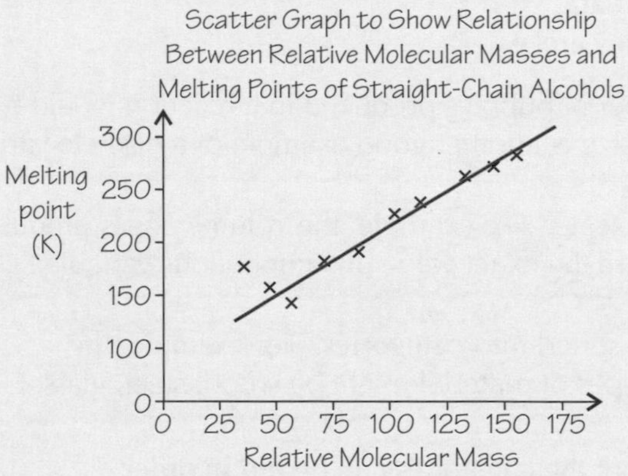


### Scatter Graphs Show the Relationships Between Variables

Correlation describes the **relationship** between two variables — the independent one and the dependent one.

Data can show:

1) **Positive correlation** — as one variable **increases** the other **increases**. The graph on the left shows positive correlation.
2) **Negative correlation** — as one variable **increases** the other **decreases**.
3) **No correlation** — there is **no relationship** between the two variables.

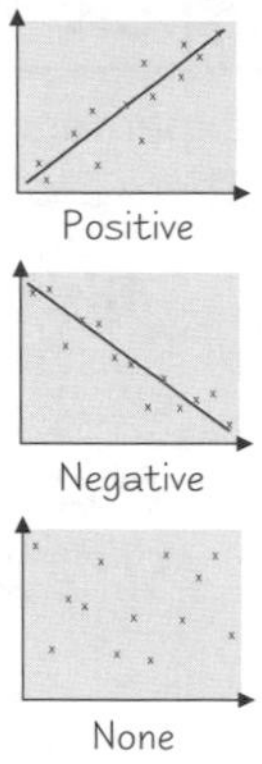


There are also pie charts. These are normally used to display categoric data.

**Whatever type of graph you make, you'll ONLY get full marks if you:**

- Choose a sensible scale — don't do a tiny graph in the corner of the paper.
- Label both axes — including units.
- Plot your points accurately — using a sharp pencil.

## *Correlation* **Doesn't Necessarily** *Mean* **Cause** *— Don't Jump to Conclusions*

1) Ideally, only **two** quantities would **ever** change in any experiment — everything else would remain **constant**.
2) But in experiments or studies outside the lab, you **can't** usually control all the variables. So even if two variables are correlated, the change in one may **not** be causing the change in the other. Both changes might be caused be a **third variable**.

Watch out for bias too — for instance, a bottled water company might point these studies out to people without mentioning any of the doubts.

**Example**

For example: Some studies have found a correlation between **drinking chlorinated tap water** and the risk of developing certain cancers. So some people argue that this means water shouldn't have chlorine added.

**BUT** it's hard to control all the variables (e.g. lifestyle factors) between people who do drink tap water and people who don't.

Or, the cancer risk could be affected by something else in tap water — or by whatever the non-tap water drinkers drink instead...

# Practical and Investigative Skills

## Don't Get **Carried Away** When Drawing Conclusions

The **data** should always **support** the conclusion. This may sound obvious but it's easy to **jump** to conclusions. Conclusions have to be **specific** — not make sweeping generalisations.

**Example**

The rate of an enzyme-controlled reaction was measured at **10 °C, 20 °C, 30 °C, 40 °C, 50 °C and 60 °C**. All other variables were kept constant, and the results are shown in this graph.

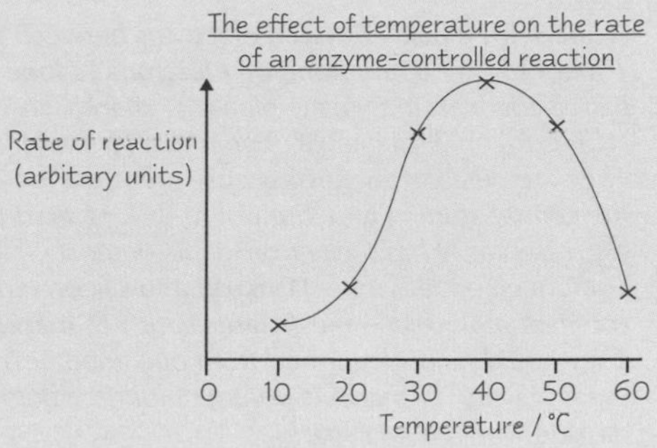


A science magazine **concluded** from this data that enzyme X works best at **40 °C**. The data **doesn't** support this.

The enzyme **could** work best at 42 °C or 47 °C but you can't tell from the data because **increases** of **10 °C** at a time were used. The rate of reaction at in-between temperatures **wasn't** measured.

All you know is that it's faster at **40 °C** than at any of the other temperatures tested.

**Example**

The experiment above **ONLY** gives information about this particular enzyme-controlled reaction. You can't conclude that **all** enzyme-controlled reactions happen faster at a particular temperature — only this one. And you can't say for sure that doing the experiment at, say, a different constant pressure, wouldn't give a different optimum temperature.

## You Need to Look **Critically** at Your Results

There are a few bits of lingo that you need to understand. They'll be useful when you're evaluating how convincing your results are.

1) **Valid results** — Valid results answer the original question. For example, if you haven't **controlled all the variables** your results won't be valid, because you won't be testing just the thing you wanted to.

2) **Accurate** — Accurate results are those that are **really close** to the **true** answer.

3) **Precise results** — These are results taken using **sensitive instruments** that measure in **small increments**, e.g. pH measured with a meter (pH 7.692) will be **more precise** than pH measured with paper (pH 7).

It's possible for results to be precise **but not** accurate, e.g. a balance that weighs to 1/1000 th of a gram will give precise results but if it's not **calibrated** properly the results won't be accurate.

You may have to calculate the percentage error of a measurement.
E.g. if a balance is calibrated to within 0.1 g, and you measure a mass as 4 g, then the percentage error is: $(0.1 \div 4) \times 100 = 2.5\%$.
Using a larger quantity reduces the percentage error. E.g. a mass of 40 g has a percentage error of: $(0.1 \div 40) \times 100 = 0.25\%$.

4) **Reliable results** — **Reliable** means the results can be **consistently reproduced** in independent experiments. And if the results are reproducible they're more likely to be **true**. If the data isn't reliable for whatever reason you **can't draw** a valid **conclusion**.

For experiments, the **more repeats** you do, the **more reliable** the data. If you get the **same result** twice, it could be the correct answer. But if you get the same result **20 times**, it'd be much more reliable. And it'd be even more reliable if everyone in the class got about the same results using different apparatus.

## Work **Safely** and **Ethically** — Don't Blow Up the Lab or Harm Small Animals

In any experiment you'll be expected to show that you've thought about the **risks and hazards**. It's generally a good thing to wear a lab coat and goggles, but you may need to take additional safety measures, depending on the experiment. For example, anything involving nasty gases will need to be done in a fume cupboard.

You need to make sure you're working **ethically** too. This is most important if there are other people or animals involved. You have to put their welfare first.

# Answers

## Section 1 — Elements and Bonding

### Page 5 — The Periodic Table and Bonding

1 a)

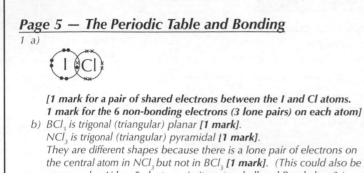

**[1 mark for a pair of shared electrons between the I and Cl atoms. 1 mark for the 6 non-bonding electrons (3 lone pairs) on each atom]**

b) *$BCl_3$ is trigonal (triangular) planar* ***[1 mark]****.*
*$NCl_3$ is trigonal (triangular) pyramidal* ***[1 mark]****.*
*They are different shapes because there is a lone pair of electrons on the central atom in $NCl_3$ but not in $BCl_3$* ***[1 mark]****. (This could also be expressed as N has 5 electrons in its outer shell and B only has 3.)*

c) *Sodium chloride is ionic* ***[1 mark]*** *and silicon dioxide giant covalent (or giant molecular – must state 'giant')* ***[1 mark]****.*
*They could be distinguished from one another by trying to dissolve them in water* ***[1 mark]****. Sodium chloride would dissolve but silicon dioxide would not* ***[1 mark]****.*
*(Alternatively testing the electrical conductivity of their molten state* ***[1 mark]*** *– liquid sodium chloride conducts but silicon dioxide does not* ***[1 mark]****.)*
When a question asks you to describe a test, it's important to state the results of the test and what the results tell you. Don't just name a test — you won't get full marks.

### Page 7 — Electronegativity and Intermolecular Forces

1 a)

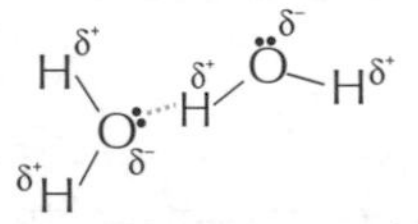


**[1 mark for hydrogen bond shown between O of one molecule and H on the other, and 1 mark for $\delta^+$ on all H atoms and $\delta^-$ on both oxygen atoms]**

b) *Permanent dipole-permanent dipole bonding* ***[1 mark]***

2 a) *Oxygen* ***[1 mark]*** *Electronegativity decreases as you move down a group (and S is beneath O in Group 6)* ***[1 mark]****.*

b)

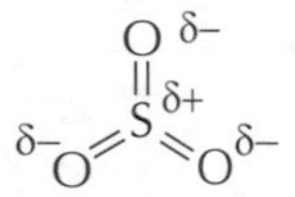


**[1 mark for $\delta^+$ on the S atom, 1 mark for $\delta^-$ on all three O atoms]**

c) *$SO_3$ is non-polar overall* ***[1 mark]****. The three polar S=O bonds point in different directions, so their polarities cancel each other out* ***[1 mark]****.*

## Section 2 — Kinetics

### Page 9 — Rate Graphs and Orders

1 a) *1st order* ***[1 mark]***

b)

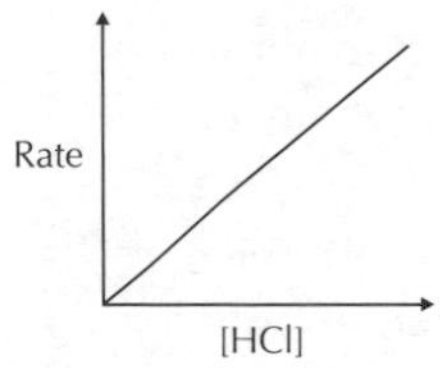


**[1 mark for correctly labelled axes, 1 mark for straight line passing through the origin]**

c) *The volume* ***[1 mark]*** *of hydrogen gas produced in a unit time* ***[1 mark]****.*
*OR*
*The reduction of mass* ***[1 mark]*** *due to the gas given off in a unit time* ***[1 mark]****.*

2 a) *E.g. Gas volume of $O_{2(g)}$* ***[1 mark]*** *using, e.g. a gas syringe* ***[1 mark]****.*

b)

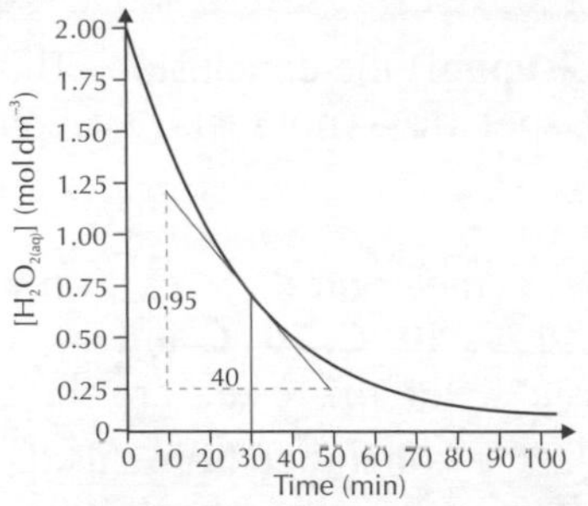


**[1 mark for $[H_2O_{2(aq)}]$ on y-axis and time on x-axis. 1 mark for points accurately plotted. 1 mark for best-fit smooth curve. 1 mark for tangent to curve at 30 minutes.]**
*Rate after 30 minutes = $0.95 \div 40 \approx 0.024$ mol dm$^{-3}$ min$^{-1}$*
**[1 mark for rate within range 0.024 ± 0.01, 1 mark for units]**

### Page 11 — Initial Rates and Half-Life

1 *Comparing experiments 1 and 2: when [D] is doubled and [E] is kept constant the initial rate quadruples* ***[1 mark]****. So the reaction is 2nd order with respect to [D]* ***[1 mark]****.*
*Comparing experiments 1 and 3: when [E] doubles and [D] is kept constant the initial rate doubles* ***[1 mark]****. So the reaction is 1st order with respect to [E]* ***[1 mark]****.*
Always explain your reasoning carefully — state which concentrations are constant and which are changing.

2 a)

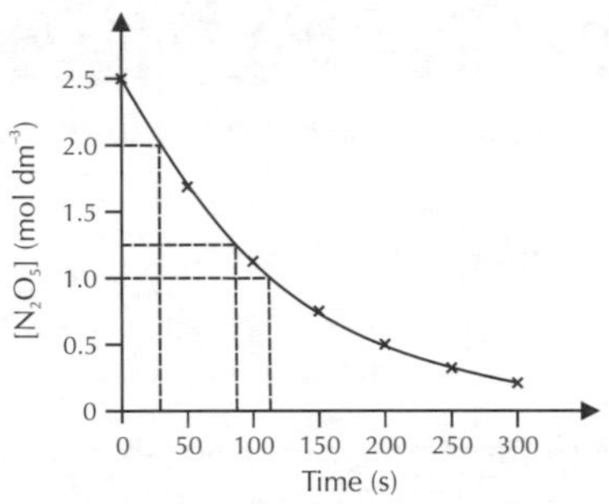


**[1 mark for $[N_2O_5]$ on y-axis and time on x-axis, 1 mark for points plotted accurately, 1 mark for best-fit smooth curve]**

b) i) *Time value = 85 s*
**[1 mark for horizontal dotted line from 1.25 on y-axis to curve and vertical dotted line from curve to x-axis. 1 mark for correct time, allow 85 ± 2]**

ii) *Time value for $[N_2O_5]$ = 2.0 mol dm$^{-3}$: 113 s*
*Time value for $[N_2O_5]$ = 1.0 mol dm$^{-3}$: 28 s*
*Time value difference = 113 – 28 = 85*
**[1 mark for vertical dotted lines from curve at 2.0 mol dm$^{-3}$ and at 1.0 mol dm$^{-3}$. 1 mark for correct time difference, allow 85 ± 4]**

c) *The order of reaction = 1* ***[1 mark]*** *because the half-life of ≈ 85 s is independent of concentration* ***[1 mark]****.*

### Page 13 — Rate Equations

1 a) *Rate = $k[NO_{(g)}]^2[H_{2(g)}]$*
**[2 marks, otherwise 1 mark for correct equation apart from incorrect orders of reactants]**

b) i) *$0.00267 = k \times (0.004)^2 \times 0.002$* ***[1 mark]***
*$k = 0.00267 \div (3.2 \times 10^{-8}) = 83\,437.5$*
*Units: $k$ = mol dm$^{-3}$ s$^{-1}$ ÷ [(mol dm$^{-3}$)$^2$ × (mol dm$^{-3}$)] = mol$^{-2}$ dm$^6$ s$^{-1}$*
*$k = 0.00267 \div (3.2 \times 10^{-8}) = 83\,437.5$ dm$^6$ mol$^{-2}$ s$^{-1}$*
*(or $k = 8.34 \times 10^4$ dm$^6$ mol$^{-2}$ s$^{-1}$)*
**[1 mark for answer, 1 mark for units]**

ii) *It would decrease* ***[1 mark]****.*
If the temperature decreases, the rate decreases too.
A lower rate means a lower rate constant.

# Answers

2 a) Rate = $k[CH_3COOC_2H_5][H^+]$ **[1 mark]**

b) $2.2 \times 10^{-3} = k \times 0.25 \times 2.0$ **[1 mark]**

$k = 2.2 \times 10^{-3} \div 0.5 = 4.4 \times 10^{-3}$ **[1 mark]**

Units: $k = (mol\ dm^{-3}\ s^{-1}) \div [(mol\ dm^{-3}) \times (mol\ dm^{-3})] = mol^{-1}\ dm^{3}\ s^{-1}$

**[1 mark for answer, 1 mark for units]**

c) If the volume doubles, the concentration of each reactant halves to become 1 mol $dm^{-3}$ and 0.125 mol $dm^{-3}$ respectively **[1 mark]**.

So the rate = $4.4 \times 10^{-3} \times 1 \times 0.125 = 5.5 \times 10^{-4}$ mol $dm^{-3}$ $s^{-1}$ **[1 mark]**.

3 The rate equation is: Rate = $k[X][Y]$ **[1 mark]**

Rate is proportional to [X], so increasing [X] by 3.33% increases the rate by 3.33% also **[1 mark]**.

However, increasing the temperature by 10 K doubles the rate.

So temperature has a greater effect **[1 mark]**.

## Page 15 — Rates and Reaction Mechanisms

1 a) rate = $k[H_2][ICl]$ **[1 mark]**

b) i) One molecule of $H_2$ and one molecule of ICl **[1 mark]**.

If the molecule is in the rate equation, it must be in the rate-determining step **[1 mark]**.

ii) Incorrect **[1 mark]**. $H_2$ and ICl are both in the rate equation, so they must both be in the rate-determining step OR the order of the reaction with respect to ICl is 1, so there must be only one molecule of ICl in the rate-determining step **[1 mark]**.

2 a) The rate equation is first order with respect to HBr and $O_2$ **[1 mark]**

So only 1 molecule of HBr (and $O_2$) is involved in the rate-determining step **[1 mark]**

There must be more steps as 4 molecules of HBr are in the equation **[1 mark]**.

b) $HBr + O_2 \rightarrow HBrO_2$ (rate-determining step) **[1 mark]**

$HBr + HBrO_2 \rightarrow 2HBrO$ **[1 mark]**

$HBr + HBrO \rightarrow H_2O + Br_2$ **[1 mark]**

$HBr + HBrO \rightarrow H_2O + Br_2$ **[1 mark]**

Part b) is pretty tricky — you need to do a fair bit of detective work and some trial and error. Make sure you use all of the clues in the question...

## Page 17 — Rate Calculations

1 a) Comparing experiments 1 and 3: when [X] is doubled and [Y] is kept constant, the initial rate also doubles **[1 mark]**. So the reaction is 1st order with respect to [X] **[1 mark]**.

b) Comparing experiments 1 and 2: trebling [Y] increases the rate by a factor of 9 **[1 mark]**. $9 = 3^2$, so the reaction is 2nd order with respect to [Y] **[1 mark]**.

c) rate = $k[X][Y]^2$ **[1 mark]**

## Page 19 — Activation Energy

1 a) Activation energy is the minimum amount of energy particles need to react **[1 mark]**.

b) i)

| T | $k$ | 1/T | ln $k$ |
|---|---|---|---|
| 305 | 0.181 | 0.00328 | –1.709 |
| 313 | 0.468 | **0.00319** | **–0.759** |
| 323 | 1.34 | **0.00310** | **0.293** |
| 333 | 3.29 | 0.00300 | 1.191 |
| 344 | 10.1 | **0.00291** | **2.313** |
| 353 | 22.7 | 0.00283 | 3.122 |

**[1 mark for all 3 1/T values, 1 mark for all 3 ln k values]**

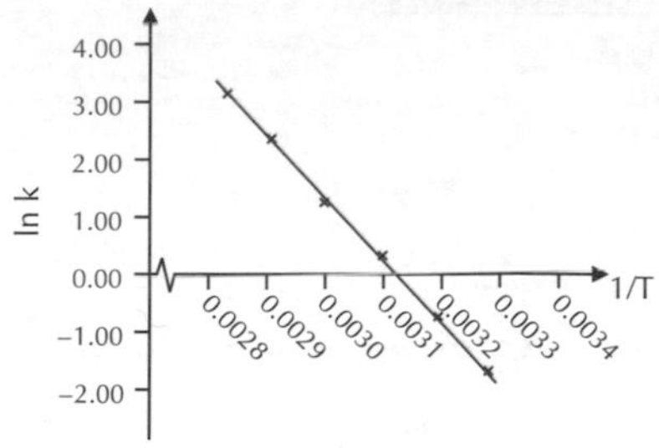


**[1 mark for at least 5 points plotted accurately, 1 mark for line of best fit]**

ii) Any correct determination of gradient **[1 mark]**

Value = – 10750 ± 250 **[1 mark]**

iii) Gradient of graph in part (i) = $-E_a/R = -10750$ **[1 mark]**.

$E_a = 10750 \times 8.31$ **[1 mark]**

= 89 333 J $mol^{-1}$ OR 89.3 kJ $mol^{-1}$ **[1 mark]**

## Page 21 — Catalysts

1 a) Rate = $k[CH_3CH_2CH_2Br][OH^-]$ **[1 mark for each correct term, including rate constant]**. The reaction is second order overall **[1 mark]**.

b) When all of the enzymes molecules are bound to reactant molecules (the enzyme is saturated) **[1 mark]**, adding more reactant can't make the reaction any faster because there are no enzyme molecules available to interact with the extra reactant **[1 mark]**.

## Page 23 — Halogenoalkanes and Reaction Mechanisms

1 D **[1 mark]**

1-chloropentane is a primary halogenoalkane which means it will reacts using an $S_N2$ mechanism. So both 1-chloropentane and sodium hydroxide must be in the rate equation, as the rate will depend on the concentration of both them.

2 A **[1 mark]**

A tertiary halogenoalkane reacts using an $S_N1$ mechanism. The rate determining step for an $S_N1$ mechanism is the dissociation of the halogenoalkane to form a carbocation.

3 a) 1-iodobutane is a primary iodoalkane **[1 mark]**

b) Rate = $k[CH_3CH_2CH_2CH_2I][OH^-]$ **[1 mark]**

c) Mechanism is $S_N2$

**[2 marks, otherwise 1 mark for $S_N$ or nucleophilic substitution]**

d)

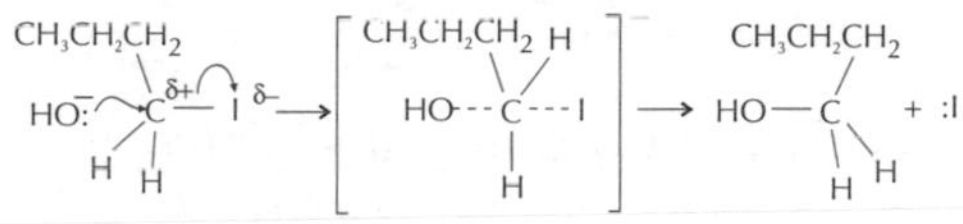


**[3 marks, 1 mark for each correct stage]**

## Section 3 — Equilibria

## Page 25 — Dynamic Equilibria

1 a) A dynamic equilibrium is one in which both forward and reverse reactions are still proceeding **[1 mark]** at the same rate **[1 mark]**.

b) i) The value of the equilibrium constant would be unchanged **[1 mark]** because the temperature remains constant **[1 mark]**.

ii) The value of the equilibrium constant would change **[1 mark]** because the temperature has changed **[1 mark]**.

Not enough information is given for you to say whether the value increases or decreases.

iii) $K_c = \frac{[PCl_3][Cl_2]}{[PCl_5]}$ **[1 mark]**

We know that for the reverse reaction at this temperature:

$K_c = \frac{[PCl_5]}{[PCl_3][Cl_2]}$ which has a numerical value of 125

So for this reaction, $K_c$ has a numerical value of $1 \div 125 = 0.08$ **[1 mark]**.

# Answers

## Page 27 — Equilibrium Constants

1
$$K_c = \frac{[H_2][I_2]}{[HI]^2} \textbf{ [1 mark]}$$

$$\Rightarrow [HI]^2 = \frac{[H_2][I_2]}{K_c} = \frac{2.0 \times 0.3}{0.0167} = 35.93 \textbf{ [1 mark]}$$

$$\Rightarrow [HI] = \sqrt{35.93} = 6.0 \text{ mol dm}^{-3}$$

The vessel has a volume of 1 $dm^3$ so there are 6 moles of HI **[1 mark]**.

2 a) i) mass/$M_r$ = 42.5/46 = 0.92 **[1 mark]**
ii) moles of $O_2$ = mass/$M_r$ = 14.1/32 = 0.44 **[1 mark]**
moles of NO = 2 × moles of $O_2$ = 0.88 **[1 mark]**
moles of $NO_2$ = 0.92 – 0.88 = 0.04 **[1 mark]**

b) Concentration of $O_2$ = 0.44 ÷ 22.8 = 0.019 mol $dm^{-3}$
Concentration of NO = 0.88 ÷ 22.8 = 0.039 mol $dm^{-3}$
Concentration of $NO_2$ = 0.04 ÷ 22.8 = 1.75 × $10^{-3}$ mol $dm^{-3}$
**[1 mark]**

$$K_c = \frac{[NO]^2[O_2]}{[NO_2]^2} \textbf{ [1 mark]}$$

$$\Rightarrow K_c = \frac{(0.039)^2 \times (0.019)}{(1.75 \times 10^{-3})^2} \textbf{ [1 mark]} = 9.4 \textbf{ [1 mark]} \text{ mol dm}^{-3} \textbf{ [1 mark]}$$

(Units = (mol $dm^{-3})^2$ × (mol $dm^{-3}$) /(mol $dm^{-3})^2$ = mol $dm^{-3}$)

## Page 29 — Gas Equilibria

1 a) $K_p = \frac{p(SO_2)p(Cl_2)}{p(SO_2Cl_2)}$ **[1 mark]**

b) $Cl_2$ and $SO_2$ are produced in equal amounts,
so $p(Cl_2) = p(SO_2)$ = 60.2 kPa **[1 mark]**
Total pressure = $p(SO_2Cl_2) + p(Cl_2) + p(SO_2)$ **[1 mark]**
so $p(SO_2Cl_2)$ = 141 – 60.2 – 60.2 = 20.6 kPa **[1 mark]**

c) $K_p = \frac{(60.2)(60.2)}{(20.6)}$ **[1 mark]** = 176 **[1 mark]** kPa **[1 mark]**
(Units = (kPa × kPa)/ kPa = kPa)

2 a) $p(O_2)$ = ½ × p(NO) **[1 mark]** = ½ × 36 = 18 kPa **[1 mark]**
b) $p(NO_2)$ = total pressure – p(NO) – $p(O_2)$ **[1 mark]**
= 99 – 36 – 18 = 45 kPa **[1 mark]**

c) $K_p = \frac{p(NO_2)^2}{p(NO)^2 p(O_2)}$ **[1 mark]** $= \frac{(45)^2}{(36)^2(18)}$ **[1 mark]**
= 0.0868 **[1 mark]** $kPa^{-1}$ **[1 mark]**
(Units = $kPa^2$/($kPa^2$ × kPa) = $kPa^{-1}$)

## Page 31 — Equilibrium Constants and Entropy

1 a) $\Delta S_{total}$ = 175.8 – (57 200 ÷ (273 + 60)) **[1 mark]** = 4.03 J $K^{-1}$ $mol^{-1}$ **[1 mark]**
b) lnK = $\Delta S_{total}$ ÷ R = 4.03 ÷ 8.31 = **[1 mark]** 0.484
K = $e^{0.484}$ =1.62 **[1 mark]**
c) $\Delta S_{total}$ = 175.8 – (57 200 ÷ 433) **[1 mark]** = 43.7 J $K^{-1}$ mol $^{1}$
**[1 mark]** lnK = $\Delta S_{total}$ ÷ R = 43.7 ÷ 8.31 = 5.26 **[1 mark]**
K = $e^{5.26}$ = 192.2 **[1 mark]**
d) At 60 °C the equilibrium is approximately balanced between product and reactant **[1 mark]**. The increase in temperature has shifted the position of equilibrium well over to the right **[1 mark]**.

## Page 33 — Le Chatelier's Principle

1 a) If the temperature of the system is increased, the position of equilibrium moves to the left **[1 mark]**. This decreases the equilibrium concentration of $CH_3OH_{(g)}$ **[1 mark]**.
b) If the pressure of the system is decreased, the position of equilibrium moves to the left **[1 mark]**. This decreases the equilibrium concentration of $CH_3OH_{(g)}$ **[1 mark]**.
c) A catalyst has no effect on the position of equilibrium **[1 mark]** so there is no change to the equilibrium concentration of $CH_3OH_{(g)}$ **[1 mark]**.

2 a) $T_2$ is lower than $T_1$ **[1 mark]**.
A decrease in temperature shifts the position of equilibrium in the exothermic direction, producing more product **[1 mark]**. More product means $K_p$ increases **[1 mark]**.
A negative ΔH means the forward direction's exothermic — it gives out heat.
b) The yield of $SO_3$ increases **[1 mark]**. (A decrease in volume means an increase in pressure. This shifts the equilibrium position to the right.) $K_p$ is unchanged **[1 mark]**.

## Page 35 — Equilibria in Industrial Processes

1 a) Lower temperatures would favour/increase the yield of the forward reaction, which is exothermic **[1 mark]**. The reaction would be too slow at lower temperatures **[1 mark]**, so the temperature is a compromise between maximum yield and a faster reaction **[1 mark]**.
b) Catalysts have no affect on product yield **[1 mark]**.
c) Any unreacted $SO_2$ and $O_2$ could be recycled back into the reaction vessel **[1 mark]**.
d) **Any two from the following, up to a maximum of 4 marks:**
- Whether the reaction will go **[1 mark]**.
The entropy changes involved must be greater than –100 J$K^{-1}mol^{-1}$ **[1 mark]**.
- How fast the reaction will go **[1 mark]**.
If a substance reacts too slowly, a catalyst may need to be added or the temperature or pressure of the reaction system may need to be increased **[1 mark]**.
- The potential to increase the atom economy of the process **[1 mark]**.
The greater the atom economy, the less the waste — this is better for the environment and will reduce costs **[1 mark]**.
- Whether there are ways of saving energy consumption **[1 mark]**.
This is better for the environment and will reduce costs **[1 mark]**.
- What safety procedures need to be in place **[1 mark]**.
If high temperatures and pressures are used, safety measures will have to be in place to protect workers and the environment **[1 mark]** OR if the products / waste products are toxic / highly flammable, safety measures will have to be in place to protect workers and the environment **[1 mark]**.

# Section 4 — Acids and Bases

## Page 38 — Acids and Bases

1 a) $H^+$ or $H_3O^+$ and $SO_4^{2-}$ **[1 mark]**
b) $2H^+_{(aq)} + Mg_{(s)} \rightarrow Mg^{2+}_{(aq)} + H_{2(g)}$ **[1 mark]**
c) $SO_4^{2-}$ **[1 mark]**
d) The acid dissociates / ionises in water as follows:
$H_2SO_4 + 2H_2O \rightleftharpoons 2H_3O^+ + SO_4^{2-}$ **[1 mark]**
The equilibrium position lies almost completely to the right **[1 mark]**.

2 a) $HCN_{(aq)} + H_2O_{(l)} \rightleftharpoons H_3O^+_{(aq)} + CN^-_{(aq)}$
OR $HCN_{(aq)} \rightleftharpoons H^+_{(aq)} + CN^-_{(aq)}$ **[1 mark]**
b) The equilibrium position lies to the left **[1 mark]**.
c) The pairs are HCN and $CN^-$ **[1 mark]**
AND $H_2O$ and $H_3O^+$ **[1 mark]**.
d) $H^+$ **[1 mark]**

## Page 41 — pH Calculations

1 a) $K_a = \frac{[H^+][A^-]}{[HA]}$ **[1 mark]**

b) Assume [HA] = 0.280 because only a very small amount of the HA will dissociate **[1 mark]**.

$$K_a = \frac{[H^+]^2}{[HA]} \Rightarrow 5.60 \times 10^{-4} = \frac{[H^+]^2}{0.280}$$

$[H^+] = \sqrt{(5.60 \times 10^{-4}) \times 0.280}$ = 0.0125 mol $dm^{-3}$ **[1 mark]**
pH = $-\log_{10}[H^+] = -\log_{10}(0.0125)$ = 1.90 **[1 mark]**

2 $[H^+] = 10^{-2.65}$ = 2.24 × $10^{-3}$ mol $dm^{-3}$ **[1 mark]**

$K_a = \frac{[H^+]^2}{[HX]}$ **[1 mark]** $= \frac{(2.24 \times 10^{-3})^2}{0.15}$
= 3.34 × $10^{-5}$ **[1 mark]** mol $dm^{-3}$ **[1 mark]**

# Answers

3 a) $[H^+] = 10^{-2.6} = 2.51 \times 10^{-3}$ mol dm$^{-3}$ **[1 mark]**

$K_a = \dfrac{[H^+]^2}{[C_6H_5COOH]}$ **[1 mark]** $= \dfrac{(2.51\times10^{-3})^2}{0.1}$

$= 6.3\times10^{-5}$ **[1 mark]** mol dm$^{-3}$ **[1 mark]**

b) $[H^+] = \sqrt{K_a[C_6H_5COOH]}$ **[1 mark]**

$= \sqrt{(6.3\times10^{-5})\times0.01} = 7.9\times10^{-4}$ mol dm$^{-3}$ **[1 mark]**

c) $pH = -\log_{10}[H^+] = -\log(7.9\times10^{-4}) = 3.1$ **[1 mark]**

d) $[H^+] = \sqrt{6.3\times10^{-5}\times1} = 7.9\times10^{-3}$ **[1 mark]**
so $pH = -\log(7.9\times10^{-3}) = 2.10$ **[1 mark]**

e) As the solution is diluted by a factor of 10 the pH increases by 0.5 **[1 mark]**.

## Page 43 — pH Curves, Titrations and Indicators

1 a) Any strong monoprotic acid, e.g. HCl, $HNO_3$ **[1 mark]**
Any strong alkali, e.g. NaOH, KOH **[1 mark]**
The shape tells you that this is a strong acid/strong base titration curve.

b) Any indicator that changes colour between pH 3 and pH 11, e.g. methyl orange, phenolphthalein **[1 mark]**.

2 a)

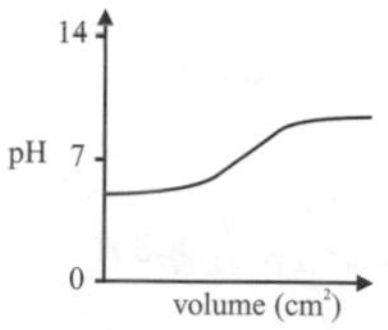


**[1 mark for general shape correct, 1 mark for approximate start and finish pHs correct]**

b) pH 7 **[1 mark]**

3 a) Y **[1 mark]**

b) $NaOH_{(aq)} + CH_3COOH_{(aq)} \rightarrow CH_3COONa_{(aq)}$ **[1 mark]** $+ H_2O_{(aq)}$
**[1 mark for correct equation]**

c) Any indicator that changes colour between pH 7 and pH 12, e.g. phenolphthalein **[1 mark]**.
This indicator is suitable because it changes colour over the vertical part of the pH curve OR it will change colour at the equivalence point/end point of the titration **[1 mark]**.

## Page 45 — Titration Calculations

1 a) $HCl_{(aq)} + NaOH_{(aq)} \rightarrow NaCl_{(aq)} + H_2O_{(l)}$ **[1 mark]**

b) i) 25.6 cm³ **[1 mark]**

ii) moles NaOH $= \dfrac{0.1\times25.6}{1000}$ **[1 mark]** $= 2.56\times10^{-3}$ **[1 mark]**

c) Concentration of HCl $= \dfrac{(2.56\times10^{-3})\times1000}{25}$ **[1 mark]**
$= 0.1024$ mol dm$^{-3}$ **[1 mark]**

2 a) $H_2SO_{4(aq)} + 2NaOH_{(aq)} \rightarrow Na_2SO_{4(aq)} + 2H_2O_{(l)}$ **[1 mark]**

b) i) No. of moles NaOH $= \dfrac{0.1\times35.65}{1000}$ **[1 mark]** $= 3.565\times10^{-3}$ **[1 mark]**

ii) No. of moles $H_2SO_4$ = No. of moles NaOH ÷ 2
$= 1.78\times10^{-3}$ **[1 mark]**

iii) Concentration of $H_2SO_4 = \dfrac{(1.78\times10^{-3})\times1000}{25}$ **[1 mark]**
$= 0.07$ mol dm$^{-3}$ **[1 mark]**

3 Equation: $HCl_{(aq)} + NaOH_{(aq)} \rightarrow NaCl_{(aq)} + H_2O_{(l)}$ **[1 mark]**

No. of moles NaOH $= \dfrac{0.25\times10}{1000}$ **[1 mark]** $= 2.5\times10^{-3}$ **[1 mark]**

No. of moles HCl = No. of moles NaOH $= 2.5\times10^{-3}$ **[1 mark]**

Volume HCl $= \dfrac{(2.5\times10^{-3})\times1000}{0.1}$ **[1 mark]** = 25 cm³ **[1 mark]**.

## Page 47 — Buffer Action

1 a) $K_a = \dfrac{[C_6H_5COO^-][H^+]}{[C_6H_5COOH]}$ **[1 mark]**

$\Rightarrow [H^+] = 6.4\times10^{-5}\times\dfrac{0.40}{0.20} = 1.28\times10^{-4}$ mol dm$^{-3}$ **[1 mark]**

$pH = -\log_{10}(1.28\times10^{-4}) = 3.9$ **[1 mark]**

b) The buffer solution contains benzoic acid and benzoate ions in equilibrium: $C_6H_5COOH \rightleftharpoons H^+ + C_6H_5COO^-$ **[1 mark]**
Adding $H_2SO_4$ increases the concentration of $H^+$ **[1 mark]**.
The equilibrium shifts left to reduce the concentration of $H^+$, so the pH will only change very slightly **[1 mark]**.

2 a) $CH_3(CH_2)_2COOH \rightleftharpoons H^+ + CH_3(CH_2)_2COO^-$ **[1 mark]**

b) $[CH_3(CH_2)_2COOH] = [CH_3(CH_2)_2COO^-]$,
so $[CH_3(CH_2)_2COOH] \div [CH_3(CH_2)_2COO^-] = 1$ **[1 mark]**
and $K_a = [H^+]$. $pH = -\log_{10}(1.5\times10^{-5})$ **[1 mark]** = 4.8 **[1 mark]**
If the concentrations of the weak acid and the salt of the weak acid are equal, they cancel from the $K_a$ expression and the buffer $pH = pK_a$.

## Section 5 — Isomerism and Carbonyl Compounds

## Page 49 — Formulas and Isomers

1 a) Any two from: pentan-1-ol, pentan-2-ol, pentan-3-ol **[1 mark for each]**.

b) E-pent-2-ene **[1 mark]**.
Z-pent-2-ene **[1 mark]**.

c) propene **[1 mark]**.
cyclopropane **[1 mark]**.

2 a) The property of having stereoisomers, which are molecules with the same structural formula **[1 mark]**, but with a different orientation of their bonds in space **[1 mark]**.

b) For example:

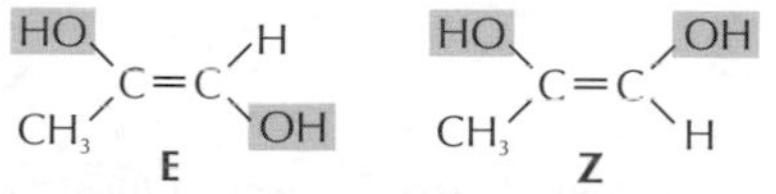


**[1 mark for each correct structure, 1 mark for correct E/Z labels.]**

## Page 51 — Optical Isomerism and Chirality

1 a)

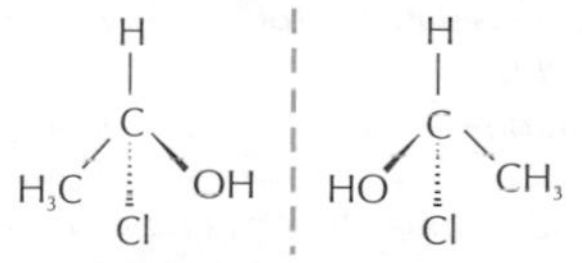


**[1 mark for each correctly drawn structure — they don't have to be orientated in the same way as in the diagram above, as long as the molecules are mirror images of each other.]**

b) The molecules have an asymmetric carbon/a chiral carbon/a carbon with four different groups attached **[1 mark]**.

c) Optically active molecules rotate the plane of plane-polarised light **[1 mark]**.

2 a)

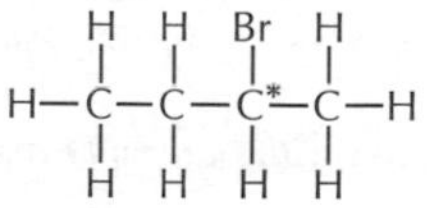


**[1 mark]**

It doesn't really matter how you mark the chiral centre, as long as you've made it clear which carbon you've marked.

b) Since the butan-2-ol solution is a racemic mixture, it must contain equal amounts of both enantiomers **[1 mark]**. The two enantiomers will exactly cancel out each other's light-rotating effect **[1 mark]**.

c) The reaction has proceeded via an $S_N1$ mechanism **[1 mark]**.
You know this because the original solution contained a single optical isomer, but the product is a racemic mixture **[1 mark]**.

# Answers

## Page 54 — Pharmaceutical Synthesis

1 a) 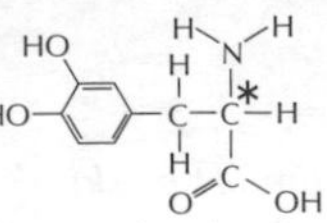 **[1 mark]**

The chiral carbon is the one with 4 different groups attached.

b) i) *The racemic mixture contains both DOPA enantiomers **[1 mark]**. The other enantiomer may have harmful side effects **[1 mark]**.*

ii) *Smaller doses of the pure drug will be needed **[1 mark]**.*

2 a) *'Combinatorial chemistry' is a process of synthesising a large number **[1 mark]** of structurally similar (or related) **[1 mark]** compounds at the same time.*

b) *Small differences in the structures of molecules can have large effects on their properties as a drug **[1 mark]**. Testing many similar compounds allow you to find the one that has the most powerful medicinal properties/minimal side effects **[1 mark]**.*

## Page 57 — Aldehydes and Ketones

1 a) *Oxidation **[1 mark]***

b) *Ethanal **[1 mark]**. Functional group is carbonyl (C=O) **[1 mark]**.*

c) i) *If the ethanal is left in the reaction mixture it may oxidise further **[1 mark]** to form ethanoic acid **[1 mark]**.*

ii) *Propan-2-ol oxidises to a ketone **[1 mark]**, which cannot be oxidised any further **[1 mark]**.*

Propan-2-ol oxidises to a ketone rather than an aldehyde because it's a secondary alcohol.

2 ***X** is butan-2-ol*

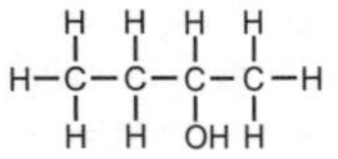

***[1 mark for any <u>secondary</u> alcohol, 1 mark for name, 1 for structure]***

***Y** is butanone*

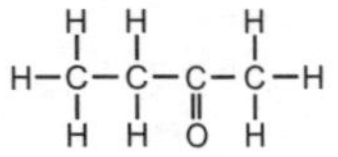

***[1 mark for any ketone, 1 mark for name, 1 for structure]***

## Page 59 — More on Aldehydes and Ketones

1 a) *Butanal **[1 mark]** and butanone (or butan-2-one) **[1 mark]***

b) *Tollens' reagent/silver nitrate dissolved in aqueous ammonia **[1 mark]***
*silver mirror with butanal **[1 mark]***
*no reaction with butanone **[1 mark]***
*OR*
*Fehling's or Benedict's solution (or copper(II) ions dissolved in NaOH or $Na_2CO_3$) **[1 mark]***
*brick-red precipitate with butanal **[1 mark]***
*no reaction with butanone **[1 mark]***
*OR*
*Iodine in the presence of an alkali **[1 mark]***
*no reaction with butanal **[1 mark]***
*straw-yellow precipitate/antiseptic smell with butanone **[1 mark]***
*OR*
*Acidified dichromate(VI) ions/potassium dichromate(VI) and dilute sulfuric acid **[1 mark]***
*solution changes colour from orange to green with butanal **[1 mark]***
*no reaction with butanone **[1 mark]***

c) *butanoic acid **[1 mark]***

2 a) 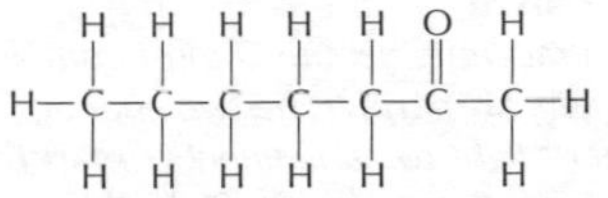 **[1 mark]**

*Brady's reagent tells you that it is a carbonyl compound **[1 mark]**.*
*Tollens' reagent tells you that it is not an aldehyde **[1 mark]**.*
*The iodine test tells you that it has a methyl carbonyl group **[1 mark]**.*

b) *You can measure the melting point of the precipitate with Brady's reagent **[1 mark]**. Each carbonyl compound gives a precipitate with a specific melting point which can be looked up in tables **[1 mark]**.*

c) 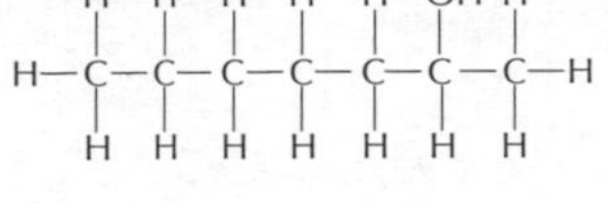 **[1 mark]**

## Page 61 — Carboxylic Acids

1 a) *Propanoic acid **[1 mark]***

b) *Propan-1-ol **[1 mark]***

The '1' is really important here. You wouldn't get the mark for just saying 'propanol', because if you reacted propan-2-ol and acidified potassium dichromate(VI), you'd get a ketone instead.

c) $CH_3CH_2COOH_{(aq)} + KOH_{(aq)} \rightarrow CH_3CH_2COOK_{(aq)} + H_2O_{(l)}$ ***[1 mark]***

2 a) 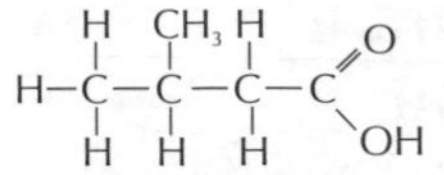 **[1 mark]**

b) $2CH_3COOH_{(aq)} + Na_2CO_{3(s)} \rightarrow 2CH_3COONa_{(aq)} + H_2O_{(l)} + CO_{2(g)}$
***[1 mark for correct reactants and products, 1 mark for equation correctly balanced.]***

c) 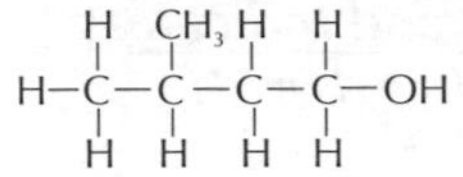 **[1 mark]**

*3-methylbutan-1-ol **[1 mark]***
*Reducing agent: $LiAlH_4$ (in dry diethyl ether) **[1 mark]***

d) *Esterification OR condensation **[1 mark]***

## Page 64 — Esters

1 a) $CH_3COOH + CH_3CH(CH_3)CH_2CH_2OH \rightarrow CH_3COOCH_2CH_2CH(CH_3)CH_3 + H_2O$
***[1 mark for reactants correct, 1 mark for products correct.]***

b) *ethanoic acid **[1 mark]***

c) *Heat OR warm OR reflux **[1 mark]** and (concentrated sulfuric) acid catalyst **[1 mark]**.*

2 a) *2-methylpropyl ethanoate **[1 mark]***

b) *Flavouring/perfume OR solvent OR plasticiser **[1 mark]***

c) *Ethanoic acid **[1 mark]*** 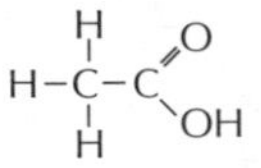 **[1 mark]**

*2-methylpropan-1-ol **[1 mark]*** 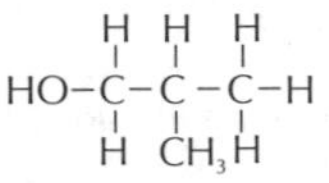 **[1 mark]**

*This is acid hydrolysis **[1 mark]***

d) *With sodium hydroxide, sodium ethanoate is produced, but in the reaction in part (c), ethanoic acid is produced **[1 mark]**.*

## Page 67 — Fatty Acids and Fats

1 a) $C_{17}H_{35}COOH$ *or* $C_{18}H_{36}O_2$ ***[1 mark]***

b) i) *Triglycerides **[1 mark]***

ii) *The triester must be saturated because stearic acid is saturated/contain no double bonds. **[1 mark]***

2 a) *'Cis' means that the hydrogen atoms attached to the carbon atoms either side of the double bond are on the same side **[1 mark]***

b) *Trans fatty acids increase the levels of 'bad' cholesterol/decrease the level of 'good' cholesterol in the body. **[1 mark]** 'Bad' cholesterol increases the risk of heart disease and strokes/'good' cholesterol decreases the risk of heart disease and strokes. **[1 mark]***

## Page 69 — Acylation

1 a) $CH_3COCl + CH_3CH_2NH_2 \rightarrow CH_3CONHCH_2CH_3 + HCl$ ***[1 mark]***

b)

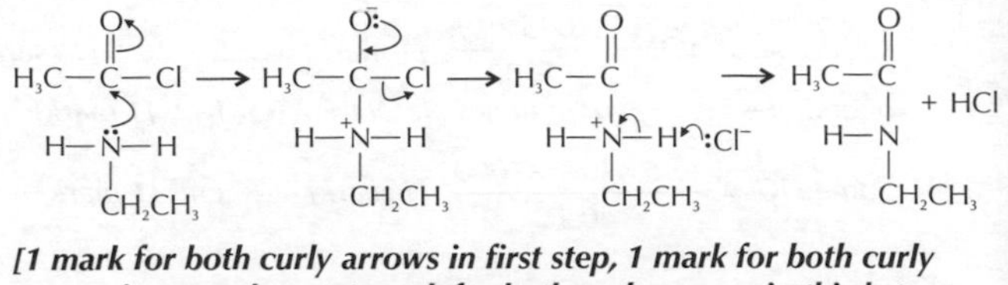

***[1 mark for both curly arrows in first step, 1 mark for both curly arrows in second step, 1 mark for both curly arrows in third step, 1 mark for structures of reactants and product correct.]***

# Answers

2 a) $CH_3CH_2COCl + CH_3CH_2OH \rightarrow CH_3CH_2COOCH_2CH_3 + HCl$
**[1 mark for ester product correct, 1 mark for all other reactants and products correct]**
*Product is ethyl propanoate* **[1 mark]**.
b) *The reaction between propanoyl chloride and ethanol is irreversible OR faster* **[1 mark]**.
c) *Propanoic acid* **[1 mark]**.

## Section 6 — More Organic Chemistry

### Page 71 — Benzene

1 a) $C_7H_8$ or $C_6H_5CH_3$ **[1 mark]**
b) *Aromatic OR arenes* **[1 mark]**
c) *A: 1,3-dichlorobenzene* **[1 mark]**
*B: nitrobenzene* **[1 mark]**
*C: 2,4-dimethylphenol* **[1 mark]**

2 a) *The model suggests that there should be two different bond lengths in the molecule, corresponding to C=C and C–C* **[1 mark]**
b) *X-ray diffraction* **[1 mark]**
c) *X ray diffraction shows that all the carbon–carbon bond lengths in benzene are actually the same, which doesn't fit the Kekulé model.* **[1 mark]**

### Page 73 — Reactions of Benzene

1 a) i) *A: nitrobenzene* **[1 mark]**
*B + C: concentrated nitric acid* **[1 mark]**
*and concentrated sulfuric acid* **[1 mark]**
*D: warm, not more than 55 °C* **[1 mark]**
When you're asked to name a compound, give its name, not its formula.
ii) *This is an electrophilic substitution reaction with nitrobenzene as the electrophile. See page 72 for the mechanism.*
**[1 mark for each of the three steps.]**
iii) $HNO_3 + H_2SO_4 \rightarrow H_2NO_3^+ + HSO_4^-$ **[1 mark]**
$H_2NO_3^+ \rightarrow NO_2^+ + H_2O$ **[1 mark]**
b) i) *G: benzenesulfonic acid* **[1 mark]**
*E + F: concentrated sulfuric acid, heat under reflux OR fuming sulfuric acid, warm*
**[1 mark for reagent, 1 mark for appropriate conditions for that reagent]**.
ii) *Sulfur trioxide/$SO_3$* **[1 mark]**

### Page 75 — More Reactions of Benzene

1 a) *Reagent: bromoethane / chloroethane* **[1 mark]**
*Catalyst: a halogen carrier e.g. $AlCl_3$* **[1 mark]**
b) *The electrophile is formed as follows:*
$CH_3CH_2Cl + AlCl_3 \rightarrow CH_3CH_2^+ + AlCl_4^-$ **[1 mark]**
*For the mechanism see page 74.* **[1 mark for correct structures of intermediates, 1 mark for the correct structure of products, 1 mark for correct positions of curly arrows.]**
c) *The catalyst polarises* **[1 mark]** *the chloroethane molecule to produce a carbocation/positive charge/positively charged ion* **[1 mark]**. *This can then act as an electrophile/attack/react with the benzene ring* **[1 mark]**.

2 a) $H_3C-C^+{=}O$ **[1 mark]**
b)  **[1 mark]**
c) *For example, the aluminium only has 6 electrons in its outer shell, or the aluminium has an incomplete outer shell* **[1 mark]**.

### Page 77 — Phenols

1 a) 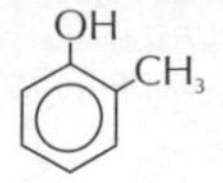 **[1 mark]**
b) $2Na + 2C_7H_7OH \rightarrow 2C_7H_7ONa + H_2$ **[1 mark]**
c) *4.8 dm³ of $H_2$ = 4.8 ÷ 24 = 0.2 moles* **[1 mark]**
*From eqn:*
*2 moles of $C_7H_7OH$ give 1 mole of $H_2$*
*So 0.4 moles of $C_7H_7OH$ give 0.2 moles of $H_2$* **[1 mark]**
*$M_r$ of $C_7H_7OH$ is (7 × 12) + (7 × 1) + 16 + 1 = 108*
*Mass of 0.4 moles of $C_7H_7OH$ is 108 × 0.4 = 43.2g* **[1 mark]**

2 a) *With benzene, there will be no reaction* **[1 mark]** *but with phenol a reaction will occur which decolorises the bromine water / gives a precipitate / smells of antiseptic* **[1 mark for any of these observations]**
b) *2,4,6-tribromophenol* **[1 mark]**
c) *Electrons from one of oxygen's p-orbitals overlap with the benzene ring's delocalised system, increasing its electron density* **[1 mark]**. *This makes the ring more likely to be attacked by electrophiles.* **[1 mark]**
d) *Electrophilic substitution* **[1 mark]**

### Page 80 — Amines

1 a) *It can accept protons/H⁺ ions, or it can donate a lone pair of electrons* **[1 mark]**.
b) *Methylamine is stronger as the nitrogen lone pair is more available* **[1 mark]** *— the methyl group/$CH_3$ pushes electrons onto/increases electron density on the nitrogen* **[1 mark]**. *Phenylamine is weaker as the nitrogen lone pair is less available* **[1 mark]** *— nitrogen's electron density is decreased as it's partially delocalised around the benzene ring* **[1 mark]**.

2 a) $CH_3CH_2NH_2 + 3CH_3Br \rightarrow CH_3CH_2(CH_3)_3N^+Br^- + 2HBr$
**[1 mark]** *for correct structure/formula of the quaternary salt*
**[1 mark]** *for correct balanced equation*
b) *An excess of $CH_3Br$* **[1 mark]**
c) *For example, as a surfactant, in fabric conditioners or in hair products* **[1 mark]**.

3 a) *You get a mixture of primary, secondary and tertiary amines, and quaternary ammonium salts* **[1 mark]**.
b) i) *$LiAlH_4$ and dry diethyl ether* **[1 mark]**, *followed by dilute acid* **[1 mark]**
*OR reflux* **[1 mark]** *with sodium metal and ethanol* **[1 mark]**.
ii) *It's too expensive* **[1 mark]**.
iii) *Metal catalyst such as platinum or nickel* **[1 mark]** *and high temperature and pressure* **[1 mark]**.

### Page 83 — Reactions of Amines

1 a) *Azo dyes* **[1 mark]**
b) *The -N=N- group* **[1 mark]**
c) 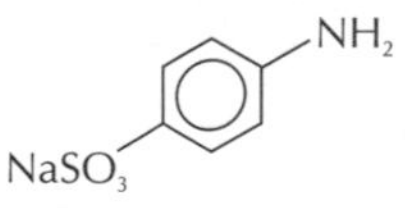 or 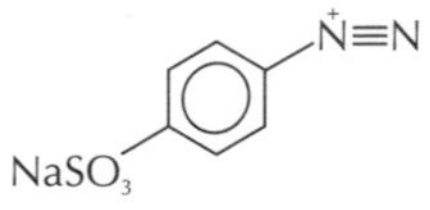 **[1 mark]**

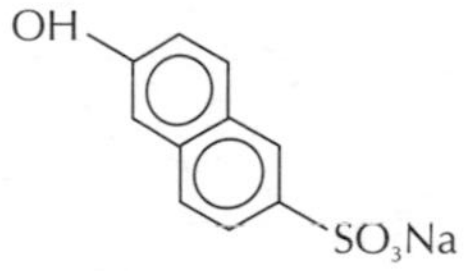 **[1 mark]**

As a first step, make sure you remember the basic overall reaction, e.g. phenylamine + phenol = azo dye, then learn the actual equations and reaction conditions.

### Page 85 — More About Azo Dyes

1 a) i) *Benzene rings* **[1 mark]**, *N=N/azo group* **[1 mark]**, *oxygen lone pairs* **[1 mark]**.
ii) *$-SO_3^-Na^+$/sodium sulfonate group* **[1 mark]**
b) *Ionic attraction* **[1 mark]** *between $-SO_3^-$ (in dye)* **[1 mark]** *and $-NH_3^+$ (in protein)* **[1 mark]**.

# Answers

2 a) Colourless **[1 mark]**

b) i) Delocalised systems contain molecular orbitals that are close together in energy **[1 mark]** which allows them to absorb wavelengths / frequencies of visible light **[1 mark]**, resulting in coloured molecules.

ii) Adding functional groups to a chromophore can increase the delocalisation **[1 mark]**, reducing the energy gap between molecular orbitals, so that different frequencies / wavelengths are absorbed **[1 mark]**, changing the molecule's colour.

## Page 88 — Amino Acids and Proteins

1 a) An amino acid in which the amino and carboxyl groups are attached to the same carbon atom **[1 mark]**.

b)

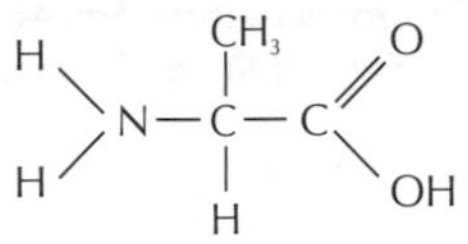

**[1 mark — structure of $NH_2$ and COOH not required]**

c) The $CH_3$ group **[1 mark]**.

d)

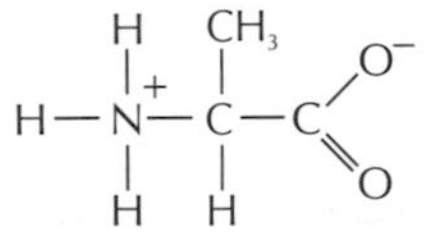

**[1 mark]**

2 a) A molecule made by joining 2 amino acids **[1 mark]**.

b)

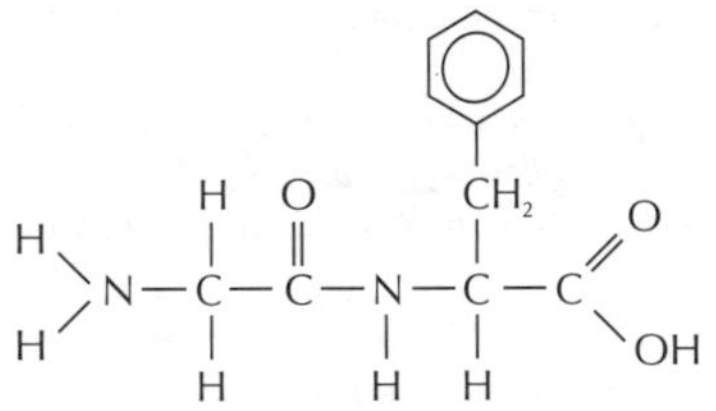

***OR***

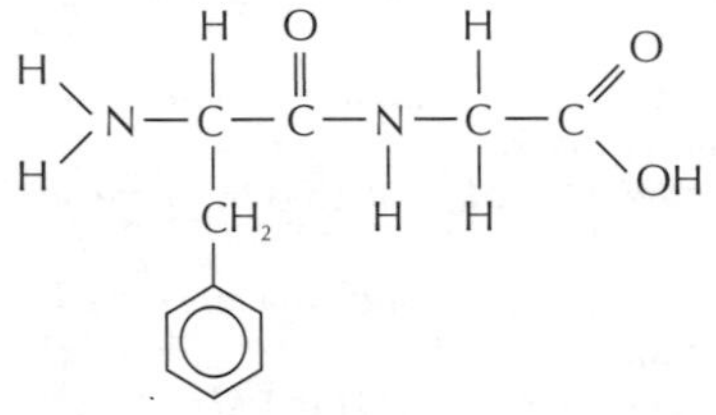

**[1 mark — structure of $NH_2$ and COOH not required]**

c) A condensation reaction involves a water molecule being removed as two other molecules are joined **[1 mark]**.

d) Glycine is not chiral as the central carbon atom is not joined to four different groups **[1 mark]**.

## Page 90 — DNA

1 a)

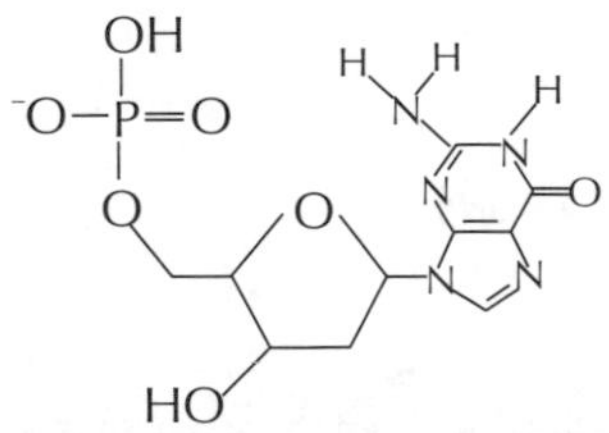

**[1 mark for the correct attachment of deoxyribose to the phosphate. 1 mark for guanine correctly attached to ribose]**

b) DNA codes for specific amino acids with sequences of three bases called base triplets **[1 mark]**. Different sequences of bases/base triplets code for the different amino acids that make up a protein **[1 mark]**.

## Page 92 — More DNA

1 a) By hydrogen bonds **[1 mark]** between bases **[1 mark]**.

b) Bases connect to one another in specific pairs **[1 mark]**, so the sequence of bases on the DNA strand defines the sequence of free nucleotides which connect to it **[1 mark]**.

c) TAACGT **[2 marks if all correct, 1 mark deducted for each mistake]**.

2 a) Sections of the DNA molecule vary from person to person. Genetic fingerprinting is a molecular technique which is able to break down and analyse these sections **[1 mark]**. It can be used to identify people based on samples of their DNA **[1 mark]**.

b) DNA profiles collected in the UK are stored on a national database, so there are concerns over e.g. who could access the information / what the information could be used for / the consequences of adding the DNA of innocent people to a database containing the DNA of criminals **[1 mark for any sensible concern]**.

## Page 94 — RNA and Protein Synthesis

1 a) DNA does not contain uracil/only RNA contains uracil **[1 mark]**.

b) Four amino acids (or for three amino acids, plus partially for two others) **[1 mark]**. Each amino acid is coded for by a triplet of bases **[1 mark]**.

c) –TTCCACGTAGCT– **[2 marks for all correct, 1 mark deducted for each mistake.]**

Remember — thymine in DNA is replaced by uracil in RNA and that uracil pairs with adenine.

2 a) Transcription **[1 mark]** occurs in the cell nucleus **[1 mark]**.

b) A codon **[1 mark]**. The bases are complementary pairs of the base triplets in DNA **[1 mark]**.

c) i) ribosome **[1 mark]**.

ii) Translation begins when a ribosome reads a start codon **[1 mark]**. As this codon is always the same, it always causes the addition of the same amino acid **[1 mark]**.

3 A tRNA has an anticodon at one end and glycine attached at the other **[1 mark]**. The anticodon on the tRNA involved is –CCA– (it's complementary to the mRNA codon) **[1 mark]**. The tRNA anticodon binds to the codon on the mRNA **[1 mark]**. The same thing happens with the next codon and a peptide link is formed with the adjacent amino acid **[1 mark]**.

## Page 96 — Enzymes

1 a) The enzyme only catalyses a specific reaction **[1 mark]** (or only works with a particular substrate).

b) Enzymes have an active site with a particular shape **[1 mark]**. Only a certain substrate will fit into this site **[1 mark]**.

2 a) i) Molecules have less (thermal/kinetic) energy **[1 mark]** at low temperatures, so collide less often and with less energy **[1 mark]**.

ii) Above optimum temperature the enzyme is denatured **[1 mark]**, the shape of the active site changes and so the substrate no longer fits into the active site **[1 mark]**.

c) pH **[1 mark]**.

3 a) Inhibitors **[1 mark]**.

b) A molecule may have a very similar shape to the substrate **[1 mark]** and so fit into the active site **[1 mark]**. This blocks the active site, preventing the substrate from entering **[1 mark]**.

## Page 99 — Polymers

1 a) Polypropene **[1 mark]**

b) Addition polymerisation **[1 mark]**

c)

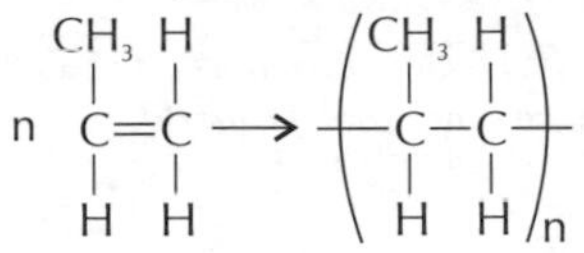

**[2 marks]**

# Answers

2 a) i) 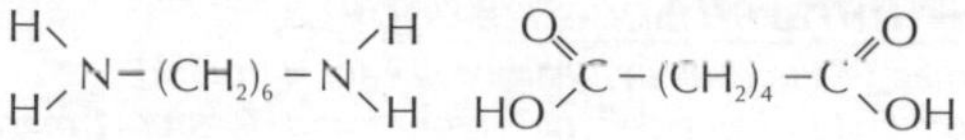

**[1 mark each]**

ii) There are six carbon atoms in each monomer/reagent **[1 mark]**.

Don't forget to count the carbons in the carboxyl groups too.

iii) Amide/peptide link **[1 mark]**

b) i) 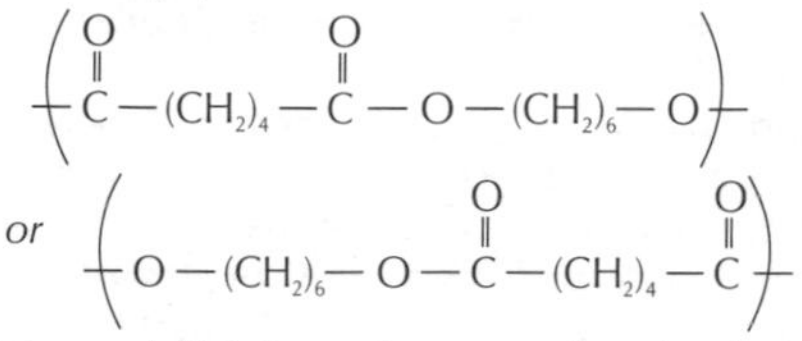 **[1 mark]**

ii) For each link formed, one small molecule (water) is eliminated **[1 mark]**.

## Page 101 — Polymer Properties

1 a) Polymer A **[1 mark]**

The more crystalline a polymer is, the stronger it is **[1 mark]**. Since HDPE is stronger than LDPE, it's likely to be the more crystalline polymer **[1 mark]**.

b) When you increase the crystallinity of a polymer, you force the polymer chains to lie closer together **[1 mark]**. The intermolecular forces between the chains will get stronger **[1 mark]**. This means that you will have to put more energy in to separate the chains, so the melting point of the polymer will increase **[1 mark]**.

c) Cold-drawing **[1 mark]**

2 a) In unplasticised PVC the polymer chains are closely packed together **[1 mark]**. So the intermolecular forces between the chains are very strong **[1 mark]**.

That's why PVC has a high glass transition temperature too.

b) Plasticiser molecules get in between the polymer chains, and reduce the effect of intermolecular forces **[1 mark]**, so the chains can move around more **[1 mark]**. This makes the PVC more flexible **[1 mark]**.

## Page 103 — Polymers and the Environment

1 a) i) A: condensation polymer/polyamide/polypeptide/protein **[1 mark]**
B: addition polymer **[1 mark]**

ii) A: 6-aminohexanoic acid **[1 mark]**
B: propene **[1 mark]**

b) A **[1 mark]**

c) Advantages include: it is cheap and easy, it doesn't require waste plastics to be separated or sorted **[1 mark]**.
Disadvantages include: it requires large areas of land, decomposing waste may release methane/greenhouse gases, leaks from landfill sites can contaminate water supplies **[1 mark]**.

## Section 7 — Synthesis and Analysis

## Page 105 — Organic Functional Groups

1 a) A — hydroxyl / OH **[1 mark]**
B — hydroxyl / OH and alkenyl / C = C **[1 mark]**
C — hydroxyl /OH and phenyl /  **[1 mark]**

b) C **[1 mark]**

c) A **[1 mark]**

d) C **[1 mark]**

2 a) carbonyl / ketone OR amide ($-CONH_2$) **[1 mark]** and (primary) amine / amino **[1 mark]**

b) i) C=O **[1 mark]**

ii) It is a double-ended molecule **[1 mark]** with 2 amine / amino groups **[1 mark]**.

3 a) phenyl **[1 mark]**, hydroxyl **[1 mark]** and ester **[1 mark]**

b) ester **[1 mark]**

c) Expanded structure (with C and H atoms showing):

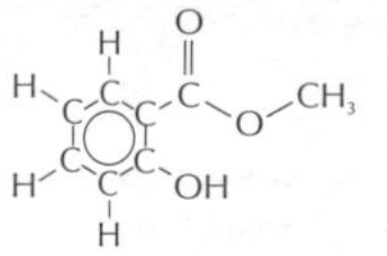

So molecular formula of methyl salicylate is $C_8H_8O_3$. **[1 mark]**

d) 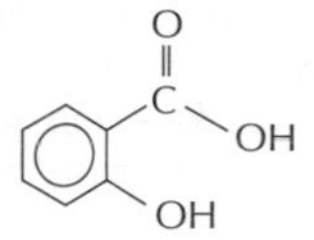 **[1 mark]**

Look back at esters on p62 if you had trouble with this one.

## Page 107 — Types of Reaction

1 a) Electrophile because of positive charge **[1 mark]**.

b) Nucleophile because of lone pair of electrons on N **[1 mark]**.

c) Nucleophile because of negative charge **[1 mark]**.

d) Electrophile because H atoms have no lone pairs **[1 mark]**.

2 a) i) addition **[1 mark]**

ii) addition **[1 mark]**

iii) substitution **[1 mark]**

b) i) $CH_3(CN)C(OH)CH_3$ or 2-hydroxy-2-methylpropanenitrile **[1 mark]**. Nucleophile **[1 mark]**

ii) $CH_3CH_2Br$ or bromoethane **[1 mark]**. Electrophile **[1 mark]**

iii) $CH_3CH_2OH$ or ethanol **[1 mark]**. Nucleophile **[1 mark]**

## Page 109 — Organic Synthesis

1 Step 1: The methanol is refluxed **[1 mark]** with $K_2Cr_2O_7$ **[1 mark]** and sulfuric acid **[1 mark]** to form methanoic acid **[1 mark]**.
Step 2: The methanoic acid is reacted under reflux **[1 mark]** with ethanol **[1 mark]** using an acid catalyst **[1 mark]**.

2 Step 1: React propane with bromine **[1 mark]** in the presence of UV light **[1 mark]**. Bromine is toxic and corrosive **[1 mark]** so great care should be taken. Bromopropane is formed **[1 mark]**.
Step 2: Bromopropane is then refluxed **[1 mark]** with sodium hydroxide solution **[1 mark]**, again a corrosive substance so take care **[1 mark]**, to form propanol **[1 mark]**.

## Page 111 — More on Organic Synthesis

1 $$\%\text{ atom economy} = \frac{12 + (3 \times 1) + 16 + 1}{12 + (3 \times 1) + 80 + 23 + 16 + 1} \times 100 = 23.7\%$$

**[1 mark for product on top line, reactants on bottom. 1 mark for numbers correct on top line. 1 mark for numbers correct on bottom line. 1 mark for correct answer overall]**.

2 a) To add extra nutrients to the soil, i.e. fertilisers **[1 mark]**.
To kill pests (weeds, insects, moulds), i.e. pesticides **[1 mark]**.
To neutralise acid in soil/raise pH/control pH of soil **[1 mark]**.

b) Any two points with matching explanations from:
Nitrates from fertiliser getting into rivers/lakes/drinking water **[1 mark]** causing excessive growth of plants (eutrophication)/harmful to health (of young children/babies)/blue baby syndrome **[1 mark]**.
Pesticides may not only kill the pest/not selective **[1 mark]**.
Can kill beneficial insects/plants/organisms/reduce biodiversity **[1 mark]**. Pesticides may not easily break down/may be too stable **[1 mark]**. Can build up in environment/accumulate in food chain/bioaccumulate **[1 mark]**.
**[4 marks in total, up to 2 for each problem]**

## Page 113 — Practical Techniques

1 a) The purer sample will have the higher melting point **[1 mark]**, so the sample that melts at 69 °C is purer **[1 mark]**.

b) To purify the sample you could dissolve it in propanone **[1 mark]** and allow it to partially recrystallise **[1 mark]**. You'd then filter the crystals **[1 mark]**, then wash them with propanone **[1 mark]** and dry them **[1 mark]**.

c) The purity could be checked by measuring the boiling point or melting point. **[1 mark]** OR by spectroscopic means. **[1 mark]**

# Answers

## Page 115 — Chromatography

1 a) $R_f \text{ value} = \frac{\text{Distance travelled by spot}}{\text{Distance travelled by solvent}}$ ***[1 mark]***

*$R_f$ value of spot A = 7 ÷ 8 = 0.875* ***[1 mark]***

The $R_f$ value has no units, because it's a ratio.

b) *Substance A has moved further up the plate because it's less strongly adsorbed* ***[1 mark]*** *onto the stationary phase* ***[1 mark]*** *than substance B* ***[1 mark]***.

2 a) *The mixture is injected into a stream of carrier gas, which takes it through a tube over the stationary phase* ***[1 mark]***. *The components of the mixture dissolve in the stationary phase* ***[1 mark]***, *evaporate into the mobile phase* ***[1 mark]***, *and redissolve, gradually travelling along the tube to the detector* ***[1 mark]***.

b) *The substances separate because they have different solubilities in the stationary phase* ***[1 mark]***, *so they take different amounts of time to move through the tube* ***[1 mark]***.

c) *The areas under the peaks will be proportional to the relative amount of each substance in the mixture OR the area under the benzene peak will be three times greater than the area under the ethanol peak* ***[1 mark]***.

## Page 118 — Mass Spectrometry

1 a) *88* ***[1 mark]***

b) *A has a mass of 43, so it's probably $CH_3CH_2CH_2$* ***[1 mark]***.
*B has a mass of 45, so it's probably COOH* ***[1 mark]***.
*C has a mass of 73, so it's probably $CH_2CH_2COOH$* ***[1 mark]***.

c) *Since the molecule is a carboxylic acid that contains the three fragments that you found in part (b), it must have this structure:*

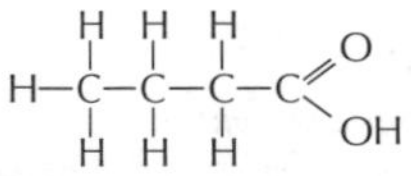

***[1 mark]***

*This is butanoic acid* ***[1 mark]***.

Make sure you check that the $M_r$ of your molecule is what it should be from the spectrum — $M_r$ of butanoic acid = 88.

## Page 120 — NMR Spectroscopy

1 a) *The peak at $\delta = 0$ is produced by the reference compound, tetramethylsilane/TMS* ***[1 mark]***.

b) *All three carbon atoms in the molecule $CH_3CH_2CH_2NH_2$ are in different environments* ***[1 mark]***. *There are only two peaks on the carbon-13 NMR spectrum shown* ***[1 mark]***.

The $^{13}C$ NMR spectrum of $CH_3CH_2CH_2NH_2$ has three peaks of equal height — because it has three carbon environments, and one carbon atom in each.

c) *Structure:*

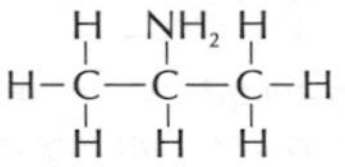

***[1 mark]***.

*This molecule has two carbon environments, with two carbons in one, and one carbon in the other* ***[1 mark]***. *So it would produce the spectrum shown.*

The 2 carbon environments are $CH_3$–$CH(NH_2)$–$CH_3$ and $CH(NH_2)$–$(CH_3)_2$.

## Page 122 — Proton NMR

1 a) *A $CH_2$ group adjacent to a halogen* ***[1 mark]***.

You've got to read the question carefully — it tells you it's a halogenoalkane. So the group at 3.6 p.p.m. can't have oxygen in it. It can't be halogen-$CH_3$ either, as this has 3 hydrogens in it.

b) *A $CH_3$ group* ***[1 mark]***.

c) *$CH_2$ added to $CH_3$ gives a mass of 29, so the halogen must be chlorine with a mass of 35.5* ***[1 mark]***.
*So a likely structure is $CH_3CH_2Cl$* ***[1 mark]***.

d) *The quartet at 3.6 p.p.m. is caused by 3 protons on the adjacent carbon* ***[1 mark]***. *The n + 1 rule tells you that 3 protons give 3 + 1 = 4 peaks* ***[1 mark]***.
*Similarly the triplet at 1.3 p.p.m. is due to 2 adjacent protons* ***[1 mark]*** *giving 2 + 1 = 3 peaks* ***[1 mark]***.

## Page 124 — Infrared Spectroscopy

1 a) *A's due to an O–H group in a carboxylic acid* ***[1 mark]***.
*B's due to a C=O in an aldehyde, ketone, acid or ester* ***[1 mark]***.
*C's due to a C–O in an alcohol, ester or acid* ***[1 mark]***.

b) *The spectrum suggests it's a carboxylic acid, so it's got a COOH group* ***[1 mark]***. *This group has a mass of 45, so the rest of the molecule has a mass of 74 – 45 = 29, which is likely to be $C_2H_5$* ***[1 mark]***.
*So the molecule could be $C_2H_5COOH$ — propanoic acid* ***[1 mark]***.

2 a) *X is due to an O–H group in an alcohol or phenol* ***[1 mark]***.
*Y is due to C–H bonds* ***[1 mark]***.
*Z is due to a C–O group in an alcohol, ester or acid* ***[1 mark]***.

b) *The spectrum suggests it's an alcohol, so it's got an OH group* ***[1 mark]***. *This group has a mass of 17, so the rest of the molecule has a mass of 46 – 17 = 29, which is likely to be $C_2H_5$* ***[1 mark]***.
*So the molecule could be $C_2H_5OH$ — ethanol* ***[1 mark]***.

## Page 127 — Combining Spectra

1 a) *Mass of molecule = 73* ***[1 mark]***.

You can tell this from the mass spectrum — the mass of the molecular ion is 73.

b) *Structure of the molecule:*

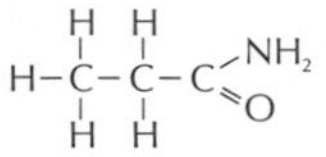

***[1 mark]***

*Explanation: Award* **1 mark** *each for the following pieces of reasoning, up to a total of* ***[5 marks]***:

- *IR spectrum shows medium absorbance trough at about 3500 $cm^{-1}$, suggesting an amine, or amide.*
- *IR spectrum has trough at about 1700 $cm^{-1}$, suggesting C=O group.*
- *$^{13}C$ NMR spectrum shows the molecule has three carbon environments with the same number of carbons in each.*
- *$^{13}C$ NMR spectrum shows a shift of about 170, which corresponds to a carbonyl group (ester, amide or carboxylic acid).*
- *$^{1}H$ NMR spectrum has a quartet at $\delta \approx 2$, and a triplet at $\delta \approx 1$ — this splitting pattern matches a $CH_2CH_3$ group.*
- *Mass spectrum peak at m/z = 15 corresponds to $CH_3$ group.*
- *Mass spectrum peak at m/z = 29 corresponds to $CH_2CH_3$ group.*
- *Mass spectrum peak at m/z = 44 corresponds to $CONH_2$ group.*

2 a) *Mass of molecule = 60* ***[1 mark]***.

You can tell this from the mass spectrum — the mass of the molecular ion is 60.

b) *Structure of the molecule:*

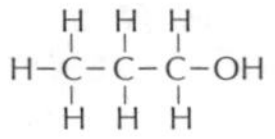

***[1 mark]***

*Explanation: Award* **1 mark** *each for the following pieces of reasoning, up to a total of* ***[5 marks]***:

- *IR spectrum has a strong absorbance trough at 3300 $cm^{-1}$, suggesting an OH group.*
- *IR spectrum has a trough at 1200 $cm^{-1}$, suggesting a C–O group.*
- *Mass spectrum peak at m/z = 15 corresponds to $CH_3$ group.*
- *Mass spectrum peak at m/z = 17 corresponds to OH group.*
- *Mass spectrum peak at m/z = 29 corresponds to $C_2H_5$ group.*
- *Mass spectrum peak at m/z = 31 corresponds to $CH_2OH$ group.*
- *Mass spectrum peak at m/z = 43 corresponds to $C_3H_7$ group.*
- *$^{13}C$ NMR spectrum has 3 peaks, so there are 3 carbon environments.*
- *$^{13}C$ NMR spectrum peak at $\delta \approx 60$ corresponds to C–O group.*
- *$^{1}H$ NMR spectrum peak at $\delta \approx 1$ corresponds to $-CH_3$.*
- *$^{1}H$ NMR spectrum peak at $\delta \approx 1.5$ corresponds to $-CH_2-$.*
- *$^{1}H$ NMR spectrum peak at $\delta \approx 2$ corresponds to –OH.*
- *$^{1}H$ NMR spectrum peak at $\delta \approx 3.5$ corresponds to $-CH_2O-$.*
- *$^{1}H$ NMR spectrum integration trace of 2, 1, 2, 3 matches the number of H atoms in $CH_3CH_2CH_2OH$.*
- *$^{1}H$ NMR spectrum has 4 peaks, so there are 4 proton environments.*
- *$^{1}H$ NMR spectrum has a sextuplet, a quartet, a triplet and a singlet — this splitting pattern matches the arrangement of H atoms in $CH_3CH_2CH_2OH$.*

# Answers

## Section 8 — Thermodynamics

### Page 129 — Enthalpy Changes

1 a) *Bonds broken* | *Bonds formed*

*$4 \times C{-}H = 4 \times 412 = 1648$* | *$2 \times C{=}O = 2 \times 743 = 1486$*

*$2 \times O{=}O = 2 \times 496 = 992$* | *$4 \times O{-}H = 4 \times 463 = 1852$* **[1 mark]**

*$(1648 + 992) - (1486 + 1852) = -698$ kJ mol$^{-1}$*

**[1 mark for 698 kJ mol$^{-1}$, 1 mark for negative sign on final answer]**

b) *Some of the bond enthalpies used are averages* **[1 mark]**. *These may be different from the actual ones in the substances* **[1 mark]**.

### Page 131 — Lattice Enthalpy

1 a)

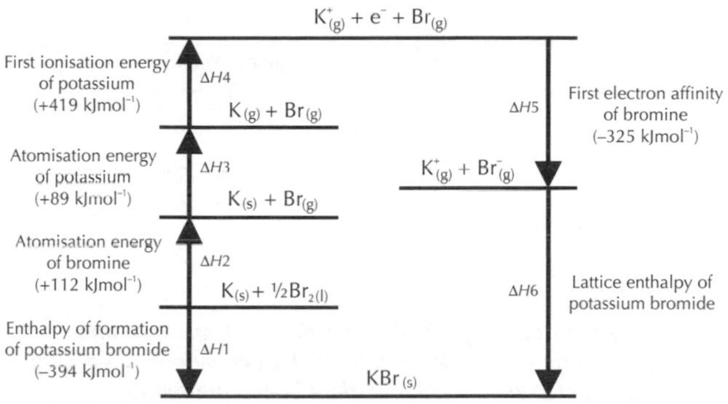


**[1 mark for left of cycle. 1 mark for right of cycle. 1 mark for formulas/state symbols. 1 mark for correct directions of arrows.]**

b) *Lattice enthalpy, $\Delta H6 = -\Delta H5 - \Delta H4 - \Delta H3 - \Delta H2 + \Delta H1$*

*$= -(-325) - (+419) - (+89) - (+112) + (-394)$* **[1 mark]**

*$= -689$* **[1 mark]** *kJ mol$^{-1}$* **[1 mark]**

*Award marks if calculation method matches cycle in part (a).*

2 a) *X: 2 × the atomisation enthalpy of chlorine*

*OR the bond dissociation enthalpy of chlorine* **[1 mark]**

*Y: the 2nd ionisation enthalpy of copper* **[1 mark]**

*Z: 2 × the 1st electron affinity of chlorine* **[1 mark]**

b) *The enthalpy of formation of copper(II) chloride* **[1 mark]**.

*The lattice enthalpy of copper(II) chloride* **[1 mark]**.

*The atomisation enthalpy of copper* **[1 mark]**.

### Page 133 — Enthalpies of Solution and Neutralisation

1 a)

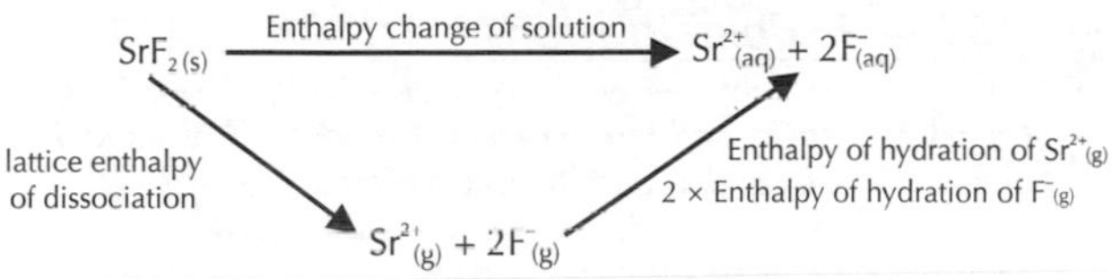


**[1 mark for each of the 4 enthalpy changes labelled, 1 mark for a complete, correct cycle.]**

Don't forget — you have to double the enthalpy of hydration for $F^-$ because there are two in $SrF_2$.

b) *$+2492 + (-1480) + (2 \times -506)$* **[1 mark]** *$= 0$ kJ mol$^{-1}$* **[1 mark]**

In enthalpy cycles for the enthalpy change of solution, you have to use lattice enthalpy of dissociation = –(lattice enthalpy of formation).

2 *By Hess's law:*

*Enthalpy change of solution of $MgCl_{2(s)}$*

*= –lattice enthalpy of formation of $MgCl_{2(s)}$*

*+ enthalpy of hydration of $Mg^{2+}_{(g)}$*

*+ [2 × enthalpy of hydration of $Cl^-_{(g)}$]* **[1 mark]**

*$= -(-2526) + (-1920) + [2 \times (-364)]$* **[1 mark]**

*$= 2526 - 1920 - 728 = -122$ kJ mol$^{-1}$* **[1 mark]**

3 a) *$H_2SO_4 + 2NaOH \rightarrow Na_2SO_4 + 2H_2O$* **[1 mark]**

b) *200 ml of 2.75 mol dm$^{-3}$ acid will contain $2.75 \times 0.2 = 0.55$ moles* **[1 mark]**

*The volume of the solution is 400 ml, so the mass of the solution is 0.4 kg, so m = 0.4.*

*$\Delta H = -mc\Delta T = -0.4 \times 4.18 \times 38 = -63.54$ kJ for 0.55 moles of acid* **[1 mark]**

*1 mole of water is given by 0.5 moles of acid.*

*So 0.5 moles of acid will produce $(0.5 \div 0.55) \times -63.54 = -57.76$ kJ* **[1 mark]**

### Page 135 — Entropy

1 a) *Entropy is a measure of the number of ways that particles can be arranged* **[1 mark]**, *as well as the number of ways that energy can be shared out between particles* **[1 mark]**.

b) i) *Entropy will increase* **[1 mark]** *because 2 moles of solid is converted into 2 moles of solid and 1 mole of gas — so there are more particles, and gas particles have more entropy than those in solids* **[1 mark]**.

ii) *Entropy will increase* **[1 mark]** *because 1 mole of solid and 1 mole of gas are converted into 2 moles of gas, and gas particles have more entropy than those in solids* **[1 mark]**.

iii) *Entropy will decrease* **[1 mark]** *because 4 moles of gas are converted into 2 moles of gas, and there is less entropy when there are fewer particles* **[1 mark]**.

iv) *Entropy will decrease* **[1 mark]** *because 1½ moles of gas are converted into 1 mole of liquid, and there is less entropy when there are fewer particles, and liquid particles have less entropy than gas particles* **[1 mark]**.

2 *Reaction is not likely to be spontaneous* **[1 mark]** *because there is a decrease in entropy* **[1 mark]**.

### Page 137 — Entropy Change

1 a) *You would expect an increase in the entropy of the system* **[1 mark]** *because a solid is combining with a substance in solution to produce another solution, a liquid and a gas — this leads to an increase in disorder* **[1 mark]**.

b) *This reaction is endothermic, so the entropy change of the surroundings will be negative* **[1 mark]**, *this means that the entropy change of the system must be sufficiently positive to counteract this change* **[1 mark]**. *The total entropy change will be positive and the reaction will be spontaneous* **[1 mark]**.

2 a) *You would expect $\Delta S_{system}$ to be negative, i.e. a decrease in entropy of the system* **[1 mark]** *because a solid is combining with a gas to produce only a solid so there's a decrease in disorder* **[1 mark]**.

b) *$\Delta S_{system} = S_{products} - S_{reactants}$* **[1 mark]**

*$= (2 \times 26.9) - ((2 \times 32.7) + 205) = 53.8 - 270.4$* **[1 mark]**

*$= -216.6$ J K$^{-1}$ mol$^{-1}$* **[1 mark, include units]**

c) *$\Delta S_{surroundings} = -\Delta H/T = -(-1\,204\,000 \div 298)$* **[1 mark]**

*$= +4040.3$ J K$^{-1}$ mol$^{-1}$* **[1 mark]**

*$\Delta S_{total} = \Delta S_{system} + \Delta S_{surroundings} = (-216.6) + 4040.3$* **[1 mark]**

*$= +3824$ J K$^{-1}$ mol$^{-1}$* **[1 mark]**

### Page 139 — Free-Energy Change

1 a) *$\Delta S_{system} = 48 - 70 = -22$ J K$^{-1}$ mol$^{-1}$* **[1 mark]**

b) *250 K: $\Delta G = -6 \times 10^3 - 250 \times -22 = -500$* **[1 mark]**.

*$\Delta G$ is negative so the reaction is feasible at 250 K* **[1 mark]**.

*At 300 K, $\Delta G = -6 \times 10^3 - 300 \times -22 = 600$* **[1 mark]**.

*$\Delta G$ is positive so the reaction is not feasible at 300 K* **[1 mark]**.

2 a) *$\Delta G = 117 \times 10^3 - (550 \times 175) = +20\,750$ J mol$^{-1}$* **[1 mark]**.

*The value of $\Delta G$ is positive at 550 K, so the reaction will not occur spontaneously at this temperature* **[1 mark]**.

b) *$T = \Delta H \div \Delta S_{system} = 117 \times 10^3 \div 175$* **[1 mark]** *= 669 K* **[1 mark]**.

# Answers

## Section 9 — Period 3, Redox and Electrochemistry

### Page 141 — Period 3 Elements and Oxides

1 a) $SO_3$ **[1 mark]**, $SO_{3(g)} + H_2O_{(l)} \rightarrow H_2SO_{4(aq)}$ **[1 mark]**
b) i) $Na_2O$ **[1 mark]**, $Na_2O_{(s)} + H_2O_{(l)} \rightarrow 2NaOH_{(aq)}$ **[1 mark]**
ii) $Na_2O$ has a giant lattice structure **[1 mark]** with ionic bonds **[1 mark]**, that take a lot of energy to break **[1 mark]**.

2 a) $P_{4(s)} + 5O_{2(g)} \rightarrow P_4O_{10(s)}$ or $4P_{(s)} + 5O_{2(g)} \rightarrow P_4O_{10(s)}$ **[1 mark]**
b) i) $P_4O_{10(s)} + 6H_2O_{(l)} \rightarrow 4H_3PO_{4(aq)}$ **[1 mark]**
ii) The solution is acidic, with a pH of 0-2 **[1 mark]**.
c) $P_4O_{10(aq)} + 12KOH_{(aq)} \rightarrow 4K_3PO_{4(aq)} + 6H_2O_{(l)}$ **[1 mark]**

### Page 143 — Redox Equations

1 a) The oxidation state of Cl = −1
so Ti + (4 × −1) = 0, Ti = +4 **[1 mark]**
b) The oxidation state of O = −2
so (2 × V) + (5 × −2) = 0, V = +5 **[1 mark]**
c) The oxidation state of O = −2
so Cr + (4 × −2) = −2, Cr = +6 **[1 mark]**
d) The oxidation state of O = −2
so (2 × Cr) + (7 × −2) = −2, Cr = +6 **[1 mark]**

2 a) $2MnO_{4\,(aq)}^- + 16H^+_{(aq)} + 10I^-_{(aq)} \rightarrow 2Mn^{2+}_{(aq)} + 8H_2O_{(l)} + 5I_{2(aq)}$
**[1 mark for correct reactants and products, 1 mark for correct balancing]**
You have to balance the number of electrons before you can combine the half-equations. And always double-check that your equation definitely balances. It's easy to slip up and throw away marks.
b) Mn has been reduced **[1 mark]** from +7 to +2 **[1 mark]**.
I has been oxidised **[1 mark]** from −1 to 0 **[1 mark]**.
c) Reactive metals have a tendency to lose electrons, so are good reducing agents **[1 mark]**. $I^-$ is already in its reduced form **[1 mark]**.

### Page 145 — Electrode Potentials

1 a) $Zn_{(s)} \mid Zn^{2+}_{(aq)} \parallel Ag^+_{(aq)} \mid Ag_{(s)}$
**[1 mark for zinc on the left and silver on the right, 1 mark for the oxidised products in the middle.]**
b) +0.80 V − (−0.76 V) = 1.56 V **[1 mark]**
c) The concentration of $Zn^{2+}$ ions or $Ag^+$ ions was not 1.00 mol $dm^{-3}$ **[1 mark]**. The pressure wasn't 100 kPa **[1 mark]**.
The difference can't be due to temperature, because it was standard during the experiment (25 °C is the same as 298 K).
d) $Zn_{(s)} + 2Ag^+_{(aq)} \rightarrow Zn^{2+}_{(aq)} + 2Ag_{(s)}$ **[1 mark]**
e) The zinc half-cell. It has a more negative standard electrode potential/it's less electronegative **[1 mark]**.

### Page 147 — The Electrochemical Series

1 a) $Zn_{(s)} + Ni^{2+}_{(aq)} \rightleftharpoons Zn^{2+}_{(aq)} + Ni_{(s)}$ **[1 mark]**
$E^\circ$ = (−0.25) − (−0.76) = +0.51 V **[1 mark]**
b) $2MnO_{4\,(aq)}^- + 16H^+_{(aq)} + 5Sn^{2+}_{(aq)} \rightleftharpoons 2Mn^{2+}_{(aq)} + 8H_2O_{(l)} + 5Sn^{4+}_{(aq)}$ **[1 mark]**
$E^\circ$ = (+1.51) − (+0.15) = +1.36 V **[1 mark]**
c) No reaction **[1 mark]**. Both reactants are in their oxidised form **[1 mark]**.
d) $Ag^+_{(aq)} + Fe^{2+}_{(aq)} \rightleftharpoons Ag_{(s)} + Fe^{3+}_{(aq)}$ **[1 mark]**
$E^\circ$ = (+0.80) − (+0.77) = +0.03 V **[1 mark]**

2 a) $KMnO_4$ **[1 mark]** because it has a more positive/less negative electrode potential **[1 mark]**
b) $MnO_4^- + 8H^+ + 5Fe^{2+} \rightarrow Mn^{2+} + 4H_2O + 5Fe^{3+}$ **[1 mark]**
$Cr_2O_7^{2-} + 14H^+ + 6Fe^{2+} \rightarrow 2Cr^{3+} + 7H_2O + 6Fe^{3+}$ **[1 mark]**
c) Cell potential for the first reaction is +1.51 − 0.77 = 0.74 V **[1 mark]**
Cell potential for the second reaction is + 1.33 − 0.77 = 0.56 V **[1 mark]**

3 a) $Cu^{2+}_{(aq)} + 2e^- \rightleftharpoons Cu_{(s)}$ **[1 mark]**
$Ni^{2+}_{(aq)} + 2e^- \rightleftharpoons Ni_{(s)}$ **[1 mark]**
b) 0.34 − (−0.25) = 0.59 V **[1 mark]**
c) $Ni_{(s)} + Cu^{2+}_{(aq)} \rightleftharpoons Cu_{(s)} + Ni^{2+}_{(aq)}$ **[1 mark]**
d) i) If the copper solution was more dilute, the E of the copper half-cell would be lower, so the overall cell potential would be smaller **[1 mark]**.
ii) If the nickel solution was more concentrated, the E of the nickel half-cell would be higher (more positive/ less negative), so the overall cell potential would be lower. **[1 mark]**

### Page 149 — Storage and Fuel Cells

1 a)

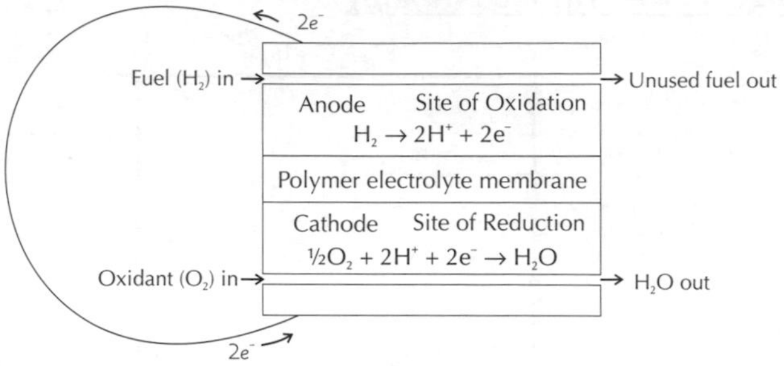


**[1 mark for naming anode and cathode. 1 mark for anode half-equation. 1 mark for cathode half equation. 1 mark for showing $H_2$/ fuel and $O_2$/ oxidant in and unused fuel and $H_2O$ out. 1 mark for showing correct direction of flow of electrons in circuit.]**
b) Correctly label anode as site of oxidation and cathode as site of reduction **[1 mark]**.
c) Possible advantages – more efficient/release less pollution **[1 mark]**
Possible disadvantages – problems storing and transporting hydrogen/ manufacturing hydrogen currently requires energy from fossil fuels/ fuel cells are expensive **[1 mark]**

2 a) $Pb_{(s)} + 2H_2SO_{4(aq)} + PbO_{2(s)} \rightleftharpoons 2PbSO_{4(s)} + 2H_2O_{(l)}$ **[1 mark]**
$E^\circ$ = 1.69 − (−0.36) = +2.05 V **[1 mark]**
b) Any two from:
Lower cost over a long period of time **[1 mark]**.
Longer life span because they can be recharged **[1 mark]**.
Can supply more power than non-rechargeable batteries **[1 mark]**.
Use fewer resources because they are reusable and don't need to be replaced as often **[1 mark]**.

### Page 152 — Redox Titrations

1 a) $MnO_4^- + 8H^+ + 5Fe^{2+} \rightarrow Mn^{2+} + 4H_2O + 5Fe^{3+}$
**[1 mark for $MnO_4^-$ and $Mn^{2+}$ correct, 1 mark for $5Fe^{2+}$ and $5Fe^{3+}$ correct, 1 mark for $8H^+$ and $4H_2O$ correct]**.
b) Number of moles = (concentration × volume) ÷ 1000
Moles of $MnO_4^-$ = (0.4 × 11.5) ÷ 1000 = 4.6 × $10^{-3}$ **[1 mark]**
Moles of $Fe^{2+}$ = moles of $MnO_4^-$ × 5 **[1 mark]** = 2.3 × $10^{-2}$ **[1 mark]**
c) Mass of substance = moles × relative atomic mass
Mass of iron in solution = (2.3 × $10^{-2}$) × 55.8 = 1.2834 g **[1 mark]**
% iron in steel wool = (1.2834 ÷ 1.3) × 100 **[1 mark]** = 98.7 % **[1 mark]**

2 a) A redox reaction **[1 mark]**.
b) Number of moles = (concentration × volume) ÷ 1000
Number of moles = (0.5 × 10) ÷ 1000 **[1 mark]** = 0.005 **[1 mark]**
c) Number of moles = (concentration × volume) ÷ 1000
Number of moles = (0.1 × 20) ÷ 1000 **[1 mark]** = 0.002 **[1 mark]**
d) 1 mole of $MnO_4^-$ ions needs 5 moles of electrons to be reduced.
So to reduce 0.002 moles of $MnO_4^-$, you need (0.002 × 5) = 0.01 moles of electrons **[1 mark]**.
The 0.005 moles of tin ions must have lost 0.01 moles of

# Answers

*electrons as they were oxidised OR all of these electrons must have come from the tin ions* **[1 mark]**.
*Each tin ion changed its oxidation state by 0.01 ÷ 0.005 = 2* **[1 mark]**.
*The oxidation state of the oxidised tin ions is (+2) + 2 = +4* **[1 mark]**.

3 a) *The number of moles of thiosulfate used = (19.33 × 0.15) ÷ 1000 = 0.0029 moles* **[1 mark]**.
*From the iodine-thiosulfate equation, the number of moles of $I_2$ = half the number of moles of thiosulfate, so in this case the number of moles of $I_2$ = 0.00145* **[1 mark]**.
b) *From the equation, 2 copper ions produce 1 iodine molecule* **[1 mark]**, *so the number of moles of copper ions = 2 × 0.00145 = 0.0029* **[1 mark]**.
c) *In 250 cm$^3$ of the copper solution there are: (250 ÷ 25) × 0.0029 = 0.029 moles of copper* **[1 mark]**.
*1 mole of copper is 63.5 g, so in the alloy there are: 0.029 × 63.5 = 1.84 g of copper* **[1 mark]**.
*Percentage of copper in the alloy = (1.84 ÷ 4.20) × 100 = 42.8%* **[1 mark]**.

## Section 10 — Transition Metals

### Page 155 — Transition Metals — The Basics

1 a) *$1s^2\ 2s^2\ 2p^6\ 3s^2\ 3p^6\ 3d^{10}$ or [Ar] $3d^{10}$* **[1 mark]**
b) *No, it doesn't* **[1 mark]**. *A transition metal is an element that can form at least one stable ion with an incomplete d-subshell* **[1 mark]**, *but $Cu^+$ ions have a full 3d subshell* **[1 mark]**.
c) *copper(II) sulfate ($CuSO_{4(aq)}$)* **[1 mark]**

2 a) i) *$1s^22s^22p^63s^23p^63d^{10}4s^2$* **[1 mark]**
ii) *$1s^22s^22p^63s^23p^63d^{10}$* **[1 mark]**
iii) *$1s^22s^22p^63s^23p^63d^54s^1$* **[1 mark]**
iv) *$1s^22s^22p^63s^23p^63d^3$* **[1 mark]**
*(allow use of shorthand [Ar] to represent $1s^22s^22p^63s^23p^6$)*
b) *A transition metal is one that has at least one stable ion* **[1 mark]** *with an incomplete/partially filled d-shell* **[1 mark]**.
*Zinc has only one stable ion (2+)* **[1 mark]** *and this has 10 electrons in the d-subshell/the subshell is full* **[1 mark]**.

3 a) i) *$1s^2\ 2s^2\ 2p^6\ 3s^2\ 3p^6\ 3d^5$* **[1 mark]**
ii) *$1s^2\ 2s^2\ 2p^6$* **[1 mark]**
b) *Iron can exist in two different oxidation states, $Fe^{2+}$ and $Fe^{3+}$* **[1 mark]**.
*Aluminium can only exist in one oxidation state, $Al^{3+}$* **[1 mark]**.
*Iron can form coloured compounds/solutions* **[1 mark]**.
*Aluminium forms only colourless/white compounds/solutions* **[1 mark]**.

### Page 157 — Complex Ions

1 a) *A complex ion is a metal ion surrounded by coordinately bonded ligands* **[1 mark]**.
b) *A lone pair of electrons from the N atom is donated to/forms a coordinate bond with the central iron ion* **[1 mark]**.
c)

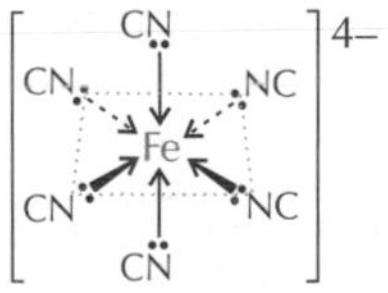


**[1 mark]**

2 a) *A bidentate ligand has two lone pairs of electrons* **[1 mark]**, *so it can form two coordinate bonds with the central metal ion* **[1 mark]**.
b) *6* **[1 mark]**
Each ethanedioate ligand forms two bonds with the $Fe^{3+}$ ion — so that's 6 altogether.
c) *Octahedral* **[1 mark]**
Complex ions with a coordination number of 6 are usually octahedral.

### Page 159 — Variable Oxidation States — Chromium

1 a) *Reduction/redox* **[1 mark]**
b) *Degas all the liquids by bubbling nitrogen through them (to remove any oxygen)* **[1 mark]**. *Do all stages of the experiment in an inert atmosphere (e.g. nitrogen or carbon dioxide)* **[1 mark]**.

2 a) *$Cr_2O_7^{2-} + 14H^+ + 6e^- \rightarrow 2Cr^{3+} + 7H_2O$* **[1 mark]**
b) i) *The two half-equations are:*
*$Cr_2O_7^{2-} + 14H^+ + 6e^- \rightarrow 2Cr^{3+} + 7H_2O$*
*$CH_3CH_2OH \rightarrow CH_3CHO + 2H^+ + 2e^-$*
*So the full equation is:*
*$Cr_2O_7^{2-} + 3CH_3CH_2OH + 8H^+ \rightarrow 2Cr^{3+} + 3CH_3CHO + 7H_2O$*
**[1 mark for correct reactants, 1 mark for correct products, 1 mark for correct balancing]**
Don't forget to balance the half-equations by adding $H_2O$, $H^+$ and $e^-$.
ii) *The solution will change from orange to green* **[1 mark]**.
c) i) *$SO_2 + 2H_2O \rightarrow SO_4^{2-} + 4H^+ + 2e^-$* **[1 mark]**
ii) *$Cr_2O_7^{2-} + 3SO_2 + 2H^+ \rightarrow 2Cr^{3+} + 3SO_4^{2-} + H_2O$* **[1 mark]**
For this one, you needed to triple everything in the half-equation from c(i) so that it has the same number of electrons as the half-equation in a).

### Page 161 — Variable Oxidation States — Cu and Co

1 a) *Ligand substitution* **[1 mark]** *(accept 'ligand exchange')*
b) *A lone pair of electrons* **[1 mark]**.
c) *B only* **[1 mark]**
d) *B is changing from octahedral* **[1 mark]** *to tetrahedral* **[1 mark]**.
*The $Cl^-$ ligands are bigger than the $H_2O$ ligand* **[1 mark]** *so fewer of them can fit around the metal ion* **[1 mark]**.

2 a) *Both form a blue precipitate when first added to a solution of copper(II) ions* **[1 mark]** *but only excess ammonia solution will make this dissolve forming an (intense) blue solution* **[1 mark]**.
b) i) *$[Cu(H_2O)_6]^{2+} + 2NH_3 \rightarrow [Cu(H_2O)_4(OH)_2] + 2NH_4^+$*
**[1 mark for two ammonia molecules, 1 mark for correct formula of precipitate complex — allow $Cu(OH)_2$]**
ii) *$[Cu(H_2O)_6]^{2+} + 4NH_3 \rightarrow [Cu(H_2O)_2(NH_3)_4]^{2+} + 4H_2O$*
**[1 mark for four ammonia molecules, 1 mark for correct formula of complex ion formed — allow $[Cu(NH_3)_4]^{2+}$]**

### Page 163 — Formation of Coloured Ions

1 a) *Some frequencies of visible light are absorbed by the ion causing electrons to jump into a higher energy level* **[1 mark]**. *The remaining frequencies of light are reflected/transmitted, and combine to make up the colour seen* **[1 mark]**.
b) *Change in oxidation state* **[1 mark]**, *ligand* **[1 mark]** *or coordination number* **[1 mark]**.

2 *Prepare a range of dilutions of known concentrations* **[1 mark]**.
*Measure the absorbance of the solutions* **[1 mark]**.
*Plot a graph of concentration versus absorbance* **[1 mark]**.

3 a) *$\Delta E$ is the energy absorbed* **[1 mark]** *when an electron moves from the ground state to a higher energy level/excited state* **[1 mark]**.
*OR $\Delta E$ is the difference between the ground state energy* **[1 mark]** *and the energy of an excited electron* **[1 mark]**.
b) i) *$Cu^+$ [Ar] $3d^{10}$* **[1 mark]**
ii) *$Cu^{2+}$ [Ar] $3d^9$* **[1 mark]**
c) *$Cu^{2+}$* **[1 mark]** *because it has an incomplete d-subshell* **[1 mark]**.

### Page 165 — Transition Metal Catalysts

1 a) *Vanadium(V) is reduced* **[1 mark]** *to vanadium(IV)*
*$V_2O_5 + SO_2 \rightarrow V_2O_4 + SO_3$* **[1 mark]**
*Vanadium(IV) is oxidised* **[1 mark]** *to vanadium(V)*
*$V_2O_4 + \frac{1}{2}O_2 \rightarrow V_2O_5$* **[1 mark]**
b) i) *Impurities* **[1 mark]** *are adsorbed onto the surface of the catalyst* **[1 mark]**.
*Example: lead in petrol poisons catalytic converter*
*or: sulfur in hydrogen poisons the iron catalyst in the Haber Process* **[1 mark]**
ii) *Reduced efficiency* **[1 mark]**, *increased cost* **[1 mark]**.

# Answers

2 a) Homogeneous — reactants and products in the same phase **[1 mark]**
Heterogeneous — reactants and products in different phases **[1 mark]**
b) i) homogeneous **[1 mark]**
ii)

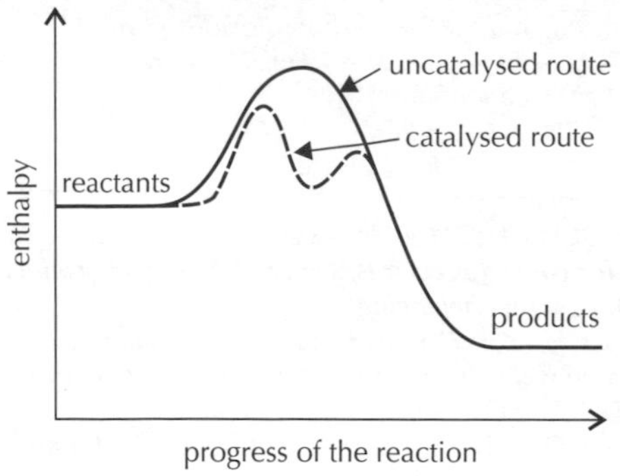


***[1 mark for enthalpy level of products lower than that of reactants, 1 mark for uncatalysed reaction having the greater activation energy, 1 mark for a catalysed reaction curve with two humps.]***

## Page 168 — Other Uses of Transition Metals

1 a) The $Sn/Sn^{2+}$ system has a more positive (greater) standard electrode potential value than the $Fe/Fe^{2+}$ system. **[1 mark]** This means that the iron would oxidise in preference to the tin and so the tin cannot act as a sacrificial protector. **[1 mark]**
b) This is a sacrificial method of protection **[1 mark]** since the $Zn/Zn^{2+}$ system has a more negative (lower) standard electrode potential value than the $Fe/Fe^{2+}$ system. **[1 mark]** This means that the zinc would oxidise in preference to the iron. **[1 mark]**

2 The impure copper is used as the anode **[1 mark]** and a small piece of pure copper is used as the cathode **[1 mark]**. The electrolyte in the cell is a copper salt **[1 mark, accept named copper compound]**. At the anode the copper is oxidised: $Cu_{(s)} \rightarrow Cu^{2+}_{(aq)} + 2e^-$ **[1 mark]**. The copper ions travel through the electrolyte to the cathode but the impurities fall to the bottom of the cell **[1 mark]**. At the cathode the copper ions are reduced back to copper: $Cu^{2+}_{(aq)} + 2e^- \rightarrow Cu_{(s)}$ **[1 mark]**.

3 a) Aldehydes and ketones **[1 mark]**.
b) silver mirror/precipitate **[1 mark]**
c) i) $[Ag(NH_3)_2]^+$ **[1 mark]**
ii) linear **[1 mark]**
iii) colourless **[1 mark]**

## Section 11 — Inorganic Reactions

## Page 171 — Water and Carbon Dioxide

1 To boil water hydrogen bonds between water molecules must be broken **[1 mark]**. Since hydrogen bonds are very strong in comparison to other intermolecular forces they require a lot of energy to break, **[1 mark]** which is why the boiling point of water is very high when compared to similar molecules that are not capable of hydrogen bonding **[1 mark]**.

2 Water is a polar solvent **[1 mark]**. Capsaicin is a non-polar molecule so it cannot/doesn't easily form bonds with polar solvents like water **[1 mark]**. So it will not dissolve very easily in water **[1 mark]**.

3 a) Elevated levels of $CO_2$ are thought to be responsible for climate change/global warming/$CO_2$ is a greenhouse gas **[1 mark]**.
b) $CO_2$ will dissolve in water — the oceans act as a carbon sink because they can store vast amounts of $CO_2$ **[1 mark]**. This has helped to slow/reduce increases in atmospheric $CO_2$ **[1 mark]**, which may have slowed down the effects of global warming due to $CO_2$ **[1 mark]**.
It also increases the acidity of the oceans **[1 mark]**. This may harm or kill species which are pH sensitive **[1 mark]**. Other species will suffer due to food chains being disturbed **[1 mark]**.
c) Plants remove $CO_2$ from the atmosphere by photosynthesis **[1 mark]**, and store it as glucose and other carbon-based compounds **[1 mark]**. Deforestation has reduced green plant coverage on the Earth **[1 mark]**, reducing photosynthesis and the amount of $CO_2$ being removed from the atmosphere **[1 mark]**.

## Page 173 — Nitrogen Chemistry

1 a) i) −3 **[1 mark]**
ii) +5 **[1 mark]**
b) N is being oxidised **[1 mark]**. It is losing electrons/gaining oxygen/its oxidation state increases **[1 mark]**.
c) $NH_4^+ + 3H_2O \rightarrow NO_3^- + 10H^+ + 8e^-$
**[1 mark for 3 moles of $H_2O$ on left of arrow**
**1 mark for 10 moles of $H^+$ and 8 moles of $e^-$ on right of arrow]**

2 a) $N_2 + O_2 \rightarrow 2NO$ **[1 mark for left-hand side, 1 mark for right]** (allow $0.5N_2 + 0.5O_2 \rightarrow NO$).
b) N has an oxidation state of +2 in NO **[1 mark]**.
c) A brown colour would appear (nitrogen dioxide is brown) **[1 mark]**.

## Page 176 — Metal-Aqua Ions

1 $Fe^{3+}$ has a higher charge density than $Fe^{2+}$ **[1 mark]**.
This means $Fe^{3+}$ polarises water molecules more **[1 mark]**, weakening the O-H bond more **[1 mark]** and making it more likely that $H^+$ ions are released into the solution **[1 mark]**.

2 A blue precipitate **[1 mark]** of copper hydroxide forms in the blue solution **[1 mark]** of copper sulfate. On addition of excess ammonia, the precipitate dissolves **[1 mark]** to give a deep blue solution **[1 mark]**.
$[Cu(H_2O)_6]^{2+}_{(aq)} + 2OH^-_{(aq)} \rightleftharpoons Cu(H_2O)_4(OH)_{2(s)}$ **[1 mark]** $+ 2H_2O_{(l)}$
$Cu(H_2O)_4(OH)_{2(s)} + 4NH_{3(aq)} \rightleftharpoons$
$[Cu(NH_3)_4(H_2O)_2]^{2+}_{(aq)}$ **[1 mark]** $+ 2H_2O_{(l)} + 2OH^-_{(aq)}$
**[1 additional mark for each balanced equation.]**

3 a) i) $[Cr(H_2O)_6]^{3+}$ **[1 mark]**
ii) $Cr(H_2O)_3(OH)_3$ **[1 mark]**
iii) $[Cr(NH_3)_6]^{3+}$ **[1 mark]**
b) $Cr(H_2O)_3(OH)_{3(aq)} + 6NH_{3(aq)} \rightarrow [Cr(NH_3)_6]^{3+}_{(aq)} + 3H_2O_{(l)} + 3OH^-_{(aq)}$ **[1 mark]**

4 a) i) Formation of a brown precipitate **[1 mark]**
ii) Formation of a green precipitate **[1 mark]**
b) $[Fe(H_2O)_6]^{2+}_{(aq)} + CO_3^{2-}_{(aq)} \rightarrow FeCO_{3(aq)} + 6H_2O_{(aq)}$ **[1 mark]**
c) i) Formation of a brown precipitate **[1 mark]**
ii) $Fe^{2+}$ has been oxidised to $Fe^{3+}$ by the oxygen in the air **[1 mark]**

## Page 178 — Substitution Reactions

1 a) $[Cu(H_2O)_6]^{2+}_{(aq)} + 4Cl^-_{(aq)} \rightarrow CuCl_4^{2-}_{(aq)}$ **[1 mark]** $+ 6H_2O_{(l)}$
**[1 mark for balanced equation]**
$CuCl_4^{2-}$ is yellow (allow green, which is the colour you would see when you actually do the experiment) **[1 mark]**
b) $[Cu(H_2O)_6]^{2+}_{(aq)} + 3C_2O_4^{2-}_{(aq)} \rightarrow [Cu(C_2O_4)_3]^{4-}_{(aq)}$ **[1 mark]** $+ 6H_2O_{(l)}$
**[1 mark for balanced equation]**
c) $Cu(H_2O)_4(OH)_2$ **[1 mark]**, blue **[1 mark]**

2 a) $[Fe(H_2O)_6]^{3+}_{(aq)} + EDTA^{4-}_{(aq)} \rightarrow [FeEDTA]^-_{(aq)}$ **[1 mark]** $+ 6H_2O_{(l)}$
**[1 mark for balanced equation]**
b) The formation of $[FeEDTA]^-$ results in an increase in entropy **[1 mark]**, because the number of particles increases **[1 mark]**.
c) $Fe(H_2O)_3(OH)_3$ **[1 mark]**

3 a) $[Cu(H_2O)_6]^{2+}$ **[1 mark]**.
b) i) $[Cu(H_2O)_6]^{2+}_{(aq)} + 4NH_{3(aq)} \rightleftharpoons [Cu(NH_3)_4(H_2O)_2]^{2+}_{(aq)} + 4H_2O_{(l)}$
**[1 mark for correct formula of the new complex ion formed, 1 mark for the rest of the equation being correctly balanced]**
ii) $K_{stab} = \frac{[(Cu(NH_3)_4(H_2O)_2)^{2+}]}{[(Cu(H_2O)_6)^{2+}][NH_3]^4}$
**[1 mark for top of fraction correct, 1 mark for bottom of fraction correct]**

# Index

# Index

# Index

# Index